WORSHIP

THIRD EDITION

WORSHIP

A HYMNAL AND SERVICE BOOK FOR ROMAN CATHOLICS

GIA PUBLICATIONS, INC.
CHICAGO

PREFACE

This third edition of *Worship* makes its appearance in the wake of the nearly quarter-century development of the Roman Rite since the Second Vatican Council. The two previous editions, 1971 and 1975, supplied American parishes with service music and hymns which were needed to cultivate vocal prayer, both spoken and sung. These hymnals attempted to move American Catholics more toward the mainstream of Christian hymnody. The present edition reflects our perception of that growth which has taken place during this period of rapid development, as well as our vision of what is needed by way of a hymnal and service book to accompany the Church into the 21st century.

The structure of this edition represents a different direction from that taken with its predecessor. The ordering of the second edition tended to be functional, e.g, hymns in alphabetical order, while the new edition has been organized to mirror who we are and how we pray as Roman Catholics within the larger Christian community.

We begin with the *Liturgy of the Hours,* the Church's daily prayer, edited in such a way so as to enable parishes to celebrate the official rite on all Sundays, solemnities and feasts of the Lord throughout the year, plus the Office for the Dead. The Psalter, which follows, includes all of the psalms and canticles required for Morning Prayer, Evening Prayer and Night Prayer on those days, arranged for singing according to the Gelineau psalmody, as well as a wide range of alternate tones. A separate volume, *Worship - Liturgy of the Hours - Leaders' Edition,* is published for presider, cantor, lector and organist.

In our presentation of the rites for this edition, we have taken into account the fact that the average worshipper experiences these rites infrequently, and unlike his or her experience of the eucharist, is generally unfamiliar with all but certain key elements of the structure. We also remained constantly aware of the uniqueness of the assembly which gathers for weddings, funerals and infant baptism. Therefore, it was our concern that the presentation of the rites offers good practical catechesis, and when combined with competent leadership, makes possible the full and active participation of the gathered assembly.

A number of subtle, but distinctly different directions have been taken in our presentation of music for the eucharist. Complete settings of the mass ordinary texts are presented in course, and eucharistic prayer acclamations from the same source are grouped together. The most significant difference, however, is that the Order of Mass (no. 229) is presented with music rather than as text alone. We have compiled what we judge to be a basic music repertoire for the mass — music which is reprinted in both the marriage and funeral rites — and music which we would hope every parish will learn, in an effort to create a common repertoire that can be sung on those occasions when the eucharist is celebrated by an assembly gathered from different communities.

At the heart of this book is the corpus of just over 400 hymns: texts, with accompanying tunes. Texts which are based almost entirely on scripture. Texts which, we hope, will place on the lips of our assemblies words which enable them to express their faith in praise and petition; to pray in song. We have attempted to collect a body of texts which are theologically sound, embrace the fullness of liturgical practice, and are poetically substantive.

As we began the job of compiling this collection of hymns, our work took us first to the *Lectionary for Mass.* We analyzed the scriptures for each Sunday in all three cycles and for all the principal feasts and solemnities, and attempted to provide at least one "hymn for the day" either based on, or supportive of, each day's readings. In our search for hymns to include in this collection we capitalized on the great hymn writing explosion of the last twenty years and combed the rich heritage of the past. The result of this work is found in the index of Hymns for the Church Year (no. 1205) as well as the liturgical and topical indexes which follow. To support further the lectionary basis of our worshiplife as a Christian people, the entire hymn section is arranged according to the *Lectionary for Mass,* with "Ordinary Time" represented by the large selection of general hymns.

Once again, we offer two people's editions of *Worship,* one with and one without the Sunday scriptures. While we share a deep concern for the Word as aural tradition, the concern is tempered by a realization of common communication disabilities as well as acoustical limitations. There are clearly two sides to the question, and to us the verdict is still not clear. Therefore, we felt the need to continue the dialogue by making both options available.

The language of the hymn texts reflects a contemporary concern that language be just, as well as poetic. We have altered texts that use exclusive terms to refer to both men and women, and we have modernized some pronouns, verb forms and other archaisms whenever we felt the result yielded a better text for contemporary use. In rare cases, e.g., "Faith of Our Fathers," alteration seemed inadvisable, or in a few other cases, was not permitted by the copyright holder. Similarly, at our request the Grail prepared an inclusive language version of their psalm translation, but it failed to gain the approval of the National Conference of Catholic Bishops for use with the lectionary and hours.

A good deal of research was done in order to find the original harmonizations for many of the hymn tunes. In some instances this unearthed a setting which introduces a fresh "new" sound to the repertoire. The normative range of the tunes extends to a fourth-line treble clef "D". For use at an early hour, or when a tune is still unfamiliar, a low key accompaniment book with music only is available. However, under most circumstances we strongly urge that the hymns be played in the keys in which they are printed in the regular accompaniment and people's editions. In most hymns of duple meter, the half note represents the unit of pulse, while hymns having triple meter may be considered to have one beat per measure.

We are grateful to Gabe Huck who wrote the introductions and commentaries on the rites and the lectionary, and to John A. Gurrieri and Ronald F. Krisman, directors of the secretariat of the Bishops' Committee on the Liturgy, for their guidance and assistance. We also acknowledge Gabe Huck for compiling the section of devotional prayers. These are intended both for the individual and for family use in the home, and have been selected to offer a suitable range of texts for daily use.

Special acknowledgement is extended to the following for their immeasurable contributions to this project: to Catherine Salika, our bibliographer, researcher, and author of the *Worship Companion;* to Michael A. Cymbala, permissions editor; to Neil Borgstrom, editorial assistant; and to Ronald F. Krisman, W. Thomas Smith and Paul Westermeyer for their detailed evaluations of the hymn section.

The composers or sources of refrains, psalm tones, and certain other brief musical elements are identified throughout by their initials. They are: RJB, Robert J. Batastini; LB, Laurence Bevenot, OSB; IB, Ingrid Brustle; JRC, J. Robert Carroll; JJC, James J. Chepponis; MC, Michael Connolly; PC, Patricia Craig; RC,

Randolph Currie; EE, Eugene Englert; JG, Joseph Gelineau, SJ; DRH, David R. Haas; PH, Peter Hallock; MH, Marty Haugen; CWH, Clifford W. Howell, SJ; HH, Howard Hughes, SM; DH, David Hurd; RMH, Robert M. Hutmacher, OFM; DCI, David Clark Isele; MJ, Michael Joncas; CK, Columba Kelly, OSB; RKK, Robert Knox Kennedy; MK, Marie Kremer; REK, Robert E. Kreutz; RK, Ronald F. Krisman; RL, Robert LeBlanc; *LBW, Lutheran Book of Worship; LW, Lutheran Worship;* DLSM, DeLaSalle McKeon, CSJ; JAM, John Allyn Melloh, SM; DM, Douglas Mews; AGM, A. Gregory Murray, OSB; PP, Peter Peacock, OFM Cap; CAP, C. Alexander Peloquin; RP, Richard Proulx; DJR, Donald J. Reagan; JR, Joseph Roff; TFS, Thomas F. Savoy; JS, John Schiavone; FS, Frank Schoen; JBS, Joseph B. Smith; RJT, Robert J. Thompson; ST, Suzanne Toolan, SM; RCV, Ralph C. Verdi, CPPS; CW, Chrysogonus Waddell, OCSO; GW, Guy Weitz; and MEY, Michael E. Young. We are grateful to those who have composed settings especially for this edition.

Finally, we the editors once again pay tribute to our publisher, Edward J. Harris, for his confidence in our ability, his support of our decisions, and his personal integrity.

We have attempted to create a service book and hymnal for a church which moves into the third millenium of its existence. It is a movement of great confidence; confident that this Church will continue its role in the history of salvation brought about by the life, the death, the resurrection and the promise to come again of the Lord Jesus Christ.

Robert J. Batastini, General Editor and Project Director

Fred Moleck, Text Editor

Robert H. Oldershaw, Liturgical and Index Editor

Richard Proulx, Music Editor

Contents

Hymns

Lectionary

Prayers of the Individual and Household

Indexes

The Liturgy of the Hours

When darkness gives way before the sun's light and a new day begins, people of all religions have had their rites of morning: words and songs and gestures with which to pray. It has been the same at the end of the day's light, and again in the last moments before sleep.

Christians from the beginning learned ways of morning and evening and night prayer. These moments are the hinges of daily life. As they came round each day they have been occasions to repeat what every child has learned by heart: words to praise God for a new morning, to thank the Father for Christ who is our light as evening comes, to invoke God's strong protection through the hours of night.

The daily prayers of Christians were fashioned at first from very simple things: the sign of the cross, the Lord's Prayer, a few verses and songs and short psalms, intercessions. And for most Christians morning and night remain times for such simple prayers always said by heart. The portion of this book called "Prayers of the Individual and Household" (nos. 1152-1202) contains many of the texts which continue to be part of morning, evening and night prayer.

The pages of this present section offer a form of daily prayer that grew from this same tradition. When Christians have gathered in the early morning, at day's end, just before retiring, the simple prayers for the individual have grown more elaborate. The daily assemblies of men and women religious gave shape to what became known as the divine office or "liturgy of the hours." In recent times, these prayers have been restored to some of their original simplicity and are again being prayed in parish churches and Christian households.

In using and in adapting the forms of morning, evening and night prayer given below, two things are especially important. First, these are not to be prayers which could be prayed any time. Rather, they are prayers (in word, song, gesture, silence) which are prompted by the morning itself, by the evening, by the night. Their content and pace should reflect what is unique to each of these moments. Second, these prayers are not meant to be followed in and read from books. The assembly's parts are to be gradually learned by heart. Simplicity, repetition, care for times of silence, the use of refrains: all make it possible for these prayers to belong fully to those who assemble.

*The proper antiphons, readings, intercessions and prayers for each day are found in the **Worship - Liturgy of the Hours - Leaders' Edition** or **Christian Prayer**.*

INVITATORY

All make the sign of the cross on their lips.

O Lord, + o - pen my lips.   And my mouth will pro-claim your praise.

2   PSALM 95 – TO GOD WITH GLADNESS SING

The cantor sings the proper antiphon for Psalm 95.

Psalm 95
Para. by James Quinn, SJ, b.1919

CAMANO, 6 6 6 6 4 44 4
Richard Proulx, b.1937

1. To God with glad - ness sing,   Your
2. He cra - dles in his hand   The
3. Your heav'n - ly Fa - ther praise,   Ac-

Rock and Sav - ior bless;   With - in his tem - ple
heights and depths of earth;   He made the sea and
claim his on - ly Son,   Your voice in hom - age

bring Your songs of thank - ful - ness!
land, He brought the world to birth!
raise To him who makes all one!

O God of might, To you we sing, En-
O God most high, We are your sheep, On
O Dove of peace, On us de - scend That

throned as King On heav - en's height!
us you keep Your Shep - herd's eye!
strife may end And joy in - crease!

Text: © 1969, James Quinn, SJ; Music: © 1980, G.I.A. Publications, Inc.

Alternate setting found at no. 51.

MORNING PRAYER/LAUDS

The church's sense for how to pray in the morning comes from our Jewish 3
heritage. Whatever the day, whatever the difficulties, the tradition has
been to begin the day with praise for the creator. Thus the whole of morning prayer is in the verse: "O Lord, open my lips. And my mouth will
proclaim your praise." The sign of the cross, first traced on the Christian
at baptism, is again made to begin the new day and its prayer. In the
hymn and the psalms, in the scripture and intercessions, each one who
prays and the community together finds what it is to stand at the beginning of a new day as a Christian. The morning's prayer gives the day its
meaning when, through the years, these prayers become one's own.

This verse and response are omitted when the hour begins with the invitatory.

All make the sign of the cross.

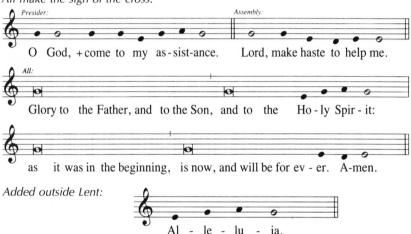

O God, +come to my as-sist-ance. Lord, make haste to help me.

Glory to the Father, and to the Son, and to the Ho-ly Spir-it:

as it was in the beginning, is now, and will be for ev-er. A-men.

Added outside Lent:

Al - le - lu - ia.

4 **HYMN**

Nocte Surgentes
Attr. to St. Gregory the Great, 540-604
Tr. by Percy Dearmer, 1867-1936, alt.

CHRISTE SANCTORIUM, 11 11 11 5
Paris Antiphoner, 1681

1. Fa - ther, we praise you, now the night is
2. Mak - er of all things, fit us for your
3. All - ho - ly Fa - ther, Son and e - qual

o - ver, Ac - tive and watch - ful, stand we all be-
man - sions; Ban - ish our weak - ness, health and whole-ness
Spir - it, Trin - i - ty bless - ed, send us your sal-

fore you; Sing - ing we of - fer pray'r and med - i-
send - ing; Bring us to heav - en, where your saints u-
va - tion; Yours is the glo - ry, gleam-ing and re-

ta - tion: Thus we a - dore you.
nit - ed Joy with - out end - ing.
sound - ing Through all cre - a - tion.

PSALMODY

The psalms, canticle and their antiphons are taken from the proper of the day.

READING

5 **RESPONSE TO THE WORD OF GOD**

Robert LeBlanc, 1984

Cantor, then all:

A. *Advent* Christ, Son of the
B. *Christmas* The Lord has
C. *Lent* Christ, Son of the
D. *Easter* Christ, Son of the living God, have mer -
E. *General* Christ, Son of the

liv - ing God,   have   mer - cy   on   us.
made   known,   alleluia,   al - le - lu -   ia.
liv - ing God,   have   mer - cy   on   us.
cy   on   us,   alleluia,   al - le - lu -   ia.
liv - ing God,   have   mer - cy   on   us.

Cantor:

A. You are the   one   who   is   to   come,
B. His   saving   power,
C. You were   wounded for our of - fenses,
D. You have   risen   from   the   dead,
E. You are seated at the right   hand   of   the Father,

All:

have   mer - cy   on   us.
alleluia,   al - le - lu -   ia.
have   mer - cy   on   us.
alleluia,   al - le - lu -   ia.
have   mer - cy   on   us.

Cantor:

Glo - ry   to   the   Fa - ther, and   to   the   Son,

and   to   the   Ho - ly   Spir   -   it:

All:

A. Christ, Son   of   the
B. The   Lord   has
C. Christ, Son   of   the
D. Christ, Son of   the   living God, have   mer   -
E. Christ, Son   of   the

liv - ing God,   have   mer - cy   on   us.
made   known,   alleluia,   al - le - lu -   ia.
liv - ing God,   have   mer - cy   on   us.
cy   on   us,   alleluia,   al - le - lu -   ia.
liv - ing God,   have   mer - cy   on   us.

6 GOSPEL CANTICLE

The cantor sings the proper antiphon.
All make the sign of the cross.

James Quinn, SJ, b.1919

FOREST GREEN, CMD
English
Harm. by Ralph Vaughan Williams, 1872-1958

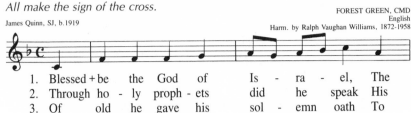

1.	Blessed + be	the	God	of	Is - ra -	el,	The
2.	Through ho - ly	proph - ets	did	he	speak	His
3.	Of	old	he	gave	his	sol - emn	oath	To
4.	O	ti - ny	child,	your	name	shall	be	The
5.	The	ris - ing	Sun	shall	shine	on	us	To

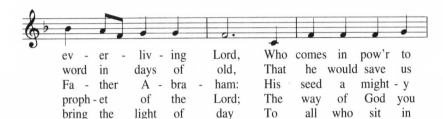

ev - er - liv - ing Lord, Who comes in pow'r to
word in days of old, That he would save us
Fa - ther A - bra - ham: His seed a might - y
proph - et of the Lord; The way of God you
bring the light of day To all who sit in

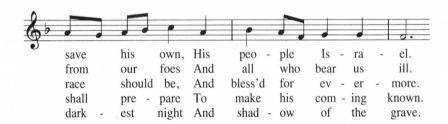

save his own, His peo - ple Is - ra - el.
from our foes And all who bear us ill.
race should be, And bless'd for ev - er - more.
shall pre - pare To make his com - ing known.
dark - est night And shad - ow of the grave.

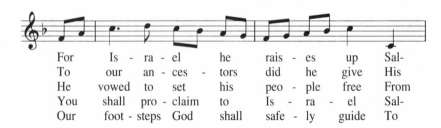

For Is - ra - el he rais - es up Sal-
To our an - ces - tors did he give His
He vowed to set his peo - ple free From
You shall pro - claim to Is - ra - el Sal-
Our foot - steps God shall safe - ly guide To

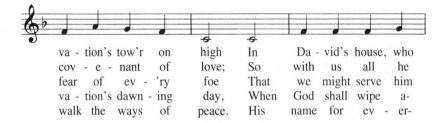

va - tion's tow'r on high In Da - vid's house, who
cov - e - nant of love; So with us all he
fear of ev - 'ry foe That we might serve him
va - tion's dawn - ing day, When God shall wipe a-
walk the ways of peace. His name for ev - er-

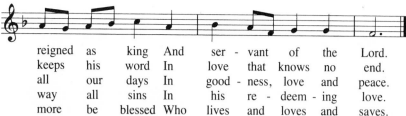

reigned	as	king	And	ser - vant	of	the	Lord.
keeps	his	word	In	love	that	knows	no	end.
all	our	days	In	good - ness,	love	and	peace.
way	all	sins	In	his	re - deem - ing	love.
more	be	blessed	Who	lives	and	loves	and	saves.

Text: © 1969, James Quinn, SJ; Harm: © Oxford University Press

Alternate setting found at no. 89.

INTERCESSIONS

7

The response will be indicated by the leader.

LORD'S PRAYER

Adapt. by Robert Snow, 1964

Our Fa - ther in heav - en, hal - lowed be your name,

your king - dom come, your will be done,

on earth as in heav - en. Give us to - day

our dai - ly bread. For - give us our sins

as we for - give those who sin a - gainst us.

Save us from the time of trial and de - liv - er

us from e - vil. For the king - dom, the pow'r

and the glo - ry are yours, now and for ev - er.

The concluding prayer follows.

8

9 *Dismissal, if the leader is not a priest or deacon:*

All may conclude the celebration by exchanging a sign of peace.

EVENING PRAYER/VESPERS 10

The church gathers in the evening to give thanks for the day that is ending. In the earliest tradition, this began with the lighting of the lamps as darkness fell and the hymn of praise of Christ who is "radiant Light...of God the Father's deathless face." The evening psalms and the Magnificat bring the day just past to focus for the Christian: "God has cast down the mighty from their thrones, and has lifted up the lowly"; "God has remembered the promise of mercy, the promise made to our ancestors." Prayers of intercession are almost always part of the church's liturgy, but those which conclude evening prayer are especially important. As day ends, the church again and again lifts up to God the needs and sorrows and failures of all the world. Such intercession is the daily task and joy of the baptized.

*The proper antiphons, readings, intercessions and prayers for each day are found in the **Worship - Liturgy of the Hours - Leaders' Edition** or **Christian Prayer.***

All make the sign of the cross.

A

Presider:
O God, + come to my as-sist-ance.

Assembly:
Lord, make haste to help me.

All:
Glory to the Father, and to the Son, and to the Ho-ly Spir-it:

as it was in the beginning, is now, and will be for ev-er. A-men.

Added outside Lent:

Al-le-lu-ia.

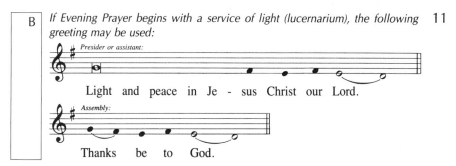

B

If Evening Prayer begins with a service of light (lucernarium), the following 11
greeting may be used:

Presider or assistant:
Light and peace in Je-sus Christ our Lord.

Assembly:
Thanks be to God.

12 HYMN

Phos Hilaron
Greek, c.200
Tr. by William G. Storey, b. 1923

JESU DULCIS MEMORIA, LM
Acc. by Richard Proulx, b.1937

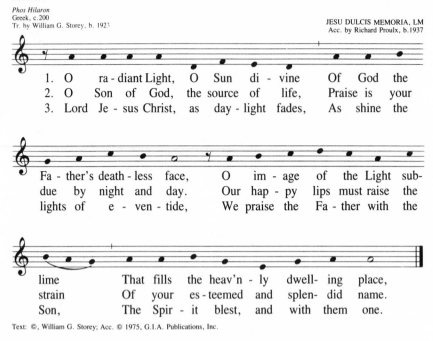

1. O ra-diant Light, O Sun di - vine Of God the
2. O Son of God, the source of life, Praise is your
3. Lord Je - sus Christ, as day-light fades, As shine the

Fa - ther's death-less face, O im - age of the Light sub-
due by night and day. Our hap - py lips must raise the
lights of e - ven - tide, We praise the Fa - ther with the

lime That fills the heav'n - ly dwell- ing place,
strain Of your es - teemed and splen- did name.
Son, The Spir - it blest, and with them one.

Text: ©, William G. Storey; Acc. © 1975, G.I.A. Publications, Inc.

13

Optional *If the lucernarium is celebrated, the evening thanksgiving may be sung.*

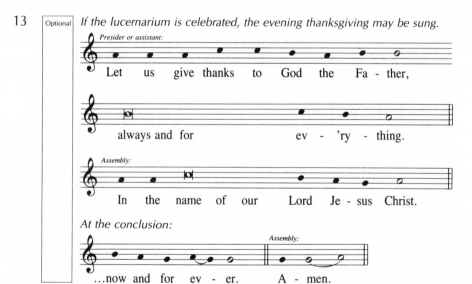

Presider or assistant:

Let us give thanks to God the Fa - ther,

always and for ev - 'ry - thing.

Assembly:

In the name of our Lord Je - sus Christ.

At the conclusion:

Assembly:

...now and for ev - er. A - men.

PSALMODY

The psalms, canticle and their antiphons are taken from the proper of the day.

READING

RESPONSE TO THE WORD OF GOD
14

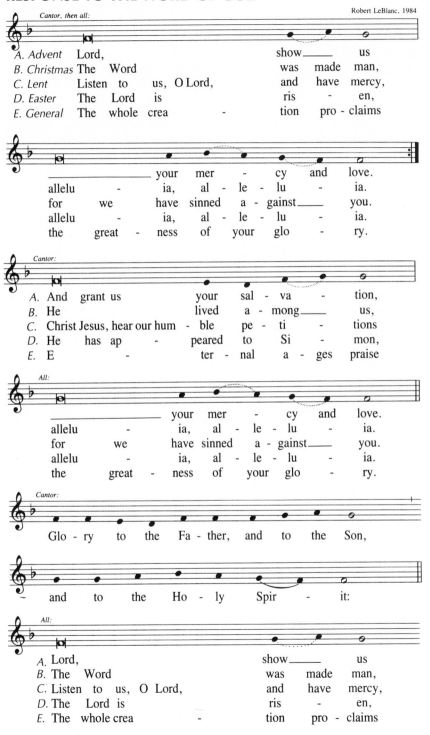

Robert LeBlanc, 1984

Cantor, then all:

A. *Advent*	Lord,		show	us	
B. *Christmas*	The Word		was	made	man,
C. *Lent*	Listen to	us, O Lord,	and	have	mercy,
D. *Easter*	The Lord	is	ris -	en,	
E. *General*	The whole crea	-	tion	pro - claims	

_____ your	mer	- cy	and	love.
allelu -	ia,	al - le - lu	-	ia.
for we	have sinned	a - gainst ___		you.
allelu -	ia,	al - le - lu	-	ia.
the great -	ness	of your glo	-	ry.

Cantor:

A. And grant us	your	sal - va	-	tion,
B. He	lived	a - mong ___		us,
C. Christ Jesus, hear our hum -	ble	pe - ti	-	tions
D. He has ap -	peared	to Si	-	mon,
E. E -	ter - nal	a - ges		praise

All:

_____ your	mer	- cy	and	love.
allelu -	ia,	al - le - lu	-	ia.
for we	have sinned	a - gainst ___		you.
allelu -	ia,	al - le - lu	-	ia.
the great -	ness	of your glo	-	ry.

Cantor:

Glo - ry to the Fa - ther, and to the Son,

and to the Ho - ly Spir - it:

All:

A. Lord,		show ___	us	
B. The Word		was	made	man,
C. Listen to us, O Lord,		and	have	mercy,
D. The Lord is		ris -	en,	
E. The whole crea	-	tion	pro - claims	

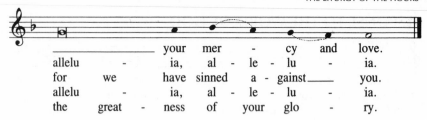

your mer - cy and love.
allelu - ia, al - le - lu - ia.
for we have sinned a - gainst____ you.
allelu - ia, al - le - lu - ia.
the great - ness of your glo - ry.

15 GOSPEL CANTICLE

The cantor sings the proper antiphon.
All make the sign of the cross.

Magnificat anima mea
Tr. by John T. Mueller. 1940

MAGNIFICAT, LMD
Michael Joncas, b.1951
Harm. by Mark V. Smith, b.1956

1. My soul + gives glo - ry to the Lord, In
2. His mer - cy goes to all who fear, From
3. He raised his ser - vant Is - ra - el, Re-

God my Sav - ior I re - joice. My
age to age and to all parts. His
mem - b'ring his e - ter - nal grace, As

low - li - ness he did re - gard, Ex-
arm of strength to all is near; He
from of old he did fore - tell To

alt - ing me by his own choice.
scat - ters those who have proud hearts.
A - bra - ham and all his race.

From this day all shall call me blest, For
He casts the might - y from their throne And
O Fa - ther, Son and Spir - it blest, In

he has done great things for me, Of
rais - es those of low de - gree; He
three - fold Name are you a - dored, To

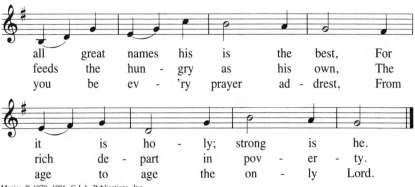

all great names his is the best, For
feeds the hun - gry as his own, The
you be ev - 'ry prayer ad - drest, From

it is ho - ly; strong is he.
rich de - part in pov - er - ty.
age to age the on - ly Lord.

Music: © 1979, 1986, G.I.A. Publications, Inc.

Alternate settings found at nos. 87 and 88.

INTERCESSIONS 16

The response will be indicated by the leader.

LORD'S PRAYER

Adapt. by Robert Snow, 1964

Our Fa - ther in heav - en, hal - lowed be your name,

your king - dom come, your will be done,

on earth as in heav - en. Give us to - day

our dai - ly bread. For - give us our sins

as we for - give those who sin a - gainst us.

Save us from the time of trial and de - liv - er

us from e - vil. For the king - dom, the pow'r

and the glo - ry are yours, now and for ev - er.

The concluding prayer follows.

17   DISMISSAL

A

Priest or deacon: The Lord be with you.   Assembly: And also with you.

Priest or deacon: May almight - y God bless you,   the Fa - ther,

and   the   Son,   and the Holy   Spir - it.

All: A - men! A - men!   MJ

Priest or deacon: Go in peace.   Assembly: Thanks be to God.

18   B   *Dismissal, if the leader is not a priest or deacon:*

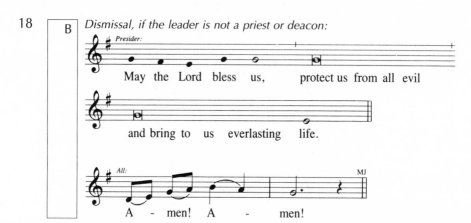

Presider: May the Lord bless us,   protect us from all evil

and bring to us everlasting life.

All: A - men! A - men!   MJ

All may conclude the celebration by exchanging a sign of peace.

NIGHT PRAYER/COMPLINE   19

The church's prayers at night are direct and simple. The Christian remembers with sorrow the day's evil and failure, and places this before the mercy of God. Before surrendering to sleep, there is prayer for God's protection through the night and an expression of acceptance: "Now, Lord, you may dismiss your servant." The night prayer concludes by binding together the sleep of this night with the final falling asleep in the Lord: "May the all-powerful Lord grant us a restful night and a peaceful death." Night's last words are often a gentle invocation of our mother, "When this exile is ended, show us your womb's blessed fruit, Jesus."

*The proper antiphons, readings, intercessions and prayers for each day are found in the **Worship—Liturgy of the Hours—Leaders' Edition** or **Christian Prayer.***

All make the sign of the cross.

O God,+come to my as-sist-ance.   Lord, make haste to help me.

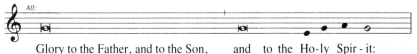

Glory to the Father, and to the Son,   and to the Ho-ly Spir-it:

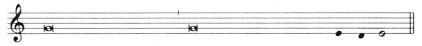

as it was in the beginning, is now and will be for ev - er. A-men.

Added outside Lent:

Al - le - lu - ia.

Optional | *A brief examination of conscience may be made. At its conclusion, the following may be said:*

**I confess to almighty God,
and to you, my brothers and sisters,
that I have sinned through my own fault
in my thoughts and in my words,
in what I have done,
and in what I have failed to do;
and I ask blessed Mary, ever virgin,
all the angels and saints,
and you, my brothers and sisters,
to pray for me to the Lord our God.**

20 **HYMN**

Benedictine Nuns of St. Mary's Abbey
West Malling, Kent, 1967

TE LUCIS ANTE TERMINUM, LM
Adapt. by Howard Hughes, SM, b.1930

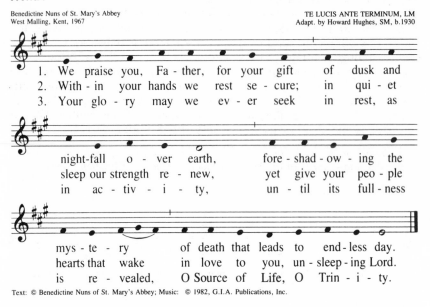

1. We praise you, Fa - ther, for your gift of dusk and
2. With - in your hands we rest se - cure; in qui - et
3. Your glo - ry may we ev - er seek in rest, as

night-fall o - ver earth, fore - shad - ow - ing the
sleep our strength re - new, yet give your peo - ple
in ac - tiv - i - ty, un - til its full - ness

mys - te - ry of death that leads to end - less day.
hearts that wake in love to you, un - sleep - ing Lord.
is re - vealed, O Source of Life, O Trin - i - ty.

Text: © Benedictine Nuns of St. Mary's Abbey; Music: © 1982, G.I.A. Publications, Inc.

PSALMODY

The psalm, antiphon and psalm prayer are taken from the proper of the day of the week.

21 **READING**

RESPONSORY

In Manus Tuas
Sarum Tone
Adapt. by Richard Proulx, 1984

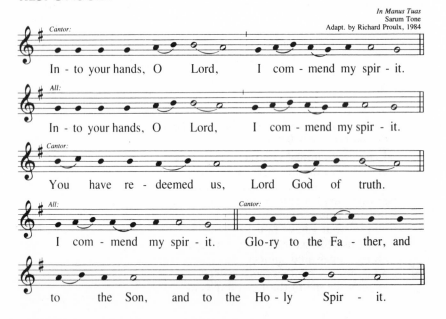

Cantor:
In - to your hands, O Lord, I com - mend my spir - it.

All:
In - to your hands, O Lord, I com - mend my spir - it.

Cantor:
You have re - deemed us, Lord God of truth.

All:
I com - mend my spir - it. Cantor: Glo - ry to the Fa - ther, and

to the Son, and to the Ho - ly Spir - it.

In - to your hands, O Lord, I com - mend my spir - it.

GOSPEL CANTICLE

22

Antiphon

Nunc Dimittis
Sarum Tone
Adapt. by Richard Proulx, 1984

Pro - tect us, Lord, as we stay a - wake; watch

o - ver us as we sleep, that a - wake we may keep

watch with Christ, and a - sleep rest in his peace.

Verses

1. Lord, now you let your ser - vant go in peace: your word has

been ful - filled. 2. My own eyes have seen the sal - va - tion

which you have prepared in the sight of ev - 'ry peo - ple.

3. A light to re - veal you to the na - tions and the glory

of your peo - ple Is - ra - el. 4. Glory to the

Fa - ther, and to the Son and to the

Ho - ly Spir - it: as it was in the be - gin - ning,

is now, and will be for ev - er. A - men.

Alternate setting found at no. 90. For a metrical setting of the "Nunc Dimittis" use hymn no. 691, stanzas 1,2,& 5.

23 PRAYER

CONCLUSION

Presider:

May the all-powerful Lord grant us a restful night and a peaceful death.

All: MJ

A - men! A - men!

The Marian antiphon, "Salve Regina," no. 703, or during Easter season, "Regina Caeli," no. 443, may follow.

Antiphon I

Bless-ed are   they   who de - light   in the law   of the Lord.

Psalm Tone

Gelineau Tone

Beatus vir qui non abiit

1 **Hap**py in**deed** is the màn
  who **fol**lows not the **coun**sel of the **wíck**ed,
  nor **lin**gers in the **way** of sìnners
  nor **sits** in the **com**pany of scórners,
2 but whose de**light** is the **law** of the Lòrd
  and who **pon**ders his **law** day and níght.

3 **He** is like a **tree** that is plànted
  be**side** the **flow**ing wáters,
  that **yields** its **fruit** in due sèason
  and whose **leaves** shall **never** fáde;
  and **all** that he **does** shall pròsper.
4 Not **so** are the **wick**ed, not só!

  For **they** like **win**nowed chàff
  shall be **driv**en away by the wínd.
5 When the **wick**ed are **judged** they shall not stànd,
  nor find **room** among **those** who are júst;
6 for the **Lord** guards the **way** of the jùst
  but the **way** of the **wick**ed leads to doóm.

  Give **praise** to the **Fa**ther Almìghty,
  to his **Son**, Jesus **Christ**, the Lórd,
  to the **Spir**it who **dwells** in our heàrts,
  both **now** and for ever. Amén.

25 Psalm 4

Antiphon

Have mer - cy, Lord, and hear my prayer.

Psalm Tone

Gelineau Tone

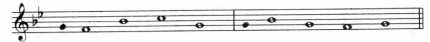

Cum invocarem

2 When I **call**, an**s**wer me, O **God** of **justice**;
from **anguish** you re**leased** me, have **mercy** and **hear** me!

3 O **men**, how **long** will your **hearts** be **closed**,
will you **love** what is **futile** and **seek** what is **false**?

4 It is the **Lord** who grants **favors** to **those** whom he **loves**;
the **Lord hears** me whenever I **call** him.

5 Fear him; do not **sin**: **pon**der on your **bed** and be **still**.
6 Make **justice** your **sacrifice** and **trust** in the **Lord**.

7 "What can **bring** us **hap**piness?" **many say**.
Lift up the **light** of your **face** on **us**, O **Lord**.

8 You have **put** into my **heart** a **greater joy**
than **they** have from a**bun**dance of **corn** and new **wine**.

9 I will **lie** down in **peace** and **sleep** comes at **once**
for **you** alone, **Lord**, make me **dwell** in **safety**.

Give **praise** to the **Father**, the **Son** and **Holy Spirit**,
both **now** and for **ages unending**. Amen.

Psalm 6   26

Antiphon

Re - turn, O Lord, and res - cue my soul.

Psalm Tone

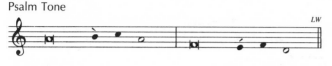

Gelineau Tone

Domine, ne in furore

²**Lord**, do not re**prove** me ìn your **an**ger;
  punish me **not**, ín your **rage**.
³Have **mer**cy on me, **Lord**, I hàve no **strength**;
  Lord, **heal** me, my **bod**y is **racked**,
⁴my **soul** is **rá**cked with **pain**.

  But **you**, O **Lòrd**...how **long**?
⁵**Return**, Lord, **res**cúe my **soul**.
  Save me in your **mer**cìful **love**;
⁶for in **death no** one re**mem**bers you;
  from the **grave**, **who** can gíve you **praise**?

⁷**I** am ex**haus**ted wìth my **groan**ing;
  every **night** I drench my **pil**low with **tears**;
  I be**dew** my **béd** with **weep**ing.
⁸My **eye** wastes a**wày** with **grief**;
  I have grown **old** sur**round**ed bý my **foes**.

⁹**Leave** me, all **you** whò do evil,
  for the **Lord** has **héard** my **weep**ing.
¹⁰The **Lord** has **hèard** my **plea**,
  the **Lord** will ac**cép**t my **prayer**.
¹¹All my **foes** will re**tire** ìn con**fusion**,
  foiled and **sud**denlý con**found**ed.

⁹**Give praise** to the **Fa**thèr Al**mighty**,
  to his **Son**, Jesus **Christ**, the **Lord**,
  to the **Spir**it who **dwells** ìn our **hearts**,
  both **now** and for **e**vér. **Amen**.

27 Psalm 8

Antiphon I

How great is your name,　O Lord　our God, through　all the earth!

Antiphon II

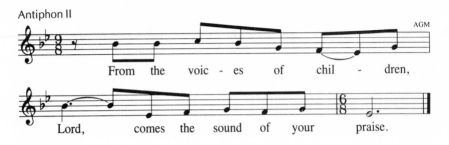

From　the　voic - es　of　chil - dren,

Lord,　comes　the　sound　of　your　praise.

Psalm Tone

Chant tone 5
Acc. by RJB

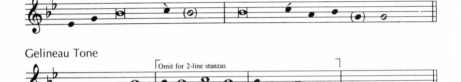

Gelineau Tone

Domine, Dominus noster

*2 How **great** is your **name**, O Lòrd our **God**
  thro´ugh **all** the **earth**!

Your **maj**esty is **praised** above the **hèav**ens;
3 on the **lips** of chi´ldren and of **babes**
  you have found **praise** to **foil** your **è**nemy,
  to **si**lence the fo´e and the **reb**el.

4 When I see the **heav**ens, the **work** of yòur **hands**,
  the **moon** and the sta´rs which you ar**ranged**,
5 what is **man** that you should **keep** him in mìnd,
  mortal **man** tha´t you **care** for **him**?

6 Yet you have **made** him little **less** than a gòd;
  with **glory** and hón**or** you **crowned** him,
7 gave him **pow**er over the **works** of yòur **hand**,
  put **all** things ún**der** his **feet**.

Omitted when Antiphon I is used.

8 **All** of them, **sheep** and **càttle**,
yes, **e**ven thé **sav**age **beasts**,
9 **birds** of the **air**, and **fìsh**
that **make** their **way** throúgh the **wa**ters.

*10 How **great** is your **name**, O Lòrd our **God**
throúgh **all** the **earth**!

Give **glo**ry to the **Fa**ther Al**mìght**y,
to his **Son**, Jésus **Christ**, the **Lord**,
to the **Spir**it who **dwells** in òur **hearts**,
both **now** and for **é**ver. **Amen**.

28 Psalm (12)13

Antiphon

I trust in your mer - ci - ful love.

Psalm Tone

Gelineau Tone

Usquequo, Domine?

¹ How **long**, O **Lord**, will yòu for**get** me?
How **long** will you **híde** your **face**?
² How **long** must I bear **grief** ìn my **soul**,
this **sorrow** in my **heart** dáy and **night**?
How **long** shall my ene**mý** pre**vail**?

³ **Look** at me, **an**swer me, **Lòrd** my **God**!
Give **light** to my **eyes** lest I **fall** asléep in **death**,
⁴ lest my **en**emy **say**: "**I** have òver**come** him";
lest my **foes** re**joice** to sée my **fall**.

⁵ As for **me**, I **trust** in your **mercì**ful **love**.
Let my **heart** re**joice** in your **sá**ving **help**.
⁶ Let me **sing** to the **Lord** for his **goodn**èss to **me**,
singing **psalms** to the **name** of the **Lórd**, the Most **High**.

Give **praise** to the **Father**, the **Son** and Hòly **Spir**it,
both **now** and for **ages** unendíng. **Amen**.

Antiphon

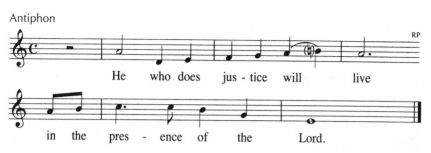

He who does jus - tice will live
in the pres - ence of the Lord.

Psalm Tone

Gelineau Tone

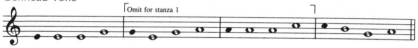

Domine, quis habitabit?

¹ Lord, **who** shall be admitted to your **tent**
   and **dwell** on your holy **moun**tain?

² He who **walks** without **fault**,
   he who **acts** with **justice**
   and **speaks** the **truth** from his **heart**,
³ he who does not **slan**der with his **tongue**,

he who **does** no **wrong** to his **broth**er,
who **casts** no **slur** on his **neigh**bor,
⁴ who **holds** the **god**less in dis**dain**,
but **hon**ors those who **fear** the **Lord**;

he who **keeps** his **pledge**, come what **may**,
⁵ who **takes** no **in**terest on a **loan**
and ac**cepts** no **bribes** against the **in**nocent.
Such a man will **stand** firm for **ever**.

Give **praise** to the **Fath**er, Al**mighty**,
to his **Son**, Jesus **Christ**, the **Lord**,
to the **Spir**it who **dwells** in our **hearts**,
both **now** and for **ever**. **A**men.

30 Psalm (15)16

Antiphon

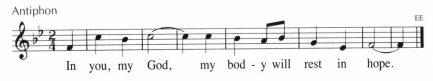

In you, my God, my bod-y will rest in hope.

Psalm Tone

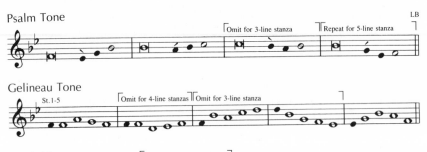

Gelineau Tone

Conserva me, Domine

¹ **Preserve** me, **God**, I take **ref**ùge in **you**.
² I **say** to the **Lord**: "**You** áre my **God**.
My **hap**piness **lies** in **y**óu **alone**."

³ He has **put** into my **heart** a **mar**vèlous **love**
for the **faithful ones** who **dwell** ín his **land**.
⁴ Those who **choose** other **gods** incrèase their **sorrows**.
Never will I **offer** their **offer**íngs of **blood**.
Never will I **take** their **name** upón my **lips**.

⁵ O **Lord**, it is **you** who are my **port**ìon and **cup**,
it is **you** yourself who **áre** my **prize**.
⁶ The **lot** marked **out** for me is **m**ỳ **delight**,
welcome in**deed** the **her**itage that **fá**lls to **me**!

⁷ I will **bless** the **Lord** who **g**ìves me **coun**sel,
who **even** at **night** dir**éct**s my **heart**.
⁸ I **keep** the **Lord** ever **ìn** my **sight**;
since **he** is at my **right** hand, **I** sháll stand **firm**.

9 And so my **heart** re**joi**ces, my **soul** is **glad**;
even my **bod**y shall **rést** in **safe**ty.
10 For **you** will not **leave** my **soul** am**òng** the **dead**,
nor **let** your beloved **knów** de**cay**.

11 You will **show** me the **pàth** of **life**,
the **full**ness of **joy** ín your **pres**ence,
at your **right** hand **hap**pi**néss** for **ever**.

Give **praise** to the **Fathèr** Al**might**y,
to his **Son**, Jesus **Chríst**, the **Lord**,
to the **Spir**it who **dwells** ìn our **hearts**,
both **now** and forevér. **Amen**.

31 Psalm (21)22

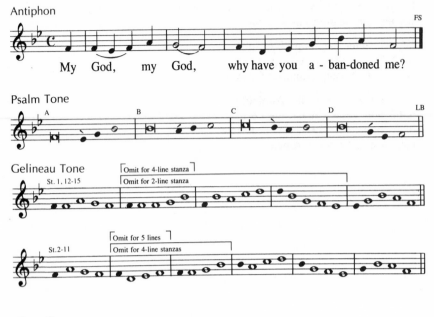

Antiphon

My God, my God, why have you a - ban-doned me?

Psalm Tone

Gelineau Tone

Omit for 4-line stanza
Omit for 2-line stanza
St. 1, 12-15

Omit for 5 lines
Omit for 4-line stanzas
St. 2-11

Deus, Deus meus

²My **God**, my **God**, **why** have you forsaken me?
   You are **far** from my **plea** and the **cry** of my dis**tress**.
³O my **God**, I call by **day** and you **give** no **reply**;
   I **call** by **night** and I **find** no **peace**.

⁴Yet **you**, O **God**, are **holy**,
   en**throned** on the **praises** of Israel.
⁵In **you** our **fathers** put their **trust**;
   they **trusted** and you **set** them **free**.   *[Repeat C + D]*
⁶When they **cried** to **you**, they es**caped**.
   In you they **trusted** and **never** in **vain**.

⁷But **I** am a **worm** and no **man**,   *[Omit B + C]*
   the butt of **men**, laughing-**stock** of the **people**.
⁸**All** who **see** me de**ride** me.
   They curl their **lips**, they **toss** their **heads**.
⁹"He **trusted** in the **Lord**, let him **save** him;
   let him re**lease** him if **this** is his **friend**."

¹⁰ Yes, it was **you** who **took** me from the **womb**,
  en**trust**ed me to my **mo**ther's **breast**.
¹¹ To **you** I was com**mit**ted from my **birth**,
  from my **mother**'s womb **you** have béen my **God**.   *[Repeat C + D]*
¹² Do not **leave** me a**lone** in my **distress**;
  come **close**, there is **none** élse to **help**.

¹³ **Many bulls** have sur**round**ed me,
  fierce **bulls** of **Bash**an clóse me **in**.
¹⁴ A**gainst** me they **open** wìde their **jaws**,
  like **lions**, **rend**íng, and **roar**ing.

¹⁵ Like **water I** àm poured **out**,
  dis**joint**ed are áll my **bones**.
  My **heart** has becòme like **wax**,
  it is **melt**ed withín my **breast**.   *[Repeat C + D]*
¹⁶ **Parched** as burnt **clay** is my **throat**,
  my **tongue cleaves** tó my **jaws**.

¹⁷ **Many dogs** have sur**round**ed me,
  a **band** of the **wick**éd be**set** me.
  They tear **holes** in my **hands** ànd my **feet**,
¹⁶ and **lay** me in the **dúst** of **death**.

¹⁸ I can **count** every **one** òf my **bones**.
  These **people stare** at mé and **gloat**;
¹⁹ they di**vide** my **cloth**ìng a**mong** them.
  They **cast lots** fór my **robe**.

²⁰ O **Lord**, do not **leave** mè a**lone**,   *[Omit B + C]*
  my **strength**, make **háste** to **help** me!
²¹ **Res**cue my **soul** fròm the **sword**,
  my **life** from the **grip** óf these **dogs**.
²² Save my **life** from the **jaws** òf these **lions**,
  my poor **soul** from the **horns** óf these **oxen**.

²³ I will **tell** of your **name** tò my **breth**ren,
  and **praise** you where **they** áre as**sem**bled.
²⁴ "You who **fear** the **Lord**, gìve him **praise**;
  all **sons** of **Ja**cob, give him **glory**.
  Re**vere** him, Is**rá**el's **sons**.

²⁵ For **he** has nevèr de**spised**
  nor **scorned** the poverty óf the **poor**.
  From **him** he has not **hid**dèn his **face**,
  but he **heard** the **poor** man whén he **cried**."

26 **You** are my **praise** in the grèat assembly.
My **vows** I will **pay** before th**óse** who **fear** him,
27 The **poor** shall **eat** and shall hàve their **fill**.
They shall **praise** the **Lord**, th**óse** who **seek** him.   [Repeat D]
May their **hearts live** for evér and **ever**!

28 All the **earth** shall remember and return tò the **Lord**,
all **fam**ilies of the **nations** worshíp before him;
29 for the **king**dom is the **Lord's**, he is **ruler** òf the **nations**.
30 They shall **wor**ship him, **all** the **mighty** óf the **earth**;   [Repeat D]
before him shall **bow** all who go **down** tó the **dust**.

31 And my **soul** shall live for **him**, my chìldren **serve** him.
They shall **tell** of the **Lord** to generations yét to **come**,
32 declare his **faithfulness** to **peoples** yèt un**born**:
"**These things** the L**órd** has **done**."

Give **praise** to the **Father**, the **Son** and Hòly **Spir**it,   [Omit B + C]
both **now** and for **ages** unendíng. **Amen**.

32   Psalm (22)23

Antiphon I

Antiphon II

Antiphon III

The Lord is my shep-herd, noth-ing shall I want: he leads me by safe paths, noth-ing shall I fear.

Psalm Tone

Gelineau Tone

Dominus regit me

¹ The **Lord** is mỳ ˏshepherd;
   there is **noth**ing I shall **want**.
² **Fresh** and **green** are thè pastures
   where he **gives** me ré**pose**.
   Near **restful wa**ters hè **leads** me,
³ to re**vive** my droopíng **spirit**.

He **guides** me along the rìght **path**;
   he is **true** tó his **name**.
⁴ If I should **walk** in the **valley** òf **darkness**
   no **e**vil would Í **fear**.
   You are **there** with your **crook** and yòur **staff**;
   with **these** you give mé **comfort**.

⁵ You have pre**pared** a **ban**quet fòr **me**
   in the **sight** óf my **foes**.
   My **head** you ˏhave a**noint**ed wìth **oil**,
   my **cup** is ové**rflowing**.

⁶ Surely **good**ness and **kind**ness shàll **follow** me
   all the **days** óf my **life**.
   In the **Lord's** own **house** shall Í **dwell**
   for **ev**er ánd **ever**.

To the **Fa**ther and **Son** gìve **glory**,
   give **glory** tó the **Spir**it.
   To God who **is**, who **was**, and whò **will** be
   for **ev**er ánd **ever**.

33　Psalm (24)25

Antiphon

To you I lift up my soul, O Lord my God.

Psalm Tone

Gelineau Tone

Ad te, Domine, levavi

¹To you, O **Lord**, I **lift** up my **soul**.
²I **trust** you, let me **not** be disáppointed;
 do not **let** my enemìes **triumph**.
³Those who **hope** in you shall **not** be disáppointed,
 but only **those** who **wan**tonly bréak **faith**.

⁴**Lord,** make me knòw your **ways**.
 Lord, teach me yóur **paths**.
⁵Make me **walk** in your **truth,** ánd **teach** me,
 for **you** are **God** mỳ **savior**.

 In **you** I **hope** àll day **long**
⁷ᶜbecause of your **good**ness, Ó **Lord**.
⁶Remember your **mer**cỳ, **Lord,**
 and the **love** you have **shown** from óf **old**.
⁷Do not remember the **sins** of mỳ **youth**.
 In your **love** remembér **me**.

⁸The **Lord** is gòod and up**right**.
 He shows the **path** to **those** whó **stray**,
⁹he guides the **hum**ble in the rìght **path**,
 he **teach**es his **way** to thé **poor**.

¹⁰His **ways** are **faith**fulnèss and **love**
 for those who **keep** his **cove**nant ánd **will**.
¹¹**Lord,** for the **sake** of yòur **name**
 for**give** my **guilt,** for it ís **great**.

12 If **any**one **fe**ars the **Lord**
  he will **show** him the **path** he shóuld **choose**.
13 His **soul** shall **live** in **hap**piness
  and his **chil**dren shall poss**ess** thé **land**.
14 The Lord's **friend**ship is for **those** who rè**vere** him;
  to **them** he reveals hís **cov**enant.

15 My **eyes** are **al**ways òn the **Lord**,
  for he **res**cues my **feet** from thé **snare**.
16 **Turn** to **me** and hàve **mer**cy
  for **I** am **lone**ly ánd **poor**.

17 Re**lie**ve the **an**guish òf my **heart**
  and set me **free** from **my** dístress.
18 **See** my af**flic**tion and mỳ **toil**
  and **take** all my **sins** áway.

19 **See** how **man**y àre my **foes**,
  how **vi**olent their **hat**red fór **me**.
20 Pre**serve** my **life** and res**cù**e me.
  Do not disap**point** me, **you** are mý **refuge**.
21 May **in**nocence and **up**rightness pro**tect** me,
  for my **hope** is in **you**, Ó **Lord**.

22 **Re**deem Israèl, O **God**,
  from **all its** dístress.
  To the **Fa**ther, the **Son** and Holỳ **Spir**it,
  give **praise** for ever. Ámen.

34 Psalm (26)27

Antiphon

IB

I will sing and make mu - sic for the Lord.

Psalm Tone

LB

Repeat for 6-line stanzas

Gelineau Tone

Repeat for 6-line stanzas

St. 6

Dominus illuminatio

¹The **Lord** is my **light** ànd my **help**;
whom sháll I **fear**?
The **Lord** is the **strong**hold òf my **life**;
before **whom** sháll I **shrink**?

²When **evildoè**rs draw **near**
to **devoúr** my **flesh**,
it is **they**, my **enemì**es and **foes**,
who **stumblé** and **fall**.

³Though an **army** encàmp **against** me
my **heart** wóuld not **fear**.
Though **war** break òut **against** me
even **then** wóuld I **trust**.

⁴There is **one** thing I **ask** òf the **Lord**,
for **thís** I **long**,
to **live** in the **house** òf the **Lord**,
all the **days** óf my **life**,
to **savor** the **sweet**ness òf the **Lord**,
to be**hóld** his **temple**.

⁵For **there** he keeps me **safe** ìn his **tent**,
in the **dáy** of evil.
He **hides** me in the **shelter** òf his **tent**,
on a **rock** he séts me **safe**.

⁶And **now** my **head** shàll be **raised**
above my **foes** whó sur**round** me,
and I shall **offer** with**in** his **tent**
a **sac**rifìce of **joy**.
I will **sing** and make **mu**sic fór the **Lord**.

⁷O **Lord**, hear my **voice** whèn I **call**;
have **mer**cý and **an**swer.
⁸Of **you** my **he**àrt has **spo**ken:
"**Séek** his **face**."

It is your **face**, O **Lord**, thàt I **seek**;
⁹**hide** nót your **face**.
Dis**miss** not you **serv**ànt in **anger**;
you have beén my **help**.

Do not a**ban**don òr for**sake** me,
O **Gód** my **help**!
¹⁰Though **father** and **moth**èr for**sake** me,
the **Lord** wíll re**ceive** me.

¹¹In**struct** me, **Lord**, ìn your **way**;
on an evén path **lead** me.
When they **lie** in am**bùsh** ¹²pro**tect** me
from my e**né**my's **greed**.
False **wit**nesses rìse a**gainst** me,
breathíng out **fury**.

¹³I am **sure** I shall **see** thè Lord's **good**ness
in the **land** óf the **liv**ing.
¹⁴Hope in **him**, hold **firm** ànd take **heart**.
Hope ín the **Lord**!

Praise the **Fa**ther, the **Son** and Hòly **Spir**it,
both **now** ánd for **ever**,
the God who **is**, who **was**, and ìs to **come**,
at the **end** óf the **ages**.

35   Psalm (30)31

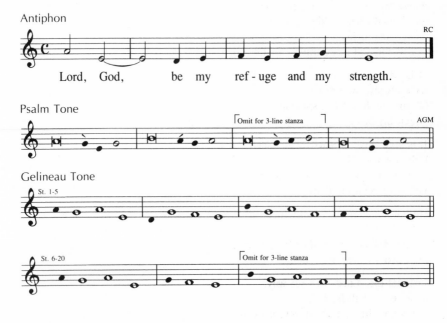

Antiphon

Lord,   God,   be   my   ref - uge   and my   strength.

In te, Domine, speravi

²In **you**, O **Lord**, Ì take **refuge**.
Let me **never** be **pút** to **shame**.
In your **jus**tice, sèt me **free**,
³**hear** me and **speed**ily **rés**cue me.

Be a **rock** of **refù**ge for **me**,
a **might**y **strong**hóld to **save** me,
⁴for **you** are my **ròck**, my **strong**hold.
For your **name's** sake, **lead** mé and **guide** me.

⁵**Release** me from the **snares** thèy have **hid**den
for **you** are my **réf**uge, **Lord**.
⁶Into your **hands** I comm**ènd** my **spir**it.
It is **you** who will re**deém** me, **Lord**.

O **God** of **truth**, ⁷yòu de**test**
those who **wor**ship **false** and **ém**pty **gods**.
⁸As for **me**, I **trust** ìn the **Lord**;
let me be **glad** and re**joice** ín your **love**.

You, who have **seen** mỳ af**flic**tion
and taken **heed** of my **sóul's** dis**tress**,
⁹have not **hand**ed me **over** tò the **ene**my,
but **set** my **feét** at **large**.

¹⁰ Have **mercy** on **mè**, O **Lord**,
   for I am **ín** dis**tress**.
   Tears have **wastèd** my **eyes**,
   my **throat**, ánd my **heart**.

¹¹ For my **life** is **spènt** with **sorrow**
   and my **yéars** with **sighs**.
   Affliction has **broken** dòwn my **strength**
   and my **bones** wáste a**way**.

¹² In the **face** of **àll** my **foes**
   I am **à** re**proach**,
   an **ob**ject of **scorn** tò my **neigh**bors
   and of **fear** tó my **friends**.

   Those who **see** me **ìn** the **street**
   run **far** awáy from **me**.
¹³ I am like a **dead** màn for**got**ten,
   like a **thing** thrówn a**way**.

¹⁴ I have **heard** the **slan**der òf the **crowd**,
   fear is áll a**round** me,
   as they **plot** togethèr a**gainst** me,
   as they **plan** to táke my **life**.

¹⁵ But as for **me**, I **trùst** in **you**, Lord;
   I say: "**You** áre my **God**.
¹⁶ My **life** is in your **hands**, delìver me
   from the **hands** of thóse who **hate** me.

¹⁷ Let your **face shine** òn your **ser**vant.
   Save me **ín** your **love**.
¹⁸ Let me **not** be put to **shame** fòr I **call** you,
   let the **wickéd** be **shamed**!

   Let them be **si**lenced **ìn** the **grave**,
¹⁹ let **ly**ing **líps** be **mute**,
   that speak **haugh**tily a**gàinst** the **just**
   with **pride** ánd con**tempt**."

²⁰ How **great** is the **gòod**ness, **Lord**,
   that you **keep** for thóse who **fear** you,
   that you **show** to **thòse** who **trust** you
   in the **síght** of **men**.

²¹ You **hide** them in the **shel**ter òf your **pres**ence
   from the **plott**íng of **men**;
   you **keep** them **safe** withìn your **tent**
   from dispúting **tongues**.

²²**Bless**ed be the **Lord** who has **shown** me
the **won**ders óf his **love**
in a **fort**ífied **city**.

²³"**I** am far re**moved** from your **sight**,"
I **said** in mý **alarm**.
Yet you **heard** the **voice** òf my **plea**
when I **crí**ed for **help**.

²⁴**Love** the **Lord**, àll you **saints**.
He **guá**rds his **faith**ful
but the **Lord** will re**pay** tò the **full**
those who áct with **pride**.

²⁵Be **strong**, let your **heàrt** take **cour**age,
all who **hope** ín the **Lord**.
Praise the **Fa**ther, the **Son**, and Hòly **Spir**it,
for **evér** and **ever**.

36   Psalm (33)34

Antiphon

Psalm Tone

Gelineau Tone

Benedicam Dominum

²I will **bless** the **Lord** at àll **times**,
his **praise al**ways ón my **lips**;
³in the **Lord** my **soul** shall make ìts **boast**.
The **hum**ble shall **hear** and bé **glad**.

⁴Glorify the **Lord** with **me**.
  Together let us **praise** his **name**.
⁵I **sought** the Lord and he **an**swered me;
  from all my **ter**rors he **set** mé **free**.

⁶**Look** towards **him** and be **ra**diant,
  let your **faces** **not** bé **abashed**.
⁷This **poor** man **called**; the Lòrd **heard** him
  and **res**cued him from **all** his **dí**stress.

⁸The **an**gel of the **Lord** is èn**camped**
  around **those** who re**vere** hím, to **res**cue them.
⁹Taste and **see** that the **Lord** ìs **good**.
  He is **hap**py who seeks **refuge** ín **him**.

¹⁰**Revere** the **Lord**, you hìs **saints**.
  They lack **noth**ing, **those** whó revere him.
¹¹Strong **lions** suffer **want** and gò **hun**gry
  but **those** who seek the **Lord** lack nó **bless**ing.

¹²**Come**, children ànd **hear** me
  that I may **teach** you the **fear** óf the **Lord**.
¹³Who is **he** who **longs** fòr **life**
  and many **days**, to en**joy** his **pró**sperity?

¹⁴Then **keep** your **tongue** fròm **evil**
  and your **lips** from **speak**íng de**ceit**.
¹⁵Turn a**side** from **evil** and dò **good**;
  seek and **strive** aftér **peace**.

¹⁶The **Lord** turns his **face** against thè **wick**ed
  to de**stroy** their re**mem**brance fróm the **earth**.
¹⁷The **Lord** turns his **eyes** to thè **just**
  and his **ears** to **their** áppeal.

¹⁸They **call** and the Lòrd **hears**
  and **res**cues them in **all** théir **distress**.
¹⁹The Lord is **close** to the **brok**ènhearted;
  those whose **spir**it is **crushed** he wíll **save**.

²⁰**Many** are the **tri**als of thè **just** man
  but from them **all** the **Lórd** will **res**cue him.
²¹He will keep **guard** over **all** hìs **bones**,
  not **one** of his **bones** shall bé **broken**.

²²Evil brings **death** to thè **wick**ed;
  those who **hate** the góod are **doomed**.
²³The Lord **ran**soms the **souls** of hìs **ser**vants.
  Those who **hide** in him shall **not** be cóndemned.

Give **praise** to the **Father** Àl**mighty**,
  to his **Son**, Jesus **Chríst** the **Lord**,
  to the **Spir**it who **dwells** in òur **hearts**,
  both **now** and for **ever**. À**men**.

37   Psalm (41)42

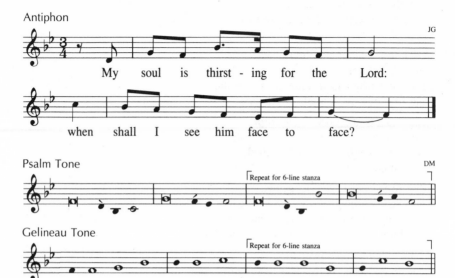

Antiphon

My soul is thirst - ing for the Lord:

when shall I see him face to face?

Psalm Tone

Repeat for 6-line stanza

Gelineau Tone

Repeat for 6-line stanza

Quemadmodum

² **Like** the **dèer** that **yearns**
for **rún**ning **streams**,
so my **sòul** is **yearn**ing
for **yóu**, my **God**.

³ **My soul** is **thirst**ing for **God**,
the **God** óf my **life**;
when can I **entèr** and **see**
the **fáce** of **God**?

⁴ **My tears** have be**còme** my **bread**,
by **níght**, by **day**,
as I **hear** it **said** all thè day **long**:
"**Where** ís your **God**?"

⁵ **These** things will **Ì** re**mem**ber
as I **pour** oút my **soul**,
how I would **lead** the re**jòi**cing **crowd**
into the **hóuse** of **God**,
amid **cries** of **glad**ness ànd thanks**giving**,
the **throng** wíld with **joy**.

⁶ **Why** are you cast **dòwn**, my **soul**,
why **gróan** with**in** me?
Hope in **God**;/I will **pràise** him **still**,
my **savior** ánd my **God**.

*7*My **soul** is cast dòwn within me
 as I thínk of **you**,
 from the **coun**try of **Jor**dan ànd Mount **Her**mon,
 from the **Híll** of **Mi**zar.

*8***Deep** is callìng on **deep**,
 in the róar of **wat**ers;
 your **tor**rents and àll your **waves**
 swept óver **me**.

*9*By **day** the **Lòrd** will **send**
 his lóving **kind**ness;
 by **night** I will sìng to **him**,
 praise the **God** óf my **life**.

*10*I will **say** to **Gòd**, my **rock**:
 "**Why** have yóu for**got**ten me?
 why do **Í** go **mourn**ing,
 op**pressed** bý the **foe**?"

*11*With **cries** that **pierce** me tò the **heart**,
 my ene**mí**es re**vile** me,
 saying to me àll day **long**:
 "**Where** ís your **God**?"

*12***Why** are you cast dòwn, my **soul**,
 why gróan with**in** me?
 Hope in **God**; I will pràise him **still**,
 my **sav**ior ánd my **God**.

Praise the **Fa**ther, the **Son** and Hóly **Spir**it,
 both **now** ánd for **ever**,
 the God who **is**, who **was** ànd who **will** be,
 world wíthout **end**.

38 Psalm (42)43

Antiphon I

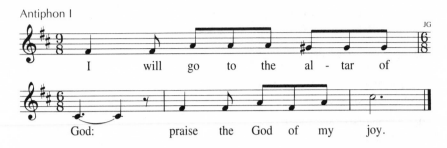

I will go to the al - tar of God: praise the God of my joy.

Antiphon II

Send forth your light and your truth: let these be my guide.

Psalm Tone

Gelineau Tone

Judica me, Deus

¹ Defend me, O **God**, and plèad my **cause**
against a **gó**dless **na**tion.
From de**ceit**ful and **cù**nning **men**
rescue mé, O **God**.

² Since **you**, O **God**, àre my **strong**hold,
why havẹ yóu re**ject**ed me?
Why do **I** go **mourn**ing,
op**pressed** bý the **foe**?

³ O **send** forth your **light** ànd your **truth**;
let **these** bé my **guide**.
Let them **bring** me to your **hò**ly **moun**tain
to the **place** whére you **dwell**.

⁴ And I will **come** to the **al**tàr of **God**,
the **God** óf my **joy**.
My re**deem**er, I will **thank** you òn the **harp**,
O **Gód**, my **God**!

⁵ **Why** are you cast dòwn, my **soul**,
why **gróan** withín me?
Hope in **God**; I will **pràise** him **still**,
my **sav**ior ánd my **God**.

Praise the **Fa**ther, the **Son** and Hòly **Spir**it,
both **now** ánd for **ever**,
the God who **is**, who **was** ànd who **will** be,
world wíthout **end**.

39 Psalm (45)46

Antiphon (Obligatory after stanzas 1, 2, and 3)

AGM

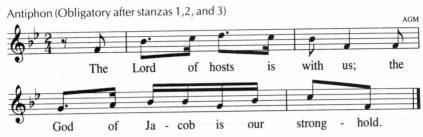

The Lord of hosts is with us; the
God of Ja - cob is our strong - hold.

Psalm Tone

Psalm tone 8-g
Acc. by RP

Gelineau Tone

Omit for final stanza

Deus noster refugium

²**God** is for **us** a **refuge** and **strength**,
a **help**er close at **hand**, in **time** of dis**tress**,
³so **we** shall not **fear** though the **earth** should **rock**,
though the **moun**tains **fall** into the **depths** of the **sea**;
⁴even **though** its **wa**ters **rage** and **foam**,
even **though** the **moun**tains be **shaken** by its **waves**.

⁵The **wa**ters of a **riv**er give **joy** to God's **city**,
the **holy place** where the **Most** High **dwells**.
⁶**God** is with**in**, it **cannot** be **shaken**;
God will **help** it at the **dawn**ing of the **day**.
Nations are in **tu**mult, **king**doms are **shaken**;
he **lifts** his **voice**, the **earth** shrinks **away**.

⁹**Come**, consi**der** the **works** of the **Lord**,
the re**doubt**able **deeds** he has **done** on the **earth**.
¹⁰He puts an **end** to **wars** over **all** the **earth**;
the **bow** he **breaks**, the **spear** he **snaps**.
¹¹"Be **still** and **know** that **I** am **God**,
supreme among the **na**tions, su**preme** on the **earth!**"

Give **praise** to the **Fa**ther, the **Son** and Holy **Spi**rit
both **now** and for **ages** un**end**ing. **Amen**.

Antiphon

Sing praise to our king, sing praise:

for God is king of all the earth.

Psalm Tone

Gelineau Tone

Omnes gentes, plaudite

²All **peoples**, **clap** your **hands**,
  cry to **God** with **shouts** of **joy**!
³For the **Lord**, the Most **High**, we
    must **fear**,
  great **king** over **all** the **earth**.

⁴He sub**dues peoples un**der us
  and **nations un**der our **feet**.
⁵Our **inher**itance, our **glory**, is from
    him,
  given to **Já**cob out of **love**.

⁶God goes **up** with **shouts** of **joy**;
  the Lord goes **up** with **trum**pet
    blast.
⁷Sing **praise** for **God**, sing **praise**,
  sing **praise** to our **king**, sing **praise**.

⁸God is **king** of **all** the **earth**.
  Sing **praise** with **all** your **skill**.
⁹God is **king** over the **nations**;
  God **reigns** on his **holy throne**.

¹⁰The **princes** of the **peoples** are
    assembled
  with the **people** of **Á**braham's **God**.
  The **rulers** of the **earth** belong to **God**,
  to **God** who **reigns** over **all**.

Give **praise** to the **Father** Al**might**y,
  to his **Son**, **Jé**sus **Christ** the **Lord**,
  to the **Spir**it who **dwells** in our
    hearts,
  both **now** and for **ever**. **Amen**.

41 Psalm (50)51

Antiphon I

Have mer - cy, Lord   cleanse me from   all   my   sins.

Antiphon II

Lord, if you will, you can   make me   clean.

Psalm Tone

Gelineau Tone

Miserere mei, Deus

³ Have **mer**cy on me, **God**, ìn your **kind**ness.
  In your com**pas**sion blot **out** my óffence.
⁴ O **wash** me more and **more** from mỳ **guilt**
  and **cleanse** me **from** mý **sin**.

⁵ My of**fen**ces trulỳ I **know** them;
  my **sin** is **al**ways béfore me.
⁶ Against **you**, you a**lone**, have Ì **sinned**;
  what is **e**vil in your **sight** I háve **done**.

  That you may be **jus**tified **when** yòu give **sen**tence
  and be with**out** re**proach** when yóu **judge**,
⁷ O **see**, in **guilt** I wàs **born**,
  a **sin**ner was **I** cónceived.

⁸ **In**deed you love **truth** ìn the **heart**;
  then in the **se**cret of my **heart** teach mé **wis**dom.
⁹ O **pu**rify me, **then** I shall bè **clean**;
  O **wash** me, I shall be **whit**er thán **snow**.

¹⁰ Make me **hear** re**joic**ìng and **glad**ness,
  that the **bones** you have **crushed** máy **thrill**.
¹¹ From my **sins** turn a**way** yòur **face**
  and **blot** out **all** mý **guilt**.

¹² A **pure** heart cre**ate** for mè, O **God**,
 put a **stead**fast **spir**it wíthin me.
¹³ Do not **cast** me a**way** from yòur **pres**ence,
 nor de**prive** me of your **holý spir**it.

¹⁴ Give me a**gain** the **joy** òf your **help**;
 with a **spir**it of **fer**vor sústain me,
¹⁵ that I may **teach** transgrèssors yòur **ways**,
 and **sin**ners may re**turn** tó **you**.

¹⁶ O **res**cue me, **Gòd**, my **help**er,
 and my **tongue** shall **ring** out yóur **good**ness.
¹⁷ O **Lord**, open mỳ **lips**,
 and my **mouth** shall de**clare** yóur **praise**.

¹⁸ For in **sac**rifice you **take** nò de**light**,
 burnt **off**ering from **me** you would ré**fuse**;
¹⁹ my **sac**rifice, a con**trìte spir**it,
 a **hum**bled, contrite **heart** you will nót **spurn**.

²⁰ In your **good**ness, show **fav**òr to **Zi**on;
 re**build** the **walls** of **Jé**ru**sa**lem.
²¹ **Then** you will be **pleased** with lawfùl **sac**rifice,
 burnt **off**erings **whol**ly cònsumed,
 then you will be **off**ered young **bulls** on yóur **al**tar.

Give **glo**ry to the **Fath**èr Al**might**y,
 to his **Son**, Jesus **Christ**, thé **Lord**,
 to the **Spir**it who **dwells** in oùr **hearts**,
 both **now** and for **ev**er. **Á**men.

42 Psalm (62)63:2-9

Antiphon I

My soul is thirst-ing for you, O Lord, thirst-ing for you my God.

Antiphon II

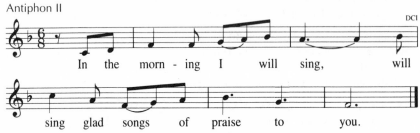

In the morn-ing I will sing, will sing glad songs of praise to you.

Psalm Tone

Gelineau Tone

Deus, Deus meus

2 O **God**, you are my **God**, for yòu I
   long;
   for yóu my **soul** is **thirst**ing.
   My **bod**y pìnes for **you**
   like a **dry**, weary lánd with**out** **wat**er.
3 So I **gaze** on **you** in the sànctuary
   to **see** your **stréngth** and your **glory**.

4 For your **love** is bètter than **life**,
   my líps will **speak** your **praise**.
5 So I will **bless** you àll my **life**,
   in your **name** I will líft up my
   hands.
6 My **soul** shall be **filled** as wìth a
   banquet,

my **mouth** shall **práise** you with **joy**.

7 On my **bed** I remèmber **you**.
   On **you** I múse through the **night**
8 for **you** have bèen my **help**;
   in the **shad**ow of your **wíngs** I
   rejoice.
9 My **soul** clìngs to **you**;
   your **ríght** hand **holds** me **fast**.

Give **praise** to the Fàther Al**mighty**,
to his **Son**, Jésus **Christ** the **Lord**,
to the **Spir**it who **dwèlls** in our
   hearts,
both **now** and for **éver**. Amen.

Psalm (63)64   43

Antiphon

The just will re-joice in the Lord;
their hearts will be filled with glo-ry.

Psalm Tone

Gelineau Tone

Exaudi, Deus

²Hear my **voice**, O **God**, as I
   com**plain**,
guard my **life** from **dread** óf the **foe**.
³**Hide** me from the **band** òf the
   wicked,
from the **throng** of **those** whó do
   evil.

⁴They **sharp**en their **tòngues** like
   swords;
they **aim** bitter **wórds** like **ar**rows
⁵to **shoot** at the **inno**cènt from
   ambush,
shooting **sud**denlý and **reck**lessly.

⁶They **scheme** their **èvil course**;
they con**spire** to **lay** sécret **snares**.
They **say**: "**Whò** will **see** us?
⁷**Who** can **search** óut our **crimes**?"

He will **search** who **searchès** the
   mind
and **knows** the **depths** òf the **heart**.
⁸**God** has **shot** them wìth his **ar**row
and **dealt** them **súd**den **wounds**.

⁹Their own **tongue** has **brought** thèm
   to **ru**in
and **all** who **sée** them **mock**.

¹⁰**Then** will **àll** men **fear**;
they will **tell** what **Gód** has **done**.
They will under**stànd** God's **deeds**.
¹¹The **just** will re**joice** ín the **Lord**
and **fly** to **hìm** for **ref**uge.
All the **up**right **héarts** will **glory**.

Give **praise** to the **Fathèr** Al**might**y,
to his **Son**, Jesus **Chríst**, the **Lord**,
to the **Spir**it who **dwells** ìn our
   hearts,
both **now** and for **evér**. **Amen**.

44 Psalm (70)71

Antiphon

I will sing of your sal - va - tion.

Psalm Tone

Gelineau Tone

In te, Domine, speravi

¹ In **you, O Lord,** I take **ref**uge;
Let me **never** be **put** to **shame**.
² In your **jus**tice res**cue** me, **free** me;
pay **heed** to **me** and **save** me.

³ Be a **rock** where **I** can take **ref**uge,
a **might**y strong**hold** to **save** me;   *[Repeat B]*
for **you** are my **rock**, my **strong**hold.
⁴ **Free** me from the **hand** of the **wick**ed,
from the **grip** of the un**just**, of the **op**pressor.

⁵ It is **you, O Lord,** who are my **hope**,
my **trust, O Lord**, since my **youth**.   *[Repeat B]*
⁶ On **you** I have **leaned** from my **birth**,
from my mother's **womb** you have **been** my **help**.
My **hope** has **al**ways **been** in **you**.

⁷ My **fate** has filled **man**y with **awe**
but **you** are **my** strong **ref**uge.
⁸ My **lips** are **filled** with your **praise**,
with your **glory all** the day **long**.   *[Repeat C + D]*
⁹ Do not re**ject** me **now** that **I** am **old**;
when my **strength** fails do **not** forsake me.

¹⁰ For my **en**emies are **speak**ing about me;
those who **watch** me take **coun**sel to**geth**er
¹¹ saying: "**God** has for**sak**en him; **fol**low him,
seize him; there is **no** one to **save** him."   *[Repeat C + D]*
¹² O **God**, do not **stay** far **off**:
my **God**, make **haste** to **help** me!

¹³Let them be **put** to **shame** ànd de**stroyed**,
all **those** who **séek** my **life**.
Let them be **covered** with **shame** ànd con**fu**sion,
all **those** who **séek** to **harm** me.

¹⁴But as for **me**, I will **à**lways **hope**
and **praise** you **móre** and **more**.
¹⁵My **lips** will **tell** òf your **justice**
and **day** by **day** óf your **help**   *[Repeat D]*
(though I can **never** téll it **all**).

¹⁶I will de**clare** the **Lord's** mìghty **deeds**
pro**claim**ing your **jus**tice, yóurs a**lone**.
¹⁷O **God**, you have **taught** me fròm my **youth**
and I pro**claim** your **wón**ders **still**.

¹⁸**Now** that I am **old** ànd grey-**head**ed,   *[Omit B + C]*
do not for**sáke** me, **God**.
Let me **tell** of your **power** tò all **ages**,
¹⁹praise your **strength** and **justice** tó the **skies**,
tell of **you** who have **wòrked** such **won**ders.
O **God**, who ís like **you**?

²⁰You have **bur**dened me with **bìt**ter **troub**les
but **you** will give me **báck** my **life**.
You will **raise** me from the **depths** òf the **earth**;
²¹you will ex**alt** me and con**sole** mé a**gain**.

²²So I will **give** you **thanks** òn the **lyre**
for your **faith**ful **lóve**, my **God**.
To **you** will I **sing** ͵wìth the **harp**,
to **you**, the **Holy** Óne of **Israel**.   *[Repeat C + D]*
²³When I **sing** to you my **lips** shàll re**joice**
and my **soul**, which **you** háve re**deemed**.

²⁴And **all** the day **lòng** my **tongue**
shall **tell** the **tale** óf your **jus**tice:
for **they** are put to **shame** ànd dis**graced**,
all **those** who **séek** to **harm** me.

Give **praise** to the **Fathèr** Al**mighty**,
to his **Son**, Jesus **Chríst**, the **Lord**,
to the **Spir**it who **dwells** ìn our **hearts**,
both **now** and for **evér**. **Amen**.

45 Psalm (83)84

Antiphon

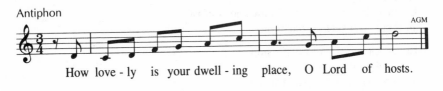

How love - ly is your dwell - ing place, O Lord of hosts.

Psalm Tone

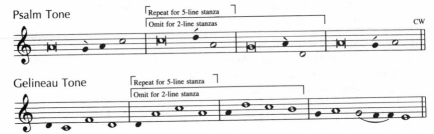

Gelineau Tone

Quam dilecta

²How **lovely** **is** your **dwell**ing place,
Lord, **God** óf **hosts**.

³My **soul** is **long**ìng and **yearn**ing,
is **yearn**ing for the **courts** of the **Lord**.
My **heart** and my **soul** ring our their **joy**
to **God**, the **liv**íng **God**.

⁴The **sparrow** her**self** fìnds a **home**
and the **swall**ow a **nest** for her **brood**;
she **lays** her **young** by your **al**tars,
Lord of **hosts**, my **king** and mý **God**.

⁵They are **hap**py, who **dwell** ìn your **house**,
for **ever** **sing**ing yóur **praise**.
⁶They are **hap**py, whose **strength** is ìn **you**,
in whose **hearts** are the **roads** tó **Zion**.

⁷As they **go** through the **Bìt**ter **Valley**
they **make** it a **place** óf **springs**,
[the **autumn** rain **cov**ers it wíth **blessings**].
⁸They **walk** with **ever** growìng **strength**,
they will **see** the God of **gods** ín **Zion**.

⁹O **Lord** God of **hosts**, hèar my **prayer**,
give **ear**, O **God** óf **Jacob**.
¹⁰Turn your **eyes**, O **God**, oùr **shield**,
look on the **face** of your ánoint**ed**.

11 **One** day with**in** your **courts**
   is **bet**ter than a **thous**ánd **else**where.
   The **thresh**old of the **house** òf **God**
   I pre**fer** to the **dwell**ings of thé **wick**ed.

12 For the Lord **God** is a **ram**pàrt, a **shield**;
   he will **give** us his **fa**vor ánd **glo**ry.
   The **Lord** will not re**fuse** anỳ **good**
   to **those** who **walk** withóut **blame**.

13 **Lord**, Gòd of **hosts**,
   happy the **man** who **trusts** ín **you**.

Give **praise** to the **Fa**thèr Al**might**y,
   to his **Son,** Jesus **Christ** thé **Lord,**
   to the **Spir**it who **dwells** in òur **hearts**,
   both **now** and for **ever**. Ámen.

46 Psalm (85)86

Antiphon

O Lord, our God, un-wea-ried is your love for us.

Psalm Tone

Gelineau Tone

Inclina, Domine

¹Turn your **ear**, O **Lord**, ànd give **an**swer
for **I** am **póor** and **need**y.
²**Pre**serve my **life**, for **Ì** am **faith**ful;
save the **ser**vant who **trústs** in **you**.

³You are my **God**, have **mer**cy òn me, **Lord**,
for **I** **cry** to you **all** thé day **long**.
⁴Give **joy** to your **serv**ànt, O **Lord**,
for to **you** I **lift** úp my **soul**.

⁵O **Lord**, you are **good** ànd for**giv**ing,
full of **love** to **áll** who **call**.
⁶Give **heed**, O **Lord**, tò my **prayer**
and at**tend** to the **sound** óf my **voice**.

⁷In the **day** of dis**tress** Ì will **call**
and **sure**ly **you** wíll re**ply**.
⁸Among the **gods** there is **none** like yòu, O **Lord**,
nor **work** to com**páre** with **yours**.

⁹All the **na**tions shall **come** tò a**dore** you
and **glo**rify your **nàme**, O **Lord**,
¹⁰for you are **great** and do **mar**vèlous **deeds**,
you who al**óne** are **God**.

¹¹**Show** me, **Lòrd**, your **way**
so that **I** may **walk** ín your **truth**.
Guide my **heart** to **féar** your **name**.

12 I will **praise** you, Lord my **God**, with àll my **heart**
and **glo**rify your **ná**me for **ever**;
13 for your **love** to **me** hàs been **great**,
you have **saved** me from the **depths** óf the **grave**.

14 The **proud** have **ris**èn a**gainst** me;
ruthless **men** séek my **life**;
to **you** they **pá**y no **heed**.

15 But **you**, God of **mer**cy ànd com**pas**sion,
slow to an**gér**, O **Lord**,
a**bound**ing in **lò**ve and **truth**,
16 **turn** and take **pit**ý on **me**.

O **give** your **strength** tò your **ser**vant
and **save** your **hánd**maid's **son**.
17 **Show** me a **sign** òf your **fa**vor
that my **foes** may **see** tó their **shame**
that you con**sole** me and **give** mé your **help**.

Give **praise** to the **Fa**thèr Al**might**y,
to his **Son**, Jesus **Chríst**, the **Lord**,
to the **Spir**it who **dwells** ìn our **hearts**,
both **now** and for **evér**. **Amen**.

47 Psalm (87)88

Antiphon

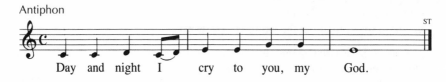

Day and night I cry to you, my God.

Psalm Tone

Gelineau Tone

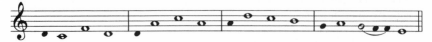

Domine, Deus

² Lord my **God**, I call for **help** by **day**;
I **cry** at **night** before you.
³ Let my **prayer** come **into** your **pres**ence.
O **turn** your **ear** to my **cry**.

⁴ For my **soul** is **filled** with **evils**;
my **life** is on the **brink** of the **grave**.
⁵ I am **reck**oned as **one** in the **tomb**;
I have **reached** the **end** of my **strength**,

⁶ like one **alone** among the **dead**,
like the **slain** lying in their **graves**,
like **those** you re**mem**ber no **more**,
cut **off**, as they **are**, from your **hand**.

⁷ You have **laid** me in the **depths** of the **tomb**,
in **plac**es that are **dark**, in the **depths**.
⁸ Your **anger weighs** down u**pon** me;
I am **drowned** beneath your **waves**.

⁹ You have **tak**en away my **friends**
and **made** me **hateful** in their **sight**.
Im**pris**oned, I **cannot** e**scape**;
¹⁰ my **eyes** are **sunk**en with **grief**.

I **call** to you, **Lord**, all the day **long**;
to **you** I **stretch** out my **hands**.
¹¹ Will you **work** your **won**ders for the **dead**?
Will the **shades stand** and **praise** you?

¹²Will your **love** be **told** ìn the **grave**
or your **faith**fulness **among** thé **dead**?
¹³Will your **won**ders be **known** in thè **dark**
or your **jus**tice in the **land** of óblivion?

¹⁴As for **me**, Lord, I **call** to yòu for **help**;
in the **morn**ing my **prayer** comes béfore you.
¹⁵**Lord**, **why** do you rèject me?
Why do you **hide** yóur **face**?

¹⁶**Wretch**ed, close to **death** fròm my **youth**,
I have **borne** your **tri**als; I ám **numb**.
¹⁷Your **fu**ry has **swept** down ùpon me;
your **ter**rors have **ut**terly déstroyed me.

¹⁸They sur**round** me all the **day** lìke a **flood**,
they as**sail** me **all** tógether.
¹⁹**Friend** and **neigh**bor you have **tak**en àway;
my **one** com**pan**ion ìs **dark**ness.

Give **praise** to the **Fa**thèr Al**might**y,
to his **Son**, Jesus **Christ**, thé **Lord**,
to the **Spir**it who **dwells** in òur **hearts**
both **now** and for **ever**. Ámen.

48 Psalm (89)90

Antiphon

In ev-'ry age, O Lord, you have been our ref - uge.

Psalm Tone

Gelineau Tone

Domine, refugium

¹O **Lord, you** have been our **refuge**
from **one** generation to the **next**.
²Before the **mount**ains were **born**
or the **earth** or the **world** brought **forth**,
you are **God**, without beginning or **end**.

³You **turn** men **back** into **dust**
and **say**: "Go **back**, sons of **men**."
⁴To your **eyes** a **thou**sand **years**
are like **yes**terday, **come** and **gone**,
no **more** than a **watch** in the **night**.

⁵You **sweep** men away like a **dream**,
like **grass** which springs **up** in the **morn**ing.
⁶In the **morn**ing it **springs** up and **flowers**;
by **evening** it **with**ers and **fades**.

⁷So **we** are de**stroyed** in your **an**ger,
struck with **ter**ror in your **fury**.
⁸Our **guilt** lies o**pen** be**fore** you,
our **secrets** in the **light** of your **face**.

⁹All our **days** pass a**way** in your **an**ger.
Our **life** is over like a **sigh**.
¹⁰Our **span** is se**ven**ty **years**
or **eigh**ty for **those** who are **strong**.

And **most** of these are **emp**tiness and **pain**.
They pass **swift**ly and **wé** are **gone**.
11 Who **un**derstands the **power** òf your **an**ger
and **fears** the **strength** óf your **fury**?

12 Make us **know** the **short**ness òf our **life**
that **we** may gain **wisd**óm of **heart**.
13 Lord, re**lent**! Is your **ang**èr for **ever**?
Show **pity** tó your **ser**vants.

14 In the **morn**ing, **fill** us wìth your **love**;
we shall ex**ult** and re**joice** áll our **days**.
15 Give us **joy** to **bal**ance òur af**fliction**
for the **years** when we **kné**w mis**for**tune.

16 Show **forth** your **work** tò your **ser**vants;
let your **glory shine** ón their **chil**dren.
17 Let the **fa**vor of the **Lord** bè up**on** us:
give suc**cess** to the **work** òf our **hands**,
(give suc**cess** to the **work** óf our **hands**).

Give **praise** to the **Fath**èr Al**mighty**,
to his **Son**, Jesus **Chríst**, the **Lord**,
to the **Spir**it who **dwells** ìn our **hearts**,
both **now** and for **ev**ér. A**men**.

49 Psalm (90)91

Antiphon I

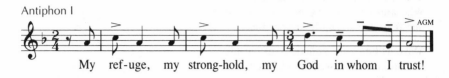

My ref-uge, my strong-hold, my God in whom I trust!

Antiphon II

Call up - on the Lord and he will hear you.

Antiphon III

Night holds no ter-rors for me sleep - ing un-der God's wings.

Psalm Tone

Gelineau Tone

Qui habitat

¹ He who **dwells** in the **shel**ter of the Most **High**
and a**bides** in the **shade** of the **Ál**mighty
² **says** to the **Lord**: "My **ref**uge,
my **strong**hold, my **God** in whom **Í** **trust!**"

³ It is **he** who will **free** you from the **snare**
of the **fow**ler who **seeks** to de**stroy** you;
⁴ **he** will con**ceal** you with his **pin**ions
and **un**der his **wings** you will find **refuge.**

⁵ You will not **fear** the **ter**ror of the **night**,
nor the **arrow** that **flies** by **day**
nor the **plague** that **prowls** in the **dark**ness
nor the **scourge** that lays **waste** at **noon.**

⁷A **thous**and may **fall** át your **side**,
 ten thousand **fall** at yóur **right**,
 you, it will **never** àp**proach**;
⁴ᶜhis **faith**fulness is **buck**ler ánd **shield**.

⁸Your **eyes** have onlý to **look**,
 to **see** how the **wick**ed are ré**paid**,
⁹**you** who have said: "**Lord**, mỳ **refuge**!"
 and have **made** the Most **High** yóur **dwell**ing.

¹⁰Upon **you** no evìl shall **fall**,
 no **plague** ap**proach** where yoú **dwell**.
¹¹For **you** has he com**mand**ed hìs **angels**,
 to **keep** you in **all** yóur **ways**.

¹²They shall **bear** you upòn their **hands**
 lest you **strike** your **foot** against á **stone**.
¹³On the **lion** and the **vi**per you wìll **tread**
 and **tram**ple the young **lion** and thé **drag**on.

¹⁴Since he **clings** to me in **love**, Ì will **free** him,
 pro**tect** him for he **knows** mý **name**.
¹⁵When he **calls** I shall **an**swer: "I àm **with** you."
 I will **save** him in dis**tress** and give hím **glory**.

¹⁶With **length** of **life** I wìll **content** him;
 I shall **let** him see my **sav**íng **pow**er.
 To the **Fa**ther, the **Son** and Holỳ **Spir**it
 give **praise** for **ever**. Ámen.

50 Psalm (92)93

Antiphon I

The Lord is King for ev - er - more.

Antiphon II

Al - le - lu - ia, al - le - lu - ia, al - le - lu - ia.

Psalm Tone

Psalm tone 8-g
Acc. by RP

Gelineau Tone

Dominus regnavit

¹ The Lord is **king**, with **maj**esty enr**ō**bed;
the **Lord** has **robed** himself with m**ì**ght,
he has **gird**ed hims**é**lf with **pow**er.

The **world** you made **firm**, not to be m**ō**ved;
² your **throne** has stood **firm** from of **ò**ld.
From all etern**ít**y, O **Lord**, you **are**.

³ The **wa**ters have **lift**ed up, O **Lō**rd,
the **wa**ters have **lift**ed up their v**ò**ice,
the **wa**ters have **lift**ed **ú**p their **thun**der.

⁴ **Great**er than the **roar** of mighty **wat**ērs,
more **glor**ious than the **surg**ings of the s**è**a,
the **Lord** is gl**ó**rious on **high**.

⁵ **Tru**ly, your de**crees** are to be **trust**ēd.
Holiness is **fit**ting to your h**ò**use,
O **Lord**, unt**íl** the **end** of **time**.

Give **glo**ry to the **Father** Al**might**ȳ,
to his **Son**, Jesus **Christ**, the **Lò**rd,
to the **Spir**it who dw**é**lls in our **hearts**.

Antiphon I

O come, let us wor - ship the Lord.

Antiphon II

Let us bow down be - fore the Lord, the God who made us.

Psalm Tone

Gelineau Tone

Venite, exultemus

¹Come, **ring** out our **jòy** to the **Lord**;
  hail the **róck** who <u>saves</u> us.
²Let us **come** befòre him, giving **thanks**,
  with **songs** lét us **hail** the <u>**Lord**</u>.

³A **mighty God** is the **Lōrd**,
  a **great** kìng above all **gods**.
⁴In his **hand** are the **dépths** of <u>the</u> <u>**earth**</u>;
  the **heights** of the **moun**tains are **hīs**.
⁵To **him** belongs the **sèa**, for he **made** it,
  and the **dry** land **sháped** by <u>his</u> <u>**hands**</u>.

⁶Come **in**; let us **bòw** and bend **low**;
  let us **kneel** befóre the **God** who **made** us
⁷for **he** is our **God** and **wē**
  the **peo**ple who belòng to his **pas**ture,
  the **flock** that is **léd** by <u>his</u> <u>**hand**</u>.

O that to**day** you would **lis**ten to his **vōice**!
⁸"**Hard**en not your **hèarts** as at **Mer**ibah,
  as on that **day** at **Más**sah in the **des**ert
⁹when your **fa**thers **pùt** me to the **test**;
  when they **tried** me, thóugh they saw my <u>**work**</u>.

¹⁰ For forty **years** I was **wear**ied of these **peopl**ē
and I **said**:'Their **hè**arts are a**stray**,
these **peo**ple d**ó** not **know** my **ways**'.
¹¹ **Then** I took an **ò**ath in my **an**ger:
'**Nev**er shall they **én**ter <u>my</u> <u>**rest**</u>.'"

Give **glo**ry to the **Fà**ther Al**might**y,
to his **Son**, J**é**sus **Christ**, the <u>**Lord**</u>,
to the **Spir**it who **dwè**lls in our **hearts**,
both **now** and for **é**ver. <u>A</u>-<u>**men**</u>.

Antiphon I

Great is the Lord, wor-thy of praise; tell all the na-tions

"God is King"; spread the news of his love.

Antiphon II

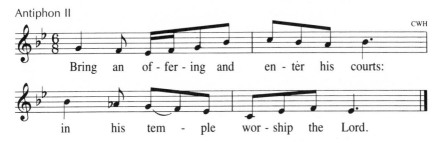

Bring an of-fer-ing and en-ter his courts:

in his tem - ple wor-ship the Lord.

Psalm Tone

Chant tone 5
Acc. by RJB

Gelineau Tone

For 3-line stanzas   For 4-line stanzas

Cantate Domino

¹O **sing** a new **song** to the **Lōrd**,
 sing to the **Lord** all the **eàrth**.
²O **sing** to the **Lórd**, bless his **name**.

Pro**claim** his **help** day by **dāy**,
³**tell** among the **na**tions his **glòry**
 and his **won**ders amóng all the **peo**ples.

⁴The Lord is **great** and **wor**thy of **prāise**,
 to be **feared** above all **gòds**;
⁵the **gods** of the **héath**ens are **naught**.

It was the **Lord** who **made** the **heavēns**,
⁶his are **majesty** and **state** and **pòwer**,
 and **splen**dor in hís **holy place**.

7 Give the **Lord**, you **fam**ilies of **peopl**ēs,
  give the **Lord glor**y and **pò**wer;
8 give the **Lord** the **glór**y of his **name**.

  Bring an **off**ering and **en**ter his **cō**urts,
9 **wor**ship the **Lord** in his **tè**mple,
  O **earth**, **trém**ble be**fore** him.

10 Pro**claim** to the **na**tions: "God is **kī**ng."
  The **world** he made **firm** in its **plà**ce;
  he will **judge** the **pé**oples in **fair**ness.

11 Let the **heav**ens re**joice** and earth be **glà**d,
  let the **sea** and all with**ín** it thunder **praise**,
12 let the **land** and all it **bears** re**joì**ce,
  all the **trees** of the **wó**od shout for **joy**

13 at the **pres**ence of the **Lord** for he **cò**mes,
  he **có**mes to **rule** the **earth**.
  With **justice** he will **rule** the **wò**rld,
  he will **judge** the **pé**oples with his **truth**.

  Give **praise** to the **Fa**ther Al**mìgh**ty,
  to his **Son**, Jé**sus Christ** the **Lord**,
  to the **Spir**it who **dwells** in **ò**ur **hearts**,
  both **now** and for **é**ver. **Amen**.

Antiphon I

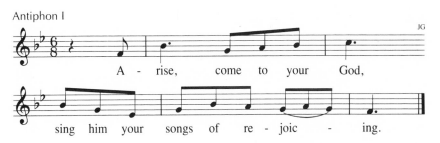

A - rise, come to your God, sing him your songs of re - joic - ing.

Antiphon II

Al - le - lu - ia, al - le - lu - ia, al - le - lu - ia.

Psalm Tone

Chant tone 8-g
Acc. by RP

Gelineau Tone

Jubilate Deo

¹ Cry out with **joy** to the **Lord**, all the **ēarth**.
² **Serve** the Lord with **glàd**ness.
Come be**fore** him, **sí**nging for **joy**.

³ Know that **he**, the Lord, is **Gōd**.
He **made** us, we be**lòng** to **him**,
we are his **peo**ple, the **shéep** of his **flock**.

⁴ **Go** within his **gates**, giving **thānks**.
Enter his **courts** with **sòngs** of **praise**.
Give **thanks** to **hím** and **bless** his **name**.

⁵ **In**deed, how **good** is the **Lōrd**,
eter**nal** his **mer**ciful **lòve**.
He is **faith**ful **fróm age** to **age**.

Give **glo**ry to the **Fa**ther Al**míght̄y**,
to his **Son**, Jesus **Chrìst**, the **Lord**,
to the **Spir**it who **dwélls** in our **hearts**.

54 Psalm (101)102

Antiphon

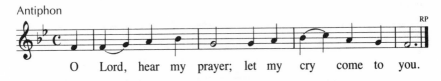

O Lord, hear my prayer; let my cry come to you.

Psalm Tone

Gelineau Tone

Domine, exaudi

2 O **Lord, lis**ten to my **pràyer**
and let my **cry** for **help reach** yóu.
3 Do not **hide** your **face** from mè
in the **day** of **my** distréss.
Turn your **ear** to**wards** mè
and an**swer** me **quick**ly whén I **call.**

4 For my **days** are **van**ishing like **smòke,**
my **bones** burn a**way** like a **fíre.**
5 My **heart** is **with**ered like the **gràss.**
I for**get** to **eat** my **bréad.**
6 I **cry** with **all** my **stréngth**
and my **skin clings** tó my **bones.**

7 I have be**come** like a **pel**ican in the **wildèr**ness,
like an **owl** in **desolate plac**és.
8 I **lie** awake and I **mòan**
like some **lonely bird** on a **róof.**
9 All day **long** my **foes** revìle me;
those who **hate** me use my **name** ás a **curse.**

10 The **bread** I **eat** is **ashè**s;
my **drink** is **min**gled with **téars.**
11 In your **an**ger, **Lord**, and your **furỳ**
you have **lift**ed me **up** and thrown me **dówn.**
12 My **days** are like a **passing shà**dow
and I **with**er away líke the **grass.**

¹³ But **you**, O **Lord**, will en**dure** for ever
and your **name** from **age** to **áge**.
¹⁴ **You** will a**rise** and have **mer**cy on **Zi**on:
for **this** is the **time** to have **mercy**,
(yes, the **time** ap**point**ed has **cóme**)
¹⁵ for your **ser**vants **love** her **very** st**ones**,
are **moved** with **pity** even **fór** her **dust**.

¹⁶ The **nations** shall **fear** the **name** of the **Lórd**
and **all** the earth's **kings** your **glorý**,
¹⁷ when the **Lord** shall **build** up **Zion** ag**àin**
and ap**pear** in **all** his **gló**ry.
¹⁸ **Then** he will **turn** to the **prayers** of the **hélp**less;
he will **not** des**píse** their **prayers**.

¹⁹ Let **this** be **writ**ten for **ages** to **cóme**
that a **peo**ple yet un**born** may **praise** the **Lórd**;
²⁰ for the **Lord** leaned **down** from his **sanc**tuary on **hígh**.
He looked **down** from **heav**en to the **eárth**
²¹ that **he** might **hear** the **groans** of the **prìs**oners
and **free** those con**démned** to **die**.

²⁹ The **sons** of your **ser**vants shall **dwell** un**troublèd**
and their **race** shall en**dure** before **yóu**
²² that the **name** of the **Lord** may be pro**claimed** in **Zì**on
and his **praise** in the **heart** of Jerus**á**lem,
²³ when **peoples** and **king**doms are **gath**ered tog**èth**er
to **pay** their **hom**age t**ó** the **Lord**.

²⁴ He has **brok**en my **strength** in mid-**coùrse**;
he has **short**ened the **days** of my **lí**fe.
²⁵ I **say** to **God**: "Do not **take** me aw**ày**
before my **days** are comp**lète**,
you, whose **days** last from **áge** to **age**.

²⁶ Long a**go** you **found**ed the e**àrth**
and the **heav**ens are the **work** of your **hánds**.
²⁷ They will **per**ish but **you** will re**màin**.
They will **all** wear **out** like a **gár**ment.
You will **change** them like **clothes** that are **chànged**.
²⁸ But **you** neither **change**, nor **háve** an **end**."

Give **praise** to the **Father** Al**mightỳ**,
to his **Son**, Jesus **Christ**, the **Lórd**,
to the **Spir**it who **dwells** in our **heàrts**,
both **now** and for **ever**. **Á**men.

55 Psalm (102)103

Benedic, anima mea

¹My **soul**, give **thanks** tò the **Lord**,
all my **being**, **bléss** his holy **name**.
²My **soul**, give **thanks** tò the **Lord**
and **nev**er **forget** áll his **bless**ings.

³It is **he** who for**gives** àll your **guilt**,
who **heals** every **óne** of your **ills**,
⁴who re**deems** your **life** fròm the **grave**,
who **crowns** you with **love** ánd com**pass**ion,
⁵who **fills** your **life** wìth good **things**,
re**new**ing your **youth** líke an **eagle**'s.

⁶The **Lord** does **deeds** of **jùs**tice,
gives **judge**ment for **áll** who are op**pressed**.
⁷He made **known** his **ways** to **Mòs**es
and his **deeds** to **Ís**rael's **sons**.

⁸The **Lord** is com**pass**ion ànd **love**,
slow to **ang**er and **rích** in **mer**cy.
⁹His **wrath** will **come** to àn **end**;
he will **not** be **áng**ry for **ever**.
¹⁰He does not **treat** us ac**cord**ing tò our **sins**,
nor re**pay** us ac**córd**ing to our **faults**.

11 For as the **heav**ens are **high** abòve the **earth**
so **strong** is his **love** for thóse who **fear** him.
12 As **far** as the **east** is fròm the **west**
so **far** does hé re**move** our **sins**.

13 As a **fa**ther has com**pas**sion òn his **sons**,
the Lord has **pit**y on thóse who **fear** him;
14 for he **knows** of **what** wè are **made**,
he re**mem**bers thát **we** are **dust**.

15 As for **man**, his **days** are like **gràss**;
he **flow**ers like the **fló**wer of the **field**;
16 the wind **blows** and hè is **gone**
and his **place** never **sées** him a**gain**.

17 But the **love** of the **Lord** is ever**làst**ing
upon **those** who **hóld** him in **fear**;
his **jus**tice reaches **out** to children's **chil**dren
18 when they **keep** his **cov**enant ìn **truth**,
when they **keep** his **wíll** in their **mind**.

19 The **Lord** has set his **sway** in **hèav**en,
and his **king**dom is **rú**ling over **all**.
20 Give **thanks** to the **Lord**, all his **an**gels,
mighty in **pow**er, ful**fill**ing hìs **word**,
who **heed** the **vóice** of his **word**.

21 Give **thanks** to the **Lord**, àll his **hosts**,
his **ser**vants whó **do** his **will**.
22 Give **thanks** to the **Lord**, all his **works**,
in **ev**ery **place** whère he **rules**.
My **soul**, give **thánks** to the **Lord**!

Give **praise** to the **Fa**ther Al**mìght**y,
to his **Son**, Jésus **Christ** the **Lord**,
to the **Spir**it who **dwells** in òur **hearts**,
both **now** and for **év**er. **Amen**.

56   Psalm (103)104

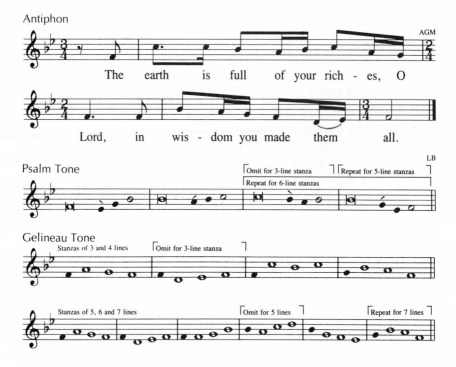

Antiphon

The earth is full of your rich - es, O
Lord, in wis - dom you made them all.

Psalm Tone

Omit for 3-line stanza   Repeat for 5-line stanzas
Repeat for 6-line stanzas

Gelineau Tone

Stanzas of 3 and 4 lines   Omit for 3-line stanza

Stanzas of 5, 6 and 7 lines   Omit for 5 lines   Repeat for 7 lines

Benedic, anima mea

¹ **Bless** the **Lòrd**, my **soul**!
Lord **God**, how **gréat** you **are**,
clothed in **maj**estỳ and **glory**,
² **wrapped** in **light** as ín a **robe**!

You **stretch** out the **heav**ens lìke a **tent**.
³ Above the **rains** you **buíld** your **dwell**ing.
You **make** the **clòuds** your **char**iot,
you **walk** on the **wings** óf the **wind**;
⁴ you **make** the **wìnds** your **mes**sengers
and **flash**ing **fíre** your **ser**vants.

⁵ You **found**ed the **earth** òn its **base**,
to stand **firm** from **áge** to **age**.
⁶ You **wrapped** it with the **o**cean lìke a **cloak**:
the **wa**ters stood **high**er thán the **moun**tains.

⁷ At your **threat** they **took** to **flight**;
  at the **voice** of your **thun**der they **fled**.
  ⁸ They **rose** over the **moun**tains and flowed **down**
  to the **place** which **you** had ap**point**ed.
  ⁹ You set **lim**its they **might** not **pass**
  lest they re**turn** to **cov**er the **earth**.

¹⁰ You make **springs** gush **forth** in the **val**leys;
  they **flow** in be**tween** the **hills**.
  ¹¹ They give **drink** to all the **beasts** of the **field**;
  the wild **ass**es **quench** their **thirst**.
  ¹² On their **banks** dwell the **birds** of **heaven**;
  from the **branch**es they **sing** their **song**.

¹³ From your **dwell**ing you **wat**er the **hills**;
  earth drinks its **fill** of your **gift**.
  ¹⁴ You **make** the grass **grow** for the **cat**tle
  and the **plants** to **serve** man's **needs**,

  that he may **bring** forth **bread** from the **earth**
  ¹⁵ and **wine** to **cheer** man's **heart**;
  oil to **make** his face **shine**
  and **bread** to **strength**en man's **heart**.

¹⁶ The **trees** of the **Lord** drink their **fill**,
  the **ce**dars he **plant**ed on **Leb**anon;
  ¹⁷ there the **birds** build their **nests**;
  on the **tree**top the **stork** has her **home**.
  ¹⁸ The **goats** find a **home** on the **moun**tains
  and **rabbits** **hide** in the **rocks**.

¹⁹ You made the **moon** to **mark** the **months**;
  the **sun** knows the **time** for its **set**ting.
  ²⁰ When you **spread** the **dark**ness it is **night**
  and all the **beasts** of the **for**est creep **forth**.
  ²¹ The young **lions** **roar** for their **prey**
  and **ask** their **food** from **God**.

²² At the **ris**ing of the **sun** they **steal** away
  and **go** to **rest** in their **dens**.
  ²³ **Man** goes **forth** to his **work**,
  to **labor** till **eve**ning **falls**.

²⁴ How **many** are your **works**, O **Lord**!
  In **wis**dom you have **made** them **all**.
  The **earth** is **full** of your **rich**es.

²⁵ **There** is the **sea**, vàst and **wide**,
with its **moving swárms** past **count**ing,
living **things**, grèat and **small**.
²⁶ The **ships** are **móv**ing **there**
and the **mon**sters you **máde** to **play** with.

²⁷ **All** of **these** lòok to **you**
to **give** them their **food** ín due **sea**son.
²⁸ You **give** it, they **gathèr** it **up**;
you **o**pen your **hand**, they háve their **fill**.

²⁹ You **hide** your **face**, they àre dis**mayed**;
you take **back** your **spir**ít, they **die**,
re**turn**ing to the **dust** from whìch they **came**.
³⁰ You **send** forth your **spir**it, they áre created;
and you re**new** the **face** óf the **earth**.

³¹ May the **glo**ry of the **Lord** làst for **ev**er!
May the **Lord** re**joice** ín his **works**!
³² He **looks** on the **earth** ànd it **trem**bles;
the **moun**tains send forth **smoke** át his **touch**.

³³ I will **sing** to the **Lord** àll my **life**,
make **mu**sic to my **God** whíle I **live**.
²⁴ May my **thoughts** be **pleas**ìng to **him**.
I **find** my **joy** ín the **Lord**.
³⁵ Let **sin**ners **van**ish from the **earth**
and the **wick**ed exìst no **more**.
Bless the **Lórd**, my **soul**.

Give **praise** to the **Fathèr** Al**might**y,
to his **Son**, Jesus **Chríst**, the **Lord**,
to the **Spir**it who **dwells** ìn our **hearts**,
both **now** and for **evér**. **Amen**.

Psalm (109)110:1-5, 7   57

Antiphon

The Lord said to my Lord: ·
"Sit at my right hand."

Psalm *Dixit Dominus*

1. The Lord's reve - lation to my Master:
2. The Lord will wield from Zion
3. A prince from the day of your birth
4. The Lord has sworn an oath he will not change
5. The Mas - ter standing at your right hand
6. He shall drink from the streams by the wayside
7. To the Father, the Son and Holy Spirit

"Sit on my right; your
your scep - ter of pow'r; rule
on the ho - ly mountains; from the
"You are a priest for ever, a
will shat - ter kings in the
and there - fore he shall
give praise for ever, give

foes I will put be - neath your feet."
in the midst of all your foes.
womb be- fore the dawn I be - got you.
priest like Mel - chi - ze - dek of old."
day_____ of his wrath.
lift _____ up his head.
praise for ev - er. A - men.

58 Psalm (110)111

Antiphon

I thank you, Lord, for your faith-ful-ness and love.

Psalm Tone

Gelineau Tone

Confitebor tibi

I will **thank** the **Lord** with àll my **heart**
in the **meet**ing of the **júst** and their assembly.
2 **Great** are the **works** òf the **Lord**,
to be **pon**déred by **all** who **love** them.

3 **Majest**ic and **glor**ìous his **work**,
his **just**íce stands **firm** for **ever**.
4 He **makes** us remembèr his **won**ders.
The **Lord** is com**pás**sion and **love**.

5 He gives **food** to thòse who **fear** him;
keeps his **covenant** éver in **mind**.
6 He has **shown** his **might** tò his **people**
by **giving** them the **lánds** of the **nations**.

7 His **works** are **just**ìce and **truth**,
his **precepts** are **áll** of them **sure**,
8 standing **firm** for evèr and **ever**;
they are **made** in úprightness and **truth**.

9 He has **sent** de**liv**erance to his **people**
and es**tab**lished his **covenànt** for **ever**.
Holy his **náme**, to be **feared**.

*10*To fear the **Lord** is the **first** stàge of **wis**dom;
all who **do** so **prove** themselves **wise**.
His **práise** shall **last** for **ev**er!

Give **praise** to the **Fath**èr Al**might**y,
to his **Son**, Jésus **Christ**, the **Lord**,
to the **Spir**it who **dwells** ìn our **hearts**,
both **now** and for èver. **Amen**.

59 Psalm (111)112

Antiphon

The just man is a light

in dark - ness to the up - right.

Psalm Tone

Gelineau Tone

Omit for 3-line stanzas

Beatus vir

¹ **Happy** the **man** who fèars the **Lord**,
who **takes** delíght in his **commands**.
² His **sons** will be **powerful** on **earth**;
the **chil**dren of the úpright <u>are</u>
  blessed.

³ **Rich**es and **wealth** are ìn his **house**;
his **jus**tice stands fírm for <u>ev</u>er.
⁴ He is a **light** in the **dark**ness fòr the
  upright;
he is **gen**erous, mérciful and **just**.

⁵ The **good** man takes pitỳ and **lends**,
he con**ducts** his affáirs with <u>hon</u>or.
⁶ The **just** man will nèver **wa**ver,
he will be remémbered <u>for</u> ever.

⁷ He **has** no **fear** of èvil **news**;
with a **firm** heart he trústs in <u>the</u>
  Lord.
⁸ With a **stead**fast **heart** he wìll not
  fear;
he will **see** the dównfall of his **foes**.

⁹ Openhanded, he **gives** to the **poor**;
his **jus**tice stands fìrm for **ever**.
His **head** wíll be **raised** in **glory**.

¹⁰ The **wick**ed man **sees** and is **angry**,
grinds his **teeth** and fàdes **away**;
the de**sire** of the wícked leads to
  doom.

Give **praise** to the **Fath**èr Al**might**y,
to his **Son**, Jésus **Christ**, the **Lord**,
to the **Spir**it who **dwells** ìn our
  hearts,
both **now** and for éver. <u>A</u>men.

Antiphon

RP

God has freed us and re-deemed us with his might - y arm.

Psalm Tone

LB

Gelineau Tone

In exitu Israel

When **Israel** came **fòrth** from Egypt,
Jacob's **sons** from an **alíen peo**ple,
² **Judah** be**came thè** Lord's **temple**,
Israel be**cáme** his **king**dom.

³ The **sea fled àt** the **sight**,
the **Jor**dan turned **back ón** its **course**,
⁴ the **moun**tains **lèapt** like **rams**
and the **hills** like **yéar**ling **sheep**.

⁵ **Why** was it, **sea**, that you **fled**,
that you **turned** back, **Jor**dan, **ón** your **course**?
⁶ **Moun**tains, that you **lèapt** like **rams**,
hills, like **yéar**ling **sheep**?

⁷ **Tremble**, O **earth**, befòre the **Lord**,
in the **pres**ence of the **Gód** of **Ja**cob,
⁸ who **turns** the **rock** intò a **pool**
and **flint** into a **spríng** of **water**.

Give **praise** to the **Fathèr** Al**might**y,
to his **Son**, Jesus **Chríst**, the **Lord**,
to the **Spir**it who **dwells** in our **hearts**,
both **now** and for **evér**. **Amen**.

61 Psalm (113B)115

Antiphon

The Lord will bless those who fear him, the lit - tle no less than the great.

Psalm Tone

Gelineau Tone

Non nobis, Domine

¹ Not to **us**, Lord, **not** to **us**,
   but **to** your **name** gíve the **glory**
   for the **sake** of your **love** ànd your **truth**;
² lest the **hea**then say: "**Where** ís their **God**?"

³ But our **God**, he is ìn the **heav**ens;
   he **does** whatevér he **wills**.
⁴ Their **i**dols are **silv**èr and **gold**,
   the **work** of **hú**man **hands**.

⁵ They have **mouths** but they **cà**nnot **speak**;
   they have **eyes** but they **cá**nnot **see**;
⁶ they have **ears** but they **cà**nnot **hear**;
   they have **nos**trils but they **cá**nnot **smell**.

⁷ With their **hands** they **cà**nnot **feel**;
   with their **feet** they **cá**nnot **walk**.
   No **sound comes** fròm their **throats**.
⁸ Their **mak**ers will **come** to be like **them**
   and so will **all** who **trúst** in **them**.

⁹ Sons of **Israel**, **trust** ín the **Lord**;
   he is their **help** ánd their **shield**.
¹⁰ Sons of **Aar**on, **trust** ìn the **Lord**;
   he is their **help** ánd their **shield**.

11 You who **fear** him, **trust** in the **Lord**;
   he is their **help** ánd their **shield**.
12 He remémbers us, and **he** will **bless** us;
   he will **bless** the **sons** of **I**srael.
   He will **bless** the **sóns** of **Aar**on.

13 The **Lord** will bless **thòse** who **fear** him,
   the **lit**tle no **less** thán the **great**;
14 to **you** may the **Lord** grànt **in**crease,
   to **you** and **áll** your **chil**dren.

15 **May** you be **blessed** bỳ the **Lord**,
   the **mak**er of **heavé**n and **earth**.
16 The **heav**ens be**long** tò the **Lord**
   but the **earth** he has **givé**n to **men**.

17 The **dead** shall not **pràise** the **Lord**,
   nor **those** who go **down** intó the **si**lence.
18 But **we** who **live** blèss the **Lord**
   now and for evér. **Amen**.

   Give **praise** to the Fathèr Al**mighty**,
   to his **Son**, Jesus **Chríst**, the **Lord**,
   to the **Spir**it who **dwells** in our **hearts**,
   both **now** and for evér. **Amen**.

62 Psalm (114)116:1-9

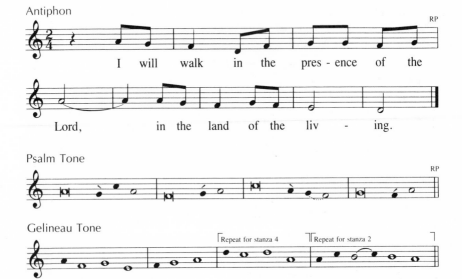

Antiphon

I will walk in the pres - ence of the Lord, in the land of the liv - ing.

Psalm Tone

Gelineau Tone

Repeat for stanza 4   Repeat for stanza 2

Dilexi, quoniam

I love the **Lord** for **he** has **heard**
the **cry** of my **appeal**;
²for he **turned** his **ear** to **me**
in the **day** when **I called him**.

³They surroun**ded** me, the **snares** of **death**,
with the **an**guish of the **tomb**;
they **caught** me, **sor**row and di**stress**.
⁴I **called** on the **Lord's name**.
O **Lord**, my **God**, de**liver me**!

⁵How **gracious** is the **Lord**, and **just**;
our **God** has **com**passion.
⁶The **Lord** pro**tects** the simple **hearts**;
I was **help**less so he **saved me**.

⁷Turn **back**, my **soul**, to your **rest**
for the **Lord** has been **good**;
⁸he has **kept** my **soul** from **death**,
(my **eyes** from **tears**)
and my **feet** from **stumbling**.

⁹I will **walk** in the **presence** of the **Lord**
in the **land** of the **living**.
Praise the **Father**, the **Son** and Holy **Spir**it,
for **ever** and **ever**.

Psalm (115)116:10-19 63

Antiphons I & II

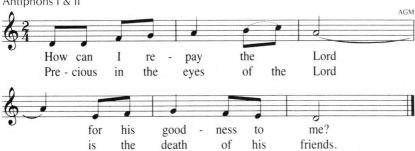

AGM

How can I re - pay the Lord
Pre - cious in the eyes of the Lord

for his good - ness to me?
is the death of his friends.

Psalm Tone

LW

Gelineau Tone

Credidi, propter

¹⁰ I **trust**ed, **e**ven wh**e**n I **said**:
"I am **sore**lý **afflict**ed,"
¹¹ and **when** I **said** in mÿ a**larm**:
"No **man** cán be **trust**ed."

¹² How **can** I re**pay** the **Lord**
for his **good**néss to **me**?
¹³ The **cup** of sal**va**tion Ì will **raise**;
I will **call** ón the **Lord's** name.

¹⁴ My **vows** to the **Lord** I wìll ful**fill**
be**fore** áll his **peo**ple.
¹⁵ O **prec**ious in the **eyes** òf the **Lord**
is the **death** óf his **faith**ful.

¹⁶ Your **ser**vant, Lord, your **serv**ànt am
I;
you have **loos**enéd my **bonds**.
¹⁷ A **thanks**giving **sacri**fìce I **make**;
I will **call** ón the **Lord's** name.

¹⁸ My **vows** to the **Lord** I wìll ful**fill**
be**fore** áll his **peo**ple,
¹⁹ in the **courts** of the **house** òf the
Lord,
in your **midst,** Ó Jeru**sa**lem.

Praise the **Fa**ther, the **Son**, and Hòly
Spirit,
both **now** ánd for **ever**,
the God who **is**, who **was** and ìs to
come
at the **end** óf the **ag**es.

64　Psalm (116)117

Antiphon

Ho - ly　is　God,　ho - ly　and　strong,

ho - ly　and　liv - ing　for　ev - er!

Psalm　　　　　　　　　　　　　　　　　　*Laudate Dominum*

Cantor:

1.　O　praise　the Lord,　all　you　na - tions,

ac - claim　him　all　you　peo - ples!

Strong is　his love　for　us;　he　is faith - ful for　ev - er.

2.　Give glo - ry　to the Fa - ther Al - might - y,

to　his　Son,　Je - sus　Christ,　the　Lord,

to　the　Spir - it　who dwells　in　our　hearts,

both　now　and　for　ev - er.　A - men.

Antiphon

Give thanks to the Lord for he is good, his love is ev - er - last - ing.

Psalm Tone

Gelineau Tone

Confitemini Domino

Give **thanks** to the **Lord** for hè is **good**,   *[Omit B + C]*
for his **love** endúres for **ever**.

²Let the **sons** of Isràel **say**:
    "His **love** endúres for **ever**."
³Let the **sons** of Aàron **say**:
    "His **love** endúres for **ever**."   *[Repeat C + D]*
⁴Let **those** who **fear** thè Lord **say**:
    "His **love** endúres for **ever**."

⁵I **called** to the **Lord** in mỳ dis**tress**;
    he **ans**wéred and **freed** me.
⁶The **Lord** is at my **side**; I dò not **fear**.
    What can **man** dó a**gainst** me?   *[Repeat C + D]*
⁷The **Lord** is at my **side** às my **help**er;
    I shall look **down** ón my **foes**.

⁸It is **bet**ter to take **refuge** ìn the **Lord**
    than to **trúst** in **men**;
⁹it is **bet**ter to take **refuge** ìn the **Lord**
    than to **trúst** in **princ**es.

¹⁰The **nations** **àll** en**com**passed me;
  in the **Lord's** náme I **crushed** them.
¹¹They **com**passed me, **com**passed mè **about**;
  in the **Lord's** náme I **crushed** them.
*{¹²They **com**passed me ab**òut** like **bees**;
  they **blazed** like a **fire** ámong **thorns**.   *[Omit C]*
  In the **Lord's** náme I **crushed** them.

¹³I was thrust **down**, thrust **dòwn** and **falling**
  but the **Lord** wás my **help**er.
¹⁴The **Lord** is my **strength** ànd my **song**;
  he wás my **savior**.   *[Repeat C + D]*
¹⁵There are **shouts** of **jòy** and **victory**
  in the **tents** óf the **just**.

The **Lord's** right **hànd** has **tri**umphed;
¹⁶his **ríght** hand **raised** me.
The **Lord's** right **hànd** has **tri**umphed;
*{¹⁷I shall not **die,** I shall **live**
  and rec**óunt** his **deeds**.
¹⁸I was **pun**ished, I was **pun**ished bỳ the **Lord**,   *[Omit B + C]*
  but **not** dóomed to **die**.

¹⁹Open to **me** the **gàtes** of **hol**iness:
  I will **enter** ánd give **thanks**.
²⁰**This** is the **Lòrd's** own **gate**
  where the **júst** may **en**ter.
²¹I will **thank** you for yòu have **an**swered   *[Omit B + C]*
  and **you** áre my **savior**.

²²The **stone** which the **buildè**rs re**ject**ed
  has be**cóme** the **cornerstone**.
²³**This** is the **work** òf the **Lord**;
  a **mar**vel ín our **eyes**.   *[Repeat C + D]*
²⁴This **day** was **made** bỳ the **Lord**;
  we re**joice** ánd are **glad**.

²⁵O **Lord**, **grant** ùs sal**vation**
  O **Lord**, gránt suc**cess**.
²⁶**Bless**ed in the **name** òf the **Lord**
  is **hé** who **comes**.   *[Repeat C + D]*
We **bless** you from the **house** òf the **Lord**;
²⁷the Lord **God** ís our **light**.

Repeat musical phrase for additional line of text.

Go **for**ward in proces**sì**on with **branch**es
even tó the **al**tar.
28 **You** are my **Gò**d, I **thank** you.
My **Gó**d, I **praise** you.
29 Give **thanks** to the **Lord** for hè is **good**;   *[Omit B + C]*
for his **love** endúres for **ev**er.

Praise the **Fa**ther, the **Son**, and Hòly **Spir**it,
both **now** ánd for **ev**er,
the God who **is**, who **was**, ànd who **will** be,
world wíthout **end**.

66 Psalm (120)121

Antiphon

The Lord will guide me and guard me for ev - er.

Psalm Tone

Gelineau Tone

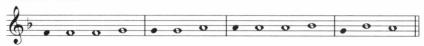

Levavi oculos

¹I **lift** up my **eyes** tò the **moun**tains;
from **where** shall cóme my **help**?
²My **help** shall **come** fròm the **Lord**
who made **heav**én and **earth**.

³May he **never** allów yòu to **stum**ble!
Let him **sleep** nót, your **guard**.
⁴**No**, he **sleeps** nòt nor **slum**bers,
Isráel's **guard**.

⁵The **Lord** is your **guard** ànd your **shade**;
at your **right** síde he **stands**.
⁶By **day** the **sun** shàll not **smite** you
nor the **moon** ín the **night**.

⁷The **Lord** will **guard** yòu from evil,
he will **guárd** your **soul**.
⁸The Lord will **guard** your gòing and **com**ing
both **now** ánd for **ev**er.

Praise the **Fa**ther, the **Son** and Hòly **Spir**it,
both **now** ánd for **ev**er,
the God who **is**, who **was** ànd who **will** be,
world wíthout **end**.

Antiphon

We shall go up with joy to the house of our God.

Psalm Tone

Gelineau Tone

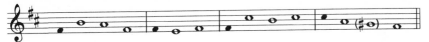

Laetatus sum

¹ I re**joiced** when I **he**̀**ard** them **say**:
"Let us **go** tó God's **house**."
² And **now** our **fe**̀**et** are **stand**ing
within your **gates**, Ó Jeru**sa**lem.

³ Jeru**sa**lem is **built** a̱s a **city**
stronglý com**pact**.
⁴ It is **there** that the **tri**̀**bes** go **up**,
the **tribes** ó**f** the **Lord**.

For **Israel's** la̱**w** it **is**
there to **praise** thé **Lord's name**.
⁵ **There** were set the **thro**̀**nes** of **judg**ment
of the **hó**use of **David**.

⁶ For the **peace** of Jeru**sa**̀**lem**, **pray**:
"**Peace** be tó your **homes**!
⁷ May **peace reign** i̱n your **walls**,
in your **pa**lá**ces**, **peace**!"

⁸ For **love** of my **brethre**̀**n** and **friends**
I say:"**Peace** u̱pon **you**!"
⁹ For **love** of the **house** o̱**f** the **Lord**
I will **ask** fór your **good**.

Praise the **Father**, the **Son** and **Hò**ly **Spir**it,
both **now** ánd for **ever**,
the God who **is**, who **was** and i̱s to **come**
at the **end** ó**f** the **ages**.

68 Psalm (122)123

Antiphon

We lift our eyes to the Lord till he show us his mer - cy.

Psalm Tone

Gelineau Tone

Ad te levavi oculos meos

¹ To **you** have I **lift**ed ùp my **eyes**,
you who **dwell** in thé **heav**ens;
² my **eyes**, like the **eyes** òf **slaves**
on the **hand** of théir **lords**.

Like the **eyes** òf a **ser**vant
on the **hand** of hér **mis**tress,
³ so our **eyes** are on the **Lord** òur **God**
till he **show** us hís **mer**cy.

⁴ Have **mer**cy on us, **Lòrd**, have **mer**cy.
We are **filled** with cóntempt.
⁵ **Indeed**, all too **full** is òur **soul**
with the **scorn** of thé **rich**,
(with the **proud** man's dísdain.)

Praise the **Fa**ther, the **Son** and Hòly **Spir**it,
both **now** and fór **ever**,
the God who **is**, who **was** and whò **will** be,
world withóut **end**.

Antiphon

The Lord has done great things for us;
we are filled with joy, we are filled with joy.

Psalm Tone

Gelineau Tone

In convertendo

¹ When the **Lord** delivered **Zi**on from **bond**age,
it **seemed** líke a **dream**.
² **Then** was our **mouth** fìlled with **laugh**ter,
on our **lips** thére were **songs**.

The **heath**ens themselves sàid: "What **mar**vels
the **Lord** wórked for **them**!"
³ What **mar**vels the **Lord** wòrked for **us**!
In**deed**, wé were **glad**.

⁴ De**liv**er us, O **Lord**, fròm our **bond**age
as **stré**ams in dry **land**.
⁵ **Those** who sòw in **tears**
sing ás they **reap**.

⁶ They go **out**, they go **out**, fùll of **tears**,
carrying **seed** fór the **sow**ing;
they come **back**, they come **back**, fùll of **song**,
carryíng their **sheaves**.

Praise the **Fa**ther, the **Son** and Hòly **Spir**it,
both **now** ánd for **ever**,
the God who **is**, who **was** ànd who **will** be,
world wíthout **end**.

70 Psalm (126)127

Antiphon

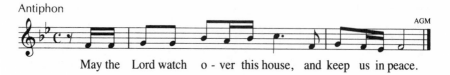

AGM

May the Lord watch o - ver this house, and keep us in peace.

Psalm Tone

LB

Gelineau Tone

Nisi Dominus

¹ If the **Lord** does not **build** the **house**,
in **vain** do its **build**ers **labor**;
if the **Lord** does not **watch** over the **city**,
in **vain** does the **watch**man keep **vigil**.

² In **vain** is your **earl**ier **ris**ing,
your **go**ing **lat**er to **rest**,
you who **toil** for the **bread** you **eat**,
when he pours **gifts** on his beloved while they **slumber**.

³ Truly **sons** are a **gift** from the **Lord**,
a **bless**ing, the **fruit** of the **womb**.
⁴ Indeed, the **sons** of **youth**
are like **arrows** in the **hand** of a **warrior**.

⁵ **O** the **happiness** of the **man**
who has **filled** his **quiver** with these **arrows**!
He will have no **cause** for **shame**
when he dis**putes** with his **foes** in the **gateways**.

Give **praise** to the **Fath**er Al**mighty**,
to his **Son**, Jesus **Christ**, the **Lord**,
to the **Spir**it who **dwells** in our **hearts**,
both **now** and for **ages** un**ending**.

Antiphon I

I place all my trust in you, my God;
all my hope is in your sav - ing word.

Antiphon II

If you, O Lord, should mark our
sins, Lord, who would sur - vive?

Antiphon III

Out of the depths I cry to you, O Lord.

Psalm Tone

Repeat for 6-line stanza

Gelineau Tone

Repeat for 6-line stanzas

De profundis

¹ Out of the **depths** I **cry** to yòu, O **Lord**,
² **Lord**, héar my **voice**!
  O **let** your **ears** bè **at**tentive
  to the **voice** óf my **pleading**.

³ If you, O Lord, should màrk our **guilt**,
  Lord, who wóuld sur**vive**?
⁴ But with **you** is **found** forgiveness:
  for **this** wé re**vere you**.

⁵My **soul** is **wait**ing fòr the **Lord**,
I **count** ón his **word**.
⁶My **soul** is **long**ing fòr the **Lord**,
more than **watch**mán for **daybreak**.
(Let the **watch**man còunt on **day**break
⁷and **Is**rael ón the **Lord**.)

Be**cause** with the **Lord** thère is **mer**cy
and **full**ness óf re**demp**tion,
⁸**Is**rael in**deed** he wìll re**deem**
from **all** íts in**iqui**ty.

To the **Fa**ther Al**mighty** give **glo**ry,
give **glo**ry tó his **Son**,
to the **Spir**it most **Holy** give **praise**,
whose **reign** ís for **ever**.

Psalm (133)134   72

Antiphon

HH

In the si-lent hours of night, bless the Lord.

Psalm

Ecce nunc

HH

1. O come, bless the Lord, all you who serve the Lord,

who stand in the house of the Lord,

in the courts of the house of our God.

2. Lift up your hands to the ho-ly place

and bless the Lord through the night.

3. May the Lord bless you from Zi-on,

he who made both heav-en and earth.

4. Glory to the Father, and the Son, and to the Ho-ly

Spir-it: as it was in the be-gin-ning,

is now, and will be for ev-er. A-men.

73 Psalm (138)139

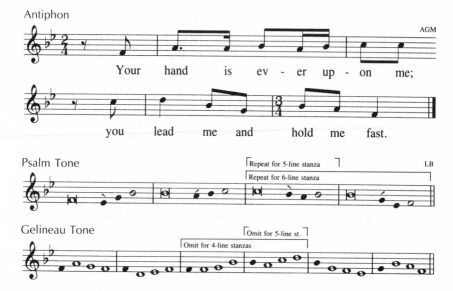

Antiphon

Your hand is ev - er up - on me;
you lead me and hold me fast.

Psalm Tone

Repeat for 5-line stanza
Repeat for 6-line stanza

Gelineau Tone

Omit for 5-line st.
Omit for 4-line stanzas

Domine, probasti

¹ O **Lord,** you **search** me ànd you **know** me,
² you **know** my **rest**ing ánd my **rising,**
 you dis**cern** my **pur**pose fròm a**far**.
³ You **mark** when I **walk** òr lie **down,**
 all my **ways** lie opén to **you**.

⁴ Before **ever** a **word** is òn my **tongue**
 you **know** it, O **Lord,** thróugh and **through**.
⁵ Be**hind** and be**fore** yòu be**siege** me,
 your **hand** ever **láid** upon me.
⁶ Too **won**derful for **mè,** this **know**ledge,
 too **high,** beyónd my **reach**.

⁷ O **where** can I **go** fròm your **spirit,**
 or **where** can I **flee** fróm your **face**?
⁸ If I **climb** the **heav**ens yòu are **there**.
 If I **lie** in the **grave,** yóu are **there**.

⁹ If I **take** the **wings** òf the **dawn**
 and **dwell** at the **sea's** fúrthest **end,**
¹⁰ even **there** your **hànd** would **lead** me,
 your **right** hand would **hóld** me **fast**.

11 If I **say**: "Let the d`a`rkness **hide** me
and the **light** around m`é` be **night**,"
12 even **dark**ness is not d`à`rk for **you**
and the **night** is as **clear** `á`s the **day**.

13 For it was **you** who creat`è`d my **being**,
knit me to**geth**er in my m`ó`ther's **womb**.
14 I **thank** you for the **won**der `ò`f my **being**,
for the **won**ders of **all** y`ó`ur creation.

Al**ready** you kn`è`w my **soul**,
15 my **bod**y held no secr`é`t from **you**
when **I** was being **fashi**`ò`ned in secret
and **mold**ed in the **depths** `ó`f the **earth**.

16 Your **eyes** saw `à`ll my **actions**,
they were **all** of them **writ**ten `í`n your **book**;
every **one** of my **days** w`à`s de**creed**
before **one** of them **came** `í`nto **being**.

17 To **me**, how myster`ì`ous your **thoughts**,
the **sum** of them **not** t`ó` be **num**bered!
18 If I **count** them, they are **more** th`à`n the **sand**;
to **fin**ish, I must be etern`á`l, like **you**.

19 O **God**, that you would sl`à`y the **wick**ed!
Men of **blood** keep f`á`r away from me!
20 With de**ceit** they reb`è`l **against** you
and **set** your des`í`gns at **naught**.

21 Do I not **hate** th`ò`se who **hate** you,
ab**hor** those who r`í`se a**gainst** you?
22 I **hate** them with a p`è`rfect **hate**
and **they** are f`ó`es to **me**.

23 O **search** me, **God**, and kn`ò`w my **heart**.
O **test** me and kn`ó`w my **thoughts**.
24 See that I **follow** n`ò`t the **wrong path**
and **lead** me in the **path** of l`í`fe e**ternal**.

Give **praise** to the **Fath**`è`r Al**might**y,
to his **Son**, Jesus **Chr**`í`st, the **Lord**,
to the **Spir**it who **dwells** `ì`n our **hearts**,
both **now** and for ev`è`r. **Amen**.

74 Psalm (140)141

Antiphon

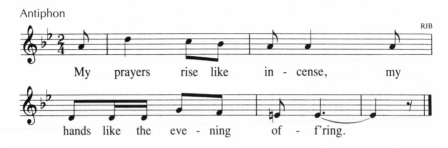

My prayers rise like in - cense, my
hands like the eve - ning of - f'ring.

Psalm Tone

Gelineau Tone

Domine, clamavi

¹I have **called** to you, **Lord**; **hast**èn to **help** me!
Hear my **voice** when I **cry** tó **you**.
²Let my **prayer** a**rise** be**fore** you lìke **incense**,
the **rais**ing of my **hands** like an **eve**ning óblation.

³**Set**, O **Lord**, a **guard** ovèr my **mouth**;
Keep **watch**, O **Lord**, at the **door** of mý **lips**!
⁴Do not **turn** my **heart** to **things** that àre **wrong**,
to **evil deeds** with **men** who áre **sinners**.

Never al**low** me to **share** ìn their **feast**ing.
⁵If a **good** man **strikes** or re**proves** me it ís **kind**ness;
but let the **oil** of the **wick**ed not a**noint** mỳ **head**.
Let my **prayer** be **ever** a**gainst** théir **malice**.

⁶Their **princ**es were thrown **down** by the **side** òf the **rock**;
then they under**stood** that my **words** wére **kind**.
⁷As a **mill**stone is **shat**tered to **piec**es on thè **ground**,
so their **bones** were **strewn** at the **mouth** of thé **grave**.

*8*To **you**, Lord **God**, my **èyes** are **turned**;
in **you** I take **ref**uge; **spare** mý **soul**!
*9*From the **trap** they have **laid** for me **keep** mè **safe**;
keep me from the **snares** of **those** who dó **e**vil.

*10*Let the **wick**ed fall **in**to the **traps** thèy have **set**
whilst I pur**sue** my **way** únharmed.
Give **praise** to the **Fa**ther, the **Son** and Holỳ **Spir**it,
both **now** and for **a**ges un**end**ing. Ámen.

75 Psalm (142)143:1-11

Antiphon

Do not hide your face from me: In you I put my trust.

Psalm Tone

Gelineau Tone

Domine, exaudi

¹**Lord**, **listen** to my **prayer**,
    turn your **ear** to my **appeal**.
    You are **faith**ful, you are **just**; give **an**swer.
²Do not **call** your **ser**vant to **judg**ment
    for **no** one is **just** in your **sight**.

³The **en**emy pur**sues** my **soul**;
    he has **crushed** my **life** to the **ground**;
    he has **made** me **dwell** in **dark**ness
    like the **dead**, long for**got**ten.   *[Repeat C + D]*
⁴**There**fore my **spir**it **fails**;
    my **heart** is **numb** with**in** me.

⁵I re**mem**ber the **days** that are **past**,
    I **pon**der **all** your **works**.
    I **muse** on what your **hand** has **wrought**
⁶and to **you** I **stretch** out my **hands**.   *[Repeat D]*
    Like a **parched** land my **soul** thirsts for **you**.

⁷**Lord**, make **haste** and **an**swer;
    for my **spir**it **fails** with**in** me.
    Do not **hide** your **face**
    lest I be**come** like **those** in the **grave**.

⁸In the **morn**ing let me **know** your **love**
    for I **put** my **trust** in **you**.
    Make me **know** the **way** I should **walk**;
    to **you** I **lift** up my **soul**.

⁹**Res**cue me, **Lord**, from my **en**emies;
I have **fled** to **you** for **ref**uge.
¹⁰**Teach** me to **do** your **will**
for **you**, O **Lord**, are my **God**.   *[Repeat C + D]*
Let your good **spir**it **guide** me
in **ways** that are **level** and **smooth**.

¹¹For your **name's** sake, **Lord**, save my **life**;   *[Omit B + C]*
in your **jus**tice save my **soul** from **dis**tress.
Give **praise** to the **Fa**ther Al**might**y,
to his **Son**, Jesus **Christ**, the **Lord**,
to the **Spir**it who **dwells** in **our hearts**,
both **now** and for **ever**. A**men**.

76 Psalm (144)145

Antiphon · RC

Your king - dom is ev - er - last-ing; you shall reign for ev - er!

Psalm Tone · REK

⌈Omit for 3-line stanza ⌈Repeat for 6-line stanza

Gelineau Tone

⌈Omit for 3-line stanza ⌈Repeat for 6-line stanza

Exaltabo te, Deus

¹ I will give you **glory**, O **God** my **King**,
I will **bless** your **name** for **ever**.
² I will **bless** you **day** after **day**
and **praise** your **name** for **ever**.
³ The Lord is **great**, **highly** to be **praised**,
his **greatness** can**not** be **measured**.

⁴ Age to **age** shall pro**claim** your **works**,
shall de**clare** your **mighty deeds**,
⁵ shall **speak** of your **splendor** and **glory**,
tell the **tale** of your **wonderful works**.

⁶ They will **speak** of your **terrible deeds**,
re**count** your **greatness** and **might**.
⁷ They will re**call** your a**bundant goodness**;
age to **age** shall **ring** out your **justice**.

⁸ The Lord is **kind** and **full** of com**passion**,
slow to **anger**, a**bounding** in **love**.
⁹ How **good** is the **Lord** to **all**,
com**passionate** to **all** his **creatures**.

¹⁰ All your **creatures** shall **thank** you, O **Lord**,
and your **friends** shall re**peat** their **blessing**.
¹¹ They shall **speak** of the **glory** of your **reign**
and de**clare** your **might**, O **God**,

12 to make **known** to **men** your mìghty **deeds**
and the **glorious spen**dor óf your **reign**.
13 **Yours** is an everlàsting **king**dom;
your **rule** lasts from áge to **age**.

The Lord is **faithful** in àll his **words**
and **loving** in áll his **deeds**.
14 The **Lord** sup**ports** àll who **fall**
and **raises all** who áre bowed **down**.

15 The **eyes** of all **crea**tures lòok to **you**
and you **give** them their **food** ín due **time**.
16 You **o**pen wìde your **hand**,
grant the de**sires** of áll who **live**.

17 The Lord is **just** in àll his **ways**.
and **loving** in áll his **deeds**.
18 He is **close** to àll who **call** him,
who **call** on **him** fróm their **hearts**.

19 He **grants** the de**sires** of thòse who **fear** him,
he **hears** their **cry** ánd he **saves** them.
20 The **Lord** pro**tects** àll who **love** him;
but the **wick**ed he will **utterl**ý de**stroy**.

21 Let me **speak** the **praise** òf the **Lord**,
let all man**kind bless** his hòly **name**,
for **ever**, for agés un**end**ing.

Give **praise** to the Fathèr Al**might**y,
to his **Son**, Jesus **Chríst**, the **Lord**,
to the **Spir**it who **dwells** ìn our **hearts**
both **now** and for evér. A**men**.

.

77 Psalm (145)146

Antiphon

I will praise my God all the days of my life.

Psalm Tone

Gelineau Tone

Lauda, anima mea

My **soul**, give **praise** to thè **Lord**;
²I will **praise** the **Lord** all mỳ **days**,
  make **mu**sic to my **God** while Í **live**.

³**Put** no **trust** ìn **princ**es,
  in mortal **men** in **whom** there is nó **help**.
⁴Take their **breath**, they re**turn** tò **clay**
  and their **plans** that **day** come tó **noth**ing.

⁵He is **hap**py who is **helped** by Jacòb's **God**,
  whose **hope** is in the **Lord** hìs **God**,
⁶who a**lone** made **heaven** ànd **earth**,
  the **seas** and **all** they cóntain.

It is **he** who keeps **faith** fòr **ever**,
⁷who is **just** to **those** who are óppressed.
  It is **he** who gives **bread** to thè **hung**ry,
  the **Lord**, who sets **prison**érs **free**,

⁸the **Lord** who gives **sight** to thè **blind**,
  who **rais**es up **those** who are bówed **down**,
⁹the **Lord**, who pro**tects** thè **stran**ger
  and up**holds** the **wid**ow ánd **or**phan.

8c It is the **Lord** who **loves** the **just**,
9c but **thwarts** the **path** of the **wick**ed.
10 The **Lord** will **reign** for **ever**,
Zion's **God**, from **age** to **age**.

Give **praise** to the **Father** **A**l**mighty**,
to his **Son**, Jesus **Christ**, the **Lord**,
to the **Spir**it who **dwells** in our **hearts**,
both **now** and for **ever**. **A**men.

78 Psalm (147)147b:12-20

Antiphon

O praise the Lord, Je - ru - sa-lem! Zi-on, praise your God!

Psalm Tone

Gelineau Tone

Lauda, Jerusalem

¹²O **praise** the **Lord**, Jerùsalem!
Zión, praise your **God**!

¹³He has **strength**ened the **bars** of your **gàtes**,
he has **blessed** the **childrén** with**in** you.
¹⁴He es**tab**lished **peace** on your **bòr**ders,
he **feeds** you with **finest wheat**.

¹⁵He **sends** out his **word** to the **eàrth**
and **swift**ly **rúns** his com**mand**.
¹⁶He **show**ers down **snow** white as **wool**,
he **scat**ters **hoarfróst** like **ash**es.

¹⁷He **hurls** down **hail**stones like **crùmbs**.
The **wat**ers are **fró**zen at his **touch**;
¹⁸he **sends** forth his **word** and it **mèlts** them;
at the **breath** of his **móuth** the waters **flow**.

¹⁹He **makes** his word **known** to **Jà**cob,
to **Israel** his **láws** and de**crees**.
²⁰He has **not** dealt **thus** with other **nà**tions;
he has **not** táught **them** his de**crees**.

Give **praise** to the **Father** Al**mìgh**ty,
to his **Son**, Jésus **Christ**, the **Lord**,
to the **Spir**it who **dwells** in our **hèarts**,
both **now** and for **év**er. **Amen**.

Antiphon

TFS

Let all cre - a - tion praise the Lord.

Psalm Tone

⌐Omit for 2-line stanza⌐   LB

Gelineau Tone

⌐Omit for 2-line stanza⌐

Laudate Dominum

Praise the **Lord** from the **heavens,**
praise him in the **heights.**
2 **Praise** him, all his **angels,**
praise him, all his **host.**

3 **Praise** him, sun and **moon,**
praise him, shining **stars.**
4 **Praise** him, highest **heavens**
and the **waters** above the **heavens.**

5 Let them **praise** the **name** of the
Lord.
He **command**ed: they were **made.**
6 He **fixed** them for **ever,**
gave a **law** which shall **not** pass
away.

7 **Praise** the **Lord** from the **earth,**
sea creatures **and** all **oceans,**
8 fire and **hail,** snow and **mist,**
stormy **winds** that obey his **word;**

9 **all** mountains and **hills,**
all **fruit** trees and **cedars,**
10 **beasts,** wild and **tame,**
reptiles and **birds** on the **wing;**

11 **all** earth's **kings** and **peo**ples,
earth's **princes** and **rul**ers;
12 **young** men and **maid**ens,
old men together with **chil**dren.

13 Let them **praise** the **name** of the
Lord,
for he **alone** is exalted.
The **splen**dor of his **name**
reaches beyond **heav**en and **earth.**

14 He ex**alts** the **strength** of his **people.**
He is the **praise** of all his **saints,**
of the **sons** of Israel,
of the **people** to **whom** he comes
close.

To the **Father,** the **Son** and **Holy**
Spirit
give **praise** for ev**er. Amen.**

80 Psalm 149

Antiphon

Sing a new song to the God of sal - va - tion.

Psalm Tone

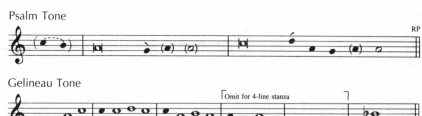

Gelineau Tone

Cantate Domino

Sing a new **song** to thè **Lord**,
his **praise** in the assémbly of the **faith**ful.
²Let **Israel** re**joice** in ìts **Mak**er,
let Zion's **sons** exúlt in their **king**.
³Let them **praise** his **name** wìth **danc**ing
and make **mu**sic with **tím**brel and **harp**.

⁴For the **Lord** takes de**light** in hìs **peo**ple.
He **crowns** the **póor** with sal**va**tion.
⁵Let the **faith**ful re**joice** in thèir **glory**,
shout for **jóy** and **take** their **rest**.
⁶Let the **praise** of **God** be on thèir **lips**
and a **two**-edged **swórd** in their **hand**,

⁷to **deal** out **venge**ance to thè **nations**
and **pun**ishment on **áll** the **peo**ples;
⁸to **bind** their **kings** ìn **chains**
and their **no**bles in **fét**ters of **iron**;
⁹to **carry** out the **sen**tence pre-òr**dained**:
this **hon**or is for **áll** his **faith**ful.

Give **praise** to the **Fa**ther Àl**might**y,
to his **Son**, Jé**sus** **Christ**, the **Lord**,
to the **Spir**it who **dwells** in òur **hearts**,
both **now** and for **év**er. **Amen**.

Antiphon

Let ev-'ry-thing that lives give praise to the Lord.

Psalm Tone

Gelineau Tone

Laudate Dominum

Praise **God** in his hòly **place**,
 praise him in his mígh**ty heav**ens.
² **Praise** him for his powèr**ful deeds**,
 praise his surpás**sing great**ness.

³ O **praise** him with sòund of **trum**pet,
 praise him with lú**te** and **harp**.
⁴ **Praise** him with **tim**brèl and **dance**,
 praise him with **strings** and **pipes**.

⁵ O **praise** him with resòun**ding cym**bals,
 praise him with clashíng of **cym**bals.
⁶ Let **ev**erything that **lives** ànd that **breathes**
 give **praise** to the **Lórd**. **Amen**.

Give **praise** to the Fathèr Al**mighty**,
 to his **Son**, Jesus **Chríst** the **Lord**,
 to the **Spir**it who **dwells** ìn our **hearts**,
 both **now** and for evér. **Amen**.

82 Isaiah 38:10-14, 17-20

Antiphon

I will sing to the Lord all the days of my life.

Psalm Tone

Gelineau Tone

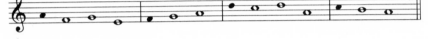

Ego dixi

1. I **said**: "So I must **go away**,
    my **life** half **spent**,
    as**signed** to the **wo**rld be**low**
    for the **rest** óf my **years**."

2. I said: "No **more** shall I **see** the **Lord**
    in the **land** óf the **living**,
    no **more** shall I **look** ùpon **men**
    with**in** this **world**.

3. My **home** is pulled **up** ànd re**moved**
    like a **shé**pherd's **tent**.
    Like a **weaver** you have **rolled** ùp my **life**,
    you **cut** it fróm the **loom**.

4. Between **evening** and **morn**ìng you **fin**ish it.
    I cry for **help** úntil **dawn**.
    I **suffer** as thòugh a **lion**
    were **break**íng my **bones**.

5. I **cry** out in **grief** lìke a **swal**low,
    I **moan** líke a **dove**.
    My **eyes** look **wearil**ỳ to **heaven**.
    Take **care** óf me, **Lord**!"

6. **You** have held **bà**ck my **life**
    from the **pí**t of **doom**.
    You have cast **far** fròm your **sight**
    every **one** óf my **sins**.

7. For the **world** below cànnot **thank** you,
   nor **death** gíve you **praise**.
   Those who go **down** tò the **grave**
   cannot **hope** fór your **mer**cy.

8. The **living**, the **liv**ìng man **thanks** you,
   as **I** dó this **day**;
   the **father** shall **tèll** his **child**ren
   of your **faíth**ful **mer**cy.

9. O **Lord**, **come** tò our **res**cue,
   and **we** shál sing **psalms**,
   sing **psalms** all the **days** òf our **life**
   in the **house** óf the **Lord**.

10. Praise the **Father**, the **Son** and Hòly **Spir**it,
    both **now** ánd for **ever**,
    the God who **is**, who **was** and ìs to **come**,
    at the **end** óf the **ages**.

83 Jeremiah 14:17-21

Antiphon

RL

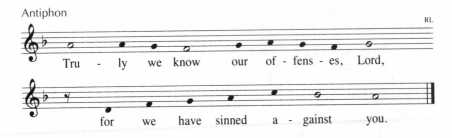

Tru - ly we know our of - fens - es, Lord,

for we have sinned a - gainst you.

Psalm Tone

Tonus Peregrinus

Deducant oculi

1. Let my eyes stréam with tears
   day and night, wíthout rest

2. over the destruction which overwhelms the virgin daughtèr
            of my people,
   over her incúrable wound.

3. If I walk out ìnto a field,
   look! those slain bý the sword:

4. if I ènter the city,
   look! those consúmed by hunger.

5. Even the prophèt and the priest
   forage in a land théy know not.

6. Have you cast Judàh off completely?
   Is Zion lóathsome to you?

7. Why have you strùck us a blow
   that cannót be healed?

8. We wait for peace, tò no avail;
   for a time of healing, but terror cómes instead.

9. We recognize, O Lord, our wickedness, the guìlt of our fathers;
   that we have sínned against you.

10. For your name's sàke spurn us <u>not</u>,
    disgrace not the throne óf your glory;

11. Remember your còvenant with <u>us</u>,
    and bréak it <u>not</u>.

12. Glory to the Father and to the Son and to thè Holy Spírit:
    as it was in the beginning, is now and will be for evér. A<u>men</u>.

84 Song of the Three Children/Daniel 3:52-57

Benedictus es, Domine

JG

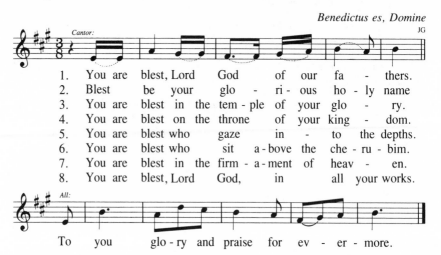

1. You are blest, Lord God of our fa - thers.
2. Blest be your glo - ri - ous ho - ly name
3. You are blest in the tem - ple of your glo - ry.
4. You are blest on the throne of your king - dom.
5. You are blest who gaze in - to the depths.
6. You are blest who sit a - bove the che - ru - bim.
7. You are blest in the firm - a - ment of heav - en.
8. You are blest, Lord God, in all your works.

To you glo - ry and praise for ev - er - more.

Song of the Three Children/Daniel 3:57-88   85

Benedicite, omnia

AGM

#				
1.	O all you	works	of the Lord,	bless the Lord:
2.	And you,	an - gels of	the Lord,	bless the Lord:
3.	And you, the	heav - ens of	the Lord,	bless the Lord:
4.	And you,	sun and	moon,	bless the Lord:
5.	And you,	stars of	the heav'ns,	bless the Lord:
6.	And you,	show - ers	and rain,	bless the Lord:
7.	And you, all	breez - es	and winds,	bless the Lord:
8.	And you,	cold and	heat,	bless the Lord:
9.	And you,	night - time	and day,	bless the Lord:
10.	And you,	moun - tains	and hills,	bless the Lord:
11.	And you, all	plants of	the earth,	bless the Lord:
12.	And you,	riv - ers	and seas,	bless the Lord:
13.	And you,	crea-tures of	the sea,	bless the Lord:
14.	And you, ev - 'ry bird	in	the sky,	bless the Lord:
15.	And you,	wild beasts	and tame,	bless the Lord:
16.	And you,	chil - dren	of men,	bless the Lord:
17.	And you,	priests of	the Lord,	bless the Lord:
18.	And you,	ser - vants of	the Lord,	bless the Lord:

All:

To him be high - est glo - ry and praise for ev - er.

86 Habakkuk 3:2-4, 13a, 15-19

Antiphon

God, my Lord, is my strength.

Psalm Tone

Domine, audivi

1. O Lord, I have heard your renown,
   and feared, O Lord, your work.
   In the course of the years revive it,
   in the course of the years make it known;
   in your **wrath** remember compassion!

2. God comes from Teman,
   the Holy One from Mount Paran.
   Covered are the heavens with his glory;
   with his **praise** the **earth** is **filled**.

3. His splendor spreads like the light;
   rays shine forth from beside him,
   where his power is concealed.
   You came forth to save your people
   to save your a**noint**ed **one**.

4. You tread the sea with your steeds
   amid the churning of the deep waters.
   I hear, and my body trembles;
   at the **sound**, my **lips quiver**.

5. Decay invades my bones,
   my legs tremble beneath me.
   I await the day of distress
   that will **come** to the **people** who **hate** us.

6. For though the fig tree blossom not
   nor fruit be on the vines,
   though the yield of the olive fail
   and the **fields** pro**duce** no **nour**ishment,

7. though the flocks disappear from the fòld
    and there be no herd in the stálls,
    yet will I rejoice ìn the Lord
    and ex**ult** in my <u>sav</u>ing **God**.

8. God, my Lord, is my strèngth;
    he makes my feet swift as those of hínds
    and enables mè to go
    up on**to** the <u>**moun**</u>tain **heights**.

9. Glory to the Father, and to the Sòn,
    and to the Holy Spírit,
    as it was in the beginnìng, is now,
    and will **be** for **ever**. **Amen**.

87 Canticle of Mary/Luke 1:46-55

Antiphon

My soul re - joic - es, my soul re - joic - es in my God.

Psalm Tone

Gelineau Tone

Stanzas 1,2,9,10   Stanzas 3-8

Magnificat anima mea

1. My **soul glor**ifi̇es the **Lord**,
   my **spir**it re**joic**es in **Gód**, my **Sa**vior.

2. He **looks** on his **ser**vant i̇n her **noth**ingness;
   hence**forth** all **ag**es will **cáll** me **bless**ed.

3. The Al**might**y works **mar**vèls for **me**.
   Holý his **name**!

4. His **mer**cy is from àge to **age**,
   on **thóse** who **fear** him.

5. He **puts** forth his àrm in **strength**
   and **scat**ters thé proud**heart**ed.

6. He **casts** the **might**y fròm their **thrones**
   and **rais**és the **low**ly.

7. He **fills** the **starv**ing wi̇th good **things**,
   sends the **rich** áway **emp**ty.

8. He pro**tects Isra**èl his **ser**vant,
   re**mem**bering his **mer**cy,

9. the **mer**cy **prom**ised tò our **fath**ers,
   for **Abra**ham and his **sóns** for **ev**er.

10. Praise the **Fath**er, the **Son** and Hòly **Spir**it,
    both **now** and for **ag**es unend**í**ng. **Amen**.

Canticle of Mary/Luke 1:46-55   88

Magnificat anima mea
JG

Cantor:

1. My soul glori- fies the
2. He looks on his servant in her

Lord, my spirit re- joices in
nothingness; hence- forth all ages will

God, my Savior. Al - le - lu - ia.
call me blessed. Al - le - lu - ia.

Cantor:

3. The Al- mighty works mar- vels for
4. His mercy is from age to

me. Ho- ly his
age on those who

name! Al - le - lu - ia.
fear him. Al - le - lu - ia.

5. He puts forth his arm in strength
6. He casts the mighty from their thrones
7. He fills the starving with good things,
8. He pro- tects Israel, his servant,

and scatters the proud- hearted.
and rais- es the lowly.
sends the rich a- way empty.
re- member- ing his mercy,

All:
Al - le - lu - ia.

Cantor:
9. the mercy promised to our fathers,
10. Praise the Father, the Son and Ho- ly Spirit,

for Abra- ham and his sons for ever.
both now and for ever, world without end.

All:
Al - le - lu - ia.

89 Canticle of Zachariah/Luke 1:68-79

Antiphon

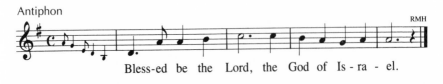

Bless-ed be the Lord, the God of Is - ra - el.

Psalm Tone

Gelineau Tone

Benedictus Dominus

1. Blessed be the **Lord**, the **God** of **I**srael!
   He has **vis**ited his **peo**ple **and** re**deemed** them.
   He has **raised** up for **us** a mighty **sà**vior
   in the **house** of **Dá**vid his **ser**vant
   as he **prom**ised by the **lips** of **hò**ly **men**,
   those who were his **próph**ets from of **old**.

2. A **sav**ior who would **free** us fròm our **foes**,
   from the **hands** of **áll** who **hate** us.
   So his **love** for our **fa**thers ìs ful**filled**
   and his holy **cov**enánt re**mem**bered.

3. He **swore** to Abraham our **fà**ther
   to **grant** ús that, **free** from **fear**,
   and **saved** from the **hands** of òur **foes**,
   we might **serve** him in **ho**liness and **jus**tice
   all the **days** of our **lives** ín his **pres**ence.

4. As for **you**, little **child**, you shàll be **called**
   a **proph**et of **Gód** the Most **High**.
   You shall go a**head** of the **Lòrd**
   to pre**pare** his **wáys** be**fore** him.

5. To make **known** to his **peo**ple their sal**và**tion,
   through for**give**néss of **all** their **sins**,
   the loving **kind**ness of the **heà**rt of our **God**
   who **vis**its us like **dáwn** from on **high**.

6. **He** will give **light** to those in **dark**ness,
   those who **dwell** in the **shad**ow òf **death**,
   and guide us intó the **way** of **peace**.

7. Give **praise** to the **Fa**ther Al**mì**ghty,
   to his **Son**, **Jé**sus **Christ**, the **Lord**,
   to the **Spir**it who **dwells** in our **heà**rts,
   both **now** and for **é**ver. **Amen**.

90 Canticle of Simeon/Luke 2:29-32

Antiphon

GW/AGM

Guard us, O Lord, while we sleep, and keep us in peace.

Psalm Tone

Chant tone 3-b
Acc. by RP

Gelineau Tone

Nunc dimittis

1. At **last** all-**pow**erful **Mas**ter,
   you give **leave** to your **ser**vant **to go**
   in **peace**, accord**ing** to **your prom**ise.

2. For my **eyes** have **seen** your sal**va**tion
   which **you** have pre**pared** for **all na**tions,
   the **light** to en**light**en the **Gen**tiles
   and give **glory** to **Is**rael, **your peo**ple.

3. Give **praise** to the **Fa**ther Al**mighty**,
   to his **Son**, Jesus **Christ**, the **Lord**,
   to the **Spir**it who **dwells** in **our hearts**,
   both **now** and for **ever**. **Amen**.

Ephesians 1:3-10 91

Antiphon

Bless - ed be God who chose us in Christ.

Psalm Tone

Benedictus Deus

1. Praised be the God and Father of our Lord Jesus Christ,
   who bestowed on us in Christ
   every spiritual blessing in the heavens.

2. God chose us in him
   before the world began
   to be holy and blameless in his sight.

3. He predestined us to be his adopted children through Jesus Christ,
   such was his will and pleasure, that all might praise the glorious favor
   he has bestowed on us in his beloved.

4. In him and through his blood, we have been redeemed,
   and our sins forgiven,
   so immeasurably generous is God's favor to us.

5. God has given us the wisdom
   to understand fully the mystery,
   the plan he was pleased to decree in Christ.

6. A plan to be carried out in Christ, in the fullness of time,
   to bring all things into one in him,
   in the heavens and on the earth.

7. Glory to the Father, and to the Son, and to the Holy Spirit:
   as it was in the beginning,
   is now, and will be for ever. Amen.

92 Philippians 2:6-11

Qui cum in forma Dei

HH

1. Though he was in the form of God, Jesus did not deem equality with God some-thing to be grasped at. JE - SUS CHRIST IS LORD!

JE - SUS CHRIST IS LORD! 2. Rather, he emptied him - self and took the form of a slave, being born in the like - ness of men. JE - SUS CHRIST IS LORD! JE - SUS CHRIST IS LORD!

3. He was known to be of hu - man es - tate, and it was thus that he hum - bled him-self, obediently accepting e - ven death, death on a cross! JE - SUS CHRIST IS LORD! JE - SUS CHRIST IS LORD!

4. Be - cause of this, God high - ly ex - alt - ed him and bestowed on him the name a - bove ev - 'ry oth - er name, JE - SUS CHRIST IS LORD! JE - SUS CHRIST IS LORD!

Cantor:

5. so that at Je - sus' name ev - 'ry knee must bend

in the heav'ns, on the earth, and un - der the earth,

and ev-'ry tongue pro-claim to the glo-ry of God the Fa - ther:

(Cantor:) JE - SUS CHRIST IS LORD! *Assembly:* JE - SUS CHRIST IS LORD!

Cantor:

6. Glo - ry to the Fa - ther, and to the Son,

and to the Ho - ly Spir - it:

as it was in the be - gin - ning, is

now, and will be for ev - er. A - men.

(Cantor:) JE - SUS CHRIST IS LORD! *Assembly: allargando* JE - SUS CHRIST IS LORD!

93 Colossians 1:12-20

Antiphon

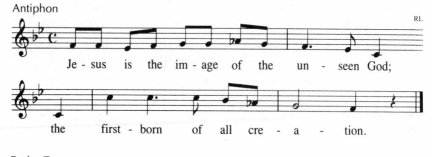

Je - sus is the im - age of the un - seen God; the first - born of all cre - a - tion.

Psalm Tone

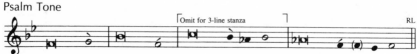

Gratias agentes

1. Let us give thanks to the Fàther
   for having made you wórthy
   to share the lot of the sáints in light.

2. He rescued us from the power of dàrkness
   and brought us into the kingdom of his beloved Són.
   Through him we hàve redemption,
   the forgiveness óf our sins.

3. He is the image of the invisible Gòd,
   the first-born of all créatures.
   In him everything in heaven and on earth wàs created,
   things visible ánd invisible.

4. All were created through hìm;
   all were created for hím.
   He is before all èlse that is.
   In him everything contínues in being.

5. It is he who is head of the body, the chùrch;
   he who is the begínning,
   the first-born òf the dead,
   so that primacy may be hís in everything.

6. It pleased God to make absolute fullness reside in hìm
   and, by means of him, to reconcile everything in his pérson,
   both on earth and ìn the heavens,
   making peace through the blóod of his cross.

7. Glory to the Father, and to the Sòn,
   and to the Holy Spírit:
   as it was in thè beginning,
   is now, and will be for éver. Amen.

94 From 1 Timothy 3:16

RMH

Cantor, then all:
Praise the Lord, all na - tions.

Cantor:
Christ man - i - fest - ed in the flesh.

Christ jus - ti - fied in the Spir - it.

Cantor, then all:
Praise the Lord, all na - tions.

Cantor:
Christ was seen by the an - gels.

Christ pro-claimed by un - be - liev - ers.

Cantor, then all:
Praise the Lord, all na - tions.

Cantor:
Christ, be - lieved through - out the world,

Christ, ex - alt - ed in glo - ry.

Cantor, then all:
Praise the Lord, all na - tions.

Antiphon

By your wounds, O Christ, we have been healed.

Psalm Tone

In hoc enim

Melody

1. Christ suf-fered for you, and left you àn ex - am - ple, to have you fol-low in hís foot-steps. 2. He did no wrong, no de - ceit was found in hìs mouth. When he was in - sult - ed, he re-turned nó in - sult. 3. When he was made to suf - fer, he did not coun - tèr with threats. In - stead he de - liv-ered him - self up to the One who judg - és just - ly. 4. In his own bod - y he brought your sins to the Cross, so that all

of us, dead to sin, could live in ac-cord with God's will. By his wounds you are healed.

Revelation 4:11; 5:9, 10, 12   96

Antiphon

Wor - thy,   wor - thy   is the Lamb that was   slain.

Psalm Tone

Dignus es

1. O Lord our God, you àre worthy
   to receive glory and honor ánd power.

2. For you have created àll things;
   by your will they came to be and wére made.

3. Worthy are you, Ò Lord,
   to receive the scroll and break open íts seals.

4. For you wère slain;
   with your blood you purchased fór God
   men and women of every race ànd tongue,
   of every people ánd nation.

5. You made of them a kingdom,
   and priests to serve òur God,
   and they shall reign on thé earth.

6. Worthy is the Lamb that wàs slain
   to receive power ánd riches,
   wisdom ànd strength,
   honor and glory ánd praise.

7. Glory to the Father, and to thè Son,
   and to the Holý Spirit:
   as it was in the bèginning,
   is now, and will be for ever. Ámen.

97 Revelation 11:17-18; 12:10b-12a

Antiphon

We praise you, O Lord, who is and who was.

Psalm Tone

Gratias agimus tibi

1. We praise you, the Lord God Almighty,
   who is and who was.
   You have assumed your great power,
   you have begun your reign.

2. The nations have raged in anger,
   but then came your day of wrath
   and the moment to judge the dead:
   the time to reward your servants the prophets
   and the holy ones who revere you,
   the great and small alike.

3. Now have salvation and power come,
   the reign of our God and the authority of his Anointed One.
   For the accuser of our brothers is cast out,
   who night and day; accused them before God.

4. They defeated him by the blood of the Lamb
   and by the word of their testimony;
   love for life did not deter them from death.
   So rejoice, you heavens, and you that dwell therein!

Revelation 15:3-4 98

Antiphon

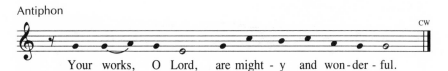

Your works, O Lord, are might - y and won - der - ful.

Psalm Tone

Omit for 2-line stanza

Magna et mirabilia

1. Mighty and wonderful àre your works,
   Lord God álmighty!
   Righteous and true àre your ways,
   O King of thé nations!

2. Who would dare refùse you honor,
   or the glory due your name, Ó Lord?

3. Since you alòne are holy,
   all nations sháll come
   and worship ìn your presence.
   Your mighty deeds are clearlý seen.

4. Glory to the Father, and tò the Son,
   and to the Holý Spirit:
   as it was in thè beginning,
   is now, and will be for ever. Ámen.

99 Revelation 19:1-7

Antiphon

All pow'r is yours, Lord God, our might-y King, al-le-lu-ia!

Refrain I

Al - le - lu - ia, al - le - lu - ia!

Verse   Refrain II

Al - le - lu - ia!

Verse   Refrain I

Al - le - lu - ia, al - le - lu - ia!

Salus, et gloria

1. Salvation, glory and power to our Gód: (Alleluia!)
   his judgements are honest and trúe. (Alleluia, alleluia!)

2. Sing praise to our God, àll you his sérvants, (Alleluia!)
   all who worship him reverently, greàt and smáll. (Alleluia, alleluia!)

3. The Lord our all-powerful Gòd is Kíng; (Alleluia!)
   let us rejoice, sing pràise, and give him glóry. (Alleluia, alleluia!)

4. The wedding feast of the Làmb has begún, (Alleluia!)
   and his bride is prepàred to wélcome him. (Alleluia, alleluia!)

5. Glory to the Father, and to the Sòn, and to the Holy Spírit, (Alleluia!)
   as it was in the beginning, is now, and will be for èver. Amén. (Alleluia,
   alleluia!)

Christian Initiation of Adults

The passage of an adult into the Christian community takes place over an extended period of time. The members of the local church, the catechists and sponsors, the clergy and the diocesan bishop take part in the journey from inquiry through the catechumenate to baptism, confirmation and eucharist. The candidates are invited by example to pray, reflect on the scriptures, to fast and to join in the community's practice of charity. They are to learn the way of Jesus from the members of the church.

This journey of the candidates and community is marked by liturgical rites; thus the community publicly acknowledges, encourages and strengthens the candidates. The first of these is the rite of becoming catechumens. It concludes the sometimes lengthy period during which those who have come to ask about the way of the church and the life of a Christian have heard the gospel proclaimed and seen it practiced. Those who then feel called to walk in this way of Christ's church ask to begin the journey toward baptism. If the church judges the inquirers ready, they are accepted into the order of catechumens (no. 101).

Those who have entered the catechumenate are already part of the household of Christ. During this time the catechumens are to hear and reflect on God's word, to learn the teachings and practices of the church, to become gradually accustomed to the ways of prayer and discipline in the church, to observe and to join in the good works of Christians. Ordinarily the catechumens are present on Sunday for the liturgy of the word but are dismissed after the homily—to continue prayer and study with their catechists—since they cannot join in the eucharist.

Rites of exorcism and blessing may be celebrated during the catechumenate. Through such rites the church prays that the catechumens will be purified, strengthened against all evil and thus eagerly grow in faith and good works. The very presence of the catechumens—at the Sunday liturgy, in these special rites and in everyday life—is itself a source of strength and blessing to the faithful.

Each year as Lent begins, the bishop, with the help of the local pastor and others involved with the catechumens, is to call those catechumens who are judged ready to prepare themselves for baptism at the Easter Vigil. Thus the catechumens become the "elect", the chosen, and for the forty days of Lent they make preparations: praying, fasting, doing good works. All the faithful join them in this. On several Sundays in Lent the rites of scrutiny take place when the assembled church prays over the elect. During Lent also the catechumens may publicly receive the words of the church's creed and of the Lord's Prayer. (The Rite of Election is found with the First Sunday of Lent, no. 787; the scrutiny rites are found with the Third, Fourth and Fifth Sundays of Lent, nos. 793, 796 and 799.)

Good Friday and Holy Saturday are days of prayer, fasting and preparation for the rites of the Easter Vigil. On the night between Saturday and Sunday, the church assembles to keep vigil and listen to many readings from scripture. Then the catechumens are called forward for baptism and confirmation. (These rites are found in the Easter Vigil, no. 818 and following.)

The newly baptized, now called neophytes, take a special place in the Sunday eucharist throughout the fifty days of Eastertime. This is a time for their full incorporation into the local community.

All of these stages of initiation take place in the midst of the community. In various rites, the faithful affirm their support for the catechumens. The daily lives of the faithful show the Christian life to the inquirers and catechumens. In turn, the faithful are strengthened and challenged in their faith by the presence of the catechumens.

Those who seek to belong to the Roman Catholic church and who are already baptized may take some part in the catechumenate but they are not baptized again. Rather, they are received into the full communion of the Roman Catholic Church.

101 ACCEPTANCE INTO THE ORDER OF CATECHUMENS

INTRODUCTORY RITES
The presider greets the assembly: candidates, sponsors, members of the parish. The candidates are asked what it is that they seek and each replies. Before or during this rite an appropriate psalm (for example, Psalm 63, no. 42) may be sung.

CANDIDATES' FIRST ACCEPTANCE OF THE GOSPEL
The presider solemnly asks if the candidates are ready to begin walking this way of the gospel. The sponsors and all present are asked if they stand ready to assist the candidates as they strive to know and follow Christ. All respond: **We are.**

SIGNING OF THE CANDIDATES WITH THE CROSS
The sign of the cross marks the candidates for their new way of life. The presider signs each on the forehead saying:

N., receive the cross on your forehead.
It is Christ himself who now strengthens you
with this sign of his love.
Learn now to know him and follow him.

Sponsors and others also sign the candidates. Ears and eyes and other senses may also be signed. The presider prays that the catechumens may share in the saving power of the cross.

INVITATION TO THE CELEBRATION OF THE WORD OF GOD

The assembly may go into the church for the liturgy of the word singing an appropriate psalm (for example, Psalm 34, no. 36).

LITURGY OF THE WORD
102

There may be one or more readings from scripture, together with a responsorial psalm. After the homily, a book containing the scriptures may be given to the new catechumens for their study and prayer throughout the time of the catechumenate.

INTERCESSIONS

All join in prayer for the new catechumens.

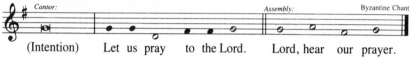

(Intention)   Let us pray   to the Lord.   Lord, hear   our prayer.

If the eucharist is to be celebrated, the catechumens are first dismissed.

RITES OF THE CATECHUMENATE
103

DISMISSAL OF THE CATECHUMENS

When the catechumens are present at Mass, they are usually dismissed after the homily. Only when they have been baptized are they able to join the faithful for the liturgy of the eucharist. After their dismissal, the catechumens remain together and are joined by their catechists or others to pray and reflect on the scripture.

CELEBRATIONS OF THE WORD OF GOD

On Sundays, after the catechetical sessions, before the liturgical seasons and at other times the catechumens and others may join for liturgy: song, reading of scripture, psalmody, prayer and silence are normally part of such a service.

MINOR EXORCISMS

At appropriate times during the catechumenate, the catechists or other ministers may lead the community in prayers of exorcism over the catechumens. These prayers acknowledge the struggle against evil and ask that God strengthen the catechumens.

BLESSINGS OF THE CATECHUMENS

Prayers of blessing and the laying on of hands may take place whenever the catechumens gather for instruction or other purposes. Catechists or other ministers ask these blessings over the catechumens.

ANOINTINGS AND PRESENTATIONS

During the catechumenate or during Lent, the candidates may be anointed with the oil of catechumens as a sign of strength given for their struggle to live the gospel. At some point in this time they are publicly presented with the church's treasury of prayer and faith, the Our Father and the Creed.

RITE OF ELECTION OR ENROLLMENT OF NAMES

See the First Sunday of Lent, no. 787.

SCRUTINIES

See the Third, Fourth and Fifth Sundays of Lent, nos. 793, 796 and 799.

PREPARATORY RITES

See Holy Saturday, no. 817.

SACRAMENTS OF INITIATION

See the Easter Vigil, no. 818.

PERIOD OF MYSTAGOGIA

"Mystagogia" refers to the fifty-day period of postbaptismal celebration when the newly baptized are gradually drawn by the community into the fullness of Christian life and prayer. The newly baptized retain a special place in the assembly and are mentioned in the prayers of intercession. A special celebration, on Pentecost or just before, may mark the conclusion of the whole period of initiation.

The Baptism of Children

Children are baptized in the faith of the church: of parents, godparents, 104
the local parish, the church throughout the world, the saints. Bringing
their children for baptism, the parents profess their commitment to make
a home where the gospel is lived. And the godparents and all members
of the community promise to support the parents in this. Thus the children enter the waters of baptism and so are joined to this people, all
baptized into the death and resurrection of Christ.

Baptism is celebrated above all at the Easter Vigil, but also on other
Sundays, for Sunday is the Lord's day, the day when the church gathers
to proclaim the paschal mystery. Baptism may take place at the Sunday
Mass and is always to be celebrated in an assembly of members of the
church.

RECEPTION OF THE CHILDREN   105

*The parents and godparents are welcomed by all. The presider asks the names of
the children and questions the parents about their own expectations and willing-
ness to take on the responsibilities this baptism brings. The godparents are asked
if they are ready to assist the parents to become Christian mothers and fathers.*

*With joy, then, the presider, the parents and godparents make the sign of the
cross on the child's forehead: "I claim you for Christ our Savior by the sign of his
cross."*

*All then go in procession to the place where the scriptures will be read. The
following antiphon, or a hymn, may be sung during this procession.*

Calvin Hampton, 1984
Acc. by Chris De Blasio, 1985

There is one God, one Fa-ther of all. There is
one God, one Fa-ther of all. He is o-ver all, and

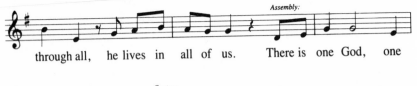

through all, he lives in all of us. There is one God, one

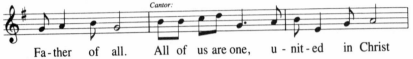

Fa-ther of all. All of us are one, u-nit-ed in Christ

Je-sus. There is one God, one Fa-ther of all.

106 LITURGY OF THE WORD

FIRST READINGS

One or more passages from scripture are read. At the conclusion of each:

Reader: This is the Word of the Lord.

Assembly: **Thanks be to God.**

RESPONSORIAL PSALM

The following psalm (or another from nos. 179 to 182) may follow the first reading.

Ps. (26)27, 1.4.8-9.13-14 / 759-2
RP

The Lord is my light and my sal-va-tion.

The Lord is my light and my help;
whom shall I fear?
The Lord is the stronghold my life;
before whom shall I shrink? ℟.

There is one thing I ask of the Lord,
for this I long,
to live in the house of the Lord,
all the days of my life,
to savor the sweetness of the Lord,
to behold his temple. ℟.

It is your face, O Lord, that I seek;
hide not your face.
Dismiss not your servant in anger;
you have been my help.
Do not abandon or forsake me,
O God my help! ℟.

I am sure I shall see the Lord's
goodness
in the land of the living.
Hope in him, hold firm and take
heart.
Hope in the Lord! ℟.

GOSPEL

107

Before the gospel reading, this acclamation is sung:

Al - le - lu - ia, al - le - lu - ia, al - le - lu - ia.

During Lent:

Praise to you, Lord Je-sus Christ, king of end-less glo-ry!

Deacon (or priest): The Lord be with you.

> *Assembly:* **And also with you.**

> *Deacon:* A reading from the holy gospel according to N.

> *Assembly:* **Glory to you, Lord.**

After the reading:

> *Deacon:* This is the gospel of the Lord.

> *Assembly:* **Praise to you, Lord Jesus Christ.**

GENERAL INTERCESSIONS

108

All join in prayer for the church, the needs of the world, the poor, the children to be baptized and their parents.

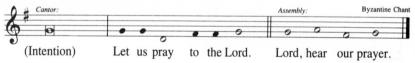

(Intention) Let us pray to the Lord. Lord, hear our prayer.

This prayer concludes with the litany of the saints which may include the patron saints of the children and of the local church.

109

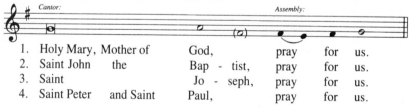

1. Holy Mary, Mother of God, pray for us.
2. Saint John the Bap - tist, pray for us.
3. Saint Jo - seph, pray for us.
4. Saint Peter and Saint Paul, pray for us.

The names of other saints may be added here. The litany concludes:

5. All you saints of God, pray for us.

110 PRAYER OF EXORCISM AND ANOINTING

The presider stands before the parents with their infants and prays that God deliver these children from the power of evil. The children may be anointed with the oil of catechumens, an anointing which makes them strong for their struggle against evil in their lives. The presider lays hands on each child to show the love and concern the Church has for them. If there is a procession to the baptistry, the following may be sung.

We come to you, Lord Je-sus, fill us with your life.

Make us chil-dren of the Fa-ther and one in you.

111 SACRAMENT OF BAPTISM

BLESSING AND INVOCATION OF GOD OVER BAPTISMAL WATER

When all are gathered at the font, the presider leads a blessing of the water, unless the baptismal water has already been blessed.

RENUNCIATION OF SIN AND PROFESSION OF FAITH

The presider then questions the parents and godparents, and they make a renunciation of sin and evil and profess their faith. The assembly listens to their responses. The presider then invites all to give their assent to this profession of faith:

This is our faith. This is the faith of the Church.

We are proud to pro-fess it, in Christ Je-sus our Lord.

A - men, a - men, a - men.

BAPTISM 112

One by one, the infants are brought to the font by their parents. There the parents express their desire to have their child baptized in the faith of the church which they have professed. The infant is then immersed in the water three times (or water is poured over the infant's head three times) as the presider says: "N., I baptize you in the name of the Father, and of the Son, and of the Holy Spirit." All may respond to each baptism with an acclamation.

Cantor then All: Howard Hughes, SM, 1977

You have put on Christ, in him you have been bap-tized.

Al - le - lu - ia, al - le - lu - ia.

ANOINTING WITH CHRISM 113

The presider anoints each child on the crown of the head with holy chrism, a mixture of oil and perfume. The word "Christ" means "anointed." The baptized child has been "Christ-ed" and the sweet smell of the anointing reminds all of this.

CLOTHING WITH THE BAPTISMAL GARMENT AND GIVING OF THE CANDLE

The infants are then clothed in baptismal garments and a candle for each of the newly baptized is lighted from the paschal candle.

Optional *The presider may touch the ears and mouth of each child: "May Jesus soon touch your ears to receive his word, and your mouth to proclaim his faith."*

CONCLUSION AND BLESSING

If baptism is celebrated at Mass, the liturgy continues with the eucharist. Otherwise, all process to the altar, carrying lighted candles. The above acclamation may be sung again during this procession. All then pray the Lord's Prayer, the parents are blessed and the liturgy concludes with a hymn of praise and thanksgiving.

Confirmation

114   Confirmation is a sacrament of initiation. With baptism and eucharist, confirmation climaxes the making of a Christian. It is the seal of baptism, the giving of the Holy Spirit. Adults are confirmed immediately after their baptism at the Easter Vigil. Children who have been baptized as infants are often confirmed some years later. The presider is the bishop or his delegate. The rite is usually celebrated within Mass; the introductory rites are done in the usual way.

115 LITURGY OF THE WORD

FIRST READINGS
One or more passages from scripture are read. At the conclusion of each:

   Reader: This is the Word of the Lord.

Assembly: **Thanks be to God.**

RESPONSORIAL PSALM
The following psalm (or another from nos. 183 to 186) may follow the first reading.

Ps. (103)104, 1.24.27-28.30-31.33-34 / 765-4
RP

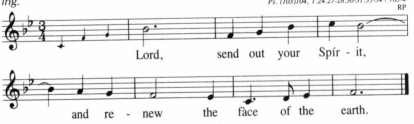

Lord, send out your Spír - it, and re - new the face of the earth.

Bless the Lord, my soul!
Lord God, how great you are.
How many are your works, O Lord!
In wisdom you have made them all.
The earth is full of your riches. ℞.

All of these look to you
to give them their food in due
  season.
You give it, they gather it up;
you open your hand, they have their
  fill. ℞.

You send forth your spirit, they are
  created;
and you renew the face of the earth.
May the glory of the Lord last for
  ever!
May the Lord rejoice in his
  works! ℞.

I will sing to the Lord all my life,
make music to my God while I live.
May my thoughts be pleasing to him.
I find my joy in the Lord. ℞.

GOSPEL

116

Before the gospel reading, this acclamation is sung:

Al - le - lu - ia,   al - le - lu - ia,   al - le - lu - ia.

During Lent:

Praise to you, Lord   Je-sus Christ,   king of end-less   glo-ry!

Deacon (or priest): The Lord be with you.

  Assembly: **And also with you.**

    Deacon: A reading from the holy gospel according to N.

  Assembly: **Glory to you, Lord.**

After the reading:

    Deacon: This is the gospel of the Lord.

  Assembly: **Praise to you, Lord Jesus Christ.**

SACRAMENT OF CONFIRMATION

117

PRESENTATION OF THE CANDIDATES

The pastor or another minister calls the candidates by name to come forward.
Sponsors may accompany candidates.

HOMILY

RENEWAL OF BAPTISMAL PROMISES

The bishop leads the candidates in the renunciation of sin and evil and the profession of their faith. When the candidates have responded, the bishop proclaims:

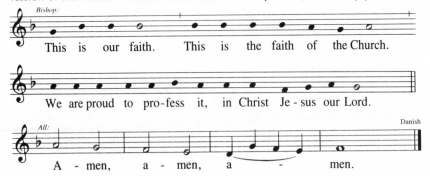

This is our faith. This is the faith of the Church.

We are proud to pro-fess it, in Christ Je - sus our Lord.

A - men, a - men, a - men.

Danish

118   **LAYING ON OF HANDS**

Over and over the church makes this gesture in the sacraments as a blessing, a sign of solidarity and of love. Here the bishop prays for the coming of the Holy Spirit on those confirmed.

ANOINTING WITH CHRISM

Chrism is a mixture of oil and perfume that has been blessed by the bishop at the end of Lent. The meaning of "Christ" is "the anointed," so in this gesture the candidate is anointed, sealed, to follow in the way of Christ. The bishop rubs the chrism into the forehead of each candidate and says: "N., be sealed with the gift of the Holy Spirit," and the newly confirmed person responds: "Amen." The bishop then says, "Peace be with you," and the newly confirmed person responds, "And also with you." The assembly may join in song during the anointing.

After the anointing, the liturgy continues with the intercessions and the liturgy of the eucharist. If confirmation is celebrated apart from Mass, the intercessions are followed by the Lord's Prayer (see nos. 246, 331 and 332), the blessing, and the concluding hymn.

Holy Communion Outside Mass

119

When for good reason communion cannot be received at Mass, the faithful may share in the paschal mystery through the liturgy of the word and the reception of holy communion.

INTRODUCTORY RITES
An appropriate hymn or psalm may be sung.

120

GREETING
If the minister is a priest or deacon, the usual form of greeting is used:
Assembly: **And also with you.**

If the minister is not a priest or deacon, another form of greeting may be used:

Assembly: **Blessed be God forever.**

PENITENTIAL RITE
The minister invites silent reflection and repentance. After some silence:
Assembly: **I confess to almighty God,**
    and to you, my brothers and sisters,
    that I have sinned through my own fault
    in my thoughts and in my words,
    in what I have done,
    and in what I have failed to do;
    and I ask blessed Mary, ever virgin,
    all the angels and saints,
    and you, my brothers and sisters,
    to pray for me to the Lord our God.
The forms found at no. 231 may also be used.

121 CELEBRATION OF THE WORD OF GOD

FIRST READINGS
One or more passages from scripture are read. At the conclusion of each:
  Reader: This is the Word of the Lord.
Assembly: **Thanks be to God.**

RESPONSORIAL PSALM
The following psalm (or another appropriate psalm) may follow the first reading.

Psalm (33)34, 2-3.4-5.6-7.8-9
RP

Taste and see the good-ness of the Lord.

I will bless the Lord at all times,
his praise always on my lips;
in the Lord my soul shall make its
    boast.
The humble shall hear and be
    glad. ℟.

Glorify the Lord with me,
together let us praise his name.
I sought the Lord and he answered
    me;
from all my terrors he set me
    free. ℟.

Look towards him and be radiant;
let your faces not be abashed.
This poor man called; the Lord heard
    him
and rescued him from all his
    distress. ℟.

The angel of the Lord is encamped
around those who revere him, to
    rescue them.
Taste and see that the Lord is good.
He is happy who seeks refuge in
    him. ℟.

122 GOSPEL
Before the gospel reading, this acclamation is sung:

Cantor, then all:
Chant Mode VI

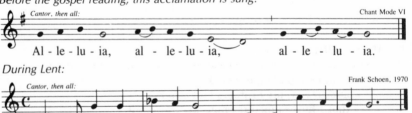

Al - le - lu - ia, al - le - lu - ia, al - le - lu - ia.

During Lent:

Cantor, then all:
Frank Schoen, 1970

Praise to you, Lord Je-sus Christ, king of end-less glo-ry!

Reader: The Lord be with you.

Assembly: **And also with you.**

Reader: A reading from the holy gospel according to N.

Assembly: **Glory to you, Lord.**

After the reading:

Reader: This is the gospel of the Lord.

Assembly: **Praise to you, Lord Jesus Christ.**

GENERAL INTERCESSIONS 123

The assembly joins in prayer for the needs of the world, of the poor and of the church.

(Intention)   Let us pray   to the Lord.   Lord, hear   our prayer.

HOLY COMMUNION 124

The minister invites all to join in the Lord's Prayer, then to exchange a sign of peace. The minister then raises the Bread and all respond to the invitation.

Assembly: **Lord, I am not worthy to receive you,**
 but only say the word and I shall be healed.

A psalm or hymn may be sung during communion. Afterwards, there may be a period of silence or the singing of a psalm or hymn. The minister then recites a concluding prayer.

CONCLUDING RITE

All are blessed and dismissed.

Minister: Go in the peace of Christ.

Assembly: **Thanks be to God.**

Reconciliation of Several Penitents

125   The sacrament of penance, also called the sacrament of reconciliation, may be celebrated with one penitent or with many. The latter form, the communal penance service, is a gathering of a few or a large number of Christians. Together they listen to the scriptures, sing psalms and hymns, pray, individually confess their sins and receive absolution, then praise God whose mercy and love are greater than our evil. In the rite of penance, the members of the church confront the struggle that was entered at baptism. There has been failure, evil done and good undone, but the penitent church comes again and again to name and renounce its sins and to return to the way of the Lord.

INTRODUCTORY RITES
An appropriate hymn or psalm may be sung.

126 **GREETING**
The presider and people greet each other in these or other words:

Presider: Grace, mercy, and peace be with you from God the Father and Christ Jesus our Savior.

Assembly: **And also with you.**

OPENING PRAYER
After silent prayer, the presider concludes the gathering rite with a solemn prayer.

127 ## CELEBRATION OF THE WORD OF GOD

FIRST READINGS
One or more passages from scripture are read. At the conclusion of each:

Reader: This is the Word of the Lord.

Assembly: **Thanks be to God.**

RESPONSORIAL PSALM

The following psalm (or another from nos. 206 through 213) may follow the first reading.

Psalm (50)51, 3-4.5-6.12-13.14-15
HH

Give back to me the joy of your sal - va - tion.

Have mercy on me, God, in your
  kindness.
In your compassion blot out my
  offense.
O wash me more and more from my
  guilt
and cleanse me from my sin. ℞.

My offenses truly I know them;
my sin is always before me.
Against you, you alone, have I
  sinned;
what is evil in your sight I have
  done. ℞.

A pure heart create for me, O God,
Put a steadfast spirit within me.
Do not cast me away from your
  presence,
nor deprive me of your holy
  spirit. ℞.

Give me again the joy of your hélp;
with a spirit of fervor sustain me,
that I may teach transgressors your
  ways
and sinners may return to you. ℞.

GOSPEL

128

Before the gospel reading, this acclamation is sung:

Cantor, then all:
Chant Mode VI

Al - le - lu - ia, al - le - lu - ia, al - le - lu - ia.

During Lent:

Cantor, then all:
Frank Schoen, 1970

Praise to you, Lord Je-sus Christ, king of end-less glo-ry!

Deacon (or priest): The Lord be with you.

  Assembly: **And also with you.**

  Deacon: A reading from the holy gospel according to N.

  Assembly: **Glory to you, Lord.**

After the reading:

  Deacon: This is the gospel of the Lord.

  Assembly: **Praise to you, Lord Jesus Christ.**

HOMILY

EXAMINATION OF CONSCIENCE
In silence or through some other manner all reflect on their lives with sorrow for their sins.

129 SACRAMENT OF PENANCE

GENERAL CONFESSION OF SINS
Kneeling (or with another posture that expresses sorrow,) all join in confession. This form may be used:

**I confess to almighty God,
and to you, my brothers and sisters,
that I have sinned through my own fault
in my thoughts and in my words,
in what I have done,
and in what I have failed to do;
and I ask blessed Mary, ever virgin,
all the angels and saints,
and you, my brothers and sisters,
to pray for me to the Lord our God.**

130 *Standing, all join in a litany using one of the following responses, or a song asking God's mercy. The Lord's Prayer is then recited or sung (see nos. 246, 331 and 332).*

    A   **We pray you, hear us.**

    B   **Lord, be merciful to me, a sinner.**

    C   **Lord, have mercy.**

131 **INDIVIDUAL CONFESSION AND ABSOLUTION**
One by one the penitents approach the priest confessors. All confess their sins, accept some fitting act of satisfaction and the counsel of the confessor. Then the priest extends his hands over the penitent's head and speaks the prayer of absolution, concluding: "Through the ministry of the Church may God give you pardon and peace, and I absolve you from your sins in the name of the Father, and of the Son, and of the Holy Spirit." The penitent responds, "Amen." (Note: On those occasions when general absolution is permitted, the rest of the rite remains the same.)

PROCLAMATION OF PRAISE FOR GOD'S MERCY 132

The presider invites all to give thanks and to show by their lives—and in the life of the whole community—the grace of repentance. A psalm, canticle or hymn may be sung to proclaim God's mercy.

Isaiah 12:1-6
RJB

Praise the Lord and call up-on his name.

I thank you, Lord, you were angry with me
but your anger has passed and you give me comfort. ℞.

Truly, God is my salvation,
I trust, I shall not fear.
For the Lord is my strength, my song,
he became my savior.
With joy you will draw water
from the wells of salvation. ℞.

Give thanks to the Lord, give praise to his name!
Make his mighty deeds known to the peoples!
Declare the greatness of his name,
sing a psalm to the Lord!
For he has done glorious deeds,
make them known to all the earth! ℞.

People of Zion, sing and shout for joy
for great in your midst is the Holy One of Israel. ℞.

CONCLUDING PRAYER OF THANKSGIVING 133

This prayer is spoken by the presider.

BLESSING AND DISMISSAL

The presider blesses all present and the deacon or other minister dismisses the assembly. All respond:

Thanks be to God.

Marriage

134   Many rituals of various kinds and origins surround a wedding. These rites of preparation and of celebration are ways for the couple, the families and friends to share in and to strengthen the making of a marriage. The marriage rite itself is the covenant made by bride and groom, the consent each gives to and accepts from each other. The church assembles to witness and bless this union.

INTRODUCTORY RITES

PROCESSION
The ministers, including bride and groom, enter in procession to appropriate music.

135   **GREETING**

Presider: In the name of the Father, and of the Son, and of the Holy Spirit.

Assembly: **Amen.**

> **A**
>
> *Presider:* The grace of our Lord Jesus Christ and the love of God and the fellowship of the Holy Spirit be with you all.
>
> *Assembly:* **And also with you.**

> **B**
>
> *Presider:* The grace and peace of God our Father and the Lord Jesus Christ be with you.
>
> *Assembly:* **Blessed be God, the Father of our Lord Jesus Christ.**
> *or:* **And also with you.**

> **C**
>
> *Presider:* The Lord be with you. *(Bishop:* Peace be with you.)
>
> *Assembly:* **And also with you.**

PENITENTIAL RITE 136

The presider invites the people to recall their sins in silence and repent of them.
After the silence, one of the following forms is used.

A   *Assembly:* **I confess to almighty God,**
and to you my brothers and sisters,
that I have sinned through my own fault
in my thoughts and in my words,
in what I have done,
and in what I have failed to do;
and I ask blessed Mary, ever virgin,
all the angels and saints,
and you, my brothers and sisters,
to pray for me to the Lord our God.

B   *Presider:* Lord, we have sinned against you:
Lord, have mercy.

Assembly: **Lord, have mercy.**

Presider: Lord, show us your mercy and love.

Assembly: **And grant us your salvation.**

C   *The presider or another minister makes a series of invocations according*
to the following pattern.

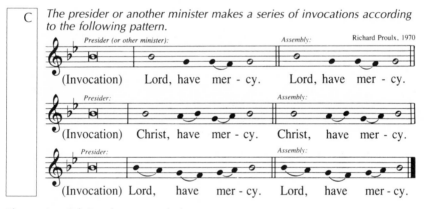

The penitential rite always concludes:

Presider: May almighty God have mercy on us, forgive us our sins, and
bring us to everlasting life.

Assembly: **Amen.**

KYRIE 137

Unless form C of the penitential rite has been used, the Kyrie follows. The people
repeat each invocation after the presider or other minister.

Christ, have mer - cy. Christ, have mer - cy.

Lord, have mer - cy. Lord, have mer - cy.

Or:

138

Richard Proulx, 1970

Ky - ri - e e - le - i - son. Ky - ri - e e - le - i - son.

Chri - ste e - le - i - son. Chri - ste e - le - i - son.

Ky - ri - e e - le - i - son. Ky - ri - e e - le - i - son.

139 **GLORIA**

The Gloria is omitted during Advent and Lent.

"A New Mass for Congregations"
Carroll Thomas Andrews, 1970

Glo - ry to God in the high - est, and

peace to his peo - ple on earth. Lord God,

heav - en - ly King, al - might - y God and Fa - ther, we

wor - ship you, we give you thanks, we praise you for your

glo - ry. Lord Je - sus Christ, on - ly Son of the

Fa - ther, Lord God, Lamb of God, you take a - way the

sin of the world: have mer - cy on us;
you are seat - ed at the right hand of the Fa - ther:
re - ceive our prayer.

Tempo primo **f**

For you a-lone are the Ho - ly One, you a - lone are the
Lord, you a - lone are the Most High,
Je - sus Christ, with the Ho - ly Spir - it, in the glo - ry of

ff

God the Fa - ther. A - men.

OPENING PRAYER   140

The gathering rites conclude with a silent prayer and a prayer spoken by the presider.

LITURGY OF THE WORD   141

FIRST READINGS

One or more passages from scriptures are read. At the conclusion of each:

  Reader: This is the Word of the Lord.

Assembly: **Thanks be to God.**

RESPONSORIAL PSALM

The following psalm (or another from nos. 187 through 192) may follow the first reading.

Psalm (32)33, 12.18.20.21.22 / 776-1
JRC

The earth is full of the good-ness, the good-ness of the Lord.

They are happy, whose God is the Lord,
the people he has chosen as his own.
The Lord looks on those who revere him,
on those who hope in his love. ℟.

Our soul is waiting for the Lord.
The Lord is our help and our shield.
In him do our hearts find joy.
We trust in his holy name. ℟.

May your love be upon us, O Lord,
as we place all our hope in you. ℟.

142 GOSPEL

Before the gospel reading, this acclamation is sung:

Chant Mode VI

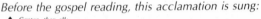

Al - le - lu - ia, al - le - lu - ia, al - le - lu - ia.

During Lent:

Frank Schoen, 1970

Praise to you, Lord Je-sus Christ, king of end-less glo-ry!

Deacon (or priest): The Lord be with you.

> *Assembly:* **And also with you.**

> *Deacon:* A reading from the holy gospel according to N.

> *Assembly:* **Glory to you, Lord.**

After the reading:

> *Deacon:* This is the gospel of the Lord.

> *Assembly:* **Praise to you, Lord Jesus Christ.**

HOMILY

143 SACRAMENT OF MARRIAGE

The presider invites the couple to give their consent to each other freely in the presence of the church. When they have done so, the presider receives their consent in the name of the church. The wedding rings, a sign of love and fidelity, are then blessed and exchanged. Unity Candle

GENERAL INTERCESSIONS

144

The church joins in prayer for the needs of the world, for the poor, for the community and for the couple.

(Intention)   Let us pray   to the Lord.   Lord, hear   our   prayer.

LITURGY OF THE EUCHARIST

145

PREPARATION OF THE GIFTS   *Music - Hymn*

Bread and wine are brought to the table. If there is no music, all may respond to the prayers of preparation:

Assembly: **Blessed be God for ever.**

The preparation concludes with the priest inviting all to pray:

Assembly: **May the Lord accept the sacrifice at your hands**
for the praise and glory of his name,
for our good, and the good of all his church.

EUCHARISTIC PRAYER

146

The presider invites the assembly to join in giving thanks and praise to God for the wonders of creation and the works of salvation.

The Lord   be   with you.   And al - so   with   you.

Lift   up   your   hearts.   We   lift   them   up   to   the   Lord.

Let   us   give   thanks   to   the   Lord   our   God.

It   is   right   to   give   him   thanks   and   praise.

During the eucharistic prayer, the assembly sings acclamations of praise and
thanksgiving. The first is the "Sanctus":

"A Community Mass"
Richard Proulx, 1970

147

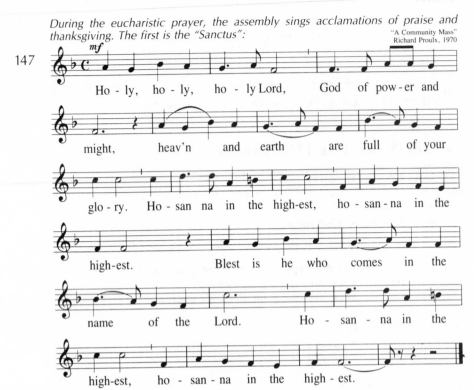

Ho - ly, ho - ly, ho - ly Lord, God of pow-er and
might, heav'n and earth are full of your
glo - ry. Ho - san na in the high-est, ho - san - na in the
high-est. Blest is he who comes in the
name of the Lord. Ho - san - na in the
high-est, ho - san - na in the high - est.

The second is the response to the invitation, "Let us proclaim the mystery of faith":

"A Community Mass"
Richard Proulx, 1970

148

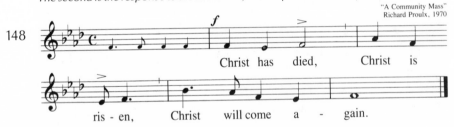

Christ has died, Christ is
ris - en, Christ will come a - gain.

Finally, the assembly ratifies the entire eucharistic prayer.

149 *Presider:* Through him, with him, in him, in the unity of the Holy Spirit, all
glory and honor is yours, almighty Father, for ever and ever.

Danish

A - men, a - men, a - men.

150 **COMMUNION RITE**

The presider invites the assembly to join in the Lord's Prayer.

Robert Snow, 1964
Acc. by Robert J. Batastini, 1975

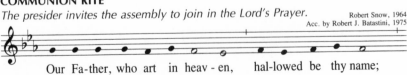

Our Fa-ther, who art in heav - en, hal-lowed be thy name;

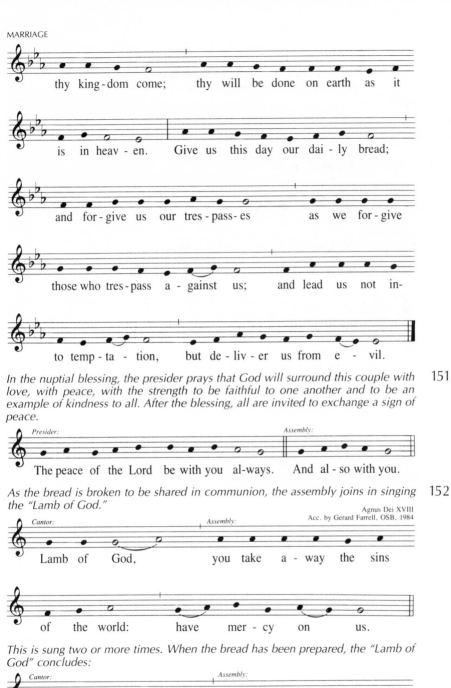

thy king-dom come; thy will be done on earth as it

is in heav-en. Give us this day our dai-ly bread;

and for-give us our tres-pass-es as we for-give

those who tres-pass a-gainst us; and lead us not in-

to temp-ta-tion, but de-liv-er us from e-vil.

In the nuptial blessing, the presider prays that God will surround this couple with 151
love, with peace, with the strength to be faithful to one another and to be an
example of kindness to all. After the blessing, all are invited to exchange a sign of
peace.

Presider: Assembly:

The peace of the Lord be with you al-ways. And al-so with you.

As the bread is broken to be shared in communion, the assembly joins in singing 152
the "Lamb of God."

Agnus Dei XVIII
Acc. by Gerard Farrell, OSB, 1984

Cantor: Assembly:

Lamb of God, you take a-way the sins

of the world: have mer-cy on us.

This is sung two or more times. When the bread has been prepared, the "Lamb of
God" concludes:

Cantor: Assembly:

Lamb of God, you take a-way the sins

of the world: grant us peace.

153 *The presider invites the assembly to share holy communion.*

Assembly: **Lord, I am not worthy to receive you,**
but only say the word and I shall be healed.

After communion there is a time of silence which is concluded with a prayer spoken by the presider.

154 CONCLUDING RITE

Presider: The Lord be with you.

Assembly: **And also with you.**

BLESSING
First the couple, then the whole assembly is blessed.

DISMISSAL

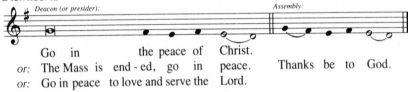

Deacon (or presider):   Assembly:

Go   in   the peace of   Christ.
or: The Mass is end-ed, go   in   peace.   Thanks be to God.
or: Go in peace to love and serve the   Lord.

The liturgy may conclude with an appropriate song or instrumental music.

[When the rite of marriage is celebrated apart from Mass, all of the above may be used but the "Liturgy of the Eucharist" is omitted. After the prayers of intercession, the nuptial blessing is given. The rite concludes with the Lord's Prayer (no. 150) and the blessing of the couple and the assembly.]

Anointing of the Sick

The sacrament of anointing is celebrated when a Christian's health is seri- ously impaired by sickness or old age. If possible, it is celebrated when the sick person is able to take part in the rite. When the sick person is able to receive holy communion, the rite of anointing may be celebrated within the liturgy of the Mass.

Through the anointing with the blessed oil of the sick, the church supports those who struggle against illness or injury and continues the healing work of Christ. The anointing is intended to bring hope and comfort to the one anointed and, to the gathered family and friends, a spirit of support and sharing in the sufferings of our brothers and sisters.

The Mass begins in the usual way, but after the greeting the presider welcomes the sick.

LITURGY OF THE WORD

FIRST READINGS
One or more passages from scripture are read. At the conclusion of each:

Reader: This is the Word of the Lord.

Assembly: **Thanks be to God.**

RESPONSORIAL PSALM

The following psalm (or another from nos. 214 through 228) may follow the first reading.

Ps.(70)71, 1-2.5-6.8-9.14-15
HH

My God, come quick-ly to help me.

In you, O Lord, I take refuge;
let me never be put to shame.
In your justice rescue me, free me;
pay heed to me and save me. ℟.

It is you, O Lord, who are my hope,
my trust, O Lord, since my youth.
On you I have leaned from my birth,
from my mother's womb you have been my help.
My hope has always been in you. ℟.

My lips are filled with your praise,
with your glory all the day long.
Do not reject me now that I am old;
When my strength fails do not forsake me. ℟.

But as for me, I will always hope
and praise you more and more.
My lips will tell of your justice
and day by day of your help. ℟.

157 GOSPEL

Before the gospel reading, this acclamation is sung:

Chant Mode VI

Al - le - lu - ia, al - le - lu - ia, al - le - lu - ia.

During Lent:

Frank Schoen, 1970

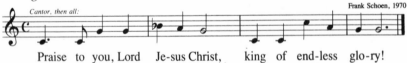

Praise to you, Lord Je-sus Christ, king of end-less glo-ry!

Deacon (or priest): The Lord be with you.

> *Assembly:* **And also with you.**

> *Deacon:* A reading from the holy gospel according to N.

> *Assembly:* **Glory to you, Lord.**

After the reading:

> *Deacon:* This is the gospel of the Lord.

> *Assembly:* **Praise to you, Lord Jesus Christ.**

HOMILY

LITURGY OF ANOINTING 158

LITANY
The assembly joins in prayers for the sick and for those who care for them.

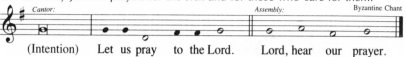

(Intention) Let us pray to the Lord. Lord, hear our prayer.

LAYING ON OF HANDS
The presider silently lays hands on the head of each sick person in a gesture of prayer, healing and solidarity.

PRAYER OVER THE OIL
If the oil is already blessed, the presider leads a prayer of thanksgiving over it. After each prayer:

Assembly: **Blessed be God who heals us in Christ.**

If the oil is not blessed, the presider leads the prayer of blessing.

ANOINTING
The presider anoints each sick person on the forehead in a sign of strength and soothing comfort.

Presider: Through this holy anointing may the Lord in his love and mercy help you with the grace of the Holy Spirit.

Assembly: **Amen.**

The presider anoints the hands of each sick person.

Presider: May the Lord who frees you from sin save you and raise you up.

Assembly: **Amen.**

The presider may anoint other parts of the body.

PRAYER AFTER ANOINTING 159
The presider prays for those who have been anointed. Then the liturgy of the eucharist is celebrated with special prayers for the sick.

[If the rite of anointing is celebrated outside of Mass, the liturgy begins with the greeting, rite of sprinkling and penitential rite. After the scriptures and homily, the liturgy of anointing is celebrated as above. Then the Lord's Prayer is recited or sung and the rite may conclude with holy communion.]

Funeral Mass

160 The rites which surround the death of a Christian extend from the Viaticum (last communion) and final prayers before death through the wake service and funeral Mass to the burial of the body or ashes. In all of this the community affirms its faith in the communion of saints and the resurrection of the dead. The family and friends are helped in their time of sorrow with prayer and song. Thus they express present grief even as they hold to the church's lasting hope. Following is the rite of the funeral Mass.

INTRODUCTORY RITES

GREETING
One of the following is spoken.

A *Presider:* The grace of our Lord Jesus Christ and the love of God and the fellowship of the Holy Spirit be with you all.

Assembly: **And also with you.**

B *Presider:* The grace and peace of God our Father and the Lord Jesus Christ be with you.

Assembly: **And also with you.**

C *Presider:* The grace and peace of God our Father, who raised Jesus from the dead, be always with you.

Assembly: **And also with you.**

D *Presider:* May the Father of mercies, the God of all consolation, be with you.

Assembly: **And also with you.**

The body is sprinkled with holy water, a reminder of baptism. The family or pall bearers spread the pall over the body, a garment like that which the Christian received at baptism. The funeral procession then moves into the church accompanied by the following song or an appropriate hymn.

Psalm (114) 115
RJB

161

Give him/her e - ter - nal rest, O Lord, and may your light shine on him/her for ev - er.

I love the Lord for he has heard
the cry of my appeal;
for he turned his ear to me
in the day when I called him. ℟.

They surround me, the snares of death,
with the anguish of the tomb;
they caught me, sorrow and distress.
I called on the Lord's name,
O Lord, our God, deliver us. ℟.

How gracious is the Lord, and just;
our God has compassion.
The Lord protects the simple hearts,
I was helpless so he saved me. ℟.

Turn back, my soul, to your rest
for the Lord has been good,
he has kept my soul from death
and my feet from stumbling. ℟.

I will walk in the presence of
the Lord
in the land of the living.
Praise the Father, the Son and
the Holy Spirit,
for ever and ever. ℟.

OPENING PRAYER
162

The presider invites all to pray and leads an opening prayer. All respond: **Amen.**

LITURGY OF THE WORD
163

FIRST READINGS

One or more passages from scripture are read. At the conclusion of each:

Reader: This is the Word of the Lord.

Assembly: **Thanks be to God.**

RESPONSORIAL PSALM

The following psalm (or another from nos. 193 through 205) may follow the first reading.

Ps.(22) 23, 1-3.3-4.5.6 / 791-1
RP

The Lord is my shep-herd; there is noth-ing I shall want.

The Lord is my shepherd;
there is nothing I shall want.
Fresh and green are the pastures
where he gives me repose.
Near restful waters he leads me,
to revive my drooping spirit. ℟.

He guides me along the right path;
he is true to his name.
If I should walk in the valley of
    darkness
no evil would I fear.

You are there with your crook and
your staff;
with these you give me comfort. ℟.

You have prepared a banquet for me
in the sight of my foes.
My head you have anointed with oil;
my cup is overflowing. ℟.

Surely goodness and kindness shall
    follow me
all the days of my life.
In the Lord's own house shall I dwell
for ever and ever. ℟.

164 GOSPEL

Before the gospel reading, this acclamation is sung:

Chant Mode VI

Al - le - lu - ia, al - le - lu - ia, al - le - lu - ia.

During Lent:

Frank Schoen, 1970

Praise to you, Lord Je - sus Christ, king of end-less glo-ry!

Deacon (or priest): The Lord be with you.

   Assembly: **And also with you.**

      Deacon: A reading from the holy gospel according to N.

   Assembly: **Glory to you, Lord.**

After the reading:

      Deacon: This is the gospel of the Lord.

   Assembly: **Praise to you, Lord Jesus Christ.**

HOMILY

GENERAL INTERCESSIONS 165

All pray for the church, the local community, those in need, the deceased and those who mourn.

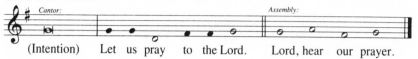

(Intention) Let us pray to the Lord. Lord, hear our prayer.

LITURGY OF THE EUCHARIST 166

PREPARATION OF THE ALTAR AND GIFTS

Bread and wine are brought to the table and the deacon or presider prepares these gifts. If there is no music, the prayers of preparation may be said aloud, and all may respond: **Blessed be God for ever.** *The presider then invites all to pray.*

Assembly: **May the Lord accept the sacrifice at your hands**
for the praise and glory of his name,
for our good, and the good of all his church.

The presider says the prayer over the gifts and all respond: **Amen.**

EUCHARISTIC PRAYER 167

This central prayer of the liturgy begins with this dialogue:

The Lord be with you. And al - so with you.

Lift up your hearts. We lift them up to the Lord.

Let us give thanks to the Lord our God.

It is right to give him thanks and praise.

The Sanctus acclamation concludes the first part of the eucharistic prayer.

168

Ho - ly, ho - ly, ho - ly Lord, God of pow-er and might,

heav'n and earth are full of your glo-ry. Ho-

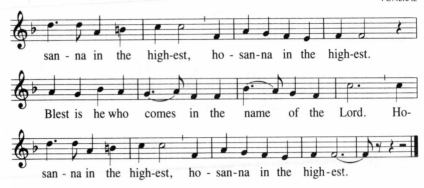

san - na in the high-est, ho - san-na in the high-est.

Blest is he who comes in the name of the Lord. Ho-

san - na in the high-est, ho - san-na in the high-est.

The following acclamation comes in response to the presider's invitation to proclaim the mystery of faith.

"A Community Mass"
Richard Proulx, 1970

169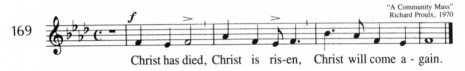

Christ has died, Christ is ris-en, Christ will come a - gain.

The eucharistic prayer concludes:

170 *Presider:* Through him, with him, in him, in the unity of the Holy Spirit, all glory and honor is yours, almighty Father, for ever and ever.

Danish

A - men, a - men, a - men.

171 **COMMUNION RITE**

The presider invites the assembly to join in the Lord's Prayer.

Adapt. by Robert Snow, 1964

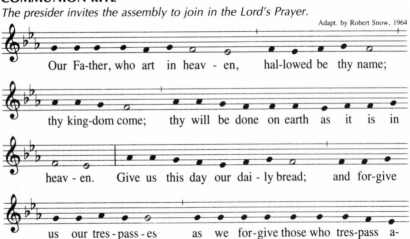

Our Fa-ther, who art in heav - en, hal-lowed be thy name;

thy king-dom come; thy will be done on earth as it is in

heav - en. Give us this day our dai - ly bread; and for-give

us our tres - pass - es as we for-give those who tres-pass a-

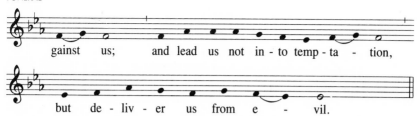

gainst us; and lead us not in-to temp-ta - tion,

but de - liv - er us from e - vil.

Presider: Deliver us, Lord…for the coming of our Savior, Jesus
Christ.

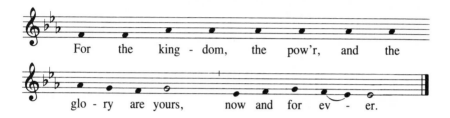

For the king - dom, the pow'r, and the

glo - ry are yours, now and for ev - er.

Following the prayer "Lord, Jesus Christ," the presider invites the sign of peace. 172

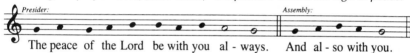

Presider: / Assembly:

The peace of the Lord be with you al - ways. And al - so with you.

All exchange a sign of peace.

As the bread is broken to be shared in communion, the assembly joins in singing 173
the "Lamb of God."

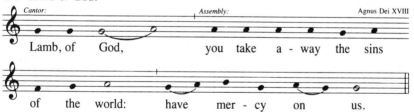

Cantor: / Assembly: / Agnus Dei XVIII

Lamb, of God, you take a - way the sins

of the world: have mer - cy on us.

*This is sung two or more times. When the bread has been prepared, the "Lamb of
God" concludes:*

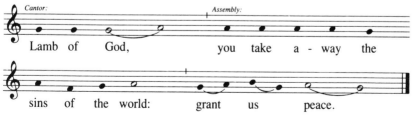

Cantor: / Assembly:

Lamb of God, you take a - way the

sins of the world: grant us peace.

174 *The presider then invites the assembly to share in the holy communion. All respond to the invitation:*

Assembly: **Lord, I am not worthy to receive you,**
but only say the word and I shall be healed.

A song or psalm may be sung during communion. After communion, a time of silence is observed. The rite concludes with the prayer after communion to which all respond: **Amen.**

175 # FINAL COMMENDATION AND FAREWELL

The ministers and assembly surround the body. After the invitation, prayer and silence, one of the following may be sung as the body is sprinkled with holy water and honored with incense.

RESPONSORY

Richard Proulx, 1975

Cantor:
Saints of God, come to his / her aid!
May Christ who called you, take you to him - self;
Give him / her e - ter - nal rest, O Lord,

Come to meet him, / her, an - gels of the Lord!
may an - gels lead you to A - bra - ham's side.
and may your light shine on him / her for ev - er.

Re - ceive his / her soul and pre - sent him / her to

God, to God the Most High.

All:
Re - ceive his / her soul and pre - sent him / her to

God, to God the Most High.

ALTERNATE RESPONSORY

ICEL, 1970

Howard Hughes, SM, 1977

I know that my Re-deem-er lives, and on the last day I shall rise a-gain; in my bod-y I shall look on God, my Sav-ior, in my bod-y I shall look on God, my Sav-ior. I my-self shall see him; my own eyes will gaze on him, my own eyes will gaze on him; in my bod-y I shall look on God, my Sav-ior, in my bod-y I shall look on God, my Sav-ior. This is the hope I cher-ish, this is the hope I cher-ish in my heart; in my bod-y I shall look on God, my Sav-ior, in my bod-y I shall look on God, my Sav-ior.

After the concluding prayer, one of the following songs or an appropriate hymn is sung while the body is being taken away.

177

In Paradisum
ICEL, 1985

TALLIS' CANON, LM
Thomas Tallis, c.1505-1585

1. May saints and an - gels lead you on,
2. Come to the peace of A - bra - ham

Es - cort - ing you where Christ has gone.
And to the sup - per of the Lamb:

Now he has called you, come to him
Come to the glo - ry of the blessed,

Who sits a - bove the ser - a - phim.
And to per - pet - ual light and rest.

178

In Paradisum
Trans. Hymnal Version, 1986

Mode VII
Acc. by Richard Proulx, 1985

In pa - ra - dí - sum de - dú - cant te án-
May choirs of an - gels es - cort you in - to

ge - li: in tu - o ad - vén - tu
par - a - dise: and at your ar - ri - val

su - scí - pi - ant te már - ty - res,
may the mar - tyrs re - ceive and wel - come you;

et per - dú - cant te in ci - vi - tá - tem san - ctam
may they bring you home in - to the ho - ly cit - y,

FUNERAL

Je - rú - sa - lem. Cho - rus an - ge - ló - rum
Jer - u - sa - lem. May the ho - ly an - gels

te su - scí - pi - at, et cum
wel - come you, and with

Lá - za - ro quon - dam páu - pe - re ae - tér-
Laz - a - rus, who lived in pov-er - ty, may you

nam há - be - as ré - qui - em.
have ev - er - last - ing rest.

Psalm Responses / Rites

BAPTISM OF CHILDREN

179   *Psalm (22) 23, 1-3. 3-4. 5.6 (no. 32)*

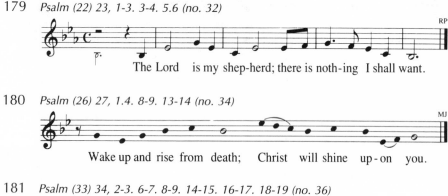

The Lord is my shep-herd; there is noth-ing I shall want.

180   *Psalm (26) 27, 1.4. 8-9. 13-14 (no. 34)*

Wake up and rise from death; Christ will shine up-on you.

181   *Psalm (33) 34, 2-3. 6-7. 8-9. 14-15. 16-17. 18-19 (no. 36)*

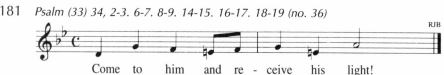

Come to him and re - ceive his light!

182   *Psalm (33) 34, 2-3. 6-7. 8-9. 14-15. 16-17. 18-19 (no. 36)*

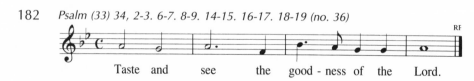

Taste and see the good - ness of the Lord.

CONFIRMATION

183   *Psalm (21) 22, 23-24. 26-27. 28. 31-32 (no. 31)*

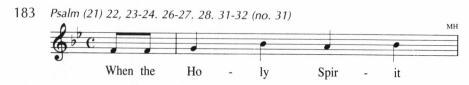

When the Ho - ly Spir - it

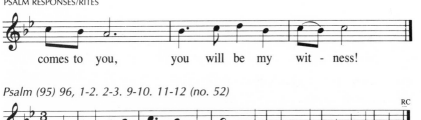

comes to you, you will be my wit - ness!

Psalm (95) 96, 1-2. 2-3. 9-10. 11-12 (no. 52)   **184**

RC

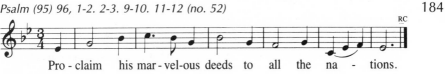

Pro - claim his mar - vel-ous deeds to all the na - tions.

Psalm (116) 117, 1. 2 (no. 64)   **185**

ST

You will be my wit-ness-es to all the world.

Psalm (144) 145, 2-3. 4-5. 8-9. 10-11. 15-16. 21 (no. 76)   **186**

DJR

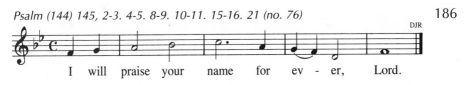

I will praise your name for ev - er, Lord.

For Confirmation, Psalm (22) 23 with the refrain "The Lord is my shepherd" (no. 179), may also be used.

MARRIAGE

Psalm (33) 34, 2-3. 4-5. 6-7. 8-9 (no. 36)   **187**

JRC

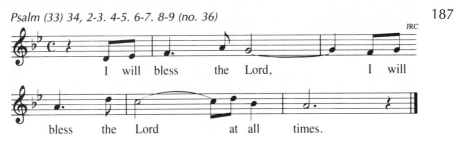

I will bless the Lord, I will

bless the Lord at all times.

Also, these verses of Psalm (33) 34 with the refrain "Taste and see" (no. 182).

Psalm (102) 103, 1-2. 8. 13. 17-18 (no. 55)   **188**

DRH

The Lord is kind and mer - ci - ful.

Psalm (102) 103, 1-2. 8. 13. 17-18 (no. 55)   **189**

HH

The Lord's kind - ness is ev - er-

last - ing   to   those   who   fear   him.

190   *Psalm (111) 112, 1-2. 3-4. 5-7. 7-8. 9 (no. 59)*

JRC

Hap-py   are those   who do   what the Lord com - mands.

191   *Psalm (144) 145, 8-9. 10. 15. 17-18 (no. 76)*

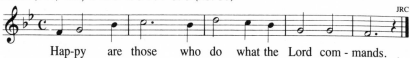

MH

The Lord   is com - pas - sion-ate to   all   his   crea-tures.

192   *Psalm 148, 1-2. 3-4. 9-10. 11-12 (no. 79)*

RJB/Acc. RP

Let   all   praise   the name of   the   Lord.

FUNERAL MASS

193   *Psalm (24) 25, 6-7. 17-18. 20-21 (no. 33)*

RJT

To   you,   O   Lord,   I   lift   my   soul.

194   *Psalm (26) 27, 1. 4. 7. 8. 9. 13-14 (no. 34)*

RP

The Lord is my light and my sal - va - tion.

195   *Psalm (26) 27, 1. 4. 7. 8. 9. 13-14 (no. 34)*

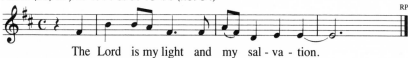

CK

I   be - lieve that   I   shall   see   the good things of the

Lord   in   the   land   of   the   liv - ing.

196   *Psalm (41) 42, 2. 3. 5; (42) 43, 3. 4. 5 (nos. 37 & 38)*

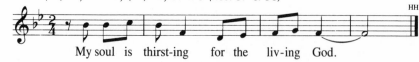

HH

My soul is thirst-ing   for the   liv-ing God.

Psalm (62) 63, 2. 3-4. 5-6. 8-9 (no. 42)　　197

My soul is thirst-ing for you, O Lord, thirst-ing for you my God.

Psalm (102) 103, 8. 10. 13-14. 15-16. 17-18 (no. 55)　　198

The Lord is kind and mer - ci - ful.

Psalm (113) 114, 5. 6; (115) 116, 10-11. 15-16 (nos. 60 & 63)　　199

I will walk in the pres-ence of the Lord, in the land of the liv - ing.

Psalm (121) 122, 1-2. 3-4. 4-5. 6-7. 8-9 (no. 67)　　200

I re - joiced when I heard them say: let us go to the house of the Lord.

Psalm (129) 130, 1-2. 3-4. 4-6. 7-8 (no. 71)　　201

I hope in the Lord, I trust in his word.

For funerals, Psalm (129) 130 with Antiphon III (no. 71) may also be used.

Psalm (142) 143, 1-2. 5-6. 7. 8. 10 (no. 75)　　202

O Lord, hear my prayer,

hear my prayer, O Lord.

BURIAL OF BAPTIZED CHILDREN

203 *Psalm (24) 25, 4-5. 6. 7. 20-21 (no. 33)*

RJT

To you, O Lord, I lift my soul.

204 *Psalm 148, 1-2. 11-12. 12-14. 14 (no. 79)*

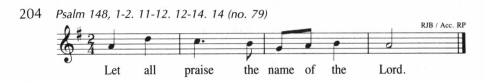

RJB / Acc. RP

Let all praise the name of the Lord.

For the Burial of Baptized Children, Psalm (22) 23 with the refrain "The Lord is my shepherd" (no. 179), and Psalms (41) 42 & (42) 43 with the refrain "My soul is thirsting" (no. 196), may also be used.

BURIAL OF NON-BAPTIZED CHILDREN

205 *Psalm (24) 25, 4-5. 6. 7. 17. 20 (no. 33)*

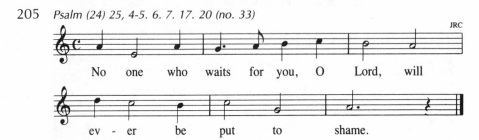

JRC

No one who waits for you, O Lord, will ev - er be put to shame.

Also, these verses of Psalm (24) 25 with the refrain "To you, O Lord" (no. 193).

PENANCE

206 *Psalm 12 (13), 2-3. 3-4. 6-7 (no. 28)*

CAP

All my hope, O Lord, is in your lov-ing kind - ness.

207 *Psalm (24) 25, 2-3. 4-5. 10-11. 15-16 (no. 33)*

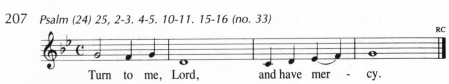

RC

Turn to me, Lord, and have mer - cy.

Psalm (30) 31, 2-3. 3-4. 5-6 (no. 35) 208

RK

You have re - deemed us, Lord, God of truth.

Psalm (89) 90, 1-2. 12-13. 14-15 (no. 48) 209

RJB

Fill us with your love, O Lord, and we will sing for joy!

Psalm (122) 123, 1-2. 2-3. 4-5 (no. 68) 210

RP

Our eyes are fixed on the Lord.

Psalm (129) 130, 1-2. 3-4. 5-7. 7-8 (no. 71) 211

JRC

With the Lord there is mer - cy,

and full - ness of re - demp - tion.

Psalm (138) 139, 1-2. 3-4. 13-14 (no. 73) 212

RP

You have searched me, and you know me, Lord.

Psalm (142) 143, 1-2. 5-6. 7. 9-10 (no. 75) 213

HH

Teach me to do your will, my God.

ANOINTING OF THE SICK

Isaiah 38, 10. 11. 12. 16. (no. 82) 214

CAP

You saved my life, O Lord; I shall not die.

215   *Psalm 6, 2-4. 4-6. 9-10 (no. 26)*   RJB

Have mer-cy   on   me,   Lord;   my strength is   gone.

216   *Psalm (24) 25, 4-5. 6-7. 8-9. 10. 14. 15-16 (no. 33)*   RJT

To   you,   O   Lord,   I   lift   my   soul.

217   *Psalm (26) 27, 1. 4. 5. 7-9. 9-10 (no. 24)*   HH

Put your hope   in the Lord;   take cour-age and be   strong.

218   *Psalm (33) 34, 2-3. 4-5. 6-7. 10-11. 12-13. 16. 19 (no. 36)*   RP

The Lord is near   to brok-en hearts, the   Lord   is   near.

Also, these verses of Psalm (33) 34 with the refrain "Taste and see" (no. 182).

219   *Psalm (41) 42, 3. 5; (42) 43, 3. 4 (nos. 37 & 38)*   RP

Like a   deer   that   longs for run-ning   streams,

so   my   soul longs   for   you,   my   God.

220   *Psalm (62) 63, 2-3. 4-6. 7-9 (no. 42)*   RP

My   soul   is   thirst-ing   for   you,   O

Lord,   thirst-ing   for   you   my   God.

221   *Psalm (85) 86, 1-2. 3-4. 5-6. 11. 12-13. 15-16 (no. 46)*   HH

Lis - ten,   Lord,   and   ans - wer   me.

Psalm (85) 86, 1-2. 3-4. 5-6. 11. 12-13. 15-16 (no. 46)   222

RJB

God, you are mer-ci-ful and kind; turn to me and have mer - cy.

Psalm (89) 90, 2. 3-4. 5-6. 10 & 12. 14. 16 (no. 48)   223

CAP

In ev-'ry age, O Lord, you have been our re - fuge.

Psalm (101) 102, 2-3. 24-25. 26-28. 19-21 (no. 54)   224

RL

O Lord, hear my prayer, and let my cry come to you.

Psalm (102) 103, 1-2. 3-4. 11-12. 13-14. 15-16. 17-18 (no. 55)   225

JS

O bless the Lord, O bless the Lord, my soul.

Psalm (102) 103, 1-2. 3-4. 11-12. 13-14. 15-16. 17-18 (no. 55)   226

CAP

The Lord is kind and mer - ci - ful;

slow to an - ger, and rich in com - pas - sion.

Psalm (122) 123, 1-2. 2-3 (no. 68)   227

ST

Our eyes are fixed on the Lord,

plead - ing for his mer - cy.

Psalm (142) 143, 1-2. 5-6. 10 (no. 75)   228

RJB

For the sake of your name, O Lord, save my life.

The Order of Mass

229 Each church gathers on the Lord's Day to listen to the scriptures, to offer prayers, to give thanks and praise to God while recalling God's gifts in creation and saving deeds in Jesus, and to share in holy communion.

In these rites of word and eucharist, the church keeps Sunday as the Lord's Day, the day of creation and resurrection, the "eighth day" when the fullness of God's kingdom is anticipated. The Mass of the Christian community has rites of gathering, of word, of eucharist, of dismissal. All those who gather constitute the assembly. One member of this assembly who has been ordained to the presbyterate, the priesthood, presides by leading the opening and closing prayers and the eucharistic prayer. A member ordained to the diaconate may assist, read the gospel and preach. Other members of the assembly are chosen and trained for various ministries: These are the readers, ushers, musicians, communion ministers. All of these assist the assembly. It is the assembly itself, all those present, that does the liturgy.

The order of Mass which follows is familiar to all who regularly join in this assembly. It is learned through repetition. This order of Mass leaves many things to the local community and to the season of the liturgical year.

INTRODUCTORY RITES

The rites which precede the liturgy of the word assist the assembly to gather as a community. They prepare that community to listen to the scriptures and to celebrate the eucharist together. The procession and entrance song are ways of expressing the unity and spirit of the assembly.

GREETING

After the sign of the cross one of the greetings is given.

Presider: In the name of the Father, and of the Son, and of the Holy Spirit.

Assembly: **Amen.**

A

Presider: The grace of our Lord Jesus Christ and the love of God and the fellowship of the Holy Spirit be with you all.

Assembly: **And also with you.**

B

Presider: The grace and peace of God our Father and the Lord Jesus Christ be with you.

Assembly: **Blessed be God, the Father of our Lord Jesus Christ.**
or: **And also with you.**

C

Presider: The Lord be with you. *(Bishop:* Peace be with you.)

Assembly: **And also with you.**

BLESSING AND SPRINKLING OF HOLY WATER   230

On Sundays, instead of the penitential rite below, the blessing and sprinkling of holy water may be done. The following or another appropriate song is sung.

Cantor, then all: Joseph Roff, 1984

Cleanse us, O Lord, from all our sins; wash us, and we shall be clean, clean as new snow. snow. I will pour clean wa-ter o-ver you and wash a-way all your sins. snow. A new heart will I give you, says the Lord.

PENITENTIAL RITE   231

The presider invites all to be mindful of human sinfulness and of the great mercy of God. After a time of silence, one of the following forms is used.

A

Assembly: **I confess to almighty God,**
and to you, my brothers and sisters,
that I have sinned through my own fault
in my thoughts and in my words,
in what I have done,
and in what I have failed to do;
and I ask blessed Mary, ever virgin,
all the angels and saints,
and you, my brothers and sisters,
to pray for me to the Lord our God.

B
Presider: Lord, we have sinned against you:
Lord, have mercy.

Assembly: **Lord, have mercy.**

Presider: Lord, show us your mercy and love.

Assembly: **And grant us your salvation.**

C
The presider or another minister makes a series of invocations according to the following pattern.

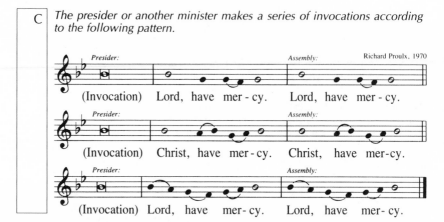

The penitential rite always concludes:

Presider: May almighty God have mercy on us, forgive us our sins, and bring us to everlasting life.

Assembly: **Amen.**

232 KYRIE

Unless form C of the penitential rite has been used, the Kyrie follows.

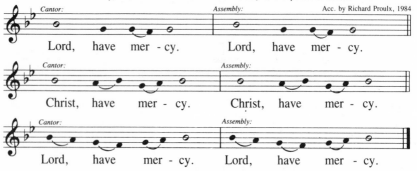

Or:

233

Chri - ste e - le - i - son. Chri - ste e - le - i - son.

Ky - ri - e e - le - i - son. Ky - ri - e e - le - i - son.

GLORIA 234

The Gloria is omitted during Advent and Lent.

"A New Mass for Congregations"
Carroll T. Andrews, 1970

Glo - ry to God in the high - est, and

peace to his peo - ple on earth. Lord God,

heav - en - ly King, al - might - y God and

Fa - ther, we wor - ship you, we give you thanks, we

praise you for your glo - ry.

Slightly slower
Choir (Congr. ad lib.):

Lord Je - sus Christ, on - ly Son of the Fa - ther,

Lord God, Lamb of God, you take a - way the

sin of the world: have mer - cy on

us; you are seat - ed at the right hand of the

Fa - ther: re - ceive our prayer.

All: f tempo primo

For you a - lone are the Ho - ly One,

you a - lone are the Lord, you a - lone are the

Most High, Je - sus Christ, with the Ho - ly Spir - it,

ff *rit.*

in the glo - ry of God the Fa - ther. A - men.

235 OPENING PRAYER

After the invitation from the presider, all pray for a while. The introductory rites conclude with the proper prayer of the day and the Amen of the assembly.

236 LITURGY OF THE WORD

When the church assembles, the book of the scriptures is opened and all listen as lectors and deacon (or presider) read from the places assigned. The first reading is normally from the Hebrew Scriptures, the second from the letters of the New Testament, and the third from the Book of Gospels. Over a three-year cycle, the church reads through the letters and gospels and a portion of the Hebrew Scriptures. During the Sundays of Ordinary Time, the letters and gospels are read in order, each Sunday continuing near the place where the previous Sunday's readings ended. During Advent/Christmas and Lent/Easter, the readings are those which are traditional and appropriate to these seasons.

The church listens to and–through the weeks and years–is shaped by the scriptures. Those who have gathered for Sunday liturgy are to give their full attention to the words of the reader. A time of silence and reflection follows each of the first two readings. After the first reading, this reflection continues in the singing of the psalm. A homily, bringing together the scriptures and the life of the community, follows the gospel. The liturgy of the word concludes with the creed, the dismissal of the catechumens and the prayers of intercession. In the latter, the assembly continues its constant work of recalling and praying for the universal church and all those in need.

This reading and hearing of the word–simple things that they are–are the foundation of the liturgical celebration. The public reading of the scriptures and the rituals which surround this–silence and psalm and acclamation, posture and gesture, preaching and litany of intercession–gather the church generation after generation. They gather and sustain and gradually make of us the image of Christ.

READING I

In conclusion:

   Reader: This is the Word of the Lord.

Assembly: **Thanks be to God.**

After a period of silence, the responsorial psalm is sung.

READING II

In conclusion:

   Reader: This is the Word of the Lord.

Assembly: **Thanks be to God.**

A time of silence follows the reading.

GOSPEL

237

Before the gospel, an acclamation is sung.

Al - le - lu - ia,   al - le - lu - ia,   al - le - lu - ia.

During Lent one of the following acclamations replaces the alleluia.

Praise to you, Lord Je-sus Christ, king of end-less glo - ry!

Or:

   B | **Praise and honor to you, Lord Jesus Christ!**

   C | **Glory and praise to you, Lord Jesus Christ!**

   D | **Glory to you, Word of God, Lord Jesus Christ!**

Deacon (or priest): The Lord be with you.

      Assembly: **And also with you.**

       Deacon: A reading from the holy gospel according to N.

      Assembly: **Glory to you, Lord.**

After the reading:

       Deacon: This is the gospel of the Lord.

      Assembly: **Praise to you, Lord Jesus Christ.**

HOMILY

238 **PROFESSION OF FAITH**

We believe in one God,
  the Father, the Almighty,
  maker of heaven and earth,
  of all that is seen and unseen.

We believe in one Lord, Jesus Christ,
  the only Son of God,
  eternally begotten of the Father,
  God from God, Light from Light,
  true God from true God,
  begotten, not made, one in Being with the Father.
  Through him all things were made.
  For us men and for our salvation he came down from heaven:

All bow at the following words up to: and became man.

  by the power of the Holy Spirit
    he was born of the Virgin Mary, and became man.
  For our sake he was crucified under Pontius Pilate;
    he suffered, died, and was buried.
    On the third day he rose again
      in fulfillment of the Scriptures;
    he ascended into heaven
      and is seated at the right hand of the Father.
  He will come again in glory to judge the living and the dead,
    and his kingdom will have no end.

We believe in the Holy Spirit, the Lord, the giver of life,
  who proceeds from the Father and the Son.
  With the Father and the Son he is worshiped and glorified.
  He has spoken through the Prophets.
  We believe in one holy catholic and apostolic Church.
  We acknowledge one baptism for the forgiveness of sins.
  We look for the resurrection of the dead,
    and the life of the world to come. Amen.

At Masses with children, the Apostles' Creed may be used: 239

**We believe in God, the Father almighty,
  creator of heaven and earth.**

**We believe in Jesus Christ, his only Son, our Lord.
  He was conceived by the power of the Holy Spirit
    and born of the Virgin Mary.
  He suffered under Pontius Pilate,
    was crucified, died, and was buried.
  He descended to the dead.
  On the third day he arose again.
  He ascended into heaven,
    and is seated at the right hand of the Father.
  He will come again to judge the living and the dead.**

**We believe in the Holy Spirit,
  the holy catholic Church,
  the communion of saints,
  the forgiveness of sins,
  the resurrection of the body,
  and the life everlasting. Amen.**

GENERAL INTERCESSIONS   240

The people respond to each petition as follows, or according to local practice.

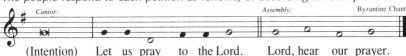

(Intention)   Let us pray   to the Lord.   Lord, hear our prayer.

LITURGY OF THE EUCHARIST   241

To do the eucharist means to give God thanks and praise. When the table has been prepared with the bread and wine, the assembly joins the presider in remembering the gracious gifts of God in creation and God's saving deeds. The center of this is the paschal mystery, the death of our Lord Jesus Christ which destroyed the power of death and his rising which brings us life. That mystery into which we were baptized we proclaim each Sunday at eucharist. It is the very shape of Christian life. We find this in the simple bread and wine which stir our remembering and draw forth our prayer of thanksgiving. "Fruit of the earth and work of human hands," the bread and wine become our holy communion in the body and blood of the Lord. We eat and drink and so proclaim that we belong to one another and to the Lord.

The members of the assembly quietly prepare themselves even as the table is prepared. The presider then invites all to lift up their hearts and join in the eucharistic prayer. All do this by giving their full attention and by singing the acclamations from the "Holy, holy" to the great "Amen." Then the assembly joins in the Lord's Prayer, the sign of peace and the "Lamb of God" litany which accompanies the breaking of bread. Ministers of communion assist the assembly to share the bread and wine. A time of silence and prayer concludes the liturgy of the eucharist.

PREPARATION OF THE ALTAR AND THE GIFTS

Bread and wine are brought to the table and the deacon or presider prepares these gifts. If there is no music, the prayers may be said aloud, and all may respond: **"Blessed be God for ever."** *The presider then invites all to pray.*

Assembly: **May the Lord accept the sacrifice at your hands**
                for the praise and glory of his name,
                for our good, and the good of all his church.

The presider says the prayer over the gifts and all respond: **Amen.**

242 EUCHARISTIC PRAYER

The central prayer of the Mass begins with this greeting and invitation between presider and assembly.

Sacramentary, 1974

Presider: The Lord be with you. *Assembly:* And al-so with you.

Presider: Lift up your hearts. *Assembly:* We lift them up to the Lord.

Presider: Let us give thanks to the Lord our God.

Assembly: It is right to give him thanks and praise.

The Sanctus acclamation is sung to conclude the introduction to the eucharistic prayer.

"A Community Mass"
Richard Proulx, 1970

243

mf
Ho - ly, ho - ly, ho - ly Lord, God of pow-er and might, heav'n and earth are full of your glo - ry. Ho - san - na in the high - est, ho - san - na in the high - est. Blest is he who comes in the name of the

Lord. Ho - san - na in the high - est, ho-

san - na in the high - est.

One of the following acclamations follows the deacon's or presider's invitation: **244**
"Let us proclaim the mystery of faith."

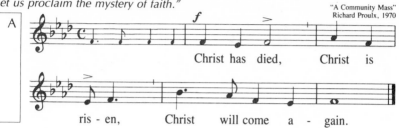

"A Community Mass"
Richard Proulx, 1970

A

f

Christ has died, Christ is

ris - en, Christ will come a - gain.

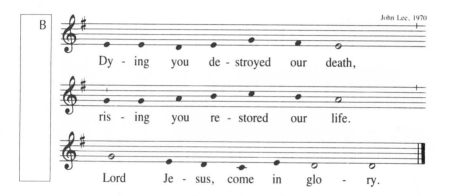

John Lee, 1970

B

Dy - ing you de - stroyed our death,

ris - ing you re - stored our life.

Lord Je - sus, come in glo - ry.

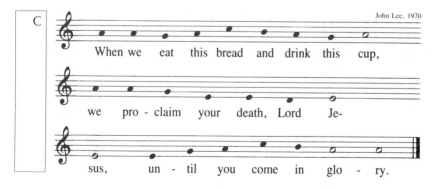

John Lee, 1970

C

When we eat this bread and drink this cup,

we pro - claim your death, Lord Je-

sus, un - til you come in glo - ry.

Adapted from *Genevan Psalter*, 1551
Harm. by Claude LeJeune, 1601

D

Lord, by your cross and re - sur - rec - tion

you have set us free.

You are the Sav - ior of the world.

The eucharistic prayer concludes:

245   *Presider:* Through him, with him, in him, in the unity of the Holy Spirit,
all glory and honor is yours, almighty Father, for ever and ever.

A - men, a - men, a - men.

246   **COMMUNION RITE**

The presider invites all to join in the Lord's Prayer.

Robert Snow, 1964
Acc. by Gerard Farrell, OSB, 1984

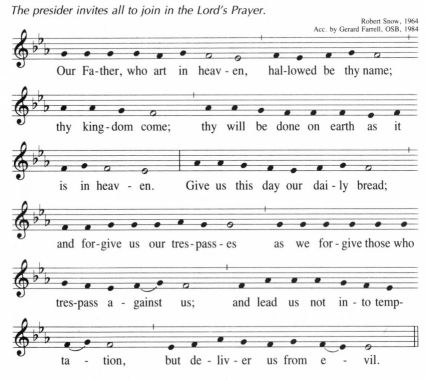

Our Fa-ther, who art in heav - en, hal-lowed be thy name;

thy king - dom come; thy will be done on earth as it

is in heav - en. Give us this day our dai - ly bread;

and for-give us our tres-pass - es as we for - give those who

tres-pass a - gainst us; and lead us not in - to temp-

ta - tion, but de - liv - er us from e - vil.

Presider: Deliver us, Lord...
for the coming of our Savior, Jesus Christ.

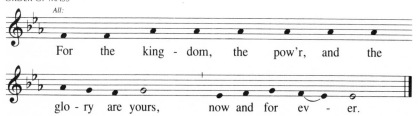

All: For the king - dom, the pow'r, and the glo - ry are yours, now and for ev - er.

Following the prayer "Lord, Jesus Christ," the presider invites the sign of peace.   247

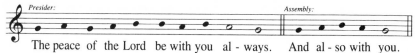

Presider: The peace of the Lord be with you al - ways. **Assembly:** And al - so with you.

All exchange a sign of peace.

Then the bread is solemnly broken and the bread and wine prepared for holy communion. The litany "Lamb of God" is sung through the breaking of the bread: 248

Agnus Dei XVIII
Acc. by Gerard Farrell, OSB, 1984

Cantor: Lamb of God, **Assembly:** you take a - way the sin of the world: have mer - cy on us.

Other invocations, such as "Bread of life" and "Prince of peace" may be added. When the preparation is completed, the litany concludes:

Cantor: Lamb of God, **Assembly:** you take a - way the sins of the world: grant us peace.

The presider then invites all to share in the holy communion.   249

       Assembly: **Lord, I am not worthy to receive you, but only say the word and I shall be healed.**

Minister of communion: The body of Christ.

       Or:

       The blood of Christ.

    Communicant: **Amen.**

A song or psalm is ordinarily sung during communion. After communion, a time of silence is observed or a song of thanksgiving is sung. The rite concludes with the prayer after communion to which all respond: **Amen.**

250 CONCLUDING RITE

The liturgy of word and eucharist ends very simply. There may be announcements of events and concerns for the community, then the presider gives a blessing and the assembly is dismissed.

GREETING AND BLESSING

Presider: The Lord be with you.

Assembly: **And also with you.**

> | Optional |
>
> *When the bishop blesses the people he adds the following:*
>
> *Bishop:* Blessed be the name of the Lord.
> *Assembly:* **Now and for ever.**
>
> *Bishop:* Our help is in the name of the Lord.
> *Assembly:* **Who made heaven and earth.**

The blessing may be in a simple or solemn form. All respond to the blessing or to each part of the blessing: **Amen.**

DISMISSAL

Go in   the peace of Christ.
or: The Mass is end - ed, go in peace.   Thanks be to God.
or: Go in peace to love and serve the Lord.

Setting One

251

KYRIE ELEISON

252

GLORIA

wor - ship you, we give you thanks, we praise you for your

glo - ry. Lord Je - sus Christ, on - ly

Son of the Fa - ther, Lord God,

Lamb of God, you take a - way the sin of the

world: have mer - cy on us; You are

seat - ed at the right hand of the Fa - ther:

re - ceive our pray'r, re - ceive, re-

ceive our pray'r. For you a - lone are the

Ho - ly One, you a - lone are the Lord, you a-

lone are the Most High, Je - sus Christ with the Ho - ly

Spir - it in the glo - ry of God the Fa - ther.

A - men. A - men.

SANCTUS

"A Community Mass"
Richard Proulx, 1970

253

Ho - ly, ho - ly, ho - ly Lord, God of pow - er and

might, heav'n and earth are

full of your glo - ry. Ho - san - na in the

high - est, ho - san - na in the high - est.

Blest is he who comes in the name of the

Lord. Ho - san - na in the high - est, ho-

san - na in the high - est.

MEMORIAL ACCLAMATION

"A Community Mass"
Richard Proulx, 1970

254

Christ has died,

Christ is ris - en, Christ will come a - gain.

255 **AMEN**

256 **AGNUS DEI**

"A Community Mass"
Richard Proulx, 1970

Lamb of God, you take a-way the sins of the world: have mer-cy on us.

Lamb of God, you take a-way the sins of the world: grant us peace.

Setting Two

KYRIE ELEISON

"Mass of the Bells"
Alexander Peloquin, 1972

Lord, have mer - cy.

Lord, have mer - cy.

Christ, have mer - cy.

Christ, have mer - cy.

Lord, have mer - cy. Lord, have

mer - cy.

258 **GLORIA** *All:*

"Mass of the Bells"
Alexander Peloquin, 1972

Glo-ry to God in the high-est, and peace to his peo-ple on

earth. Glo-ry to God in the high-est, and

peace to his peo-ple on earth. Lord God,

Cantor or T. B.:

heav-en-ly King, al-might-y God and Fa - ther.

All:

Glo-ry to God in the high-est, and peace to his peo-ple on

Cantor or S. A.:

earth. We wor-ship you, we give you thanks,

we praise you for your glo - ry. Glo-ry to God in the

All:

high-est, and peace to his peo-ple on earth.

Cantor or T. B.:

Lord Je - sus Christ, on - ly Son of the Fa - ther.

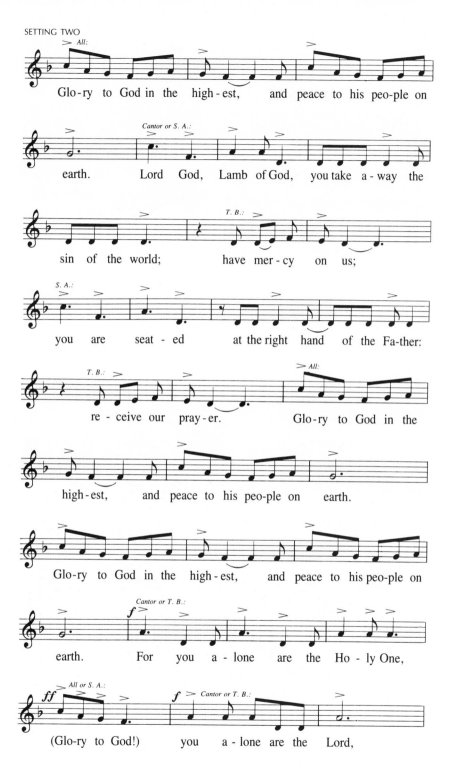

All: Glo-ry to God in the high-est, and peace to his peo-ple on earth.

Cantor or S. A.: Lord God, Lamb of God, you take a-way the sin of the world;

T. B.: have mer-cy on us;

S. A.: you are seat-ed at the right hand of the Fa-ther:

T. B.: re-ceive our pray-er.

All: Glo-ry to God in the high-est, and peace to his peo-ple on earth.

Glo-ry to God in the high-est, and peace to his peo-ple on earth.

Cantor or T. B.: For you a-lone are the Ho-ly One,

All or S. A.: (Glo-ry to God!) f Cantor or T. B.: you a-lone are the Lord,

ALLELUIA

"Mass of the Bells"
Alexander Peloquin, 1972

259

Al - le - lu - ia. Al - le - lu - ia. Al - le - lu - ia.

Al - le - lu - ia.

SANCTUS

260

Resounding and rhythmic

"Mass of the Bells"
Alexander Peloquin, 1972

Ho - ly, ho - ly, ho - ly Lord,

God of pow'r and might, heav'n and

earth are full of your glo - ry. Ho - san-

Choir or Cantor:

na in the high - est. Bless - ed is

he who comes in the name of the Lord.

Cong. and S. A.

Ho - san - na in the high - est. Ho - san-

na in the high - est. Ho - san - na in the

high-est. Ho - san - na in the

softer

high-est, high-est.

4

261 **MEMORIAL ACCLAMATION**

"Mass of the Bells"
Alexander Peloquin, 1972

Solemnly

Dy - ing you de - stroyed our death,

ris - ing you re - stored our life.

Lord Je - sus, come in glo - ry.

262 **AMEN**

"Mass of the Bells"
Alexander Peloquin, 1972

ff Resoundingly

A - men, a - men, a - men.

263 **AGNUS DEI**

"Mass of the Bells"
Alexander Peloquin, 1972

Peacefully *Cantor: mp*

mp Lamb of God, you take a - way the

sins of the world: *All:* have mer-cy on us.

Cantor or Choir: *mf*

Lamb of God, you take a - way the sins of the

world: have mer-cy on us.

Lamb of God, you take a - way the

sins of the world: grant

us peace.

Setting Three

264 **KYRIE ELEISON**

"New Plainsong"
David Hurd, 1985

Cantor: Ky - ri - e e - le - i - son. Assembly: Ky - ri - e e - le - i - son.

Cantor: Chri - ste e - le - i - son. Assembly: Chri - ste e - le - i - son.

Cantor: Ky - ri - e e - le - i - son. Assembly: Ky - ri - e e - le - i - son.

265 **GLORIA**

"New Plainsong"
David Hurd, 1980

Glo - ry to God in the high - est, and peace to his

peo - ple on earth. Lord God, heav - en - ly King, Al - might - y,

God and Fa - ther, we wor - ship you, we give you thanks,

we praise you for your glo - ry. Lord Je - sus Christ,

on - ly Son of the Fa - ther, Lord God, Lamb of God,

You take a - way the sin of the world: have mer-cy on us;

you are seat - ed at the right hand of the Fa - ther:

re - ceive our prayer. For you a - lone are the Ho - ly One,

you a - lone are the Lord, you a - lone are the

Most High, Je - sus Christ, with the Ho - ly Spir - it.

in the glo-ry of God the Fa - ther, A - men.

SANCTUS

"New Plainsong"
David Hurd, 1980

266

Ho - ly, ho - ly, ho - ly Lord, God of pow - er and might,

heav-en and earth are full of your glo - ry. Ho - san-na in the

high - est. Bless-ed is he who comes in the

name of the Lord. Ho-san-na in the high - est.

267 **MEMORIAL ACCLAMATION**

"New Plainsong"
David Hurd, 1980

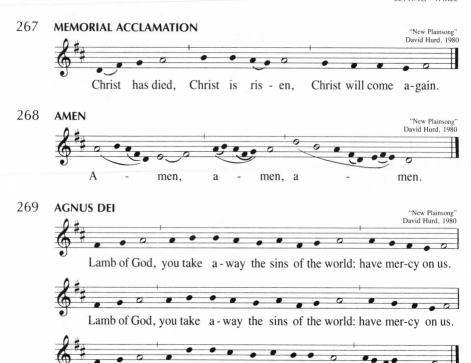

Christ has died, Christ is ris - en, Christ will come a-gain.

268 **AMEN**

"New Plainsong"
David Hurd, 1980

A - men, a - men, a - men.

269 **AGNUS DEI**

"New Plainsong"
David Hurd, 1980

Lamb of God, you take a - way the sins of the world: have mer-cy on us.

Lamb of God, you take a - way the sins of the world: have mer-cy on us.

Lamb of God, you take a-way the sins of the world: grant us peace.

Service Music

RITE OF SPRINKLING

Chant Mode VII
Adapt. by Richard Proulx, 1975

A - spér - ges me, Dó - mi - ne hys-
Cleanse me from sin, O Lord God, wash

só - po, et mun - dá - bor: la - vá - bis me,
me with hys - sop branch - es: cleanse me from guilt,

et su - per ni - vem de - al - bá - bor.
and I shall be clean as the new snow.

Mis - se - rére me - i, De - us, se - cún-
Have mer - cy on me, O my God, ac - cord-

D.C. *(ad lib)*

dum magnam miseri - cór - di - am tu - am.
ing to your great com - pas - sion.

Gló - ri - a Patri, et Filio, et Spi - rí - tu - i San - cto:
Glo - ry be to the Father
and to the Son, and to the Ho - ly Spir - it:

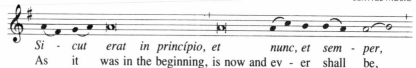

Si - cut erat in princípio, et nunc, et sem - per,
As it was in the beginning, is now and ev - er shall be,

D.C.

et in saécula sae-cu - ló-rum. A - men.
world with - out end. A - men.

271 RITE OF SPRINKLING

Moderately slow

"Festival Liturgy"
Richard Hillert, 1983

Lord Je-sus, from your wound-ed

side flowed streams of cleans-ing wa-ter. Al- le - lu - ia,

al - le - lu - ia, al - le - lu - ia. The world was

wash'd of all its sin, all life made new a - gain. Al-

le - lu - ia, al - le - lu - ia, al - le - lu - ia.

272 RITE OF SPRINKLING

Cantor, then all:

Howard Hughes, SM, 1985

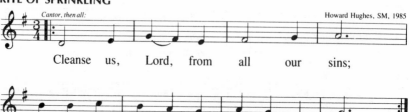

Cleanse us, Lord, from all our sins;

wash us, and we shall be clean as new snow.

I will pour clean wa-ter o-ver you and wash a-way all your sins. Cleanse us, Lord, from all our sins; wash us, and we shall be clean as new snow. A new heart, a new heart will I give you, says the Lord. Cleanse us, Lord, from all our sins; wash us, and we shall be clean as new snow. Cleanse us, Lord, from all our sins; wash us, and we shall be clean as new snow.

KYRIE

273

"Deutsche Mass"
Franz Schubert, 1826
Adapt. by Richard Proulx, 1985

Moderately (Massig)

Lord, have mer - cy. Lord, have mer - cy. Christ, have mer - cy.

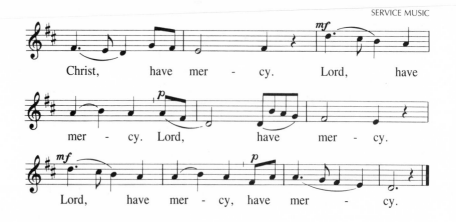

Christ, have mer - cy. Lord, have
mer - cy. Lord, have mer - cy.
Lord, have mer - cy, have mer - cy.

274 KYRIE

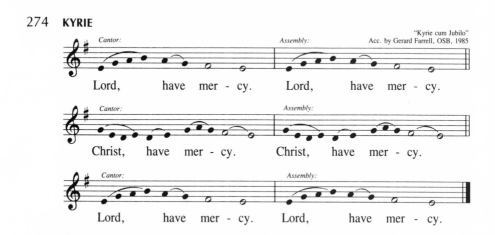

"Kyrie cum Jubilo"
Acc. by Gerard Farrell, OSB, 1985

Cantor: *Assembly:*

Lord, have mer - cy. Lord, have mer - cy.

Cantor: *Assembly:*

Christ, have mer - cy. Christ, have mer - cy.

Cantor: *Assembly:*

Lord, have mer - cy. Lord, have mer - cy.

275 KYRIE

"Music for Celebration"
David Hurd, 1979

Choir or cantor, then all:

Ky - ri - e e - le - i - son, Ky - ri - e e - le - i - son,

Ky - ri - e e - le - i - son.

Cantor:

Chri - ste e - le - i - son, Chri -

ste e - le - i - son, Chri - ste e-

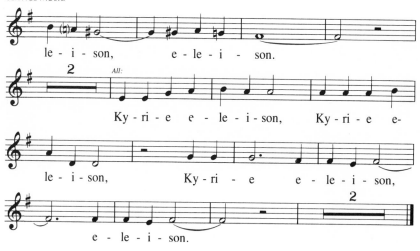

le - i - son, e - le - i - son.

2 *All:*

Ky - ri - e e - le - i - son, Ky - ri - e e-

le - i - son, Ky - ri - e e - le - i - son,

2

e - le - i - son.

GLORIA

276

John Rutter, 1972

f

Glo - ry to God in the high - est, and

peace to his peo - ple on earth.

mf

Lord God, heav'n - ly King, al -

f

might - y God and Fa - ther, we

wor - ship you, we give you thanks, we

praise you for your glo - ry.

p

Lord Je - sus Christ, on - ly Son of the

GLORIA

"Intercession Mass"
David Hurd, 1979

Glo - ry to God in the high-est, and peace to his peo - ple on earth.

2 Lord God, heav - en - ly King, al - might - y God and Fa - ther, we wor-ship you, we give you thanks, we praise you for your glo - ry.

Lord Je - sus Christ, on - ly Son of the Fa - ther,

4 Lord God, Lamb of God, you take a - way the sin of the world: have mer - cy on us; you are seat - ed at the right hand of the Fa - ther, re-

Tempo primo **f**

ceive our prayer. For

you a - lone are the Ho - ly One, you a - lone are the

Lord, you a - lone are the Most High,

Je - sus Christ, with the Ho - ly Spir - it, in the

glo - ry of God the Fa - ther. A - men.

GLORIA

"Congregational Mass"
John Lee, 1970

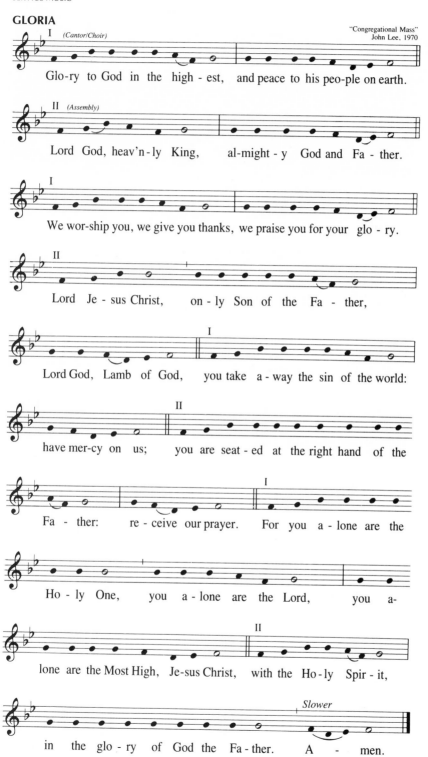

I (Cantor/Choir)
Glo-ry to God in the high-est, and peace to his peo-ple on earth.

II (Assembly)
Lord God, heav'n-ly King, al-might-y God and Fa-ther.

I
We wor-ship you, we give you thanks, we praise you for your glo-ry.

II
Lord Je-sus Christ, on-ly Son of the Fa-ther,

I
Lord God, Lamb of God, you take a-way the sin of the world:

II
have mer-cy on us; you are seat-ed at the right hand of the

I
Fa-ther: re-ceive our prayer. For you a-lone are the

Ho-ly One, you a-lone are the Lord, you a-

II
lone are the Most High, Je-sus Christ, with the Ho-ly Spir-it,

Slower
in the glo-ry of God the Fa-ther. A-men.

279 ALLELUIA

A.Gregory Murray, OSB, 1958

Al - le - lu - ia, al - le - lu - ia, al - le - lu - ia.

280 ALLELUIA

Chant-Mode II

Al - le - lu - ia, al - le - lu - ia, al - le - lu - ia.

281 ALLELUIA

Richard Proulx, 1975

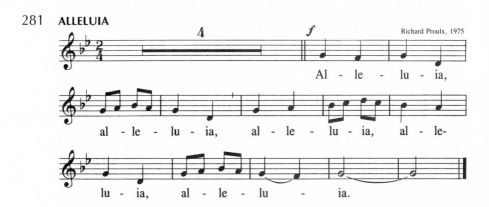

Al - le - lu - ia,

al - le - lu - ia, al - le - lu - ia, al - le -

lu - ia, al - le - lu - ia.

282 ALLELUIA

Howard Hughes, SM, 1973

Cantor:

Al - le - lu - ia, al - le - lu - ia!

Assembly:

Al - le - lu - ia, al - le - lu - ia!

Cantor:

Al - le - lu - ia,

Assembly:

al - le - lu - ia! Al - le - lu - ia, al - le - lu - ia!

Cantor:

Al - le - lu - ia, al - le - lu - ia!

Assembly:

Al - le - lu - ia,

Cantor:

al - le - lu - ia! Al - le - lu - ia, al - le - lu - ia!

Al - le - lu - ia, al - le - lu - ia!

ALLELUIA 283

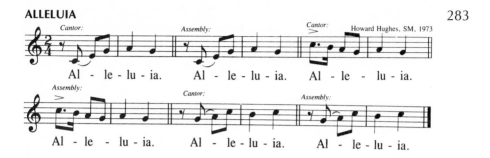

Howard Hughes, SM, 1973

Al - le - lu - ia. Al - le - lu - ia. Al - le - lu - ia.

Al - le - lu - ia. Al - le - lu - ia. Al - le - lu - ia.

ALLELUIA 284

Richard Proulx, 1980

Al - le - lu - ia, al - le-

lu - ia, al - le - lu - ia, al - le - lu - ia,

al - le - lu - ia.

ALLELUIA 285

William H. Monk, 1823-1889

Al - le - lu - ia, al - le - lu - ia, al - le - lu - ia.

ALLELUIA 286

Melchior Vulpius c.1560-1616

Al - le - lu - ia, al - le - lu - ia, al - le - lu - ia.

287 **ALLELUIA**

Taizé Community
Jacques Berthier, 1984

Al - le - lu - ia, al - le - lu - ia, al - le - lu - ia.

Al - le - lu - ia, al - le - lu - ia, al - le - lu - ia.

288 **ALLELUIA**

Jerry Sinclair, 1971
Arr. Betty C. Pulkingham, 1971

Al - le - lu - ia, al - le - lu - ia,

al - le - lu - ia, al - le - lu - ia, al - le - lu - ia,

al - le - lu - ia, al - le - lu - ia,

To repeat   *Last time*

al - le - lu - ia.   lu - ia.

289 **ALLELUIA**

Ralph C. Verdi, CPPS, 1977

Cantor: *Assembly:*

Al - le - lu - ia.   Al - le-

lu - ia.   *Cantor:*   Al - le - lu-

Assembly: ia.   Al - le - lu - ia.

Last time
Cantor: *Assembly:*

Al - le - lu - ia.   Al - le - lu - ia.

LENTEN ACCLAMATION

From "Kyrie Orbis Factor"
Acc. by David Hurd, 1979

290

Praise and hon-or, to you, O Lord Je-sus Christ.

LENTEN ACCLAMATION

From "Kyrie Orbis Factor"
Acc. by David Hurd, 1979

291

Glo-ry and praise, to you, O Lord Je-sus Christ.

LENTEN ACCLAMATION

David M. Young, 1981

292

Glo-ry and praise to you, Lord Je-sus Christ!

LENTEN ACCLAMATION

Richard Proulx, 1975

293

Glo-ry to you, O Word of God, Lord Je-sus Christ!

LENTEN ACCLAMATION

Howard Hughes, SM, 1980

294

Glo-ry to you, Word of God, Lord Je-sus Christ!

295 **CREDO**

Taizé Community
Jacques Berthier, 1984

The Apostles' Creed

1. I believe in God, the Father almighty, creator of heaven and earth.

    Refrain

2. I believe in Jesus Christ, his only Son, our Lord. He was conceived by the power of the Holy Spirit and born of the Virgin Mary.

    Refrain

3. He suffered under Pontius Pilate, was crucified, died, and was buried. He descended to the dead.

    Refrain

4. On the third day he rose again. He ascended into heaven, and is seated at the right hand of the Father. He will come again to judge the living and the dead.

    Refrain

5. I believe in the Holy Spirit, the holy catholic Church, the communion of saints, the forgiveness of sins, the resurrection of the body, and the life everlasting.

GENERAL INTERCESSIONS 296

From the Litany of the Saints

Lord, we ask you, hear our prayer.

GENERAL INTERCESSIONS 297

Taizé Community
Jacques Berthier, 1984

Ky - ri - e, Ky - ri - e e - le - i - son; Ky - ri - e,

Ky - ri - e e - le - i - son. (hum)

GENERAL INTERCESSIONS 298

Taizé Community
Jacques Berthier, 1980

Ky - ri - e, Ky - ri - e e - le - i - son. (hum)

GENERAL INTERCESSIONS 299

Ronald F. Krisman, 1977

Gra - cious Lord, hear us, we pray.

GENERAL INTERCESSIONS 300

Robert M. Hutmacher, OFM, 1979

Je - sus, Je - sus, hear our prayer.

301 **PREFACE DIALOG**

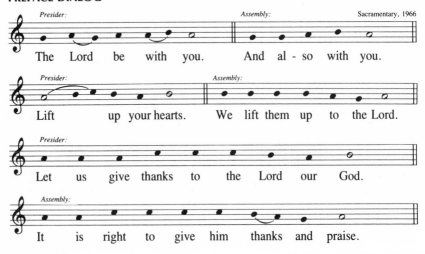

302 **SANCTUS**

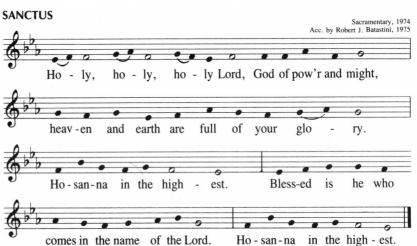

303 **MEMORIAL ACCLAMATION**

SANCTUS

"Deutsche Messe"
Franz Schubert, 1826
Adapt. by Richard Proulx, 1984

304

mp Slowly (Langsam)

Ho - ly, ho - ly, ho - ly Lord, God of

pow'r and might, Ho - ly, ho - ly,

ho - ly Lord, God of pow'r and might,

f

heav - en and earth are full,

mf

full of your glo - ry. Ho - san - na

in the high - est, ho - san - na in the

f

high - est. Bless - ed is he who comes

mp

in the name of the Lord. Ho - san - na in the

dim.

high - est, ho - san - na in the high - est.

SANCTUS

Joseph Gelineau, SJ, 1979
Adapt. from Eucharistic Prayer for Children
by Richard Proulx, 1985

305

Cantor:

Ho - ly, ho - ly, ho - ly Lord, God of pow-er and

Assembly:

might, Ho - ly, ho - ly, ho - ly Lord,

God of pow-er and might, heav'n and earth are full of your

Cantor:

glo - ry. Ho - san - na in the high - est. Ho - san-

Assembly:

na in the high - est. Blest is he who

Cantor:

comes in the name of the Lord. Ho - san - na in the high-

est. Ho - san - na in the high - est.

Assembly:

306 SANCTUS

"A Festival Eucharist"
Richard Proulx, 1975

With Majesty *f* Choir:

Ho - ly, ho - ly, ho - ly Lord,

ff All:

God of pow'r and might, ho - ly, ho - ly

ho - ly Lord, God of pow'r and might,

f Choir:

heav - en and earth are full of your glo - ry,

ff All:

God of pow'r and might. God of pow'r and

Choir: *mf*

might. Ho - san - na in the high - est, ho-

san - na in the high - est, ho - san - na in the

high - est. **ff** *All:* Ho - san - na in the high - est, ho-

san - na in the high - est, ho - san - na in the

high - est. **mf** *Choir:* Bless - ed is he who

comes in the name of the Lord. **ff** *All:* Ho-

san - na in the high - est, ho - san - na in the

high - est, ho - san - na in the high - est, ho-

san - na in the high - est.

MEMORIAL ACCLAMATION

307

"A Festival Eucharist"
Richard Proulx, 1975

f When we eat this

bread and drink this cup, we pro - claim your death, Lord

Je - sus, un - til you come in glo - ry.

308 **AMEN**

"A Festival Eucharist"
Richard Proulx, 1975

309 **SANCTUS**

"Land of Rest"
Adapt. by Marcia Pruner, 1980
Acc. by Richard Proulx, 1984

MEMORIAL ACCLAMATION

"Land of Rest"
Adapt. by Richard Proulx, 1984

310

Christ has died, Christ is ris - en,

Christ will come a - gain. Christ has died,

Christ is ris - en, Christ will come a - gain.

SANCTUS

"Mass of the Divine Word"
Howard Hughes, SM, 1981

311

All:

Ho - san - na! Ho - san - na! Ho - san - na in the high-est!

Choir or cantor:

Ho - ly, ho - ly, ho - ly Lord God of pow'r and might—

All:

Ho - san - na! Ho - san - na! Ho - san - na in the high - est! —

Cantor or choir:

heav-en and earth are full of your glo - ry.

All:

Ho - san - na! Ho - san - na! Ho - san - na in the high - est!

Cantor:

Bless-ed is he, bless-ed is he who comes in the name of the Lord.

All:

Ho - san - na! Ho - san - na! Ho - san - na in the high - est!

312 MEMORIAL ACCLAMATION

"Mass of the Divine Word"
Howard Hughes, SM, 1984

Cantor:
When we eat this bread and drink this cup,

Assembly:
When we eat this bread and drink this cup,

Cantor:
we pro - claim your death, Lord Je - sus,

Assembly:
we pro - claim your death, Lord Je - sus,

Cantor:
un - til you come in glo - ry,

Assembly:
un - til you come in glo - ry.

313 AMEN

"Mass of the Divine Word"
Howard Hughes, SM, 1984

A - men, a - men, a - men!

314 SANCTUS

"Mass of Creation"
Marty Haugen, 1984

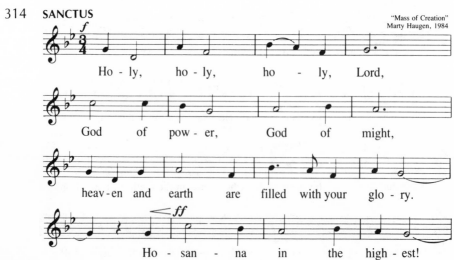

Ho - ly, ho - ly, ho - ly, Lord,

God of pow - er, God of might,

heav - en and earth are filled with your glo - ry.

Ho - san - na in the high - est!

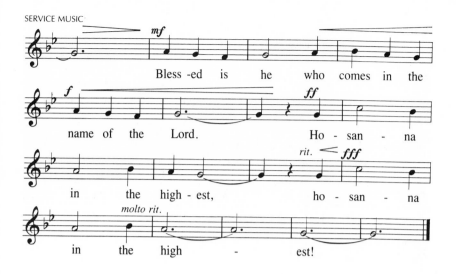

Bless-ed is he who comes in the name of the Lord. Ho-san-na in the high-est, ho-san-na in the high - est!

MEMORIAL ACCLAMATION

315

"Mass of Creation"
Marty Haugen, 1984

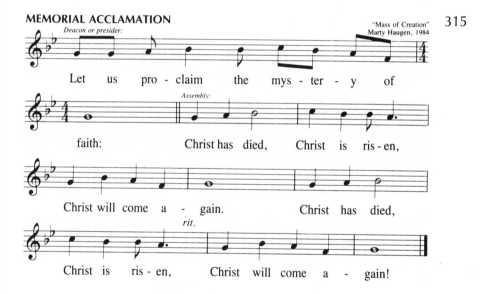

Deacon or presider:

Let us pro-claim the mys-ter-y of

Assembly:

faith: Christ has died, Christ is ris-en, Christ will come a-gain. Christ has died, Christ is ris-en, Christ will come a-gain!

AMEN

"Mass of Creation"
Marty Haugen, 1984

316

A - men, a - men, a-men! A - men, a - men, a - men!

317 EUCHARISTIC PRAYER FOR CHILDREN II

Richard Proulx, 1982

Presider: The Lord be with you. *Assembly:* And al - so with you.

Presider: Lift up your hearts. *Assembly:* We lift them up to the Lord.

Presider: Let us give thanks to the Lord our God.

Assembly: It is right to give him thanks and praise.

Three different times during the Preface we sing the following acclamation after the priest says:
...With Jesus we sing your praise:

mf Ho - san - na, ho-

san - na, ho - san - na in the high - est.

318 SANCTUS

We thank you with the angels and saints as they praise you and sing:

f Ho - ly, ho - ly, ho - ly Lord,

God of pow-er and might, heav - en and

earth are full of your glo - ry. Ho-

san - na, ho - san - na, ho - san - na in the

high - est. Ho - ly, ho - ly, ho - ly Lord, God of pow-er and might. Bless - ed is he who comes in the name of the Lord. Ho - san - na, ho - san - na, ho-san - na in the high - est.

...He promised to send the Holy Spirit, to be with us always so that we can live as your children.

Bless - ed is he who comes in the name of the Lord. Ho - san - na, ho-san - na, ho - san - na in the high - est.

319 **MEMORIAL ACCLAMATION**

The following is sung as the priest shows the consecrated host to the people,
and again when he shows the chalice:

Je - sus has giv-en his life for us.

The following is sung after each of these four texts:
...He put himself into our hands to be the sacrifice we offer you.
...all other bishops, and all who serve your people.
...Bring them home to you to be with you for ever.
...friends of Jesus the Lord will sing a song of joy.

We praise you, we

bless you, we thank you.

320 **AMEN**

...almighty Father, for ever and ever.

A - men, a - men, a - men.

A - men, a - men, a - men, a - men.

A - men, a - men, a - men.

A - men, a - men, a - men.

A - men, a - men, a - men, a - men.

*Possible endings

A - men, a - men, a - men.

MEMORIAL ACCLAMATION 321

"Mass of the Redeemer"
Richard Proulx, 1972

f

Christ has died, Christ is ris - en,

Christ will come a - gain.

MEMORIAL ACCLAMATION 322

Christus Vincit
Adapt. by Richard Proulx, 1985

Christ has died, Christ is ris - en, Christ will come a-gain.

MEMORIAL ACCLAMATION 323

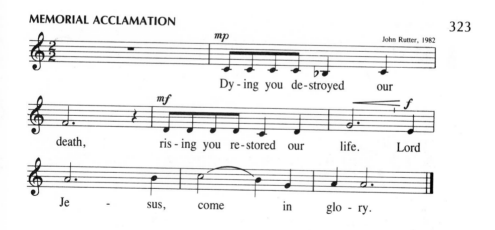

mp

John Rutter, 1982

Dy - ing you de-stroyed our

mf   *f*

death, ris - ing you re-stored our life. Lord

Je - sus, come in glo - ry.

MEMORIAL ACCLAMATION 324

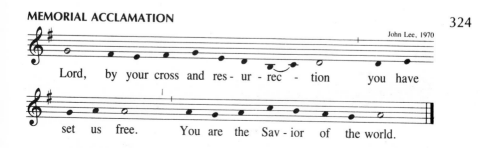

John Lee, 1970

Lord, by your cross and res - ur - rec - tion you have

set us free. You are the Sav - ior of the world.

325 MEMORIAL ACCLAMATION

Howard Hughes, SM 1975

Lord, by your cross and res - ur - rec-tion you have set us free. You are the Sav-ior of the world.

326 AMEN

Dresden
Johann G. Naumann, 1741-1801

A - men, a - men.

327 AMEN

Joseph Gelineau, 1953

A - men, A - men,

328 AMEN

Anonymous

A - men, a - men, a - men.

329 AMEN

Taizé Community
Jacques Berthier, 1980

A - men, a - men. A - men, a - men. A - men, a - men.

330 AMEN

From Sanctus VIII
Acc. by Richard Proulx, 1985

A - men. A - men. A - men.

LORD'S PRAYER

"Lyric Liturgy"
Alexander Peloquin, 1974

Let us pray with con-fi-dence to the Fa-ther in the words our Sav-ior gave us:

Our Fa-ther, who art in heav-en, hal-lowed be thy name; thy king-dom come; thy will be done on earth as it is in heav-en. Give us this day our dai-ly bread; and for-give us our tres-pass-es as we for-give those who tres-pass a-gainst us; and lead us not in-to temp-ta-tion, but de-liv-er us from e-vil.

After the prayer "Deliver Us":

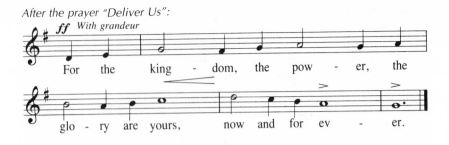

For the king - dom, the pow - er, the
glo - ry are yours, now and for ev - er.

332 LORD'S PRAYER

"A Festival Eucharist"
Richard Proulx, 1975

Our Fath - er, who art in
heav-en, hal-lowed be thy name; thy
king - dom come; thy will be done on
earth as it is in heav - en.
Give us this day our dai - ly bread; and for-
give us our tres - pass - es as
we for-give those who tres - pass a - gainst
us; and lead us not in - to temp-
ta - tion, but de - liv - er us from e - vil.

After the prayer "Deliver Us":

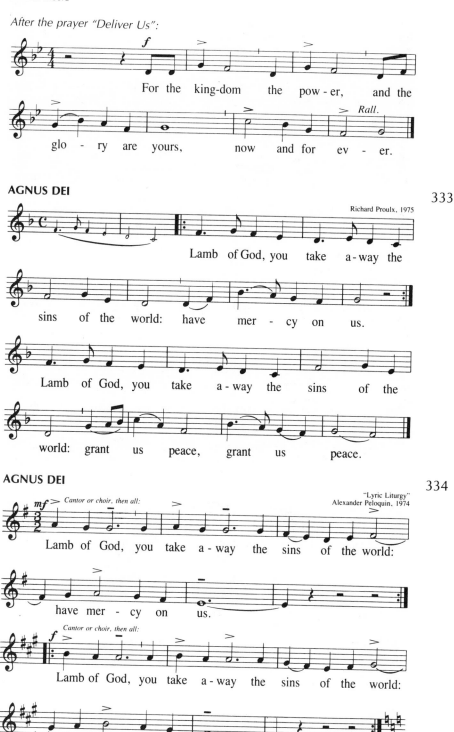

For the king-dom the pow-er, and the glo - ry are yours, now and for ev - er.

AGNUS DEI 333

Richard Proulx, 1975

Lamb of God, you take a-way the sins of the world: have mer - cy on us. Lamb of God, you take a - way the sins of the world: grant us peace, grant us peace.

AGNUS DEI 334

"Lyric Liturgy"
Alexander Peloquin, 1974

Cantor or choir, then all:

Lamb of God, you take a - way the sins of the world: have mer - cy on us.

Cantor or choir, then all:

Lamb of God, you take a - way the sins of the world: have mer - cy on us.

Lamb of God, you take a-way the
sins of the world: have mer-cy on us.

All: **ff** Lamb of God, you take a-way the
sins of the world: grant us peace.

335 **AGNUS DEI**

Cantor: Howard Hughes, SM, 1981

Lamb of God,
you take a-way the sins of the world: have

Assembly:
mer-cy on us. Have mer-cy on us.

Cantor:
Lamb of God, you take a-way the sins of the world: have

Assembly:
mer-cy on us. Have mer-cy on us.

Cantor:
Lamb of God, you take a-way the sins of the world:

Assembly:
grant us peace. Grant us peace.

AGNUS DEI

336

Ostinato Response

Do - na no - bis pa - cem.

AGNUS DEI

337

Canon

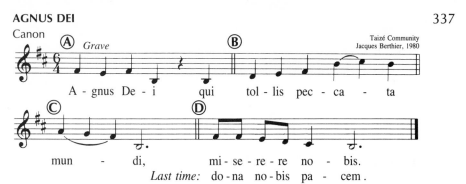

A - gnus De - i qui tol - lis pec - ca - ta

mun - di, mi - se - re - re no - bis.

Last time: do - na no - bis pa - cem.

AGNUS DEI

338

Lamb of God,

you take a - way the sins of the world, have

mer - cy on us. world, grant

us peace.

AGNUS DEI

339

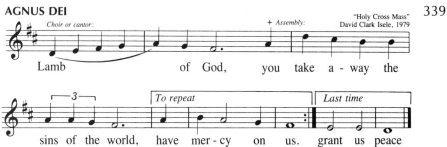

Lamb of God, you take a - way the

sins of the world, have mer - cy on us. grant us peace

Cantus Missae

INTRODUCTORY RITES

340 KYRIE

ed. Vat. XVI
Acc. by Gerard Farrell. OSB, 1985

Ky - ri - e, e - le - i - son. Ky - ri - e, e - le - i - son.

Chri - ste, e - le - i - son. Chri - ste, e - le - i - son. Ky - ri -

e, e - le - i - son. Ky - ri - e, e - le - i - son.

341 GLORIA

ed. Vat. VIII
Gerard Farrell, OSB, 1985

Glo - ri - a in ex - cel - sis De - o.

glory in heaven to God

Et in ter - ra pax ho - mi - ni - bus bo - nae vo - lun - ta - tis.

peace

Lau - da - mus te. Be - ne - di - ci - mus te.

A - do - ra - mus te. Glo - ri - fi - ca - mus te.

We adore you *We glorify you*

Gra-ti-as a-gi-mus ti-bi pro-pter ma-gnam glo-ri-am
we thank you for... great glory

tu - am. Do-mi-ne De-us, Rex cae-les-tis,
your Lord, God King of heaven

De-us Pa-ter om-ni-po-tens. Do-mi-ne Fi-li
God + Father almighty Lord, Son

u-ni-ge-ni-te, Je-su Chri-ste. Do-mi-ne
of Jesus Christ Lord

De-us, A-gnus De-i, Fi-li-us Pa-tris.
God Lamb of God Son of the father

Qui tol-lis pec-ca-ta mun-di, mi-se-re-
you take away the sins have mercy

re no-bis. Qui tol-lis pec-ca-ta mun-di, su-sci-pe
on us you take away the sins

de-pre-ca-ti-o-nem no-stram. Qui se-des ad
you are seated at

dex-ter-am Pa-tris, mi-se-re-re no-bis. Quo-ni-am tu
the right hand of the Father have mercy on us For you

so-lus San-ctus. Tu so-lus Do-mi-nus. Tu so-lus
alone are holy, you alone are the Lord you alone

Al-tis-si-mus, Je-su Chri-ste. Cum San-cto
are the most high Jesus Christ with the Holy

Spi-ri-tu, in glo-ri-a De-i
spirit in the glory of God

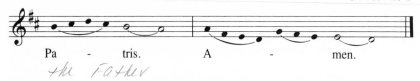

Pa - tris. A - men.

the Father

LITURGY OF THE WORD

342 THE FIRST READINGS

After the first reading:

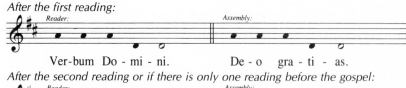

Reader: Ver-bum Do - mi - ni. Assembly: De - o gra - ti - as.

After the second reading or if there is only one reading before the gospel:

Reader: Ver - bum Do - mi - ni. Assembly: De - o gra - ti - as.

343 ALLELUIA

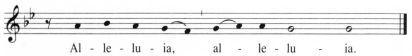

Al - le - lu - ia, al - le - lu - ia.

344 GOSPEL

Before the gospel:

Deacon or Priest: Do - mi-nus vo-bis-cum. Assembly: Et cum spi - ri - tu tu - o. Deacon: Le-cti - o san-

cti E - van-ge - li - i se-cun-dum N... Assembly: Glo - ri - a ti - bi, Do-mi-ne.

After the gospel:

Deacon: Ver-bum Do - mi - ni. Assembly: Laus ti - bi, Chri - ste.

345 CREDO

ed. Vat. III
Acc. by Gerard Farrell, OSB, 1985

Cre-do in u-num De - um, Pa - trem om - ni - po-ten-tem fa-

cto - rem cae - li et ter-rae, vi - si - bi - li-um om - ni-um

Et a - scen-dit in cae - lum, se-det ad dex-te-ram Pa - tris.

Et i - te-rum ven-tu-rus est cum glo-ri - a, ju-di-ca-re

vi - vos et mor-tu-os, cu-jus re-gni non e - rit fi - nis.

Et in Spi-ri-tum San-ctum, Do-mi-num et vi-vi-fi-can-tem:

qui ex Pa-tre Fi - li - o-que pro-ce - dit. Qui cum

Pa-tre et Fi - li - o si-mul a-do-ra-tur et con-glo-

ri - fi - ca-tur: qui lo-cu-tus est per pro - phe - tas.

Et u-nam, san-ctam, ca-tho-li-cam et a-po-sto-li-

cam Ec-cle-si-am. Con-fi-te-or u-num Ba - ptis-ma

in re-mis-si-o-nem pec-ca-to-rum. Et ex-spe-cto

re - sur-re-cti-o-nem mor-tu-o-rum. Et vi-tam ven-

tu - ri sae-cu-li. A - men.

GENERAL INTERCESSIONS

After each intention:

ex - au - di - re di - gne - ris.

Te ro - ga - mus, au - di - nos.

LITURGY OF THE EUCHARIST

PREFACE DIALOG

Do - mi - nus vo - bis - cum. Et cum Spir - i - tu tu - o.

Sur - sum cor - da. Ha - be - mus ad Do - mi - num.

Gra - ti - as a - ga - mus Do - mi - no De - o no - stro.

Di - gnum et iu - stum est.

SANCTUS

ed. Vat. XVIII
Acc. by Gerard Farrell, OSB, 1985

San - ctus, San - ctus, San - ctus Do - mi - nus De - us Sa - ba - oth.

Ple - ni sunt cae - li et ter - ra glo - ri - a tu - a. Ho - san - na

in ex - cel - sis. Be - ne - di - ctus qui ve - nit in no - mi - ne

Do - mi - ni. Ho - san - na in ex - cel - sis.

349 MEMORIAL ACCLAMATION

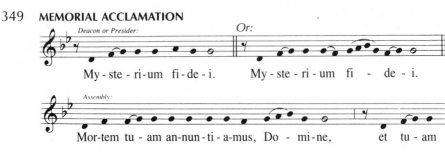

Deacon or Presider: *Or:*

My - ste - ri - um fi - de - i.   My - ste - ri - um fi - de - i.

Assembly:

Mor-tem tu - am an-nun - ti - a-mus, Do - mi-ne,   et tu - am

re - sur - re - cti - o - nem con - fi - te - mur,   do - nec ve - ni - as.

350 AMEN
After the doxology:

Assembly:

per o - mni - a sae-cu - la sae-cu - lo - rum.   A - men.

COMMUNION RITE

351 LORD'S PRAYER

Presider:

Prae-ce-ptis sa - lu - ta - ri - bus mo - ni - ti,   et di - vi - na

in - sti - tu - ti - o - ne for-ma - ti,   au - de - mus di - ce - re:

All: Acc. by Gerard Farrell, OSB, 1985

Pa - ter no-ster, qui es in cae - lis: san-cti - fi - ce - tur no - men

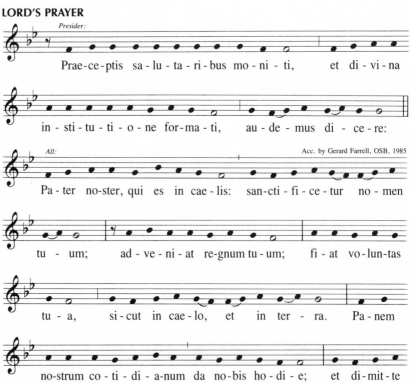

tu - um;   ad - ve - ni - at re-gnum tu - um;   fi - at vo-lun-tas

tu - a,   si - cut in cae - lo,   et in ter - ra.   Pa - nem

no-strum co - ti - di - a-num da no-bis ho - di - e;   et di - mit - te

no - bis de - bi - ta no-stra, si - cut et nos di - mit - ti - mus de-bi-

to - ri - bus no-stris; et ne nos in - du-cas in ten - ta - ti-

o - nem; sed li - be - ra nos a ma - lo.

After the prayer "Libera nos":

Qui - a tu - um est re-gnum, et po - te - stas,

et glo - ri - a in sae - cu - la.

SIGN OF PEACE 352

Presider:

Qui vivis et regnas in saecula sae - cu - lo - rum.

Assembly: *Presider:*

A - men. Pax Do - mi - ni sit sem - per

Assembly:

vo - bis - cum. Et cum spi - ri - tu tu - o.

AGNUS DEI 353

ed. Vat. XVIII
Acc. by Gerard Farrell, OSB, 1985

A - gnus De - i, qui tol - lis pec - ca - ta mun-di: mi - se - re - re no - bis.

A - gnus De - i, qui tol - lis pec - ca - ta mun - di: mi - se - re - re no - bis.

A - gnus De - i, qui tol - lis pec - ca - ta mun - di: do - na no - bis pa - cem.

CONCLUDING RITE

354 **DISMISSAL**

Deacon or Presider: *Assembly:*

I - te, mis - sa est.   De - o gra - ti - as.

For Easter Sunday and the octave of Easter:

I - te, mis-sa est, al - le - lu - ia,   al - le - lu - ia.
De - o gra - ti - as, al - le - lu - ia,   al - le - lu - ia.

When the King Shall Come Again   355

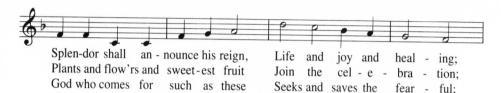

1. When the King shall come a-gain   All his pow'r re - veal - ing,
2. In the des-ert trees take root   Fresh from his cre - a - tion;
3. Strength-en fee-ble hands and knees,   Faint-ing hearts, be cheer - ful!
4. There God's high-way shall be seen   Where no roar - ing li - on,

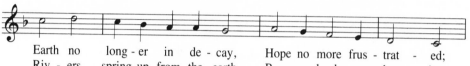

Splen-dor shall an - nounce his reign,   Life and joy and heal - ing;
Plants and flow'rs and sweet-est fruit   Join the cel - e - bra - tion;
God who comes for such as these   Seeks and saves the fear - ful;
Noth-ing e - vil or un-clean   Walks the road to Zi - on:

Earth no long - er in de - cay,   Hope no more frus - trat - ed;
Riv - ers spring up from the earth,   Bar - ren lands a - dorn - ing;
Now the deaf can hear the dumb   Sing a - way their weep - ing;
Ran-somed peo - ple home-ward bound   All your prais - es voic - ing,

This is God's re - demp-tion day   Long-ing - ly a - wait - ed.
Val - leys, this is your new birth,   Moun-tains, greet the morn - ing!
Blind eyes see the in - jured come   Walk-ing, run-ning, leap - ing.
See your Lord with glo - ry crowned,   Share in his re - joic - ing!

Text: Is. 35; Christopher Idle, b.1938. © 1982. Hope Publishing Co.
Tune: GAUDEAMUS PARITER, 7 6 7 6 D; Johann Horn, c.1495-1547

356 On Jordan's Bank

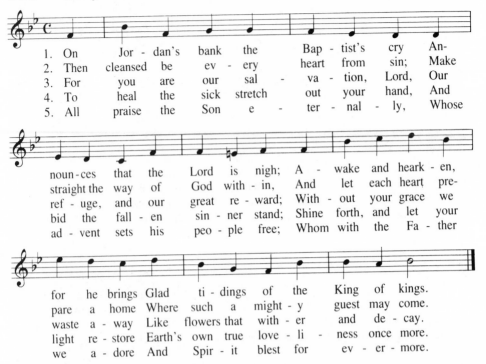

1. On Jor - dan's bank the Bap - tist's cry An-
2. Then cleansed be ev - ery heart from sin; Make
3. For you are our sal - va - tion, Lord, Our
4. To heal the sick stretch out your hand, And
5. All praise the Son e - ter - nal - ly, Whose

noun - ces that the Lord is nigh; A - wake and heark - en,
straight the way of God with - in, And let each heart pre-
ref - uge, and our great re - ward; With - out your grace we
bid the fall - en sin - ner stand; Shine forth, and let your
ad - vent sets his peo - ple free; Whom with the Fa - ther

for he brings Glad ti - dings of the King of kings.
pare a home Where such a might - y guest may come.
waste a - way Like flowers that with - er and de - cay.
light re - store Earth's own true love - li - ness once more.
we a - dore And Spir - it blest for ev - er - more.

Text: *Jordanis oras praevia*; Charles Coffin, 1676-1749; Tr. by John Chandler, 1806-1876
Tune: WINCHESTER NEW, LM; Adapt. from *Musikalisches Handbuch*, Hamburg, 1690

357 O Come, O Come, Emmanuel

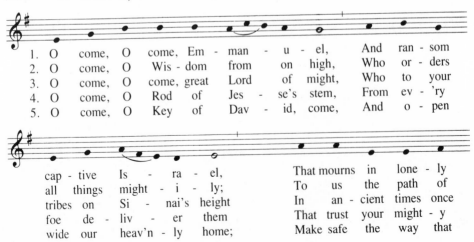

1. O come, O come, Em - man - u - el, And ran - som
2. O come, O Wis - dom from on high, Who or - ders
3. O come, O come, great Lord of might, Who to your
4. O come, O Rod of Jes - se's stem, From ev - 'ry
5. O come, O Key of Dav - id, come, And o - pen

cap - tive Is - ra - el, That mourns in lone - ly
all things might - i - ly; To us the path of
tribes on Si - nai's height In an - cient times once
foe de - liv - er them That trust your might - y
wide our heav'n - ly home; Make safe the way that

| ex | - | ile | here | Un | - | til | the | Son | of | God | ap | - | pear. |

ex - ile here Un - til the Son of God ap - pear.
knowl - edge show, And teach us in her ways to go.
gave the law, In cloud, and maj - es - ty, and awe.
pow'r to save, And give them vic - t'ry o'er the grave.
leads on high, And close the path to mis - er - y.

Re-joice! Re-joice! Em - man - u - el Shall come to you, O Is - ra - el.

6. O come, O Dayspring from on high
And cheer us by your drawing nigh;
Disperse the gloomy clouds of night,
And death's dark shadow put to flight.

7. O come, Desire of nations, bind
In one the hearts of humankind;
O bid our sad divisions cease,
And be for us our King of Peace.

Text: *Veni, veni Emmanuel*: Latin 9th C.; Tr. by John M. Neale, 1818-1866, alt.
Tune: VENI, VENI EMMANUEL, LM with refrain; Mode I; Adapt. by Thomas Helmore, 1811-1890; Acc. by Richard Proulx, b.1937, © 1975, GIA Publications, Inc.

The Voice of God Goes Out through All the World 358

1. The voice of God goes out through all the world: God's glo-ry speaks a-
2. The Lord has said: "Re - ceive my mes-sen - ger, My prom-ise to the
3. The bro - ken reed he will not tram-ple down, Nor set his heel up-
4. A - noint-ed with the Spir - it and with power, He comes to crown with
5. His touch will bless the eyes that dark-ness held, The lame shall run, the

cross the u - ni - verse. The great King's her - ald cries from star to
world, my pledge made flesh, A lamp to ev - 'ry na - tion, light from
on the dy - ing flame, He binds the wounds, and health is in his
com-fort all the weak, To show the face of jus - tice to the
halt - ing tongue shall sing, And pri-s'ners laugh in light and lib - er-

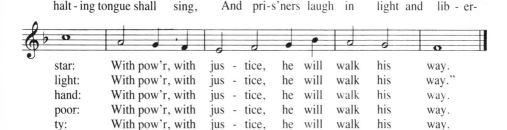

star: With pow'r, with jus - tice, he will walk his way.
light: With pow'r, with jus - tice, he will walk his way."
hand: With pow'r, with jus - tice, he will walk his way.
poor: With pow'r, with jus - tice, he will walk his way.
ty: With pow'r, with jus - tice, he will walk his way.

Text: Luke Connaughton, 1919-1979, © 1970, Mayhew McCrimmon Ltd.
Tune: TOULON, 10 10 10 10; *Genevan Psalter*, 1551; Harm. by Louis Bourgeois. c.1510-1561

359 People, Look East

1. Peo - ple, look East. The time is near Of the crown-ing of the
2. Fur-rows, be glad. Though earth is bare, One more seed is plant-ed
3. Birds, though you long have ceased to build, Guard the nest that must be
4. Stars, keep the watch. When night is dim One more light the bowl shall
5. An - gels an - nounce with shouts of mirth Him who brings new life to

year.   Make your house   fair   as   you   are   a - ble,   Trim the
there: Give up   your   strength   the   seed   to   nour - ish,   That in
filled.   E - ven   the   hour   when wings   are   fro - zen   He for
brim,   Shin - ing   be - yond   the   frost - y   weath - er,   Bright as
earth.   Set   ev - 'ry   peak   and   val - ley   hum - ming   With the

hearth and   set   the   ta - ble. Peo-ple look   East   and sing   to - day:
course the   flow'r may   flour - ish. Peo-ple look   East   and sing   to - day:
fledg - ing   time has   cho - sen. Peo-ple look   East   and sing   to - day:
sun   and   moon to - geth - er. Peo-ple look   East   and sing   to - day:
word, the   Lord is   com - ing. Peo-ple look   East   and sing   to - day:

Love   the   Guest   is   on   the   way.
Love   the   Rose   is   on   the   way.
Love   the   Bird   is   on   the   way.
Love   the   Star   is   on   the   way.
Love   the   Lord   is   on   the   way.

Text: Eleanor Farjeon, 1881-1965, © David Higham Assoc. Ltd.
Tune: BESANCON, 87 98 87; French Traditional; Harm. by Martin Shaw, 1875-1958, © Oxford University Press

Awake! Awake, and Greet the New Morn   360

1. A - wake! a - wake, and greet the new morn, For
2. To us, to all in sor - row and fear, Em-
3. In dark - est night his com - ing shall be, When
4. Re - joice, re - joice, take heart in the night, Though

an - gels her - ald its dawn - ing, Sing out your joy, for
man - u - el comes a - sing - ing, His hum - ble song is
all the world is de - spair - ing, As morn - ing light so
dark the win - ter and cheer - less, The ris - ing sun shall

soon he is born, Be - hold! the Child of our long - ing.
qui - et and near, Yet fills the earth with its ring - ing;
.qui - et and free, So warm and gen - tle and car - ing.
crown you with light, Be strong and lov - ing and fear - less;

Come as a ba - by weak and poor, To bring all hearts to-
Mu - sic to heal the bro - ken soul And hymns of lov - ing
Then shall the mute break forth in song, The lame shall leap in
Love be our song and love our prayer, And love, our end - less

geth - er, He o - pens wide the heav'n - ly door And
kind - ness, The thun - der of his an - thems roll To
won - der, The weak be raised a - bove the strong, And
sto - ry, May God fill ev - 'ry day we share, And

lives now in - side us for ev - er.
shat - ter all ha - tred and blind - ness.
weap-ons be bro - ken a - sun - der.
bring us at last in - to glo - ry.

Text: Marty Haugen, b.1950
Tune: REJOICE, REJOICE, 9 8 9 8 8 7 8 9; Marty Haugen, b.1950
© 1983, GIA Publications, Inc.

361 Take Comfort, God's People

Take com-fort, God's peo-ple, take com-fort! The

prom-ised one is on the way. Sins are par-doned,

love has con-quered: Christ will come on Christ-mas day.

1. Shout the glad tid - ings high from the hill - tops;
2. Lev - el the moun - tains, fill in the val - leys;
3. Awe - some his pow - er, might - y his scep - ter

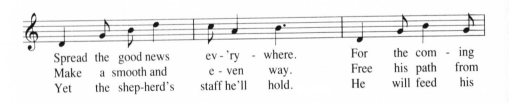

Spread the good news ev-'ry - where. For the com - ing
Make a smooth and e - ven way. Free his path from
Yet the shep-herd's staff he'll hold. He will feed his

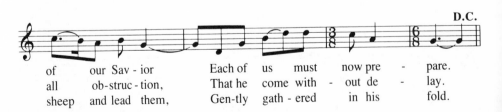

D.C.

of our Sav - ior Each of us must now pre - pare.
all ob-struc-tion, That he come with - out de - lay.
sheep and lead them, Gen-tly gath - ered in his fold.

Text: Is. 40:1-11; Omer Westendorf, b.1916
Tune: FIDDLER'S GREEN, 10 7 8 7 with refrain; Robert E. Kreutz, b.1922
© 1980, ICEL

City of God, Jerusalem 362

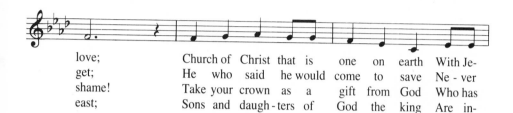

1. Cit - y of God, Je - ru - sa - lem, Where he has set his
2. Sing and be glad, Je - ru - sa - lem, For God does not for-
3. Sor - row no more, Je - ru - sa - lem, Dis - card your rags of
4. Look all a - round, Je - ru - sa - lem, Sur - vey from west to

love; Church of Christ that is one on earth With Je-
get; He who said he would come to save Ne - ver
shame! Take your crown as a gift from God Who has
east; Sons and daugh-ters of God the king Are in-

ru - sa - lem a - bove: Here as we walk this chang-ing world
failed his peo - ple yet. Though we are tempt - ed by de-spair
called you by his name. Put off your sin, and wear the robe
vit - ed to his feast. Out of their ex - ile far a - way

Our joys are mixed with tears, But the day will be soon when the
And daunt-ed by de - feat, Our in - vin - ci - ble Lord will be
Of glo - ry in its place; You will shine in his light, you will
His scat-tered fam - ily come, And the streets will re-sound with the

Sav - ior re-turns And his voice will ban-ish our fears.
seen in his strength, And his tri - umph will be com - plete.
share in his joy, You will praise his won-der - ful grace.
song of the saints When the Sav - ior wel-comes us home.

Text: Bar. 4-5; Christopher Idle, b.1938, © 1982, Hope Publishing Co.
Tune: PURPOSE, 8 6 8 7 8 6 12 8; Martin Shaw, 1875-1958, © Oxford University Press

363 Lift Up Your Heads, O Mighty Gates

1. Lift up your heads, O might - y gates; Be - hold the
2. O blest the land, the cit - y blest, Where Christ the
3. Fling wide the por - tals of your heart; Make it a
4. Come, Sav - ior, come with us a - bide; Our hearts to

King of glo - ry waits! The King of kings is
rul - er is con - fest! O hap - py hearts and
tem - ple, set a - part From earth - ly use for
you we o - pen wide: Your Ho - ly Spir - it

draw - ing near; The Sav - ior of the world is here.
hap - py homes To whom this King of tri - umph comes!
heav'n's em - ploy, A - dorned with prayer and love and joy.
guide us on, Un - til our glo - rious goal is won.

Text: Based on Ps. 24; *Macht hoch die Tür*; George Weissel, 1590-1635; Tr. by Catherine Winkworth, 1827-1878, alt.
Tune: TRURO, LM, Williams' *Psalmodia Evangelica*, 1789

364 Come, O Long Expected Jesus

1. Come, O long ex - pect - ed Je - sus, Born to set your peo - ple free;
2. Is - rael's strength and con - so - la - tion, You, the hope of all the earth,
3. Born your peo - ple to de - liv - er; Born a child and yet a king!
4. By your own e - ter - nal Spir - it Rule in all our hearts a - lone;

From our fears and sins re - lease us; Free us from cap - tiv - i - ty.
Dear de - sire of ev - 'ry na - tion, Come, and save us by your birth.
Born to reign in us for ev - er, Now your gra - cious king-dom bring.
By your all suf - fi - cient mer - it Raise us to your glo - rious throne.

Text: Hag. 2:7; Charles Wesley, 1707-1788, alt.
Tune: STUTTGART, 8 7 8 7; Christian F. Witt, 1660-1716; Harm. by Kenneth E. Smith, b.1928. © National Christian Education Council

Hills of the North, Rejoice 365

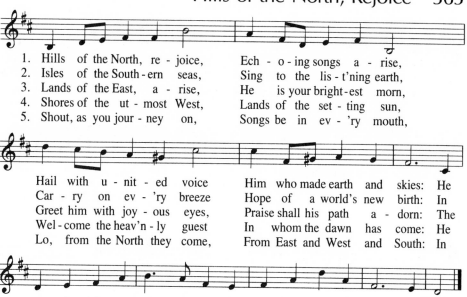

1. Hills of the North, re - joice, Ech - o - ing songs a - rise,
2. Isles of the South - ern seas, Sing to the lis - t'ning earth,
3. Lands of the East, a - rise, He is your bright - est morn,
4. Shores of the ut - most West, Lands of the set - ting sun,
5. Shout, as you jour - ney on, Songs be in ev - 'ry mouth,

Hail with u - nit - ed voice Him who made earth and skies: He
Car - ry on ev - 'ry breeze Hope of a world's new birth: In
Greet him with joy - ous eyes, Praise shall his path a - dorn: The
Wel - come the heav'n - ly guest In whom the dawn has come: He
Lo, from the North they come, From East and West and South: In

comes in right-eous - ness and love, He brings sal - va - tion from a - bove.
Christ shall all be made a - new, His word is sure, his prom - ise true.
God whom you have longed to know In Christ draws near, and calls you now.
brings a nev - er - end - ing light Who tri - umphed o'er our dark - est night.
Je - sus all shall find their rest, In him shall all the earth be blest.

Text: Editors of *English Praise*, Based on Charles E. Oakley, 1832-1865, © 1975, Oxford University Press
Tune: LITTLE CORNARD, 6 6 6 6 88; Martin Shaw, 1875-1958, © J. Curwen and Sons

Come, Lord, and Tarry Not 366

1. Come, Lord, and tar - ry not! Bring the long-looked-for day!
2. Come, for your saints still wait; Dai - ly as - cends their sigh;
3. Come, for cre - a - tion groans, Im - pa - tient of your stay,
4. Come, and make all things new, Build up this ru - ined earth;
5. Come, and be - gin your reign Of ev - er - last - ing peace;

O why these years of wait - ing here, These a - ges of de - lay?
The Spir - it and the Bride say, "Come!" Do you not hear the cry?
Worn out with these long years of ill, These a - ges of de - lay?
Re - store our fad - ed par - a - dise, Cre - a - tion's sec - ond birth.
Come, take the king - dom to your - self, Great King of right-eous - ness!

Text: Rev. 22:17, Attr. to Horatius Bonar, 1808-1889
Tune: ST. BRIDE, SM, Samuel Howard, 1710-1782

367 O Come, Divine Messiah

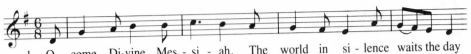

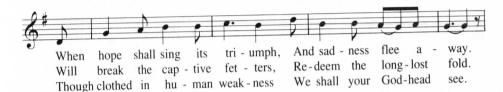

1. O come, Di-vine Mes-si-ah, The world in si-lence waits the day
2. O come, De-sired of na-tions, Whom priest and proph-et long fore-told,
3. O come, in peace and meek-ness, For low-ly will your cra-dle be:

When hope shall sing its tri-umph, And sad-ness flee a-way.
Will break the cap-tive fet-ters, Re-deem the long-lost fold.
Though clothed in hu-man weak-ness We shall your God-head see.

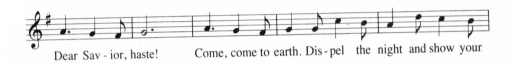

Dear Sav-ior, haste! Come, come to earth. Dis-pel the night and show your

face, And bid us hail the dawn of grace. O

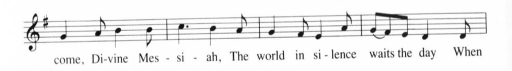

come, Di-vine Mes-si-ah, The world in si-lence waits the day When

hope shall sing its tri-umph, And sad-ness flee a-way.

Text: *Venez, divin Messie*; Abbé Simon-Joseph Pellegrin, 1663-1745; Tr. by S. Mary of St. Philip, 1877
Tune: VENEZ, DIVIN MESSIE, 7 8 7 6 with refrain; French Noël, 16th C.; Harm. by Healey Willan, 1880-1968, © 1958, Ralph Jusko Publications, Inc.

Creator of the Stars of Night 368

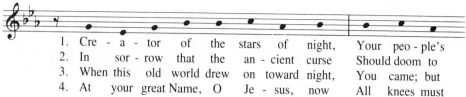

1. Cre - a - tor of the stars of night, Your peo - ple's
2. In sor - row that the an - cient curse Should doom to
3. When this old world drew on toward night, You came; but
4. At your great Name, O Je - sus, now All knees must

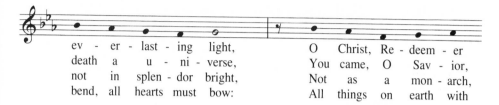

ev - er - last - ing light, O Christ, Re - deem - er
death a u - ni - verse, You came, O Sav - ior,
not in splen - dor bright, Not as a mon - arch,
bend, all hearts must bow: All things on earth with

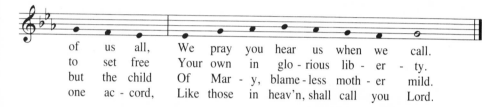

of us all, We pray you hear us when we call.
to set free Your own in glo - rious lib - er - ty.
but the child Of Mar - y, blame - less moth - er mild.
one ac - cord, Like those in heav'n, shall call you Lord.

5. Come in your holy might, we pray,
   Redeem us for eternal day;
   Defend us while we dwell below
   From all assaults of our dread foe.

6. To God Creator, God the Son,
   And God the Spirit, Three in One,
   Praise, honor, might, and glory be
   From age to age eternally.

Text: *Conditor alme siderum*, Latin 9th C.; Tr. *The Hymnal 1982*, © 1985, The Church Pension Fund
Tune: CONDITOR ALME SIDERUM, LM; Mode IV; Acc. by Gerard Farrell, OSB, b.1919, © 1986, GIA Publications, Inc.

Prepare the Way of the Lord 369

Canon

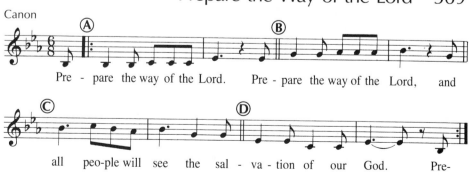

Pre - pare the way of the Lord. Pre - pare the way of the Lord, and

all peo-ple will see the sal - va - tion of our God. Pre-

Text: Luke 3:4,6; Taizé Community, 1984
Tune: Jacques Berthier, b.1923
© 1984, Les Presses de Taizé

370 Comfort, Comfort, O My People

1. Com-fort, com - fort, O my peo - ple, Speak of peace, now says our God;
2. Hark, the voice of one who's cry - ing In the des - ert far and near,
3. O make straight what long was crook-ed, Make the rough - er plac - es plain;

Com-fort those who sit in dark-ness, Mourn-ing 'neath their sor-rows' load.
Bid-ding all to full re-pent-ance Since the king-dom now is here.
Let your hearts be true and hum - ble, As be - fits his ho - ly reign.

Speak un - to Je - ru - sa - lem Of the peace that waits for them;
O that warn-ing cry o - bey! Now pre-pare for God a way;
For the glo - ry of the Lord Now o'er earth is shed a - broad;

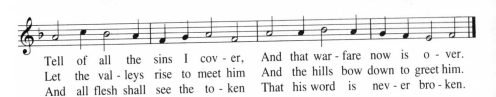

Tell of all the sins I cov - er, And that war - fare now is o - ver.
Let the val - leys rise to meet him And the hills bow down to greet him.
And all flesh shall see the to - ken That his word is nev - er bro - ken.

Text: Is. 40:1-8; *Tröstet, tröstet, meine Lieben;* Johann Olearius, 1611-1684; Tr. by Catherine Winkworth, 1827-1878, alt.
Tune: GENEVA 42, 8 7 8 7 77 88; *Genevan Psalter,* 1551; Harm. adapt. from Claude Goudimel, 1505-1572

371 Wake, O Wake, and Sleep No Longer

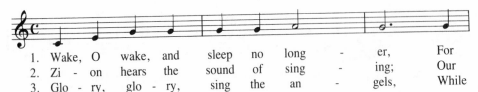

1. Wake, O wake, and sleep no long - er, For
2. Zi - on hears the sound of sing - ing; Our
3. Glo - ry, glo - ry, sing the an - gels, While

he who calls you is no stran - ger: A - wake, God's own Je-
hearts are thrilled with sud - den long - ing: She stirs, and wakes, and
mu - sic sounds from strings and cym - bals; All hu - man - kind, with

ru - sa - lem! Hear, the mid - night bells are chim - ing The
stands pre-pared. Christ, her friend, and lord, and lov - er, Her
songs a - rise! Twelve the gates in - to the cit - y, Each

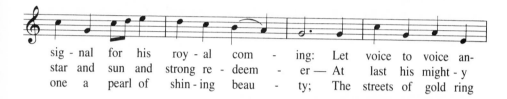

sig - nal for his roy - al com - ing: Let voice to voice an-
star and sun and strong re - deem - er — At last his might - y
one a pearl of shin - ing beau - ty; The streets of gold ring

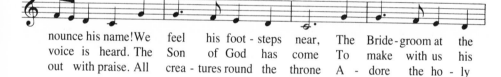

nounce his name! We feel his foot - steps near, The Bride-groom at the
voice is heard. The Son of God has come To make with us his
out with praise. All crea - tures round the throne A - dore the ho - ly

door — Al - le - lu - ia! The lamps will shine With
home: Sing Ho - san - na! The fight is won, The
One With re - joic - ing: A - men be sung By

light di - vine As Christ the sav - ior comes to reign.
feast be - gun; We fix our eyes on Christ a - lone.
ev - 'ry tongue To crown their wel - come to the King.

Text: Matt. 25:1-13; *Wachet auf, ruft uns die Stimme*, Philipp Nicolai, 1556-1608; Tr. and adapt. by Christopher Idle, b.1938. © 1982, Hope Publishing Co.
Tune: WACHET AUF, 89 8 89 8 66 4 44 8; Philipp Nicolai, 1556-1608; Harm. by J. S. Bach, 1685-1750

372 Savior of the Nations, Come

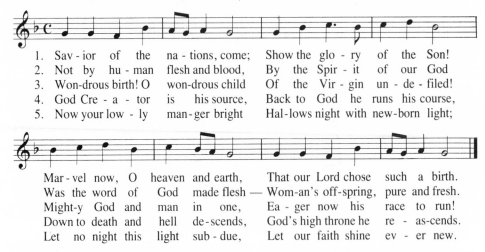

1. Sav-ior of the na-tions, come; Show the glo-ry of the Son!
2. Not by hu-man flesh and blood, By the Spir-it of our God
3. Won-drous birth! O won-drous child Of the Vir-gin un-de-filed!
4. God Cre-a-tor is his source, Back to God he runs his course,
5. Now your low-ly man-ger bright Hal-lows night with new-born light;

Mar-vel now, O heaven and earth, That our Lord chose such a birth.
Was the word of God made flesh — Wom-an's off-spring, pure and fresh.
Might-y God and man in one, Ea-ger now his race to run!
Down to death and hell de-scends, God's high throne he re-as-cends.
Let no night this light sub-due, Let our faith shine ev-er new.

Text: *Veni, Redemptor gentium;* Ascr. to St. Ambrose, 340-397; Tr. sts. 1-3a, William Reynolds, 1812-1876; Sts. 3b-5, Martin L. Seltz, 1909-1967, alt.
Tune: NUN KOMM DER HEIDEN HEILAND, 77 77; *Geystliche gesangk Buchleyn,* Wittenberg, 1524; Harm. by Melchior Vulpius, c.1560-1615

373 The King Shall Come When Morning Dawns

1. The King shall come when morn-ing dawns And
2. Not, as of old, a lit-tle child, To
3. The King shall come when morn-ing dawns And
4. And let the end-less bliss be-gin, By
5. The King shall come when morn-ing dawns And

light tri-um-phant breaks, When beau-ty gilds the
suf-fer and to die, But crowned with glo-ry
earth's dark night is past; O haste the ris-ing
wea-ry saints fore-told, When right shall tri-umph
light and beau-ty brings. Hail, Christ, the Lord! your

east-ern hills And life to joy a-wakes.
like the sun That lights the morn-ing sky.
of that morn Whose day shall ev-er last.
o-ver wrong, And truth shall be ex-tolled.
peo-ple pray: Come quick-ly, King of kings.

Text: John Brownlie, 1857-1925
Tune: ST. STEPHEN, CM; William Jones, 1726-1800

Lo, How a Rose E'er Blooming 374

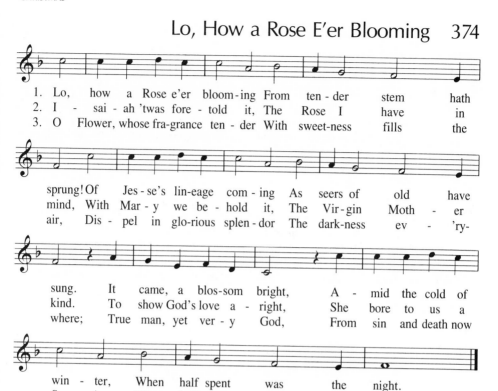

1. Lo, how a Rose e'er bloom-ing From ten - der stem hath
2. I - sai - ah 'twas fore - told it, The Rose I have in
3. O Flower, whose fra-grance ten - der With sweet-ness fills the

sprung! Of Jes - se's lin-eage com - ing As seers of old have
mind, With Mar - y we be - hold it, The Vir - gin Moth - er
air, Dis - pel in glo-rious splen - dor The dark-ness ev - 'ry-

sung. It came, a blos-som bright, A - mid the cold of
kind. To show God's love a - right, She bore to us a
where; True man, yet ver - y God, From sin and death now

win - ter, When half spent was the night.
Sav - ior, When half spent was the night.
save us, And share our ev - 'ry load.

Text: Is. 11:1; *Es ist ein' Ros' entsprungen; Speier Gebetbuch*, 1599; Tr. Sts. 1-2 by Theodore Baker, 1851-1934; St. 3, *The Hymnal*, 1940
Tune: ES IST EIN' ROS' ENTSPRUNGEN, 7 6 7 6 6 7 6; *Geistliche Kirchengesang*, Cologne, 1599; Harm. by Michael Praetorius, 1571-1621

375 See amid the Winter's Snow

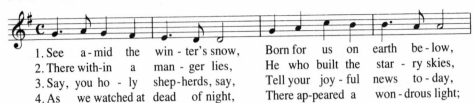

1. See a-mid the win-ter's snow, Born for us on earth be-low,
2. There with-in a man-ger lies, He who built the star-ry skies,
3. Say, you ho-ly shep-herds, say, Tell your joy-ful news to-day,
4. As we watched at dead of night, There ap-peared a won-drous light;

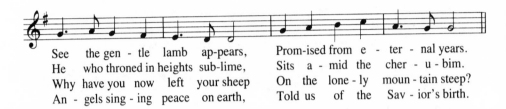

See the gen-tle lamb ap-pears, Prom-ised from e-ter-nal years.
He who throned in heights sub-lime, Sits a-mid the cher-u-bim.
Why have you now left your sheep On the lone-ly moun-tain steep?
An-gels sing-ing peace on earth, Told us of the Sav-ior's birth.

Hail that ev-er bless-ed morn, Hail re-demp-tion's hap-py dawn,

Sing through all Je-ru-sa-lem: Christ is born in Beth-le-hem.

Text: Edward Caswall, 1814-1878
Tune: HUMILITY, 77 77 with refrain; John Goss, 1800-1880

Angels We Have Heard on High 376

1. An - gels we have heard on high   Sweet-ly sing - ing o'er   the plains,
2. Shep-herds, why this ju - bi-lee?   Why your joy - ous strains pro-long?
3. Come to Beth - le - hem and see   Him whose birth the an - gels sing;
4. See him in a man - ger laid,   Whom the choirs of an - gels praise;

And the moun-tains in re-ply   Ech - o back their joy - ous strains.
Say what may the ti - dings be,   Which in - spire your heaven - ly song.
Come a - dore, on bend - ed knee,   Christ, the Lord, the new - born King.
Mar - y, Jo - seph, lend your aid,   While our hearts in love we raise.

Glo - - - - - - - - - ri - a

in ex - cel - sis De - o, Glo - - - - -

- - - ri - a in ex - cel - sis De - o.

Text: *Les anges dans nos campagnes;* French, c.18th C.;Tr. from *Crown of Jesus Music,* London, 1862
Tune: GLORIA, 7 7 7 7 with refrain; French Traditional

377 Angels, from the Realms of Glory

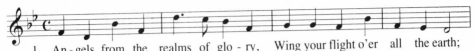

1. An - gels, from the   realms of glo - ry,   Wing your flight o'er all the earth;
2. Shep-herds, in the   fields a - bid - ing,   Watch-ing o'er your flocks by night,
3. Sag - es, leave your   con - tem-pla-tions,   Bright-er vi - sions beam a - far,
4. Though an in - fant   now we view him,   He shall fill his heav'n-ly throne,

You who sang cre - a - tion's sto - ry,   Now pro-claim Mes - si - ah's birth:
God on earth is   now re - sid - ing,   Yon-der shines the   in - fant light:
Seek the great De - sire of na - tions,   You have seen his   morn-ing star:
Ga - ther all the   na - tions to him;   Ev - ery knee shall then bow down:

Come and wor - ship, come and wor-ship, Wor-ship Christ, the   new-born King.

Text: Sts. 1-3, James Montgomery, 1771-1854; St. 4, *Christmas Box*, 1825
Tune: REGENT SQUARE, 8 7 8 7 8 7; Henry Smart, 1813-1879

378 Away in a Manger

1. A - way in a   man - ger, no   crib for a   bed,   The
2. The   cat - tle are   low - ing, the   ba - by a - wakes,   But
3. Be   near me, Lord Je - sus! I   ask you to   stay   Close

lit - tle Lord   Je - sus   laid   down his   sweet   head.   The
lit - tle Lord   Je - sus,   no   cry - ing   he   makes.   I
by   me   for   ev - er,   and   love me,   I   pray.   Bless

stars in the bright sky looked down where he lay, The
love you, Lord Je - sus! look down from the sky, And
all the dear chil - dren in your ten - der care, And

lit - tle Lord Je - sus, a - sleep on the hay.
stay by my cra - dle till morn - ing is nigh.
fit us for heav - en, to live with you there.

Text: Sts. 1-2, anonymous; St. 3, John T. McFarland, 1851-1913
Tune: CRADLE SONG, 11 11 11 11; William J. Kirkpatrick, 1838-1921; Harm. by David Willcocks, b.1919, © 1961, Oxford University Press

Silent Night, Holy Night 379

1. Si - lent night, ho - ly night, All is calm, all is bright
2. Si - lent night, ho - ly night, Shep-herds quake at the sight;
3. Si - lent night, ho - ly night, Son of God, love's pure light

Round yon Vir - gin Moth-er and Child, Ho - ly In-fant, so ten-der and mild,
Glo - ries stream from heav-en a - far, Heav'n-ly hosts sing al - le - lu - ia;
Ra - diant beams from thy ho-ly face, With the dawn of re - deem - ing grace,

Sleep in heav-en - ly peace, Sleep in heav - en - ly peace.
Christ, the Sav-ior, is born! Christ, the Sav - ior, is born!
Je - sus, Lord, at thy birth, Je - sus, Lord, at thy birth.

Text: *Stille Nacht, heilige Nacht;* Joseph Mohr, 1792-1849; Tr. John F. Young, 1820-1885
Tune: STILLE NACHT, 66 89 66; Franz X. Gruber, 1787-1863

380 'Twas in the Moon of Wintertime

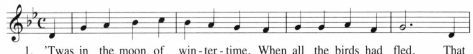

1. 'Twas in the moon of win-ter-time, When all the birds had fled, That
2. With-in a lodge of bro-ken bark The ten-der babe was found; A
3. The ear-liest moon of win-ter-time Is not so round and fair As
4. O chil-dren of the for-est free, The an-gel song is true; The

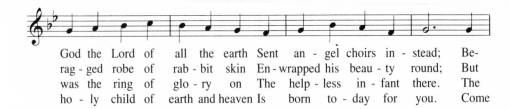

God the Lord of all the earth Sent an-gel choirs in-stead; Be-
rag-ged robe of rab-bit skin En-wrapped his beau-ty round; But
was the ring of glo-ry on The help-less in-fant there. The
ho-ly child of earth and heaven Is born to-day for you. Come

fore their light the stars grew dim, And won-d'ring hunt-ers heard the hymn:
as the hunt-er braves drew nigh, The an-gel song rang loud and high:
chiefs from far be-fore him knelt With gifts of fox and bea-ver pelt.
kneel be-fore the ra-diant boy, Who brings you beau-ty, peace, and joy.

Je-sus your king is born, Je-sus is born, in ex-cel-sis glo-ri-a.

Text: *Estennialon de tsonue Jesus ahatonhia;* St. Jean de Brebeuf, 1593-1649; Tr. by Jesse E. Middleton, 1872-1960. © Fredrick Harris Music Co. Ltd.
Tune: UNE JEUNE PUCELLE, 8 6 8 6 88 with refrain; French Melody; Harm. by Frederick F. Jackisch, b. 1922. © 1978, *Lutheran Book of Worship*

381 Unto Us a Boy Is Born

1. Un-to us a boy is born! The King of all cre-
2. Cra-dled in a stall was he With sleep-y cows and
3. Her-od then with fear was filled: "A prince," he said, "in
4. Now may Mar-y's son, who came So long a-go to
5. Al-pha and O-me-ga he! Now let the or-gan

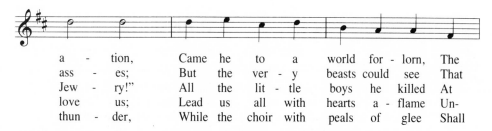

a - tion,   Came he to a   world for - lorn,   The
ass - es;   But the ver - y   beasts could see   That
Jew - ry!"   All the lit - tle   boys he killed   At
love us;   Lead us all with   hearts a - flame   Un-
thun - der,   While the choir with   peals of glee   Shall

Lord of ev - 'ry na - - - - tion.
he the world sur - pass - - - - es.
Beth-lehem in his fu - - - - ry.
to the joys a - bove - - - - us.
rend the air a - sun - - - - der.

Text: *Puer nobis nascitur;* Latin, 15th C.; Tr. by Percy Dearmer, 1867-1936. © Oxford University Press
Tune: PUER NOBIS NASCITUR, 7 7 7 7; *Piae Cantiones,* 1582; Harm. by Geoffrey Shaw, 1879-1943. © A. R. Mowbray and Co. Ltd.

While Shepherds Watched   382

1. While shep -herds watched their flocks by night, All   seat - ed   on   the
2. "Fear not," said he, for   might - y dread Had seized their trou - bled
3. "To you, in Da - vid's town, this day Is   born of Da - vid's
4. "The heav'n - ly Babe you   there shall find To   hu - man view dis-

ground, The an - gel of   the   Lord came down, And glo - ry shone a - round.
mind; "Glad ti - dings of great   joy   I   bring To   you and hu - man-kind.
line The Sav - ior, who is   Christ the Lord; And this shall be   the   sign.
played, All mean - ly wrapped in swath - ing bands, And   in   a   man - ger laid."

5. The angel spoke, and suddenly
    Appeared a shining throng
    Of angels praising God, who now
    Begin their joyful song:

6. "All glory be to God on high
    And on the earth be peace;
    Good will henceforth from heav'n to all
    Begin and never cease."

Text: Luke 2:8-14; Nahum Tate, 1652-1715
Tune: WINCHESTER OLD, CM; Christopher Tye, c.1500-c.1572; Harm. after George Kirby, fl. 1592

383 God Rest You Merry, Gentlemen

1. God   rest you mer - ry, gen - tle-men, Let noth - ing you dis - may,
2. In   Beth - le - hem in   Ju - dah This bless - ed babe was born,
3. From   God our great Cre - a - tor A   bless - ed an - gel   came,
4. The   shep-herds at those ti - dings Re - joic - ed much in mind,
5. Now   to the Lord sing prais - es, All you with - in this place,

For   Je - sus Christ our Sav - ior Was born up - on this   day,
And   laid with - in   a   man - ger Up - on this bless - ed morn:
And   un - to cer - tain shep - herds Brought ti - dings of the   same,
And   left their flocks a - feed - ing In   tem-pest, storm, and wind,
And   with true love and char - i - ty Each oth - er now em - brace;

To   save us   all from Sa - tan's power When we were gone a - stray.
For   which his moth - er Mar   - y   Did noth - ing take in   scorn.
How   that in Beth - le - hem was born The Son of God by   name.
And   went to Beth - le - hem straight-way, The bless - ed babe to   find.
This ho - ly tide of Christ - mas All oth - ers shall re - place.

O   ti - dings of   com - fort and   joy,   com-fort and

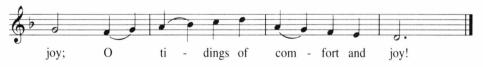

joy;   O   ti - dings of   com - fort and joy!

Text: English Carol, 18th C.
Tune: GOD REST YOU MERRY, 8 6 8 6 8 6 with refrain; English 18th C.; Harm. by John Stainer, 1840-1901

A Child Is Born in Bethlehem 384

1. A child is born in Beth - le - hem,
2. The babe who lies up - on the straw, Al - le - lu - ia.
3. Up - on this joy - ful ho - ly night,
4. We praise you, Ho - ly Trin - i - ty,

There-fore re - joice Je - ru - sa - lem,
Will rule the world for ev - er - more,
We bless your Name, O Lord of Light, Al - le - lu - ia,
A - dor - ing you e - ter - nal - ly.

al - le - lu - ia.   Our joy - ful hearts we raise,

Christ is born, O come a - dore him   In new-found songs of praise.

Text: *Puer natus in Bethlehem;* Latin 14th C.; Tr. by Ruth Fox Hume, b. 1922, © 1964, GIA Publications, Inc.
Tune: PUER NATUS, 8 8 with alleluias and refrain; Mode I; Acc. by Richard Proulx, b.1937, © 1986, GIA Publications, Inc.

385 A Stable Lamp Is Lighted

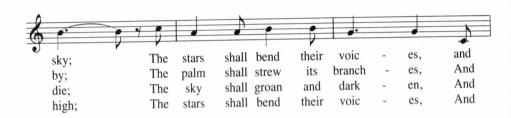

1. A sta - ble lamp is light - ed Whose glow shall wake the
2. This child through Da - vid's cit - y Shall ride in tri - umph
3. Yet he shall be for - sak - en, And yield - ed up to
4. But now, as at the end - ing, The low is lift - ed

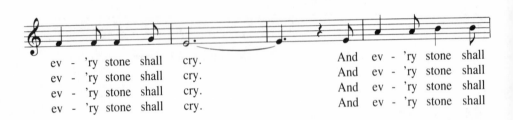

sky; The stars shall bend their voic - es, and
by; The palm shall strew its branch - es, And
die; The sky shall groan and dark - en, And
high; The stars shall bend their voic - es, And

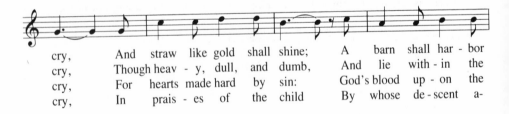

ev - 'ry stone shall cry. And ev - 'ry stone shall
ev - 'ry stone shall cry. And ev - 'ry stone shall
ev - 'ry stone shall cry. And ev - 'ry stone shall
ev - 'ry stone shall cry. And ev - 'ry stone shall

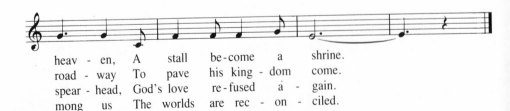

cry, And straw like gold shall shine; A barn shall har - bor
cry, Though heav - y, dull, and dumb, And lie with - in the
cry, For hearts made hard by sin: God's blood up - on the
cry, In prais - es of the child By whose de - scent a-

heav - en, A stall be - come a shrine.
road - way To pave his king - dom come.
spear - head, God's love re - fused a - gain.
mong us The worlds are rec - on - ciled.

Text: Richard Wilbur, b.1921, © 1961
Tune: ANDUJAR, 7 6 7 6 6 6 7 6; David Hurd, b.1950, © 1984, GIA Publications, Inc.

O Little Town of Bethlehem   386

1. O   lit - tle town of   Beth - le - hem, How still   we   see thee   lie!
2. For Christ is born of   Mar   -   y,   And gath - ered all   a - bove,
3. How si - lent - ly, how   si - lent - ly, The   won - drous gift is   giv'n!
4. O   ho - ly Child of   Beth - le - hem! De - scend to   us   we   pray;

A - bove thy deep and dream-less sleep The   si - lent stars go   by;
While mor - tals sleep, the   an - gels keep Their watch of won-d'ring love.
So   God im - parts to   hu - man hearts The bless - ings of his heav'n.
Cast   out our sin and en - ter in, Be   born in   us   to - day.

Yet   in   the dark streets shin - eth The ev - er - last - ing Light;
O   morn-ing stars, to - geth - er Pro - claim the ho - ly   birth!
No   ear may hear his   com - ing, But   in this world of   sin,
We   hear the Christ-mas an - gels The great glad ti - dings tell;

The   hopes and fears of   all the years Are   met   in thee   to - night.
And prais - es sing to   God the King, And peace to all   on earth.
Where meek souls will re - ceive him, still The   dear Christ en - ters in.
O   come to   us, a - bide with us, Our   Lord Em - man - u - el!

Tune: Phillips Brooks, 1835-1893
Tune: ST. LOUIS, 8 6 8 6 7 6 8 6; Lewis H. Redner, 1831-1908

387 Hark! The Herald Angels Sing

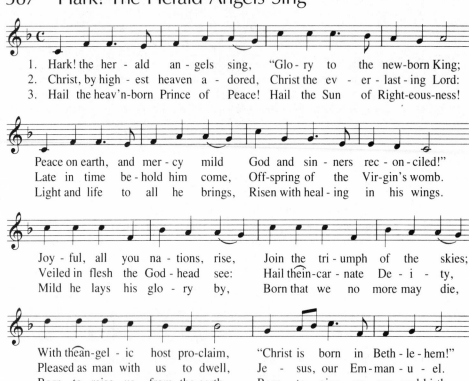

1. Hark! the her - ald an - gels sing, "Glo - ry to the new-born King;
2. Christ, by high - est heaven a - dored, Christ the ev - er - last - ing Lord:
3. Hail the heav'n-born Prince of Peace! Hail the Sun of Right-eous-ness!

Peace on earth, and mer - cy mild God and sin - ners rec - on - ciled!"
Late in time be - hold him come, Off-spring of the Vir-gin's womb.
Light and life to all he brings, Risen with heal - ing in his wings.

Joy - ful, all you na - tions, rise, Join the tri - umph of the skies;
Veiled in flesh the God - head see: Hail the in-car - nate De - i - ty,
Mild he lays his glo - ry by, Born that we no more may die,

With the an-gel - ic host pro-claim, "Christ is born in Beth - le - hem!"
Pleased as man with us to dwell, Je - sus, our Em-man - u - el.
Born to raise us from the earth, Born to give us sec - ond birth.

Hark! the her - ald an - gels sing, "Glo - ry to the new-born King!"

Text: Charles Wesley, 1707-1788, alt.
Tune: MENDELSSOHN, 77 77 D with refrain; Felix Mendelssohn, 1809-1847; Descant with harm. by David Willcocks, b.1919, © 1961, Oxford
University Press

From Heaven Above 388

1. From heav'n a - bove to earth I come To bring good
2. To you this night is born a child Of Mar - y,
3. This is the Christ, God's Son most high, Who hears your
4. The bless - ing which the Fa - ther planned The Son holds

news to ev - 'ry - one! Glad ti - dings of great joy I
cho - sen vir - gin mild; This new - born child of low - ly
sad and bit - ter cry; He will him - self your Sav - ior
in his in - fant hand, That in his king - dom bright and

bring To all the world, and glad - ly sing:
birth Shall be the joy of all the earth.
be And from all sin will set you free.
fair, You may with us his glo - ry share.

5. These are the signs which you will see
To let you know that it is he:
In manger-bed, in swaddling clothes
The child who all the earth upholds.

*6. How glad we'll be to find it so!
Then with the shepherds let us go
To see what God for us has done
In sending us his own dear Son.

*7. Look, look, dear friends, look over there!
What lies within that manger bare?
Who is that lovely little one?
The baby Jesus, God's dear Son.

*8. Welcome to earth, O noble Guest,
Through whom this sinful world is blest!
You turned not from our needs away!
How can our thanks such love repay?

*9. O Lord, you have created all!
How did you come to be so small,
To sweetly sleep in manger-bed
Where lowing cattle lately fed?

*10. Were earth a thousand times as fair
And set with gold and jewels rare,
Still such a cradle would not do
To rock a prince so great as you.

*11. For velvets soft and silken stuff
You have but hay and straw so rough
On which as king so rich and great
To be enthroned in humble state.

*12. O dearest Jesus, holy child,
Prepare a bed, soft, undefiled,
A holy shrine, within my heart,
That you and I need never part.

*13. My heart for very joy now leaps;
My voice no longer silence keeps;
I too must join the angel-throng
To sing with joy his cradle-song:

14. "Glory to God in highest heav'n,
Who unto us his Son has giv'n."
With angels sing in pious mirth:
A glad new year to all the earth!

*Stanzas 6-13 may be omitted.

Text: Luke 2:1-18; *Vom Himmel hoch da komm ich her*; Martin Luther, 1483-1546; Tr. from *Lutheran Book of Worship*, 1978, ©
Tune: VOM HIMMEL HOCH, LM; Schumann's *Geistliche Lieder*, 1539; Harm. by Hans Leo Hassler, 1564-1612

389 How Brightly Beams the Morning Star

1. How bright - ly beams the morn - ing star! What sud - den ra - diance
2. Come, heav'n - ly bride - groom, light di - vine, And deep with - in our
3. O let the harps break forth in sound! Our joy be all with

from a - far A - glow with grace and mer - cy! Of Ja-
hearts now shine; There light a flame un - dy - ing! In your
mu - sic crowned, Our voic - es rich - ly blend - ing! For Christ

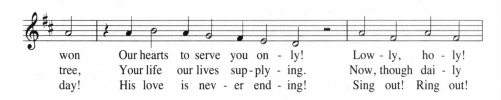

cob's race, King Da - vid's Son, Our Lord and mas - ter, you have
one bod - y let us be As liv - ing branch - es of a
goes with us all the way — To - day; to - mor - row, ev - 'ry

won Our hearts to serve you on - ly! Low - ly, ho - ly!
tree, Your life our lives sup - ply - ing. Now, though dai - ly
day! His love is nev - er end - ing! Sing out! Ring out!

Great and glo - rious, All vic - to - rious, Rich in bless - ing!
Earth's deep sad - ness May per - plex us And dis - tress us,
Ju - bi - la - tion! Ex - ul - ta - tion! Tell the sto - ry!

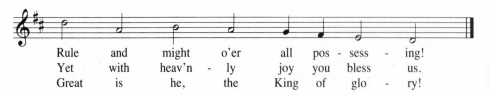

Rule and might o'er all pos - sess - ing!
Yet with heav'n - ly joy you bless us.
Great is he, the King of glo - ry!

Text: *Wie schön leuchtet der Morgenstern;* Philipp Nicolai, 1556-1608; Tr. from *Lutheran Book of Worship*, 1978, alt., ©
Tune: WIE SCHÖN LEUCHTET, 88 7 88 7 22 44 48; Philipp Nicolai, 1556-1608; Harm. by Johann H. Schein, 1586-1630

How Brightly Beams the Morning Star 390

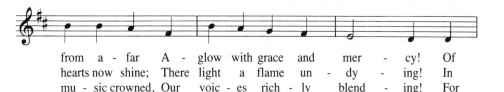

1. How bright-ly beams the morn-ing star! What sud-den ra-diance
2. Come, heav'n-ly bride-groom, light di-vine, And deep with-in our
3. O let the harps break forth in sound! Our joy be all with

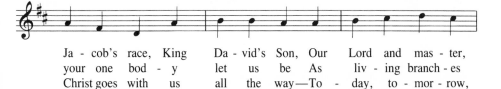

from a - far A - glow with grace and mer - cy! Of
hearts now shine; There light a flame un - dy - ing! In
mu - sic crowned, Our voic - es rich - ly blend - ing! For

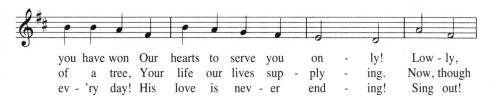

Ja - cob's race, King Da - vid's Son, Our Lord and mas - ter,
your one bod - y let us be As liv - ing branch - es
Christ goes with us all the way—To - day, to - mor - row,

you have won Our hearts to serve you on - ly! Low - ly,
of a tree, Your life our lives sup - ply - ing. Now, though
ev - 'ry day! His love is nev - er end - ing! Sing out!

ho - ly! Great and glo - rious, All vic - to - rious, Rich in
dai - ly Earth's deep sad - ness May per-plex us And dis-
Ring out! Ju - bi - la - tion! Ex - ul - ta - tion! Tell the

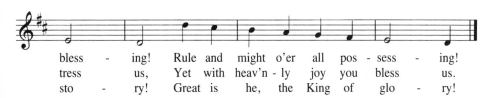

bless - ing! Rule and might o'er all pos - sess - ing!
tress us, Yet with heav'n - ly joy you bless us.
sto - ry! Great is he, the King of glo - ry!

Text: *Wie Schön leuchtet der Morgenstern;* Philipp Nicolai, 1556-1608; Tr. from *Lutheran Book of Worship,* 1978, alt., ©
Tune: WIE SCHÖN LEUCHTET, 88 7 88 7 22 44 48; Philipp Nicolai, 1556-1608; Harm. by J.S. Bach, 1685-1750

391 Good Christian Friends, Rejoice

1. Good Christ-ian friends, re - joice   With heart and soul   and   voice;
2. Good Christ-ian friends, re - joice   With heart and soul   and   voice;
3. Good Christ-ian friends, re - joice   With heart and soul   and   voice;

O   give heed   to what we   say: Je - sus Christ is   born   to - day!
Now you   hear   of end - less bliss: Je - sus Christ was   born   for   this!
Now you   need   not fear the grave: Je - sus Christ was   born   to save!

Ox   and   ass   be - fore him bow, And   he   is   in   the man - ger now.
He   has   o - pened heav-en's door, And   we   are blest   for ev - er-more.
Calls you   one   and   calls you   all   To   gain   his   ev - er-last - ing hall.

Christ is   born   to - day!   Christ   is   born   to - day!
Christ was   born   for   this!   Christ was   born   for   this!
Christ was   born   to   save!   Christ was   born   to   save!

Text: *In dulci jubilo*; Latin and German, 14th C.: Tr. by John M. Neal, 1818-1866
Tune: IN DULCI JUBILO, 66 77 77 55; Klug's *Geistliche Lieder*, Wittenberg, 1535; Harm. by Robert L. Pearsall, 1795-1856

392 O Come, All Ye Faithful/Adeste Fideles

1. O   come,   all   ye   faith - ful,   joy - ful   and   tri - um - phant, O
2.   God   of___   God, ___   Light___   of___   Light, ___
3.   Sing, choirs   of   an - gels,   sing   in   ex - ul - ta - tion,
4.   Yea,   Lord,   we   greet thee,   born this hap - py morn - ing,

1. Ad - é - ste   fi - dé - les,   laé - ti,   tri - um - phán - tes,   Ve-
2.   De - um   de   De - o,   Lu ___ men de Lu - mi - ne
3.   Can - tet   nunc   i - o,   cho - rus   an - ge - ló - rum,
4.   Er - go   qui   na - tus   Di - e   ho - di - ér - na,

come ye, O come ye to Beth - le - hem;
Lo! He comes forth from the Vir - gin's womb.
Sing, all ye cit - i - zens of heav'n a - bove!
Je - sus, to thee be all glo - ry giv'n;
ní - te, ve - ní - te in Béth - le - hem.
Ge - stant pu - él - lae ví - sce - ra.
Can - tet nunc au - la cae - lés - ti - um.
Je - su___ ti - bi sit gló - ri - a.

Come and be - hold him, born the King of an - gels;
Our ver - y God, be - got - ten not cre - a - ted,
Glo - ry to God, all glo - ry in the high - est;
Word of the Fa - ther, now in flesh ap - pear - ing;
Na - tum vi - dé - te, Re - gem an - ge - ló - rum.
De - um ve - rum, Gé - ni - tum, non fa - ctum.
Glo - ri - a, gló - ria, in ex - cél - sis De - o.
Pa - tris ae - ter - nae ver - bum ca - ro fa - ctum.

O come, let us a - dore him, O come, let us a - dore him,
Ve - ní - te a - do - ré - mus, ve - ní - te a - do - ré - mus,

O come, let us a - dore him, Christ, the Lord!
ve - ní - te a - do - ré - mus Dó - mi - num.

Text: *Adeste fideles;* John F. Wade, c.1711-1786; Tr. by Frederick Oakeley, 1802-1880, alt.
Tune: ADESTE FIDELES, Irr. with refrain; John F. Wade, c.1711-1786; Desc. with harm. by David Willcocks, b. 1919. © 1961, Oxford University Press

393 Infant Holy, Infant Lowly

1. In - fant ho - ly, In - fant low - ly, For his bed a cat - tle stall;
2. Flocks were sleep-ing: Shep-herds keep-ing Vig - il till the morn-ing new.

Ox - en low - ing, Lit - tle know-ing Christ the babe is Lord of all.
Saw the glo - ry, Heard the sto - ry, Ti - dings of a gos - pel true.

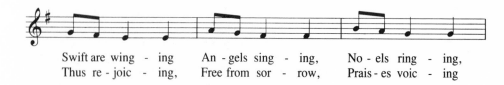

Swift are wing - ing An - gels sing - ing, No - els ring - ing,
Thus re - joic - ing, Free from sor - row, Prais - es voic - ing

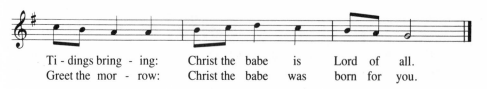

Ti - dings bring - ing: Christ the babe is Lord of all.
Greet the mor - row: Christ the babe was born for you.

Text: *W żłobie leży, ktôż pobieży,* Polish Carol; Para. by Edith M.G. Reed, 1885-1933
Tune: W ŻŁOBIE LEŻY, 44 7 44 7 4444 7; Polish Carol; Harm. by A.E. Rusbridge, 1917-1969, © Rosalind Rusbridge

394 Now Every Child That Dwells on Earth

1. Now ev-'ry child that dwells on earth, Stand up, stand up, and sing! The
2. Now ev-'ry star that dwells in sky, Look down, with shin - ing eyes: The

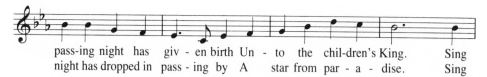

pass-ing night has giv - en birth Un - to the chil-dren's King. Sing
night has dropped in pass - ing by A star from par - a - dise. Sing

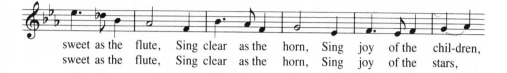

sweet as the flute, Sing clear as the horn, Sing joy of the chil-dren,
sweet as the flute, Sing clear as the horn, Sing joy of the stars,

Come Christ-mas the morn: Lit-tle Christ Je - sus our broth-er is born.
Come Christ-mas the morn: Lit-tle Christ Je - sus our broth-er is born.

Text: Eleanor Farjeon, 1881-1965, © 1927,1955, Harold Ober Associates
Tune: BERKELEY, Irregular; Leo Sowerby, 1895-1968. © The Estate of Leo Sowerby

Angel Voices Richly Blending   395

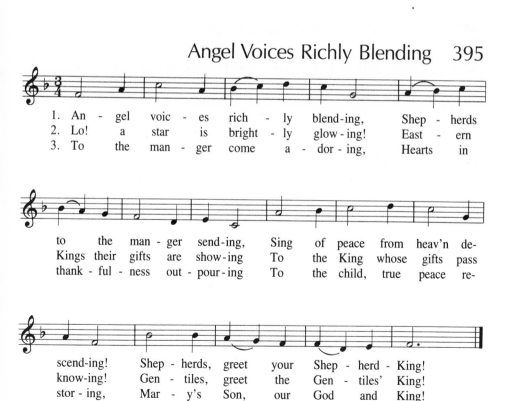

1. An - gel voic - es rich - ly blend-ing, Shep - herds
2. Lo! a star is bright - ly glow-ing! East - ern
3. To the man - ger come a - dor - ing, Hearts in

to the man - ger send-ing, Sing of peace from heav'n de-
Kings their gifts are show-ing To the King whose gifts pass
thank - ful - ness out - pour-ing To the child, true peace re-

scend-ing! Shep - herds, greet your Shep - herd - King!
know-ing! Gen - tiles, greet the Gen - tiles' King!
stor - ing, Mar - y's Son, our God and King!

Text: *Quem pastores laudavere;* German Carol, 15th C.; Adapt. by James Quinn, SJ, b. 1919, © 1969
Tune: QUEM PASTORES, 888 7; German Carol, 15th C.

396 Christ Was Born on Christmas Day

1. Christ was born on Christ-mas day: Wreathe the hol - ly, twine the bay,
2. He   is born to   set   us free,   He   is born our Lord   to   be,
3. Let   the bright red   ber - ries glow   Ev - 'ry -where in   good - ly show:
4. Chris-tians all,   re - joice and sing,   'Tis   the birth - day   of   a King,

Chri-stus na - tus ho - di - e: The Babe, the Son, the Ho - ly One of Mar-y.
Ex Ma-ri - a Vir - gi - ne: The God, the Lord, by all a-dored for ev-er.
Chri-stus na - tus ho - di - e: The Babe, the Son, the Ho - ly One of Mar-y.
Ex Ma-ri - a Vir - gi - ne: The God, the Lord, by all a-dored for ev-er.

Text: Traditional
Tune: RESONET IN LAUDIBUS, 777 11; German, 16th C.; Harm. by Ralph Vaughan Williams, 1872-1958. © Oxford University Press

397 Go Tell It on the Mountain

Go   tell it on the moun - tain,   O-ver the hills and ev - 'ry-where;

Go   tell it on the moun - tain That Je - sus Christ is born!

1. While shep-herds kept their watch-ing   O'er si - lent flocks by night,   Be-
2. The shep-herds feared and trem-bled   When lo! a - bove the earth   Rang
3. Down in   a low - ly man-ger   The hum-ble Christ was born,   And

D.C.

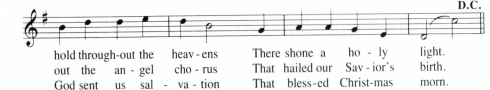

hold through-out the   heav - ens   There shone a   ho - ly   light.
out the   an - gel   cho - rus   That hailed our   Sav - ior's   birth.
God sent   us   sal - va - tion   That bless-ed   Christ-mas   morn.

Text: Afro-American Spiritual; Adapt. by John W. Work, Jr., 1871-1925. © Mrs. John W. Work III
Tune: GO TELL IT ON THE MOUNTAIN, 7 6 7 6 with refrain; Afro-American Spiritual; Harm. by Paul Sjolund, b. 1935. © Walton Music Corp.

Of the Father's Love Begotten 398

1. Of the Fa - ther's love be - got - ten,
2. O that birth for ev - er bless - ed,
3. Let the heights of heav'n a - dore him;
4. Christ, to you with God the Fa - ther,

Ere the worlds be - gan to be,
When the Vir - gin, full of grace,
An - gel hosts, his prais - es sing;
Spir - it blest e - ter - nal - ly,

He is Al - pha and O - me - ga,
By the Spir - it blest con - ceiv - ing,
Pow'rs, do - min - ions, bow be - fore him,
Hymn and chant and high thanks - giv - ing,

He the source, the end - ing he,
Bore the Sav - ior of our race;
And ex - tol our God and King;
And un - end - ing prais - es be:

Of the things that are, that have been,
And the Babe, the world's Re - deem - er,
Let no tongue on earth be si - lent,
Hon - or, glo - ry, and do - min - ion,

And that fu - ture years shall see, Ev-er-more and ev - er - more!
First re-vealed his sa - cred face, Ev-er-more and ev - er - more!
Ev - 'ry voice in con-cert ring, Ev-er-more and ev - er - more!
And e - ter - nal vic - to - ry, Ev-er-more and ev - er - more!

Text: *Corde natus ex Parentis*, Aurelius Prudentius, 348-413; Tr. by John M. Neale, 1818-1866 and Henry W. Baker, 1821-1877
Tune: DIVINUM MYSTERIUM, 8 7 8 7 8 7 7; 12th C.; Mode V; Acc. by Richard Proulx, b. 1937, © 1985, GIA Publications, Inc.

399 Joy to the World

1. Joy to the world! the Lord is come:
2. Joy to the world! the Savior reigns:
3. No more let sin and sorrows grow,
4. He rules the world with truth and grace,

Let earth receive her King;
Let us, our songs employ;
Nor thorns infest the ground;
And makes the nations prove

Let ev'ry heart prepare him room,
While fields and floods, rocks, hills, and plains
He comes to make his blessings flow
The glories of his righteousness,

And heaven and nature sing, And
Repeat the sounding joy, Re-
Far as the curse is found, Far
And wonders of his love, And

heaven and nature sing, And
peat the sounding joy, Re-
as the curse is found, Far
won-ders of his love, And

heaven, and heaven and nature sing.
peat, re-peat the sounding joy.
as, far as the curse is found.
won-ders, won-ders of his love.

Text: Ps. 98; Isaac Watts, 1674-1748
Tune: ANTIOCH, CM; Arr. from George F. Handel, 1685-1759, in T. Hawkes' *Collection of Tunes*, 1833

It Came upon the Midnight Clear 400

1. It came up-on the mid-night clear, That glo-rious song of old,
2. Still through the clo-ven skies they come, With peace-ful wings un - furled,
3. Yet with the woes of sin and strife, The world has suf-fered long;
4. For, lo, the days are has-tening on, By proph-ets seen of old,

From an-gels bend-ing near the earth To touch their harps of gold:
And still their heav'n-ly mu - sic floats O'er all the wea - ry world:
Be - neath the heav'n-ly hymn have rolled Two thou-sand years of wrong;
When with the ev - er - cir-cling years Shall come the time fore - told,

"Peace on the earth, good will to all From heaven's all gra-cious King";
A - bove its sad and low - ly plains They bend on hov-'ring wing,
And war-ring hu - man - kind hears not The ti - dings which they bring;
When peace shall o - ver all the earth Its an - cient splen-dors fling,

The world in sol - emn still-ness lay, To hear the an - gels sing.
And ev - er o'er its Ba - bel sounds The bless-ed an - gels sing.
O hush the noise and cease your strife And hear the an - gels sing.
And all the world give back the song Which now the an - gels sing.

Text: Edmund H. Sears, 1810-1876, alt.
Tune: CAROL, CMD; Richard S. Willis, 1819-1900

Canon

Gloria, Gloria 401

Glo - ri - a, glo - ri - a, in ex - cel - sis De - o!

Glo - ri - a, glo - ri - a, al - le - lu - ia, al - le - lu - ia!

Text: Luke 2:14; Taizé Community, 1978
Tune: Jacques Berthier, b.1923
© 1979, Les Presses de Taizé

402 Once in Royal David's City

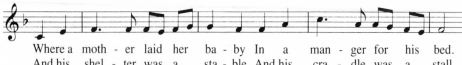

1. Once in roy - al Da - vid's cit - y Stood a low - ly cat - tle shed,
2. He came down to earth from heav - en Who is God and Lord of all,
3. And through all his won - drous child-hood He would hon - or and o - bey,
4. For he is our child - hood's pat - tern, Day by day like us he grew;
5. And our eyes at last shall see him, Thru his own re - deem-ing love;

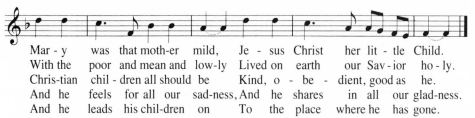

Where a moth - er laid her ba - by In a man - ger for his bed.
And his shel - ter was a sta - ble, And his cra - dle was a stall.
Love and watch the low - ly maid - en In whose gen - tle arms he lay.
He was lit - tle, weak, and help - less, Tears and smiles like us he knew:
For that child so dear and gen - tle Is our Lord in heav'n a - bove:

Mar - y was that moth-er mild, Je - sus Christ her lit - tle Child.
With the poor and mean and low-ly Lived on earth our Sav - ior ho - ly.
Chris-tian chil - dren all should be Kind, o - be - dient, good as he.
And he feels for all our sad-ness, And he shares in all our glad-ness.
And he leads his chil-dren on To the place where he has gone.

Text: Cecil Frances Alexander, 1818-1895
Tune: IRBY, 8 7 8 7 77; Henry J. Gauntlett, 1805-1876; Harm. by Arthur H. Mann, 1850-1929. © 1957, Novello and Co. Ltd.

403 Virgin-born, We Bow before You

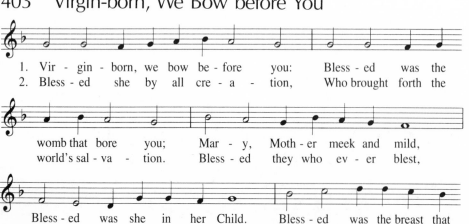

1. Vir - gin - born, we bow be - fore you: Bless - ed was the
2. Bless - ed she by all cre - a - tion, Who brought forth the

womb that bore you; Mar - y, Moth - er meek and mild,
world's sal - va - tion. Bless - ed they who ev - er blest,

Bless - ed was she in her Child. Bless - ed was the breast that
Love you most and serve you best. Vir - gin - born, we bow be-

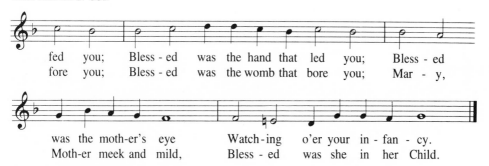

fed you; Bless - ed was the hand that led you; Bless - ed
fore you; Bless - ed was the womb that bore you; Mar - y,

was the moth-er's eye Watch-ing o'er your in - fan - cy.
Moth-er meek and mild, Bless - ed was she in her Child.

Text: Reginald Herber, 1783-1826, alt.
Tune: MON DIEU PRETE-MOI L'OREILLE, 88 77 D; Attr. to Louis Bourgeois, c.1510-1561; Harm. by Claude Goudimel, 1505-1572, alt.

Sing of Mary, Pure and Lowly   404

1. Sing of Mar - y, pure and low - ly, Vir - gin-moth - er un - de - filed,
2. Sing of Je - sus, son of 'Mar - y, In the home at Naz - a - reth.
3. Glo - ry be to God the Fa-ther; Glo - ry be to God the Son;

Sing of God's own Son most ho - ly, Who be-came her lit - tle child.
Toil and la - bor can-not wea - ry Love en - dur - ing un - to death.
Glo - ry be to God the Spir - it; Glo - ry to the Three in One.

Fair - est child of fair - est moth-er, God the Lord who came to earth,
Con - stant was the love he gave her, Though he went forth from her side,
From the heart of bless - ed Mar - y, From all saints the song as-cends,

Word made flesh, our ver - y broth-er, Takes our na - ture by his birth.
Forth to preach, and heal, and suf - fer, Till on Cal - va - ry he died.
And the church the strain re - ech-oes Un - to earth's re - mot-est ends.

Text: Roland F. Palmer, b.1891
Tune: PLEADING SAVIOR, 8 7 8 7 D; *Christian Lyre*, 1830; Harm. by Richard Proulx, b.1937, © 1986, GIA Publications, Inc.

405 The God Whom Earth and Sea and Sky

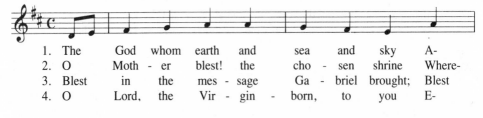

1. The God whom earth and sea and sky A-
2. O Moth - er blest! the cho - sen shrine Where-
3. Blest in the mes - sage Ga - briel brought; Blest
4. O Lord, the Vir - gin - born, to you E-

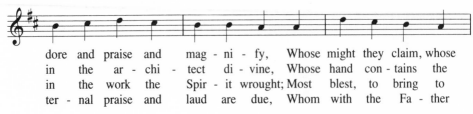

dore and praise and mag - ni - fy, Whose might they claim, whose
in the ar - chi - tect di - vine, Whose hand con - tains the
in the work the Spir - it wrought; Most blest, to bring to
ter - nal praise and laud are due, Whom with the Fa - ther

love they tell, In Mar - y's bod - y comes to dwell.
earth and sky, Has come in hu - man form to lie:
hu - man birth The long de - sired of all the earth.
we a - dore And Spir - it blest for ev - er - more.

Text: *Quem terra, pontus, aethera;* Venantius Fortunatus, c.530-609; Tr. by John M. Neale, 1818-1866, alt.
Tune: EISENACH, LM; John H. Schein, 1586-1630; Harm. by J. S. Bach, 1685-1750

406 We Three Kings of Orient Are

1. We three kings of O - ri - ent are, Bear - ing
2. Born a babe on Beth - le - hem's plain, Gold we
3. Frank - in - cense to of - fer have I; In - cense
4. Myrrh is mine: its bit - ter per - fume Breathes a
5. Glo - rious now be - hold him rise, King and

gifts we trav - erse a - far Field and foun - tain,
bring to crown him a - gain; King for - ev - er,
owns a De - i - ty nigh, Prayer and prais - ing
life of gath - 'ring gloom; Sor - rowing, sigh - ing,
God and sac - ri - fice: Heav'n sing, "Hal - le-

Moor	and	moun - tain,	Fol - low - ing	yon - der	star.
Ceas - ing	nev - er,	O - ver	us	all	to	reign.
Glad - ly	rais - ing,	Wor-ship - ing	God	on	high.
Bleed - ing,	dy - ing,	Sealed in	the	stone	cold	tomb.
lu - jah!"	"Hal - le - lu -	jah!"	earth	re - plies.

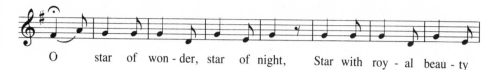

O star of won - der, star of night, Star with roy - al beau - ty

bright, West-ward lead-ing, still pro-ceed-ing, Guide us to the per-fect Light.

Text: Mt. 2:1-11; John H. Hopkins, Jr., 1820-1891
Tune: KINGS OF ORIENT, 88 44 6 with refrain; John H. Hopkins, Jr., 1820-1891

What Star Is This 407

1. What	star	is this,	with beams	so bright,	More love - ly
2. 'Tis	now	ful-filled	what God	de-creed,	"From Ja - cob
3. O	Je - sus, while	the star	of grace	Im - pels	us
4. To	God	Cre - a - tor,	heav'n - ly light,	To Christ,	re-

than	the	noon - day light?	'Tis	sent	to an -nounce	a
shall	a	star	pro - cede";	And	lo!	the east - ern
on	to	seek	your face,	Let	not	our sloth - ful
vealed	in	earth - ly night,	To	God	the Spir - it

new - born king,	Glad	ti - dings of	our God	to bring.
sag - es stand,	To	read	in heaven	the Lord's com - mand.
hearts re - fuse	The	guid - ance of	your light	to use.
blest we raise	An	end - less song	of thank - ful praise!

Text: *Quem stella sole pulchrior*, Charles Coffin, 1676-1749; Tr. by John Chandler, 1806-1876, alt.
Tune: PUER NOBIS, LM; Adapt. by Michael Praetorius, 1571-1621

408 The First Nowell

1. The first Now - ell, the an - gel did say, Was to
2. They look - ed up and saw a star Shin-ing
3. And by the light of that same star Three
4. This star drew nigh to the north - west, O'er

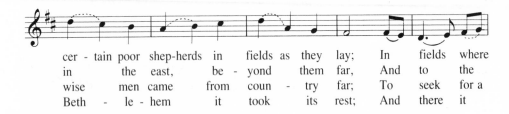

cer - tain poor shep-herds in fields as they lay; In fields where
in the east, be - yond them far, And to the
wise men came from coun - try far; To seek for a
Beth - le - hem it took its rest; And there it

they lay keep - ing their sheep, On a cold win-ter's night that
earth it gave great light, And so it con - tin - ued both
king was their in - tent, And to fol - low the star where-
did both stop and stay, Right o - ver the place where

was so deep.
day and night. Now - ell, Now - ell, Now - ell, Now-
ev - er it went.
Je - sus lay.

ell, Born is the King of Is - ra - el.

5. Then entered in those wise men three,
   Full rev'rently upon their knee,
   And offered there, in his presence,
   Their gold and myrrh and frankincense.
   Nowell, Nowell, Nowell, Nowell,
   Born is the King of Israel.

6. Then let us all with one accord
   Sing praises to our heav'nly Lord;
   Who with the Father we adore
   And Spirit blest for evermore.
   Nowell, Nowell, Nowell, Nowell,
   Born is the King of Israel.

Text: English Carol, 17th C.
Tune: THE FIRST NOWELL, Irregular; English Melody; Harm. by David Willcocks, b.1919. © 1961, Oxford University Press

As with Gladness Men of Old   409

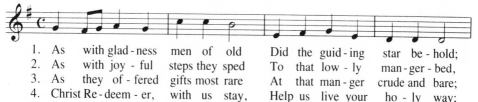

1. As   with glad-ness   men of   old   Did the guid-ing   star be-hold;
2. As   with joy-ful   steps they sped   To   that low-ly   man-ger-bed,
3. As   they of-fered   gifts most rare   At   that man-ger   crude and bare;
4. Christ Re-deem-er,   with us   stay,   Help us live your   ho-ly   way;
5. In   the heaven-ly   cit-y bright   None shall need cre-a-ted light;

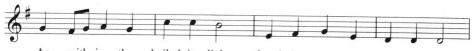

As   with joy they   hailed its light,   Lead-ing   on-ward, beam-ing bright;
There to   bend the   knee be-fore   Christ whom heaven and earth a-dore;
So   may we this   ho-ly   day,   Drawn to   you with-out   de-lay,
And when earth-ly   things are past,   Bring our   ran-somed souls   at   last
You, its   light, its   joy,   its crown,   You, its   sun which goes not down;

So, most gra-cious   Lord,   may we   Ev-er-more your   splen-dor   see.
So   may we with   hur-ried pace   Run to   seek your throne of   grace.
All   our cost-liest   treas-ures bring,   Christ, to you, our   heaven-ly   King.
Where they need no   star   to guide,   Where no clouds your glo-ry   hide.
There for ev-er   may   we sing   Al-le-lu-ias   to   our   King.

Text: William C. Dix, 1837-1898
Tune: DIX, 77 77 77; Arr. from Conrad Kocher, 1786-1872, by William H. Monk, 1823-1889

410 Songs of Thankfulness and Praise

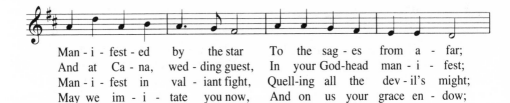

1. Songs of thank-ful - ness and praise, · Je - sus, Lord, to   you we raise,
2. Man - i - fest at   Jor - dan's stream, Proph-et, Priest, and   King su-preme;
3. Man - i - fest in   mak - ing whole   Pal - sied limbs and   faint - ing soul;
4. Grant us grace to   see you, Lord,   Mir-rored   in   your   ho - ly word;

Man - i - fest - ed   by   the star   To   the sag - es   from a - far;
And at   Ca - na,   wed - ding guest,   In   your God-head   man - i - fest;
Man - i - fest in   val - iant fight,   Quell-ing all the   dev - il's might;
May we im - i - tate   you now,   And on   us your   grace en - dow;

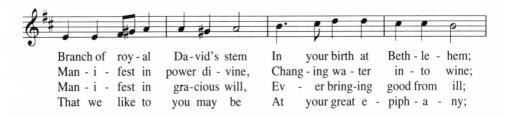

Branch of   roy - al   Da - vid's stem   In   your birth at   Beth - le - hem;
Man - i - fest in   power di - vine,   Chang - ing wa - ter   in - to   wine;
Man - i - fest in   gra-cious will,   Ev - er bring-ing   good from   ill;
That we   like to   you may be   At   your great e - piph - a - ny;

An-thems be   to   you ad - drest,   God in flesh made   man - i - fest.
An-thems be   to   you ad - drest,   God in flesh made   man - i - fest.
An-thems be   to   you ad - drest,   God in flesh made   man - i - fest.
And may praise you   ev - er   blest,   God in flesh made   man - i - fest.

Text: Christopher Wordsworth, 1807-1885
Tune: SALZBURG, 77 77 D; Jakob Hintze, 1622-1702, alt.; Harm. by J. S. Bach, 1685-1750

What Child Is This   411

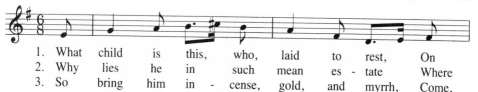

1. What child is this, who, laid to rest, On
2. Why lies he in such mean es - tate, Where
3. So bring him in - cense, gold, and myrrh, Come,

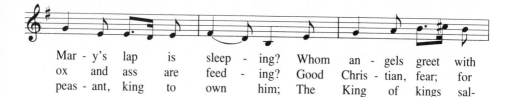

Mar - y's lap is sleep - ing? Whom an - gels greet with
ox and ass are feed - ing? Good Chris - tian, fear; for
peas - ant, king to own him; The King of kings sal-

an - thems sweet, While shep - herds watch are keep - ing?
sin - ners here The si - lent Word is plead - ing.
va - tion brings, Let lov - ing hearts en - throne him.

This, this is Christ the King, Whom shep-herds guard and an-gels sing;

Haste, haste to bring him laud, The babe, the son of Mar - y.

Text: William C. Dix, 1827-1898
Tune: GREENSLEEVES, 8 7 8 7 with refrain; English Melody, 16th C.; Harm. by John Stainer, 1840-1901

412 When John Baptized by Jordan's River

1. When John bap-tized by Jor-dan's riv - er In faith and
2. There as the Lord, bap-tized and pray - ing, Rose from the
3. O Son of Man, our na - ture shar - ing, In whose o-

hope the peo - ple came, That John and Jor-dan might de - liv - er
stream, the sin - less one, A voice was heard from heav - en say - ing,
be - dience all are blest, Sav - ior, our sins and sor - rows bear - ing,

Their trou-bled souls from sin and shame. They came to seek a new be-
"This is my own be - lov - ed Son." There as the Fa - ther's word was
Hear us and grant us this re - quest: Dai - ly to grow, by grace de-

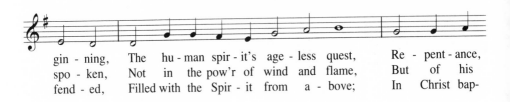

gin - ning, The hu - man spir - it's age - less quest, Re - pent-ance,
spo - ken, Not in the pow'r of wind and flame, But of his
fend - ed, Filled with the Spir - it from a - bove; In Christ bap-

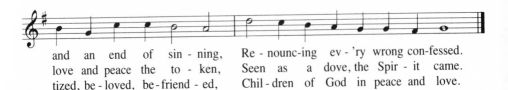

and an end of sin - ning, Re - nounc-ing ev - 'ry wrong con-fessed.
love and peace the to - ken, Seen as a dove, the Spir - it came.
tized, be - loved, be-friend - ed, Chil - dren of God in peace and love.

Text: Timothy Dudley-Smith, b.1926, © 1984, Hope Publishing Co.
Tune: RENDEZ À DIEU, 9 8 9 8 D; Louis Bourgeois, c.1510-1561

Alleluia, Song of Gladness 413

1. Al - le - lu - ia, song of glad-ness, voice of joy that can-not die;
2. Al - le - lu - ia, now re - sound-ing, true Je - ru - sa - lem and free;
3. Al - le - lu - ia we de - serve not here to chant for ev - er - more,
4. There-fore in our hymns we now pray, grant us, bless-ed Trin - i - ty,

Al - le - lu - ia is the an-them ev - er dear to choirs on high;
Al - le - lu - ia, joy - ful moth - er, all your chil - dren sing with glee;
Al - le - lu - ia our trans-gres-sions make us for a while give o'er;
At the last to keep you, East - er, in our home be - yond the sky;

In the house of God a - bid - ing thus they sing e - ter - nal - ly.
But by Bab - y - lon's sad wa - ters mourn-ing ex - iles now are we.
For the ho - ly time is com-ing bid - ding us our sins de-plore.
There to you for ev - er sing-ing Al - le - lu - ia joy - ful - ly.

Text: *Alleluia, dulce carmen;* Latin, 11th C.; John M. Neale, 1818-1866
Tune: DULCE CARMEN, 8 7 8 7 8 7; *Essay on the Church Plain Chant,* 1782

414 Hear Us, Almighty Lord/Attende Domine

Hear us, al - might - y Lord, show us your
At - tén - de Dó - mi - ne, et mi - se-

mer - cy Sin - ners we stand here be - fore you.
ré - re, Qui - a pec - cá - vi - mus ti - bi.

1. Je - sus our Sav - ior, Lord of all the na - tions,
2. Word of the Fa - ther, key-stone of God's build - ing,
3. God of com - pas - sion, Lord of might and splen - dor,
1. *Ad te Rex sum - me, óm - ni - um re - dém - ptor,*
2. *Déx - te - ra Pa - tris, la - pis an - gu - lá - ris,*
3. *Ro - gá - mus, De - us, tu - am ma - je - stá - tem:*

Christ our Re - deem - er, hear the prayers we of - fer,
Source of our glad - ness, gate - way to the King - dom,
Gra - cious - ly lis - ten, hear our cries of an - guish.
Ó - cu - los nó - stros sub - le - vá - mus flen - tes:
Ví - a sa - lú - tis já - nu - a cae - lé - stis,
Áu - ri - bus sa - cris gé - mi - tus ex - aú - di:

D.C.

Spare us and save us, com - fort us in sor - row.
Free us in mer - cy from the sins that bind us.
Touch us and heal us where our sins have wound - ed.
Ex - aú - di, Chri - ste, sup - pli - cán - tum pre - ces.
Áb - lu - e no - stri má - cu - las de - lí - cti.
Crí - mi - na no - stra plá - ci - dus in - dúl - ge.

4. Humbly confessing that we have offended,
   Stripped of illusions, naked in our sorrow,
   Pardon, Lord Jesus, those your blood has ransomed.

5. Innocent captive, you were led to slaughter,
   Sentenced by sinners when they brought false witness.
   Keep from damnation those your death has rescued.

4. *Tibi fatémur, crímina admíssa:*
   Contríto corde pándimus occúlta:
   Túa Redemptor, píetas ignóscat.

5. *Innocens captus, nec repúgnans ductus,*
   Téstibus falsis, pro ímpiis damnátus:
   Quos redemísti, tu consérva, Christe.

Text: Latin, 10th C.; Tr. by Ralph Wright, OSB, b.1938, © 1980, ICEL
Tune: ATTENDE DOMINE, 11 11 11 with refrain; Mode V; Acc. by Richard Proulx, b.1937, © 1975, GIA Publications, Inc.

Somebody's Knockin' at Your Door 415

Some-bod-y's knock-in' at your door; Some-bod-y's knock-in' at your door;

O sin - ner, why don't you an - swer? Some-bod-y's knock-in' at your

Solo: *All:*

door.
1. Knocks like Je - sus,
2. Can't you hear him? Some-bod-y's knock-in' at your door;
3. Je - sus calls you,
4. Can't you trust him?

Solo: *All:*

Knocks like Je - sus,
Can't you hear him? Some-bod-y's knock-in' at your door. O
Je - sus calls you,
Can't you trust him?

sin - ner, why don't you an-swer? Some-bod-y's knock-in' at your door.

Text: Afro-American Spiritual
Tune: SOMEBODY'S KNOCKIN', Irregular; Afro-American Spiritual; Harm. by Richard Proulx, b.1937, © 1986, GIA Publications, Inc.

416 Parce Domine

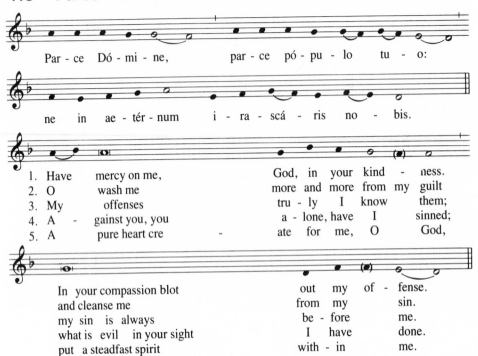

Par - ce Dó - mi - ne, par - ce pó - pu - lo tu - o:
ne in ae - tér - num i - ra - scá - ris no - bis.

1. Have mercy on me, God, in your kind - ness.
2. O wash me more and more from my guilt
3. My offenses tru - ly I know them;
4. A - gainst you, you a - lone, have I sinned;
5. A pure heart cre - ate for me, O God,

In your compassion blot out my of - fense.
and cleanse me from my sin.
my sin is always be - fore me.
what is evil in your sight I have done.
put a steadfast spirit with - in me.

Text: Joel 2:17, Psalm 51:3-6,12; Tr. The Grail, 1963, © 1963, The Grail
Tune: PARCE DOMINE, Irregular; Mode I with Tonus Peregrinus; Acc. by Robert LeBlanc, b.1948, © 1986, GIA Publications, Inc.

417 Lord, Who throughout These Forty Days

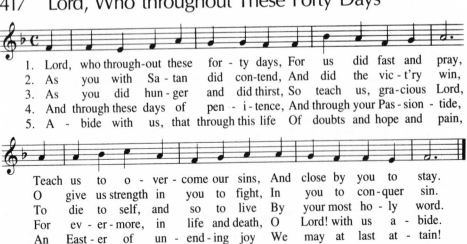

1. Lord, who through-out these for - ty days, For us did fast and pray,
2. As you with Sa - tan did con-tend, And did the vic - t'ry win,
3. As you did hun - ger and did thirst, So teach us, gra-cious Lord,
4. And through these days of pen - i - tence, And through your Pas-sion - tide,
5. A - bide with us, that through this life Of doubts and hope and pain,

Teach us to o - ver - come our sins, And close by you to stay.
O give us strength in you to fight, In you to con-quer sin.
To die to self, and so to live By your most ho - ly word.
For ev - er - more, in life and death, O Lord! with us a - bide.
An East - er of un - end - ing joy We may at last at - tain!

Text: Claudia F. Hernaman, 1838-1898, alt.
Tune: ST. FLAVIAN, CM; John's Day Psalter, 1562; Harm. based on the original faux-bourdon setting

Before the Fruit Is Ripened by the Sun   418

1. Be-fore the fruit is rip-ened by the sun,
   Be-fore the pet-als or the leaves un-coil,
   Be-fore the first fine silk-en root is spun,
   A seed is dropped and bur-ied in the soil.

2. Be-fore the East-er Al-le-lu-ias ring,
   Be-fore the mas-sive rock is rolled a-side,
   Be-fore the fear of death has lost its sting,
   A just and lov-ing man is cru-ci-fied.

3. Be-fore we gain the grace that comes through loss,
   Be-fore we live by more than bread and breath,
   Be-fore we lift in joy an emp-ty cross,
   We face with Christ the seed's re-new-ing death.

Text: John 12:20-33; Thomas H. Troeger, b.1945
Tune: RENEWING DEATH, 10 10 10 10; Carol Doran, b.1936
© 1985, Oxford University Press, Inc.

Forty Days and Forty Nights   419

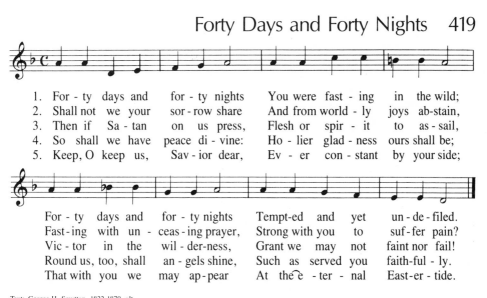

1. For-ty days and for-ty nights You were fast-ing in the wild;
   For-ty days and for-ty nights Tempt-ed and yet un-de-filed.

2. Shall not we your sor-row share And from world-ly joys ab-stain,
   Fast-ing with un-ceas-ing prayer, Strong with you to suf-fer pain?

3. Then if Sa-tan on us press, Flesh or spir-it to as-sail,
   Vic-tor in the wil-der-ness, Grant we may not faint nor fail!

4. So shall we have peace di-vine: Ho-lier glad-ness ours shall be;
   Round us, too, shall an-gels shine, Such as served you faith-ful-ly.

5. Keep, O keep us, Sav-ior dear, Ev-er con-stant by your side;
   That with you we may ap-pear At the-e-ter-nal East-er-tide.

Text: George H. Smyttan, 1822-1870, alt.
Tune: HEINLEIN, 7 7 7 7; Attr. to Martin Herbst, 1654-1681; Harm. ascr. to J. S. Bach, 1685-1750

420 Again We Keep This Solemn Fast

1. A - gain we keep this sol - emn fast, A
2. The law and proph - ets from of old In
3. More spar - ing, there - fore, let us make The
4. Let us a - void each harm - ful way That
5. We pray, O bless - ed Three in One, Our

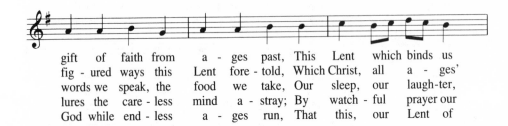

gift of faith from a - ges past, This Lent which binds us
fig - ured ways this Lent fore - told, Which Christ, all a - ges'
words we speak, the food we take, Our sleep, our laugh-ter,
lures the care - less mind a - stray; By watch - ful prayer our
God while end - less a - ges run, That this, our Lent of

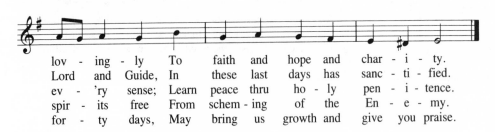

lov - ing - ly To faith and hope and char - i - ty.
Lord and Guide, In these last days has sanc - ti - fied.
ev - 'ry sense; Learn peace thru ho - ly pen - i - tence.
spir - its free From schem - ing of the En - e - my.
for - ty days, May bring us growth and give you praise.

Text: *Ex more docti mystico*; Ascr. to Gregory the Great, c.540-604; Tr. by Peter J. Scagnelli, b.1949, ©
Tune: ERHALT UNS HERR, LM; Klug's *Geistliche Lieder*, 1543; Harm. by J. S. Bach, 1685-1750

At the Cross Her Station Keeping 421

1. At the cross her sta - tion keep - ing, Mar - y stood in
2. While she wait - ed in her an - guish, See - ing Christ in
3. With what pain and de - so - la - tion, With what no - ble
4. Ev - er pa - tient in her yearn - ing, Though her tear - filled

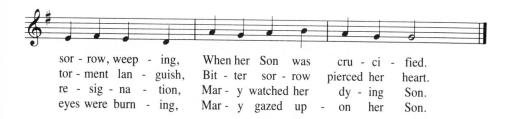

sor - row, weep - ing, When her Son was cru - ci - fied.
tor - ment lan - guish, Bit - ter sor - row pierced her heart.
re - sig - na - tion, Mar - y watched her dy - ing Son.
eyes were burn - ing, Mar - y gazed up - on her Son.

5. Who, that sorrow contemplating,
   On that passion meditating,
       Would not share the Virgin's grief?

6. Christ she saw, for our salvation,
   Scourged with cruel acclamation,
       Bruised and beaten by the rod.

7. Christ she saw with life-blood failing,
   All her anguish unavailing,
       Saw him breathe his very last.

8. Mary, fount of love's devotion,
   Let me share with true emotion
       All the sorrow you endured.

9. Virgin, ever interceding,
   Hear me in my fervent pleading:
       Fire me with your love of Christ.

10. Mother, may this prayer be granted:
    That Christ's love may be implanted
        In the depths of my poor soul.

11. At the cross, your sorrow sharing,
    All your grief and torment bearing,
        Let me stand and mourn with you.

12. Fairest maid of all creation,
    Queen of hope and consolation,
        Let me feel your grief sublime.

13. Virgin, in your love befriend me,
    At the Judgment Day defend me.
        Help me by your constant prayer.

14. Savior, when my life shall leave me,
    Through your mother's prayers receive me
        With the fruits of victory.

15. Let me to your love be taken,
    Let my soul in death awaken
        To the joys of Paradise.

Text: *Stabat mater dolorosa*; Jacopone da Todi, 1230-1306; Tr. by Anthony G. Petti, 1932-1985, ©.1971, Faber Music Ltd.
Tune: STABAT MATER, 88 7; *Mainz Gesangbuch*, 1661; Harm. by Richard Proulx, b.1937, © 1986, GIA Publications, Inc.

422 The Glory of These Forty Days

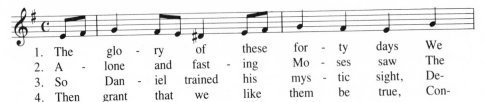

1. The glo - ry of these for - ty days We
2. A - lone and fast - ing Mo - ses saw The
3. So Dan - iel trained his mys - tic sight, De-
4. Then grant that we like them be true, Con-

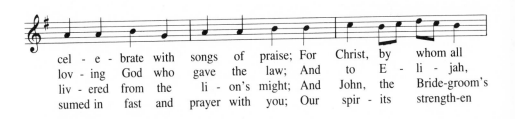

cel - e - brate with songs of praise; For Christ, by whom all
lov - ing God who gave the law; And to E - li - jah,
liv - ered from the li - on's might; And John, the Bride-groom's
sumed in fast and prayer with you; Our spir - its strength-en

things were made, Him - self has fast - ed and has prayed.
fast - ing, came The steeds and char - i - ots of flame.
friend, be - came The her - ald of Mes - si - ah's name.
with your grace, And give us joy to see your face.

Text: *Clarum decus jejunii;* Gregory the Great, c.540-604; Tr. by Maurice F. Bell, 1862-1947, © Oxford University Press
Tune: ERHALT UNS HERR, LM; Klug's *Geistliche Lieder,* 1543; Harm. by J. S. Bach, 1685-1750

423 Jesus, Remember Me

Je - sus, re - mem-ber me when you come in - to your King-dom.

Je - sus, re - mem-ber me when you come in - to your King-dom.

Text: Luke 23:42; Taizé Community, 1981
Tune: Jacques Berthier, b.1923
© 1981, Les Presses de Taizé

O Sun of Justice 424

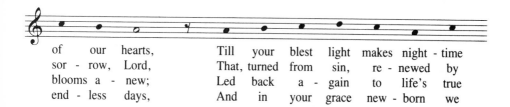

1. O Sun of jus - tice, Je - sus Christ, Dis - pel the dark - ness
2. In this our "time ac - cept - a - ble" Touch ev - 'ry heart with
3. The day, your day, in beau - ty dawns When in your light earth
4. O lov - ing Trin - i - ty, our God, To you we bow through

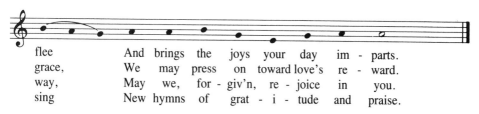

of our hearts,   Till your blest light makes night - time
sor - row, Lord,   That, turned from sin, re - newed by
blooms a - new;   Led back a - gain to life's true
end - less days,   And in your grace new - born we

flee   And brings the joys your day im - parts.
grace,   We may press on toward love's re - ward.
way,   May we, for - giv'n, re - joice in you.
sing   New hymns of grat - i - tude and praise.

Text: *Jam Christe sol justitiae;* Latin, 6th C.; Tr. by Peter J. Scagnelli, b.1949, ©
Tune: JESU DULCIS MEMORIA, LM: Mode I; Acc. by Richard Proulx, b.1937, © 1975, GIA Publications, Inc.

Salvator Mundi 425

Canon

Sal - va-tor mun - di sal - va nos.   Sal - va-tor mun - di sal - va nos.

Sal - va nos, sal - va nos.   Sal - va-tor mun - di sal - va nos.

Text: *Savior of the world, save us;* Taizé Community, 1980
Tune: Jacques Berthier, b.1923
© 1980, Les Presses de Taizé

426 By the Babylonian Rivers

1. By the Bab - y - lo - nian riv - ers We sat
2. There our cap - tors in de - ri - sion Did re-
3. How shall we sing the Lord's song In a
4. Let the Cross be be - ne - dic - tion For those

down in grief and wept; Hung our harps up - on the
quire of us a song; So we sat with star - ing
strange and bit - ter land; Can our voic - es veil the
bound in tyr - an - ny; By the power of re - sur-

wil - low, Mourned for Zi - on when we slept.
vi - sion, And the days were hard and long.
sor - row? Lord God, hold your ho - ly band.
rec - tion Loose them from cap - tiv - i - ty.

Text: Ewald Bash, b.1924, ©
Tune: KAS DZIEDAJA, 8 7 8 7; Latvian Folk Melody; Harm. by Geoffrey Laycock, b.1927, ©

427 Jesus Walked This Lonesome Valley

1. Je - sus walked this lone-some val - ley; He had to walk
2. We must walk this lone-some val - ley; We have to walk
3. You must go and stand your tri - al; You have to stand

it by him - self. O no-bod-y else could walk it
it by our - selves. O no-bod-y else can walk it
it by your - self. O no-bod-y else can stand it

for him; He had to walk it by him - self.
for us; We have to walk it by our - selves.
for you; You have to stand it by your - self.

Text: American Folk Hymn
Tune: LONESOME VALLEY, 8 8 10 8; American Folk Hymn; Harm. by Richard Proulx, b.1937, © 1975, GIA Publications, Inc.

All Glory, Laud, and Honor 428

All glo - ry, laud, and hon - or To you, Re-deem-er, King!

To whom the lips of chil - dren Made sweet ho - san - nas ring.

1. You are the King of Is - ra - el, And Da - vid's roy - al Son,
2. The com - pa - ny of an - gels Are prais - ing you on high;
3. The peo - ple of the He - brews With palms be - fore you went:
4. To you be - fore your pas - sion They sang their hymns of praise:
5. Their prais - es you ac - cept - ed, Ac - cept the prayers we bring,

Now in the Lord's Name com - ing, Our King and Bless-ed One.
And mor-tals, joined with all things Cre - a - ted, make re - ply.
Our praise and prayers and an - thems Be - fore you we pre - sent.
To you, now high ex - alt - ed, Our mel - o - dy we raise.
Great source of love and good - ness, Our Sav - ior and our King.

Text: *Gloria, laus et honor;* Theodulph of Orleans, c.760-821; Tr. by John M. Neale, 1818-1866, alt.
Tune: ST. THEODULPH, 7 6 7 6 D; Melchior Teschner, 1584-1635

Benedictus Qui Venit 429

Canon (A)   (B)

Be - ne - di - ctus qui ve - nit, Be - ne - di - ctus qui ve - nit, in

(C)   (D)

no - mi - ne, in no - mi - ne, in no - mi - ne Do - mi - ni.

Text: Mt. 21:9; Mt. 23:29; Mk. 11:9; Lk. 13:35; Ps. 118:26; Taizé Community, 1978
Tune: Jacques Berthier, b.1923
© 1979, Les Presses de Taizé

430 Hosanna in Excelsis

Canon

Ho - san - na, ho - san - na, ho - san - na in ex - cel - sis. Ho-

Text: Mt. 21:9; Mk. 11:10; Jn. 12:13; Taizé Community, 1978
Tune: Jacques Berthier, b.1923
© 1979, Les Presses de Taizé

431 Jesu, Jesu, Fill Us with Your Love

Je - su, Je - su, fill us with your love, show

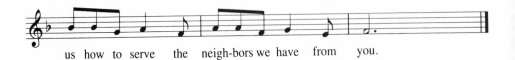

us how to serve the neigh-bors we have from you.

1. Kneels at the feet of his friends,   Si - lent - ly wash-es their
2. Neigh-bors are rich and poor,   Neigh-bors are black and
3. These are the ones we should serve,   These are the ones we should
4. Kneel at the feet of our friends,   Si - lent - ly wash-ing their

D.C.

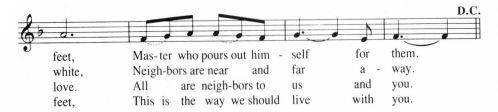

feet,   Mas- ter who pours out him - self for them.
white,   Neigh-bors are near and far a - way.
love.   All are neigh-bors to us and you.
feet,   This is the way we should live with you.

Text: John 13:3-5; Ghana Folk Song; Tr. by Tom Colvin, b.1925
Tune: CHEREPONI, Irregular; Ghana Folk song; Acc. by Jane M. Marshall, b.1924. © 1982, Hope Publishing Co.
© 1969, Hope Publishing Co.

Jesus Took a Towel 432

Je - sus took a tow - el and he gird - ed him - self, Then he

washed my feet, yes, he washed my feet, Je - sus took a ba - sin and he

knelt him-self down, And he washed, yes, he washed my feet.

1. The heav - ens are the Lord's, and the earth is his, The
2. The hour had come, the Pasch was near;

clouds are his char - iot, glo - ry his cloak; He
Je - sus loved his own, loved them to the end. O

made the moun-tains, set the lim - its of the sea; And he
Lord, let me see, let me un - der-stand Why you

D.C.

stooped and washed my feet.
stooped and washed my feet.

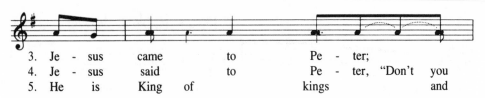

3. Je - sus came to Pe - ter;
4. Je - sus said to Pe - ter, "Don't you
5. He is King of kings and

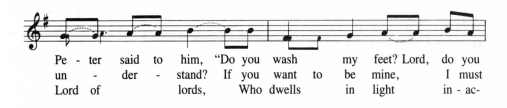

Pe - ter said to him, "Do you wash my feet? Lord, do you
un - der - stand? If you want to be mine, I must
Lord of lords, Who dwells in light in - ac-

wash my feet?" Je - sus knelt down, but
wash your feet." "Then not just my feet, but my
- ces - si - ble; No one has seen him where he

D.C.

Pe - ter cried out, "Lord, you'll nev - er wash my feet!"
head and my hands! O Lord, I want to be yours."
sits on high, Yet he stooped to wash my feet.

6. "Do you know, lit - tle chil - dren, what I've
7. Now friends, let's be glad, let our
8. Who is like you, Lord, now en-
9. O the path is rug - ged, and the

done for you? You call me Mas - ter, and you
joy be full. For God is love, and he a-
throned on high, Where you look up - on the heav - ens and the
go - ing is rough, The jour - ney is long to our

call me Lord. If I am your Mas - ter, and if
bides in us. He washed our feet, he
earth be - low? Be - fore your face the earth
heav'n - ly home, Our feet are wea - ry and

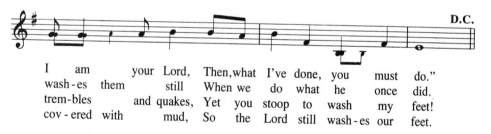

D.C.

I am your Lord, Then, what I've done, you must do."
wash - es them still When we do what he once did.
trem - bles and quakes, Yet you stoop to wash my feet!
cov - ered with mud, So the Lord still wash - es our feet.

Text: John 13; Chrysogonus Waddell, OCSO, b.1930
Tune: JESUS TOOK A TOWEL, Irregular; Chrysogonus Waddell, OCSO, b.1930
© Gethsemani Abbey

433 When I Survey the Wondrous Cross

1. When I sur - vey the won - drous cross On which the
2. For - bid it, Lord, that I should boast Save in the
3. See, from his head, his hands, his feet, Sor - row and
4. Were the whole realm of na - ture mine, That were a

Prince of glo - ry died, My rich - est gain I
death of Christ, my God; All the vain things that
love flow min - gled down; Did e'er such love and
pres - ent far too small: Love so a - maz - ing,

count but loss, And pour con - tempt on all my pride.
charm me most, I sac - ri - fice them to his blood.
sor - row meet, Or thorns com - pose so rich a crown?'
so di - vine, De - mands my soul, my life, my all.

Text: Isaac Watts, 1674-1748
Tune: ROCKINGHAM, LM; Adapted by Edward Miller, 1735-1807

434 O Sacred Head Surrounded

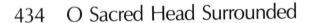

1. O Sa - cred Head sur - round - ed By crown of pierc-ing thorn!
2. I see your strength and vig - or All fad - ing in the strife,
3. In this, your bit - ter pas - sion, Good Shep - herd, think of me

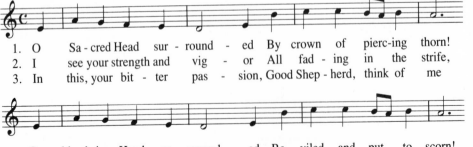

O bleed - ing Head, so wound - ed, Re - viled and put to scorn!
And death with cru - el rig - or, Be - reav - ing you of life;
With your most sweet com - pas - sion, Un - worth - y though I be:

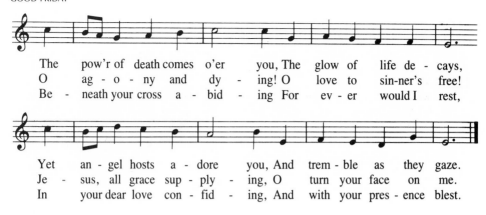

The pow'r of death comes o'er you, The glow of life de - cays,
O ag - o - ny and dy - ing! O love to sin-ner's free!
Be - neath your cross a - bid - ing For ev - er would I rest,

Yet an - gel hosts a - dore you, And trem - ble as they gaze.
Je - sus, all grace sup - ply - ing, O turn your face on me.
In your dear love con - fid - ing, And with your pres - ence blest.

Text: *Salve caput cruentatum;* Ascr. to Bernard of Clairvaux, 1091-1153; Tr. by Henry Baker, 1821-1877
Tune: PASSION CHORALE, 7 6 7 6 D; Hans Leo Hassler, 1564-1612; Harm. by J. S. Bach, 1685-1750

The Royal Banners Forward Go 435

1. The roy - al ban - ners for - ward go, The cross shines
2. There while he hung, his sa - cred side By sol - dier's
3. Ful - filled is now what Da - vid told In true pro-
4. O tree of glo - ry, tree most fair, Or - dained those

forth in mys - tic glow, Where he through whom our flesh was
spear was o - pened wide, To cleanse us in the pre - cious
phet - ic song of old, How God the na - tions' king should
ho - ly limbs to bear, How bright in roy - al robe it

made, In that same flesh our ran - som paid.
flood Of wa - ter min - gled with his blood.
be; For God is reign - ing from the tree.
stood — The pur - ple of a Sav - ior's blood!

5. Upon its arms, like balance true,
   He weighed the price for sinners due,
   The price which none but he could pay,
   And spoiled the spoiler of his prey.

6. To you, eternal Three in One,
   Let homage due by all be done:
   As by the cross you did restore,
   So rule and guide us evermore.

Text: *Vexilla Regis prodeunt;* Venantius Fortunatus, c.530-609; Tr. by John M. Neale, 1818-1866, alt.
Tune: VEXILLA REGIS, LM; Mode I; Realization in modal rhythm by Schola Antiqua, 1983, ©; Acc. by David Hurd, b.1950, © 1985, GIA
Publications, Inc.

436 Were You There

1. Were you there when they cru - ci - fied my Lord? Were you
2. Were you there when they nailed him to the tree? Were you
3. Were you there when they pierced him in the side? Were you
4. Were you there when the sun re - fused to shine? Were you

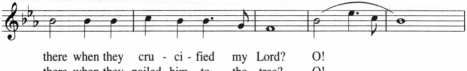

there when they cru - ci - fied my Lord? O!
there when they nailed him to the tree? O!
there when they pierced him in the side? O!
there when the sun re - fused to shine? O!

Some-times it caus - es me to trem-ble, trem-ble, trem-ble,
Some-times it caus - es me to trem-ble, trem-ble, trem-ble,
Some-times it caus - es me to trem-ble, trem-ble, trem-ble,
Some-times it caus - es me to trem-ble, trem-ble, trem-ble,

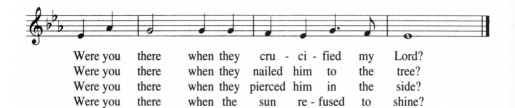

Were you there when they cru - ci - fied my Lord?
Were you there when they nailed him to the tree?
Were you there when they pierced him in the side?
Were you there when the sun re - fused to shine?

5. Were you there when they laid him in the tomb?
Were you there when they laid him in the tomb?
O! Sometimes it causes me to tremble, tremble, tremble,
Were you there when they laid him in the tomb?

6. Were you there when they rolled the stone away?
Were you there when they rolled the stone away?
O! Sometimes it causes me to tremble, tremble, tremble,
Were you there when they rolled the stone away?

Text: Afro-American Spiritual
Tune: WERE YOU THERE, 10 10 with refrain; Afro-American Spiritual; Harm. by C. Winfred Douglas, 1867-1944, © 1940, 1943, 1961, Church Pension Fund

Sing, My Tongue, the Song of Triumph   437

1. Sing, my tongue, the song of tri - umph,
2. He en - dured the nails, the spit - ting,
3. Faith - ful Cross, a - bove all oth - er,
4. Bend your boughs, O Tree of glo - ry!

Tell the sto - ry far and wide;
Vin - e - gar and spear and reed;
One and on - ly no - ble tree,
All your rig - id branch - es, bend!

Tell of dread and fi - nal bat - tle,
From that ho - ly bod - y bro - ken
None in fo - liage, none in blos - som,
For a while the an - cient tem - per

Sing of Sav - ior cru - ci - fied;
Blood and wa - ter forth pro - ceed:
None in fruit your peer may be;
That your birth be - stowed, sus - pend;

How up - on the cross a vic -
Earth and stars and sky and o -
Sweet the wood and sweet the i -
And the King of earth and heav -

tim Van - quish - ing in death he died.
cean By that flood from stain are freed.
ron And your load, most sweet is he.
en Gent - ly on your bos - om tend.

Text: *Pange, lingua, gloriosi lauream certaminis;* Venantius Fortunatus, c.530-609; Tr. from *The Three Days,* 1981
Tune: PICARDY, 8 7 8 7 8 7; French Carol; Harm. by Richard Proulx, b.1937. © 1986, GIA Publications, Inc.

438 Lord Christ, When First You Came to Earth

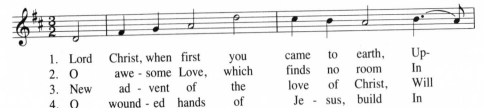

1. Lord Christ, when first you came to earth, Up-
2. O awe - some Love, which finds no room In
3. New ad - vent of the love of Christ, Will
4. O wound - ed hands of Je - sus, build In

on a cross they bound you. And mocked your sav - ing
life where sin de - nies you. And, doomed to death, shall
we a - gain re - fuse you. Till in the night of
us your new cre - a - tion: Our pride is dust, our

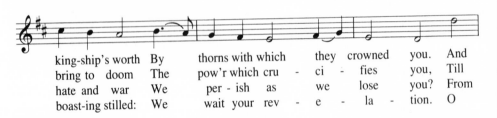

king-ship's worth By thorns with which they crowned you. And
bring to doom The pow'r which cru - ci - fies you, Till
hate and war We per - ish as we lose you? From
boast-ing stilled: We wait your rev - e - la - tion. O

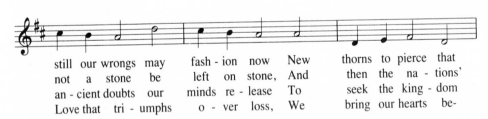

still our wrongs may fash - ion now New thorns to pierce that
not a stone be left on stone, And then the na - tions'
an - cient doubts our minds re - lease To seek the king - dom
Love that tri - umphs o - ver loss, We bring our hearts be-

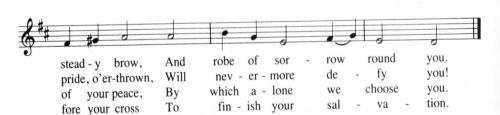

stead - y brow, And robe of sor - row round you.
pride, o'er-thrown, Will nev - er - more de - fy you!
of your peace, By which a - lone we choose you.
fore your cross To fin - ish your sal - va - tion.

Text: W. Russell Bowie, 1882-1969, alt., ©
Tune: MIT FREUDEN ZART, 8 7 8 7 88 7; Bohemian Brethren's *Kirchengesange*, 1566

My Song Is Love Unknown 439

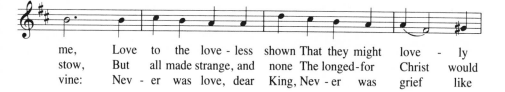

1. My song is love un - known, My Sav - ior's love for
2. He came from his blest throne, Sal - va - tion to be-
3. Here might I stay and sing, No sto - ry so di-

me, Love to the love - less shown That they might love - ly
stow, But all made strange, and none The longed-for Christ would
vine: Nev - er was love, dear King, Nev - er was grief like

be. O who am I That for my sake My
know. But O my friend, My friend in - deed, Who
thine. This is my friend, In whose sweet praise I

Lord shall take Frail flesh, and die.
at my need His life did spend.
all my days Could glad - ly spend.

Text: Samuel Crossman, c.1624-1683
Tune: LOVE UNKNOWN, 6 6 6 6 4 44 4; John Ireland, 1879-1962. © John Ireland Trust

440 All You Who Pass This Way

Refrain

All you who pass this way, look and see.

Verses

1. Is an-y sor-row like the sor-row that af-flicts me? All

2. Wo-men of Je - ru - sa-lem! Do not weep for me, but for your-selves, and for your chil - dren. All

3. Fa-ther, for - give them! they know not what they do. All

4. My God, my God, why have you a - ban-doned me? All

5. To - day you will be with me in par - a - dise. All

6. I am thirst - y. All

7. Fa - ther, in - to your hands I com-mend my spir - it. All

Text: From the Passion Gospels; Taizé Community, 1984
Tune: Jacques Berthier, b.1923
© 1984, Les Presses de Taizé

Alleluia, Alleluia, Give Thanks 441

Al - le - lu - ia, al - le - lu - ia, give thanks to the ris-en Lord.

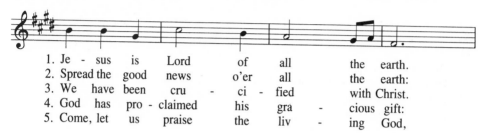

Al - le - lu - ia, al - le - lu - ia, give praise to his Name.

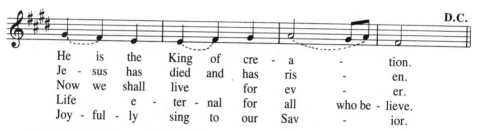

1. Je - sus is Lord of all the earth.
2. Spread the good news o'er all the earth:
3. We have been cru - ci - fied with Christ.
4. God has pro - claimed his gra - cious gift:
5. Come, let us praise the liv - ing God,

D.C.

He is the King of cre - a - tion.
Je - sus has died and has ris - en.
Now we shall live for ev - er.
Life e - ter - nal for all who be - lieve.
Joy - ful - ly sing to our Sav - ior.

Text: Donald Fishel, b.1950, © 1973, Word of God Music
Tune: ALLELUIA NO. 1, 8 8 with refrain; Donald Fishel, b.1950, © 1973, Word of God Music; Harm. by Betty Pulkingham, b.1929, Charles Mallory, b.1953, and George Mims, b.1938, © 1979, Celebration

442 Jesus Christ Is Risen Today

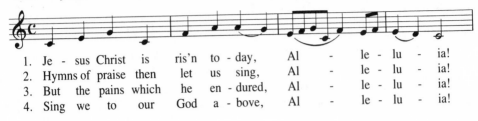

1. Je - sus Christ is ris'n to - day, Al - le - lu - ia!
2. Hymns of praise then let us sing, Al - le - lu - ia!
3. But the pains which he en - dured, Al - le - lu - ia!
4. Sing we to our God a - bove, Al - le - lu - ia!

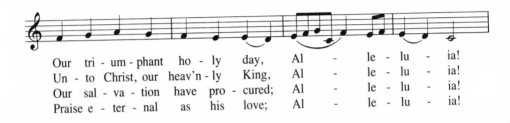

Our tri - um - phant ho - ly day, Al - le - lu - ia!
Un - to Christ, our heav'n - ly King, Al - le - lu - ia!
Our sal - va - tion have pro - cured; Al - le - lu - ia!
Praise e - ter - nal as his love; Al - le - lu - ia!

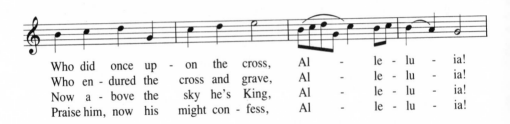

Who did once up - on the cross, Al - le - lu - ia!
Who en - dured the cross and grave, Al - le - lu - ia!
Now a - bove the sky he's King, Al - le - lu - ia!
Praise him, now his might con - fess, Al - le - lu - ia!

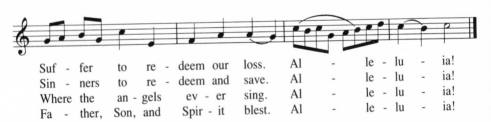

Suf - fer to re - deem our loss. Al - le - lu - ia!
Sin - ners to re - deem and save. Al - le - lu - ia!
Where the an - gels ev - er sing. Al - le - lu - ia!
Fa - ther, Son, and Spir - it blest. Al - le - lu - ia!

Text: St. 1, *Surrexit Christus hodie*, Latin, 14th C.; Para. in *Lyra Davidica*, 1708, alt.; St. 2, 3, *The Compleat Psalmodist*, c.1750, alt.; St. 4, Charles Wesley, 1707-1788
Tune: EASTER HYMN, 77 77 with alleluias; *Lyra Davidica*, 1708

O Queen of Heaven/Regina Caeli 443

O Queen of hea - ven, be joy - ful, al - le - lu - ia,
Re - gí - na cae - li,   lae - tá - re,   al - le - lú - ia,

For he whom you have hum-bly borne for us, al - le - lu - ia,
Qui - a quem me - ru - í - sti por - tá - re, al - le - lú - ia,

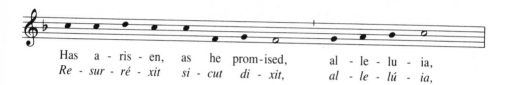

Has a - ris - en, as he prom-ised, al - le - lu - ia,
Re - sur - ré - xit si - cut di - xit, al - le - lú - ia,

Of - fer now our prayer to God, al - le - lu - ia.
O - ra pro no - bis De - um, al - le - lú - ia.

Text: Latin, 12th C.; Tr. by C. Winfred Douglas, 1867-1944, alt.
Tune: REGINA CAELI, Irregular; Mode VI; Acc. by Robert LeBlanc, b.1948, © 1986, GIA Publications, Inc.

444 Hail Thee, Festival Day

Hail thee, fes - ti - val day! Blest day that art hal-lowed for ev - er;

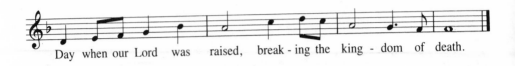

Day when our Lord was raised, break - ing the king - dom of death.

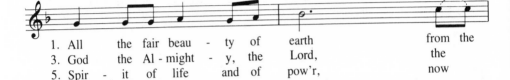

1. All   the fair beau - ty of   earth   from the
3. God   the Al - might - y, the   Lord,   the
5. Spir - it of life   and of   pow'r,   now

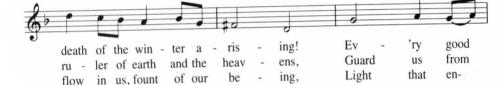

death of the win - ter a - ris - ing!   Ev - 'ry good
ru - ler of earth and the heav - ens,   Guard us from
flow in us, fount of our be - ing,   Light that en-

D.C.

gift of the year   now with its mas - ter re - turns.
harm with - out;   cleanse us from ev - il with - in.
light - ens us all,   life that in all may a - bide.

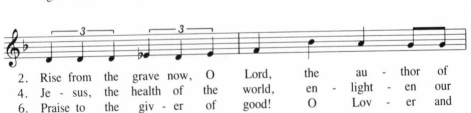

2. Rise from the grave now, O   Lord, the au - thor of
4. Je - sus, the health of the   world, en - light - en our
6. Praise to the giv - er of   good! O Lov - er and

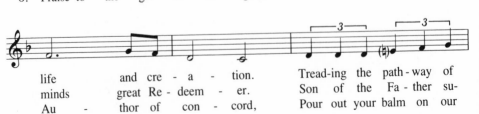

life   and cre - a - tion.   Tread-ing the path - way of
minds   great Re - deem - er.   Son of the Fa - ther su-
Au - thor of con - cord,   Pour out your balm on our

D.C.

death,	new	life	you	give	to	us	all.
preme,	on - ly	be - got	- ten	of	God.
days;	or - der	our	ways	in	your	peace.

Text: *Salve festa dies;* Venantius Fortunatus, c.530-609; Tr. composite
Tune: SALVE FESTA DIES, Irregular with refrain; Ralph Vaughan Williams, 1872-1958
© Oxford University Press

I Know That My Redeemer Lives 445

1. I	know that	my	Re -	deem	- er	lives;
2. He	lives, to	bless	me	with	his	love;
3. He	lives, and	grants	me	dai -	ly	breath;
4. He	lives, all	glo -	ry	to	his	name;

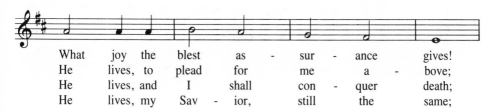

What	joy	the	blest	as -	sur -	ance	gives!
He	lives,	to	plead	for	me	a -	bove;
He	lives,	and	I	shall	con -	quer	death;
He	lives,	my	Sav -	ior,	still	the	same;

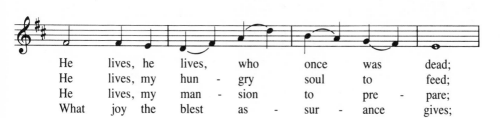

He	lives,	he	lives,	who	once	was	dead;
He	lives,	my	hun -	gry	soul	to	feed;
He	lives,	my	man -	sion	to	pre -	pare;
What	joy	the	blest	as -	sur -	ance	gives;

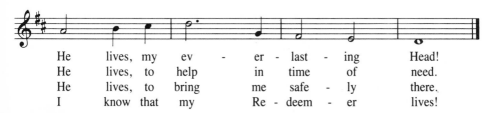

He	lives,	my	ev -	er -	last -	ing	Head!
He	lives,	to	help	in	time	of	need.
He	lives,	to	bring	me	safe -	ly	there.
I	know	that	my	Re -	deem -	er	lives!

Text: Samuel Medley, 1738-1799
Tune: DUKE STREET, LM; John Hatton, c.1710-1793

446 Morning of Splendor

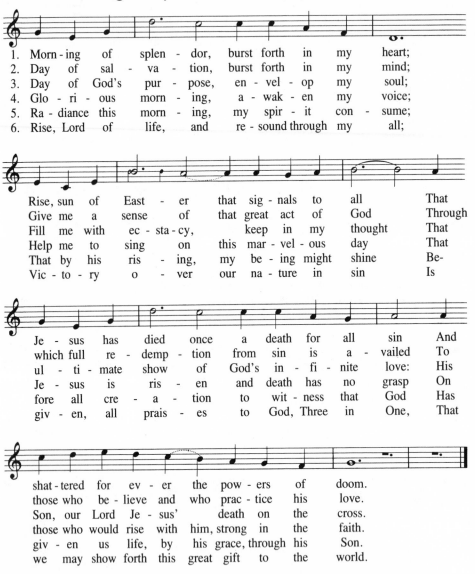

1. Morn-ing of splen - dor, burst forth in my heart;
2. Day of sal - va - tion, burst forth in my mind;
3. Day of God's pur - pose, en - vel - op my soul;
4. Glo - ri - ous morn - ing, a - wak - en my voice;
5. Ra - diance this morn - ing, my spir - it con - sume;
6. Rise, Lord of life, and re - sound through my all;

Rise, sun of East - er that sig - nals to all That
Give me a sense of that great act of God Through
Fill me with ec - sta - cy, keep in my thought That
Help me to sing on this mar - vel - ous day That
That by his ris - ing, my be - ing might shine Be-
Vic - to - ry o - ver our na - ture in sin Is

Je - sus has died once a death for all sin And
which full re - demp - tion from sin is a - vailed To
ul - ti - mate show of God's in - fi - nite love: His
Je - sus is ris - en and death has no grasp On
fore all cre - a - tion to wit - ness that God Has
giv - en, all prais - es to God, Three in One, That

shat - tered for ev - er the pow - ers of doom.
those who be - lieve and who prac - tice his love.
Son, our Lord Je - sus' death on the cross.
those who would rise with him, strong in the faith.
giv - en us life, by his grace, through his Son.
we may show forth this great gift to the world.

Text: David Hurd, b.1950
Tune: MORNING OF SPLENDOR, 10 10 11 11; David Hurd, b.1950
© 1983, GIA Publications, Inc.

O Sons and Daughters 447

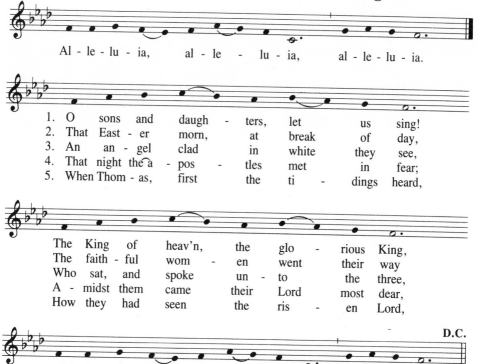

Alleluia, alleluia, alleluia.

1. O sons and daugh - ters, let us sing!
2. That East - er morn, at break of day,
3. An an - gel clad in white they see,
4. That night thea - pos - tles met in fear;
5. When Thom - as, first the ti - dings heard,

The King of heav'n, the glo - rious King,
The faith - ful wom - en went their way
Who sat, and spoke un - to the three,
A - midst them came their Lord most dear,
How they had seen the ris - en Lord,

O'er death to - day rose tri - umph - ing. Al - le - lu - ia!
To seek the tomb where Je - sus lay. Al - le - lu - ia!
"Your Lord has gone to Gal - i - lee." Al - le - lu - ia!
And said, "My peace be on all here." Al - le - lu - ia!
He doubt - ed the dis - ci - ples' word. Al - le - lu - ia!

D.C.

6. "My wounded side, O Thomas, see;
   Behold my hands, my feet," said he,
   "Not faithless, but believing be." Alleluia!

7. No longer Thomas then denied,
   He saw the feet, the hands, the side;
   "You are my Lord and God," he cried. Alleluia!

8. How blest are they who have not seen,
   And yet whose faith has constant been,
   For they eternal life shall win. Alleluia!

9. On this most holy day of days,
   To God your hearts and voices raise,
   In laud, and jubilee and praise. Alleluia!

Text: *O filii et filae*; Jean Tisserand, d.1494; Tr. by John M. Neale, 1818-1866, alt.
Tune: O FILII ET FILIAE, 888 with alleluias; Mode II; Acc. by Richard Proulx, b.1937, © 1975, GIA Publications, Inc.

448 Daylight Fades

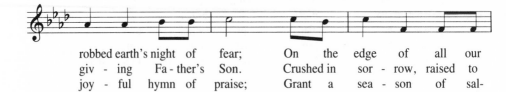

1. Day - light fades in days when death - less Light has
2. Won-drous mys - t'ry of love's giv - ing! Our for-
3. O Lord Je - sus, ris - en Sav - ior, Hear our

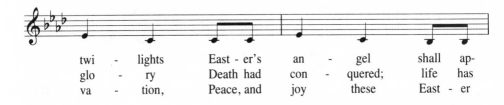

robbed earth's night of fear; On the edge of all our
giv - ing Fa - ther's Son. Crushed in sor - row, raised to
joy - ful hymn of praise; Grant a sea - son of sal-

twi - lights East - er's an - gel shall ap-
glo - ry Death had con - quered; life has
va - tion, Peace, and joy these East - er

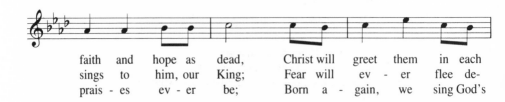

pear; When hearts bro - ken by be - liev - ing Count their
won! Once in si - lence he sub - mit - ted, Now earth
days. To our Fa - ther and the Spir - it E - qual

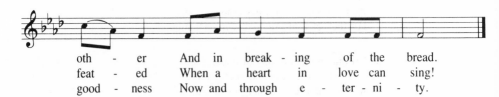

faith and hope as dead, Christ will greet them in each
sings to him, our King; Fear will ev - er flee de-
prais - es ev - er be; Born a - gain, we sing God's

oth - er And in break - ing of the bread.
feat - ed When a heart in love can sing!
good - ness Now and through e - ter - ni - ty.

Text: Lk. 24:28-35; Peter J. Scagnelli, b.1949, ©
Tune: DOMHNACH TRIONOIDE, 8 7 8 7 D; Gaelic Melody; Harm. by Richard Proulx, b.1937, © 1975, GIA Publications, Inc.

This Joyful Eastertide 449

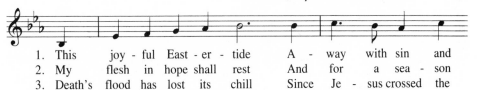

1. This joy - ful East - er - tide A - way with sin and
2. My flesh in hope shall rest And for a sea - son
3. Death's flood has lost its chill Since Je - sus crossed the

sor - row! My love, the Cru - ci - fied,
slum - ber Till trump from east to west
riv - er; Lov - er of souls, from ill

Has sprung to life this mor - row:
Shall wake the dead in num - ber:
My pass - ing soul de - liv - er:

Had Christ, who once was slain, Not burst his three - day pris - on,

Our faith had been in vain: But now has Christ a - ris - en, a-

ris - en, a - ris - en; But now has Christ a - ris - en!

Text: George R. Woodward, 1848-1934
Tune: VRUECHTEN, 6 7 6 7 D; Melody in Oudaen's *David's Psalmen*, 1685; Harm. by Paul G. Bunjes, b.1914. © 1969 Concordia Publishing House

450 Be Joyful, Mary

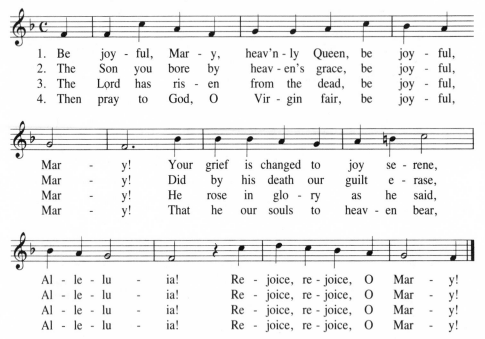

1. Be joy-ful, Mar-y, heav'n-ly Queen, be joy-ful,
2. The Son you bore by heav-en's grace, be joy-ful,
3. The Lord has ris-en from the dead, be joy-ful,
4. Then pray to God, O Vir-gin fair, be joy-ful,

Mar - y! Your grief is changed to joy se - rene,
Mar - y! Did by his death our guilt e - rase,
Mar - y! He rose in glo - ry as he said,
Mar - y! That he our souls to heav - en bear,

Al - le - lu - ia! Re - joice, re - joice, O Mar - y!
Al - le - lu - ia! Re - joice, re - joice, O Mar - y!
Al - le - lu - ia! Re - joice, re - joice, O Mar - y!
Al - le - lu - ia! Re - joice, re - joice, O Mar - y!

Text: *Regina caeli, jubila;* Latin, 17th C.; Tr. anon. in *Psallite,* 1901
Tune: REGINA CAELI, 8 5 8 4 7; Leisentritt's *Gesangbuch,* 1584, alt.

451 The Strife Is O'er

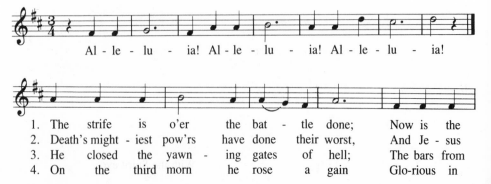

Al - le - lu - ia! Al - le - lu - ia! Al - le - lu - ia!

1. The strife is o'er the bat - tle done; Now is the
2. Death's might - iest pow'rs have done their worst, And Je - sus
3. He closed the yawn - ing gates of hell; The bars from
4. On the third morn he rose a gain Glo-rious in

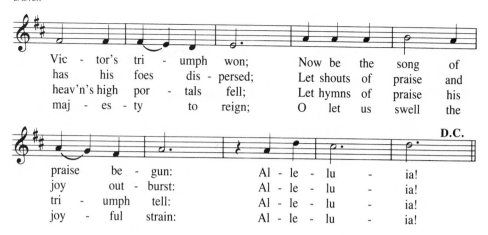

Vic - tor's tri - umph won; Now be the song of
has his foes dis - persed; Let shouts of praise and
heav'n's high por - tals fell; Let hymns of praise his
maj - es - ty to reign; O let us swell the

praise be - gun: Al - le - lu - ia!
joy out - burst: Al - le - lu - ia!
tri - umph tell: Al - le - lu - ia!
joy - ful strain: Al - le - lu - ia!

Text: *Finita iam sunt praelia*; Latin, 12th C.; Tr. by Francis Pott; 1832-1909, alt.
Tune: VICTORY, 888 with alleluias; Giovanni da Palestrina, 1525-1594; Adapt. by William H. Monk, 1823-1889

Christ the Lord Is Risen Today 452

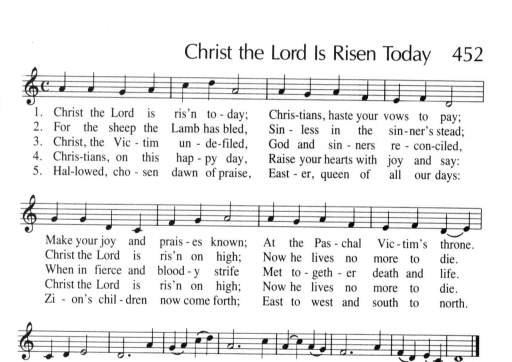

1. Christ the Lord is ris'n to - day; Chris-tians, haste your vows to pay;
2. For the sheep the Lamb has bled, Sin - less in the sin-ner's stead;
3. Christ, the Vic - tim un - de-filed, God and sin - ners re - con-ciled,
4. Chris-tians, on this hap - py day, Raise your hearts with joy and say:
5. Hal-lowed, cho - sen dawn of praise, East - er, queen of all our days:

Make your joy and prais - es known; At the Pas - chal Vic - tim's throne.
Christ the Lord is ris'n on high; Now he lives no more to die.
When in fierce and blood - y strife Met to - geth - er death and life.
Christ the Lord is ris'n on high; Now he lives no more to die.
Zi - on's chil - dren now come forth; East to west and south to north.

Al - le - lu - ia. Al - le - lu - ia. Al - le - lu - ia. Al - le - lu - ia.

6. Let the people praise you, Lord,
   Be, by all that is adored:
   Let the nations shout and sing;
   Glory to their Paschal King.

7. Hymns of glory, songs of praise,
   God on high, to you we raise:
   Risen Lord, we now adore,
   With the Spirit ever more.

Text: *Victimae paschali laudes*; Ascr. to Wipo of Burgundy, d.1048; Tr. by Jane E. Leeson, 1809-1881, alt.
Tune: SURGIT IN HAEC DIES, 77 77 with alleluias; 12th C.; Acc. by Richard Proulx, b.1937, © 1980, GIA Publications, Inc.

453 Now the Green Blade Rises

1. Now the green blade ris - es from the bur - ied grain,
2. In the grave they laid him, love by ha - tred slain,
3. Forth he came at East - er, like the ris - en grain,
4. When our hearts are win - try, griev - ing, or in pain,

Wheat that in dark earth man - y days has lain;
Think - ing that he would nev - er wake a - gain,
He that for three days in the grave had lain;
Your touch can call us back to life a - gain,

Love lives a - gain, that with the dead has been;
Laid in the earth like grain that sleeps un - seen;
Raised from the dead, my liv - ing Lord is seen;
Fields of our hearts that dead and bare have been;

Love is come a - gain like wheat a - ris - ing green.

Test: John M.C. Crum, 1872-1958, © Oxford University Press
Tune: NOËL NOUVELET, 11 10 11 10; French Carol; Harm. by Thomas Foster, b.1938, © 1986, GIA Publications, Inc.

454 Maranatha! Alleluia!

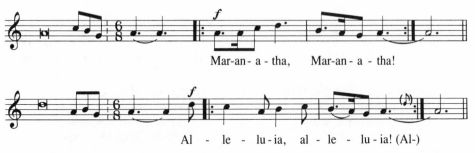

Mar-an- a - tha, Mar-an- a - tha!

Al - le - lu - ia, al - le - lu - ia! (Al-)

Text: 1 Cor. 16:22, Rev. 22:20; Taizé Community, 1978
Tune: Jacques Berthier, b.1923
© 1979, Les Presses de Taizé

Rejoice, Angelic Choirs 455

1. Re - joice, an - gel - ic choirs, re - joice! Re-
2. O earth, ex - ult in ra - diance bright, Il-
3. Let all who gath - er round this flame, The

joice now, all cre - a - tion! Let trum - pets loud - ly
lu - mined by Christ's splen - dor! Your dark - ness now is
sign of Christ's a - ris - ing, The death - less light of

raise their voice To hail the Lord's sal - va - tion; Let
put to flight; To him due prais - es ren - der! Be
Christ ac - claim, His sav - ing mer - cy priz - ing; That

all Christ's ho - ly peo - ple sing The tri - umph of their
glad, O Church! Sing out your songs! Your tem - ples fill with
all may live by faith in him Who con-quered death, de-

might-y king In fes - tal cel - e - bra - tion!
shout-ing throngs To hail the glo - rious vic - tor!
spair, and sin To make us his for ev - er.

Text: *Exsultet jam angelica;* Latin, 4th C.; Tr. by Joel W. Lundeen, b.1918. © 1978, *Lutheran Book of Worship*
Tune: MIT FREUDEN ZART, 8 7 8 7 88 7; Bohemian Brethren's *Kirchengesange,* 1556

456 Come, Ye Faithful, Raise the Strain

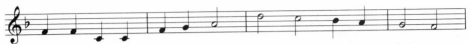

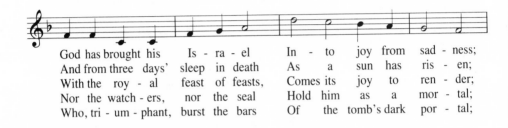

1. Come, ye faith - ful raise the strain Of tri - um - phant glad - ness;
2. 'Tis the spring of souls to - day; Christ has burst the pris - on,
3. Now the queen of sea-sons, bright With the day of splen - dor,
4. Nei - ther could the gates of death, Nor the tomb's dark por - tal,
5. "Al - le - lu - ia!" now we cry To our King im - mor - tal,

God has brought his Is - ra - el In - to joy from sad - ness;
And from three days' sleep in death As a sun has ris - en;
With the roy - al feast of feasts, Comes its joy to ren - der;
Nor the watch - ers, nor the seal Hold him as a mor - tal;
Who, tri - um - phant, burst the bars Of the tomb's dark por - tal;

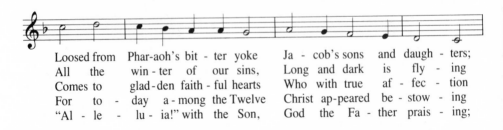

Loosed from Phar-aoh's bit - ter yoke Ja - cob's sons and daugh - ters;
All the win - ter of our sins, Long and dark is fly - ing
Comes to glad-den faith - ful hearts Who with true af - fec - tion
For to - day a - mong the Twelve Christ ap-peared be - stow - ing
"Al - le - lu - ia!" with the Son, God the Fa - ther prais - ing;

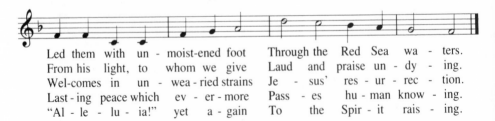

Led them with un - moist-ened foot Through the Red Sea wa - ters.
From his light, to whom we give Laud and praise un - dy - ing.
Wel-comes in un - wea - ried strains Je - sus' res - ur - rec - tion.
Last - ing peace which ev - er - more Pass - es hu - man know - ing.
"Al - le - lu - ia!" yet a - gain To the Spir - it rais - ing.

Text: Ex. 15; Ἄσωμεν πάντες λαοί; John of Damascus, c.675-c.749; Tr. by John M. Neale, 1818-1866, alt.
Tune: GAUDEAMUS PARITER, 7 6 7 6 D; Johann Horn, c.1495-1547

That Easter Day with Joy Was Bright   457

1. That East - er day with joy was bright,
2. His ris - en flesh with ra - diance glowed;
3. O Je - sus, King of gen - tle - ness,
4. O Lord of all, with us a - bide
5. All praise, to you, O ris - en Lord,

The sun shone out with fair - er light,
His wound - ed hands and feet he showed;
Who with your grace our hearts pos - sess
In this our joy - ful East - er - tide;
Now both by heaven and earth a - dored;

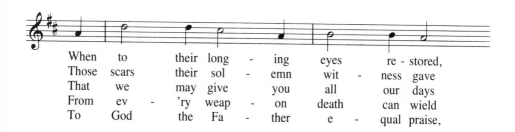

When to their long - ing eyes re - stored,
Those scars their sol - emn wit - ness gave
That we may give you all our days
From ev - 'ry weap - on death can wield
To God the Fa - ther e - qual praise,

The a - pos - tles saw their ris - en Lord.
That Christ was ris - en from the grave.
The will - ing trib - ute of our praise.
Your own re - deemed for ev - er shield.
And Spir - it blest, our songs we raise.

Text: *Claro paschali gaudio;* Latin 5th C.; Tr. by John M. Neale, 1818-1866, alt.
Tune: PUER NOBIS, LM; Adapt. by Michael Praetorius, 1571-1621

458　This Is the Feast of Victory

This is the feast of vic-to-ry for our

God. Al-le-lu - ia, al-le-lu - ia, al-

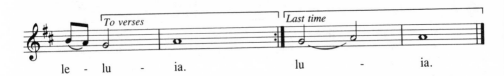

To verses　*Last time*

le-lu - ia.　lu - ia.

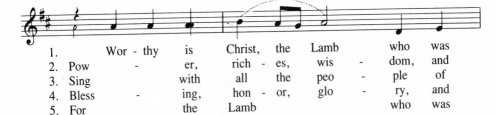

1.	Wor - thy	is	Christ,	the	Lamb		who	was
2.	Pow -	er,	rich -	es,	wis	-	dom,	and
3.	Sing		with	all	the	peo	-	ple	of
4.	Bless -	ing,	hon -	or,	glo	-	ry,	and
5.	For		the	Lamb				who	was

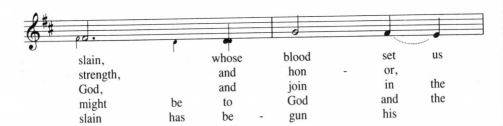

slain,		whose	blood	set	us
strength,		and	hon	-	or,
God,		and	join	in	the
might	be	to	God	and	the
slain	has	be -	gun	his	

D.C.

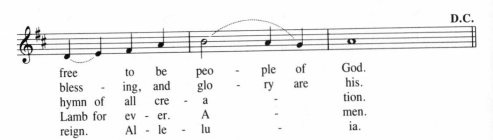

free	to	be	peo	-	ple	of	God.
bless -	ing,	and	glo	-	ry	are	his.
hymn of	all	cre	-	a	-		tion.
Lamb for	ev -	er.	A	-			men.
reign.	Al -	le -	lu	-			ia.

Text: Based on Revelations 5, © 1978, *Lutheran Book of Worship*
Tune: FESTIVAL CANTICLE, Irregular; Richard Hillert, b.1923. © 1975, Richard Hillert, Harm: © 1978, *Lutheran Book of Worship*

At the Lamb's High Feast We Sing 459

1. At the Lamb's high feast we sing Praise to our vic - to-rious King.
2. Where the Pas - chal blood is poured, Death's dark an - gel sheathes his sword;
3. Might-y vic - tim from the sky, Hell's fierce powers be - neath you lie;
4. East-er tri - umph, East - er joy, This a - lone can sin de-stroy;

Who has washed us in the tide Flow-ing from his pierc-ed side;
Is - rael's hosts tri - umph - ant go Through the wave that drowns the foe.
You have con-quered in the fight, You have brought us life and light:
From sin's power, Lord, set us free New-born souls in you to be.

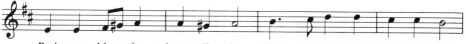

Praise we him, whose love di - vine Gives his sa - cred Blood for wine,
Praise we Christ, whose blood was shed, Pas - chal vic - tim, Pas-chal bread;
Now no more can death ap - pall, Now no more the grave en-thrall;
Fa - ther, who the crown shall give, Sa - vior, by whose death we live,

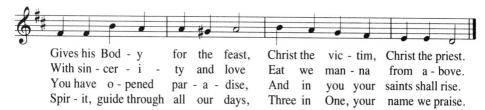

Gives his Bod - y for the feast, Christ the vic - tim, Christ the priest.
With sin - cer - i - ty and love Eat we man - na from a - bove.
You have o - pened par - a - dise, And in you your saints shall rise.
Spir - it, guide through all our days, Three in One, your name we praise.

Text: *Ad regias agni dapes;* Latin, 4th C.; Tr. by Robert Campbell, 1814-1868, alt.
Tune: SALZBURG, 77 77 D; Jakob Hintze, 1622-1702; Harm. by J.S. Bach, 1685-1750

460 At the Lamb's High Feast We Sing

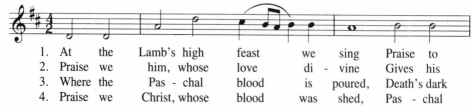

1. At the Lamb's high feast we sing Praise to
2. Praise we him, whose love di - vine Gives his
3. Where the Pas - chal blood is poured, Death's dark
4. Praise we Christ, whose blood was shed, Pas - chal

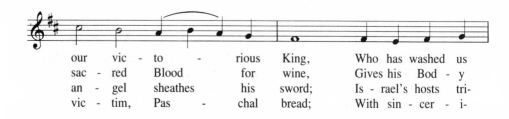

our vic - to - rious King, Who has washed us
sac - red Blood for wine, Gives his Bod - y
an - gel sheathes his sword; Is - rael's hosts tri-
vic - tim, Pas - chal bread; With sin - cer - i-

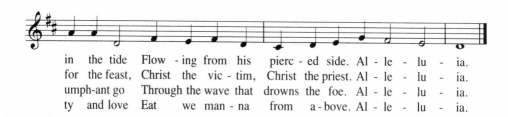

in the tide Flow - ing from his pierc - ed side. Al - le - lu - ia.
for the feast, Christ the vic - tim, Christ the priest. Al - le - lu - ia.
umph-ant go Through the wave that drowns the foe. Al - le - lu - ia.
ty and love Eat we man - na from a - bove. Al - le - lu - ia.

5. Mighty victim from the sky,
   Hell's fierce pow'rs beneath you lie;
   You have conquered in the fight,
   You have brought us life and light.
   Alleluia.

6. Now no more can death appall,
   Now no more the grave enthrall;
   You have opened paradise,
   And in you your saints shall rise.
   Alleluia.

7. Easter triumph, Easter joy,
   This alone can sin destroy;
   From sin's pow'r Lord, set us free
   Newborn souls in you to be.
   Alleluia.

8. Father, who the crown shall give,
   Savior, by whose death we live,
   Spirit, guide through all our days,
   Three in One, your name we praise.
   Alleluia.

Text: *Ad regias agni dapes*; Latin, 4th C.; Tr. by Robert Campbell, 1814-1868, alt.
Tune: SONNE DER GERECHTIGKEIT, 77 77 with alleluias; Bohemian Brethren's *Kirchengesange*, 1566

Christ the Lord Is Risen Today   461

1. Christ the Lord is ris'n to - day; Chris-tians, haste your vows to pay;
2. Christ, the vic - tim un - de - filed, God and sin - ners rec - on-ciled;
3. Hal-lowed, cho - sen dawn of praise, East - er, queen of all our days:
4. Christ, who once for sin - ners bled, Now the first - born from the dead,

Make your joy and prais - es known At the Pas - chal Vic-tim's throne;
When in fierce and blood - y strife Met to - geth - er death and life;
Zi - on's chil - dren now come forth; East to west and south to north.
Throned in end - less might and pow'r, Lives and reigns for ev - er - more.

For the sheep the Lamb has bled, Sin - less in the sin-ner's stead.
Chris-tians, on this hap - py day Raise your hearts with joy and say:
Let the peo - ple praise you, Lord, Be, by all that is, a - dored:
Hymns of glo - ry, songs of praise, Fa - ther, un - to you we raise:

Christ the Lord is ris'n on high; Now he lives, no more to die.
Christ the Lord is ris'n on high; Now he lives, no more to die.
Let the na - tions shout and sing; Glo - ry to their Pas - chal King.
Ris - en Lord, we now a-dore, With the Spir - it ev - er - more.

Text: *Victimae paschali laudes;* Ascr. to Wipo of Burgundy, d.1048; Tr. by Jane E. Leeson, 1809-1881, alt.
Tune: VICTIMAE PASCHALI, 77 77 D; Würth's *Katholisches Gesangbuch,* 1859; Revised in *Catholic Youth's Hymn Book,* 1871

462 Christ the Lord Is Risen Today

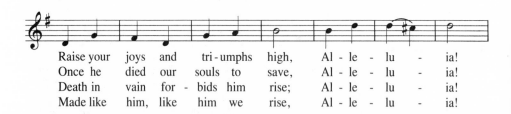

1. Christ the Lord is ris'n to - day, Al - le - lu - ia!
2. Lives a - gain our glo - rious King; Al - le - lu - ia!
3. Love's re - deem - ing work is done, Al - le - lu - ia!
4. Soar we now where Christ has led, Al - le - lu - ia!

All on earth with an - gels say. Al - le - lu - ia!
Where, O death, is now your sting? Al - le - lu - ia!
Fought the fight, the bat - tle won. Al - le - lu - ia!
Fol - l'wing our ex - alt - ed Head; Al - le - lu - ia!

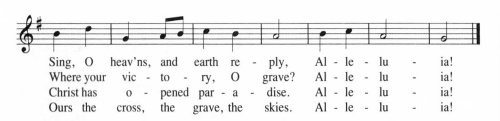

Raise your joys and tri - umphs high, Al - le - lu - ia!
Once he died our souls to save, Al - le - lu - ia!
Death in vain for - bids him rise; Al - le - lu - ia!
Made like him, like him we rise, Al - le - lu - ia!

Sing, O heav'ns, and earth re - ply, Al - le - lu - ia!
Where your vic - to - ry, O grave? Al - le - lu - ia!
Christ has o - pened par - a - dise. Al - le - lu - ia!
Ours the cross, the grave, the skies. Al - le - lu - ia!

Text: Charles Wesley, 1707-1788
Tune: GWALCHMAI, 77 77 with alleluias; Joseph D. Jones, 1827-1870

Christ the Lord Is Risen Today 463

1. Christ the Lord   is   ris'n to - day,   Al - le - lu - ia!
2. Lives a - gain our   glo - rious King; Al - le - lu - ia!
3. Love's re - deem - ing   work is   done,   Al - le - lu - ia!
4. Soar we now where Christ has led,   Al - le - lu - ia!

All   on earth with   an - gels say,   Al - le - lu - ia!
Where, O death, is   now   your sting?   Al - le - lu - ia!
Fought the fight, the   bat - tle   won.   Al - le - lu - ia!
Fol - l'wing our   ex - alt - ed   head;   Al - le - lu - ia!

Raise your joys and   tri - umphs high,   Al - le - lu - ia!
Once he died our   souls to   save,   Al - le - lu - ia!
Death in vain for - bids him   rise;   Al - le - lu - ia!
Made like him, like   him   we   rise,   Al - le - lu - ia!

Sing, O heav'ns, and   earth re - ply,   Al - le - lu - ia!
Where your vic - to - ry,   O grave?   Al - le - lu - ia!
Christ has   o - pened par - a - dise.   Al - le - lu - ia!
Ours the cross, the   grave, the skies. Al - le - lu - ia!

Text: Charles Wesley, 1707-1788
Tune: LLANFAIR, 7/ 77 with alleluias; Robert Williams, 1781-1821

464 The Head That Once Was Crowned with Thorns

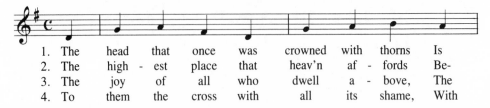

1. The head that once was crowned with thorns Is
2. The high - est place that heav'n af - fords Be -
3. The joy of all who dwell a - bove, The
4. To them the cross with all its shame, With

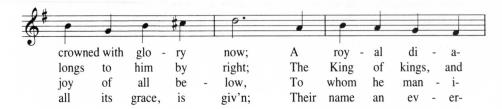

crowned with glo - ry now; A roy - al di - a-
longs to him by right; The King of kings, and
joy of all be - low, To whom he man - i-
all its grace, is giv'n; Their name an ev - er-

dem a - dorns The might - y vic - tor's brow.
Lord of lords, And heav'n's e - ter - nal light.
fests his love, And grants his name to know.
last - ing name; Their joy the joy of heav'n.

5. They suffer with their Lord below;
They reign with him above;
Their profit and their joy to know
The myst'ry of his love.

6. The cross he bore is life and health,
Though shame and death to him,
His people's hope, his people's wealth,
Their everlasting theme.

Text: Heb. 2:9-10; Thomas Kelly, 1769-1855
Tune: ST. MAGNUS, CM; Jeremiah Clarke, 1670-1707

465 Christus Resurrexit

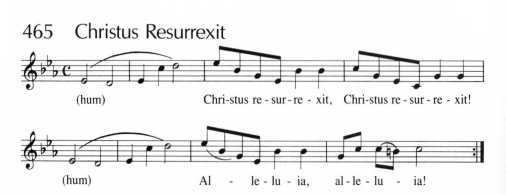

(hum) Chri-stus re - sur-re - xit, Chri-stus re - sur-re - xit!

(hum) Al - le-lu - ia, al-le-lu - ia!

Text: *Christ is risen;* Psalm 118: 1,5,6,19,21,24; Tr. composite; Taizé Community, 1982
Tune: Jacques Berthier, b.1923
© 1984, Les Presses de Taizé

Christ Is Alive! 466

1. Christ is a - live! Let Chris - tians sing.
2. Christ is a - live! No long - er bound
3. Not throned a - bove, re - mote - ly high,
4. In ev - 'ry in - sult, rift, and war
5. Christ is a - live! His Spir - it burns

His cross stands emp - ty to the sky.
To dis - tant years in Pal - es - tine,
Un - touched, un - moved by hu - man pains,
Where col - or, scorn or wealth di - vide,
Through this and ev - 'ry fu - ture age,

Let streets and homes with prais - es ring.
He comes to claim the here and now
But dai - ly, in the midst of life,
He suf - fers still, yet loves the more,
Till all cre - a - tion lives and learns

His love in death shall nev - er die.
And con - quer ev - 'ry place and time.
Our Sav - ior with the Fa - ther reigns.
And lives, though ev - er cru - ci - fied.
His joy, his jus - tice, love and praise.

Text: Rom. 6:5-11; Brian Wren, b.1936, © 1975, Hope Publishing Co.
Tune: TRURO, LM; Williams' *Psalmodia Evangelica*, 1789

467 Sing with All the Saints in Glory

1. Sing with all the saints in glo - ry, Sing the res - ur-
2. O what glo - ry, far ex - ceed - ing All that eye has
3. Life e - ter - nal! heav'n re - joic - es: Je - sus lives who
4. Life e - ter - nal! O what won - ders Crowd on faith; what

rec - tion song! Death and sor - row, earth's dark sto - ry,
yet per-ceived! Ho - liest hearts for a - ges plead - ing,
once was dead; Shout with joy, O death - less voic - es!
joy un-known, When, a - midst earth's clos - ing thun - ders,

To the for - mer days be - long. All a - round the
Nev - er that full joy con-ceived. God has prom - ised,
Child of God, lift up your head! Pa - tri - archs from
Saints shall stand be - fore the throne! O to en - ter

clouds are break - ing, Soon the storms of time shall cease;
Christ pre - pares it, There on high our wel - come waits;
dis - tant a - ges, Saints all long - ing for their heaven,
that bright por - tal, See that glow - ing fir - ma - ment,

In God's like - ness, we a - wak - en, Know-ing ev - er - last-ing peace.
Ev - 'ry hum - ble spir - it shares it, Christ has passed the e - ter - nal gates.
Proph-ets, psalm-ists, seers, and sag - es, All a - wait the glo - ry giv'n.
Know, with you, O God im - mor - tal, "Je - sus Christ whom you have sent!"

Text: 1 Cor. 15:20; William J. Irons, 1812-1883, alt.
Tune: HYMN TO JOY, 8 7 8 7 D; Arr. from Ludwig van Beethoven, 1770-1827, by Edward Hodges, 1796-1867

Look, O Look, the Sight Is Glorious 468

1. Look, O look, the sight is glo - rious, See the
2. Crown the Sav - ior! An - gels crown him! Rich the
3. Sin - ners in de - ri - sion crowned him, Mock - ing
4. Hark! those bursts of ac - cla - ma - tion! Hark! those

man of sor - rows now; From the fight re - turned vic-
tro - phies Je - sus brings; On the seat of pow'r en-
thus the Sav - ior's claim; Saints and an - gels crowd a-
loud tri - um - phant chords! Je - sus takes the high - est

to - rious, Ev - 'ry knee to him shall bow.
throne him While the vault of heav - en rings.
round him, Own his ti - tle, praise his name.
sta - tion; Oh, what joy the sight af - fords!

Crown him, crown him! Crown him, crown him! Crown him,
Crown him, crown him! Crown him, crown him! Crown him,
Crown him, crown him! Crown him, crown him! Crown him,
Crown him, crown him! Crown him, crown him! Crown him,

rit.

Crown him! Crowns be - come the vic - tor's
Crown him! Crown the Sav - ior, King of
Crown him! Spread a - broad the vic - tor's
Crown him! King of kings and Lord of

a tempo

brow. Crowns be - come the vic - tor's brow.
kings. Crown the Sav - ior, King of kings.
fame! Spread a - broad the vic - tor's fame!
lords! King of kings and Lord of lords!

Text: Rev. 7:9-15; Thomas Kelly, 1769-1855, alt.
Tune: BRYN CALFARIA, 8 7 8 7 444 77; William Owen, 1814-1893

469 A Hymn of Glory Let Us Sing

1. A hymn of glo-ry let us sing! New
2. The ho-ly ap-os-tol-ic band Up-
3. To whom the shin-ing an-gels cry, "Why
4. O ris-en Christ, as-cend-ed Lord, All

hymns through-out the world shall ring: Al - leon the Mount of Ol - ives stand. Al - le-
stand and gaze up - on the sky?" Al - le-
praise to you let earth ac - cord: Al - le-

[⌒]

lu - ia! Al - le - lu - ia! Christ, by a road be - fore un-
lu - ia! Al - le - lu - ia! And with his faith - ful fol-l'wers
lu - ia! Al - le - lu - ia! "This is the Sav - ior!" Thus they
lu - ia! Al - le - lu - ia! You are, while end - less a - ges

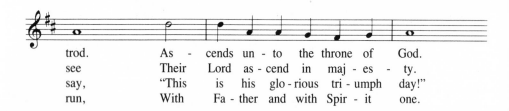

trod. As - cends un - to the throne of God.
see Their Lord as - cend in maj - es - ty.
say, "This is his glo - rious tri - umph day!"
run, With Fa - ther and with Spir - it one.

Al - le - lu - ia! Al - le - lu - ia! Al - le - lu - ia,

Al - le - lu - ia, Al - le - lu - ia!

Text: *Hymnum canamus gloria;* Venerable Bede, 673-735; Tr. *Lutheran Book of Worship,* 1978
Tune: LASST UNS ERFREUEN, LM; with alleluias; *Geistliche Kirchengesange,* Cologne, 1623; Harm. by Ralph Vaughan Williams, 1872-1958, © Oxford University Press

Lord, You Give the Great Commission 470

1. Lord, you give the great com - mis-sion: "Heal the
2. Lord, you call us to your ser - vice: "In my
3. Lord, you make the com - mon ho - ly: "This my
4. Lord, you show us love's true meas-ure: "Fa - ther,
5. Lord, you bless with words as - sur - ing: "I am

sick and preach the word." Lest the Church ne-
name bap - tize and teach." That the world may
bod - y, this my blood." Let us all, for
what they do, for - give." Yet we hoard as
with you to the end." Faith and hope and

glect its mis-sion, And the Gos - pel go un-
trust your pro-mise, Life a - bun - dant meant for
earth's true glo - ry, Dai - ly lift life heav - en-
pri - vate treas-ure, All that you so free - ly
love re - stor-ing, May we serve as you in-

heard, Help us wit - ness to your pur - pose
each, Give us all new fer - vor, draw us
ward, Ask - ing that the world a - round us
give. May your care and mer - cy lead us
tend, And, a - mid the cares that claim us,

With re - newed in - teg - ri - ty;
Clos - er in com - mun - i - ty;
Share your chil - dren's lib - er - ty;
To a just so - ci - e - ty;
Hold in mind e - ter - ni - ty;
With the

Spir - it's gifts em - power us For the work of min - is - try.

Text: Jeffrey Rowthorn, b.1934, © 1978
Tune: ABBOT'S LEIGH, 8 7 8 7 D; Cyril V. Taylor, b.1907, © 1942, 1970, Hope Publishing Co.

471 Hail the Day That Sees Him Rise

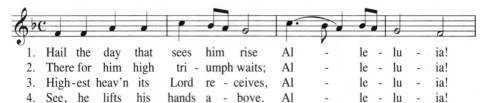

1. Hail the day that sees him rise   Al - le - lu - ia!
2. There for him high tri - umph waits;   Al - le - lu - ia!
3. High-est heav'n its Lord re - ceives,   Al - le - lu - ia!
4. See, he lifts his hands a - bove.   Al - le - lu - ia!

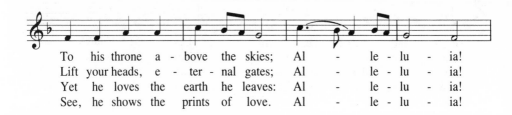

To his throne a - bove the skies;   Al - le - lu - ia!
Lift your heads, e - ter - nal gates;   Al - le - lu - ia!
Yet he loves the earth he leaves: Al - le - lu - ia!
See, he shows the prints of love.   Al - le - lu - ia!

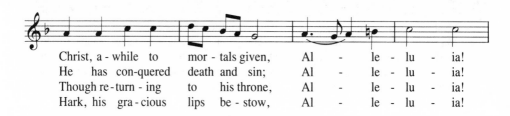

Christ, a - while to mor - tals given,   Al - le - lu - ia!
He has con-quered death and sin;   Al - le - lu - ia!
Though re - turn - ing to his throne,   Al - le - lu - ia!
Hark, his gra - cious lips be - stow,   Al - le - lu - ia!

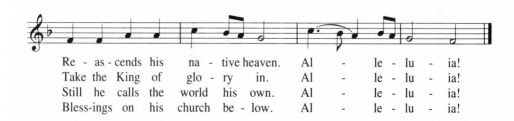

Re - as - cends his na - tive heaven.   Al - le - lu - ia!
Take the King of glo - ry in.   Al - le - lu - ia!
Still he calls the world his own.   Al - le - lu - ia!
Bless-ings on his church be - low.   Al - le - lu - ia!

5. Still for us he intercedes, Alleluia!
His prevailing death he pleads, Alleluia!
Near himself prepares our place, Alleluia!
He the first fruits of our race. Alleluia!

6. There we shall with him remain, Alleluia!
Partners of his endless reign; Alleluia!
There his face unclouded see, Alleluia!
Live with him eternally. Alleluia!

Text: Charles Wesley, 1707-1788, alt.
Tune: LLANFAIR, 77 77 with alleluias; Robert Williams, 1781-1821

Come Down, O Love Divine 472

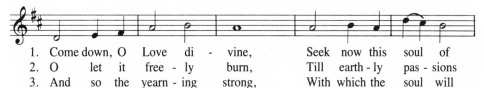

1. Come down, O Love di - vine,   Seek now this soul of
2. O   let it free - ly burn,   Till earth - ly pas - sions
3. And   so the yearn - ing strong,   With which the soul will

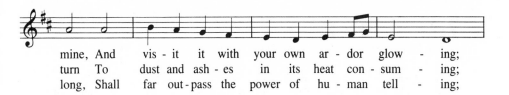

mine, And vis - it it with your own ar - dor glow - ing;
turn To   dust and ash - es in its heat con - sum - ing;
long, Shall far out - pass the power of hu - man tell - ing;

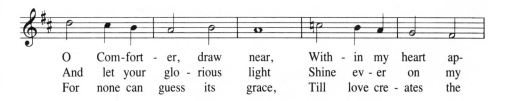

O   Com - fort - er, draw near,   With - in my heart ap -
And let your glo - rious light   Shine ev - er on   my
For none can guess its grace,   Till love cre - ates the

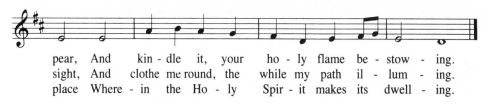

pear, And kin - dle it, your ho - ly flame be - stow - ing.
sight, And clothe me round, the while my path il - lum - ing.
place Where - in the Ho - ly Spir - it makes its dwell - ing.

Text: *Discendi, Amor Santo*; Bianco da Siena, d. c.1434; Tr. by Richard F. Littledale, 1833-1890
Tune: DOWN AMPNEY, 66 11 D; Ralph Vaughan Williams, 1872-1958, © Oxford University Press

Veni Sancte Spiritus 473

Ve - ni San - cte Spi - ri - tus.

Text: *Come Holy Spirit*; Verses drawn from the Pentecost Sequence; Taizé Community, 1978
Tune: Jacques Berthier, b.1923
© 1979, Les Presses de Taizé

474 Fire of God, Undying Flame

1. Fire of God, un - dy - ing flame,
2. Breath of God, that swept in power
3. Strength of God, your might with - in
4. Truth of God, your pierc - ing rays
5. Love of God, your grace pro - found

Spir - it who in splen - dor came, Let your heat my
In the Pen - te - cos - tal hour, Ho - ly breath, be
Con - quers sor - row, pain and sin; For - ti - fy from
Pen - e - trate my se - cret ways, May the light that
Knows not ei - ther age or bound; Come, my heart's own

soul re - fine, Till it glows with love di - vine.
now in me Source of vi - tal en - er - gy.
e - vil art All the gate - ways of my heart.
shames my sin Guide me ho - lier paths to win.
guest to be, Dwell for ev - er - more in me.

Text: Albert F. Bayly, 1901-1984, alt. © Oxford University Press
Tune: NUN KOMM DER HEIDEN HEILAND, 77 77; *Geystliche Gesank Buchleyn*, Wittenberg, 1524; Harm. by Melchior Vulpius, c.1560-1616

475 O Holy Spirit, by Whose Breath

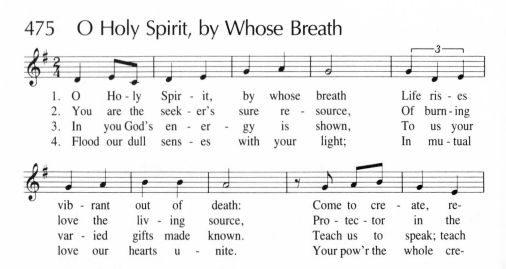

1. O Ho - ly Spir - it, by whose breath Life ris - es
2. You are the seek - er's sure re - source, Of burn - ing
3. In you God's en - er - gy is shown, To us your
4. Flood our dull sens - es with your light; In mu - tual

vib - rant out of death: Come to cre - ate, re-
love the liv - ing source, Pro - tec - tor in the
var - ied gifts made known. Teach us to speak; teach
love our hearts u - nite. Your pow'r the whole cre-

new, in	-	spire;	Come, kin-dle	in	our	hearts your	fire.
midst of		strife,	The giv-er	and	the	Lord of	life.
us	to	hear;	Yours is the	tongue and		yours the	ear.
a	-	tion fills;	Con-firm our	weak un	-	cer-tain	wills.

5. From inner strife grant us release;
   Turn nations to the ways of peace.
   To fuller life your people bring
   That as one body we may sing:

6. Praise to the Father, Christ his Word,
   And to the Spirit, God the Lord;
   To whom all honor, glory be
   Both now and for eternity.

Text: *Veni, Creator Spiritus;* Attr. to Rabanus Maurus, 776-865; Tr. by John W. Grant, b.1919, © 1971
Tune: VENI CREATOR SPIRITUS, LM; Mode VIII; Setting by Richard J. Wojcik, b.1923, © 1975, GIA Publications, Inc.

Spirit Divine, Accept Our Prayers 476

1. Spir - it di - vine,	ac - cept our prayers,	And make this
2. Come as the light;	to us re - veal	Our emp - ti-
3. Come as the fire,	and purge our hearts	Like sac - ri-
4. Come as the dove,	and spread your wings,	The wings of
5. Spir - it di - vine,	ac - cept our prayers;	Make a lost

house your home;	De - scend with all your
ness and woe,	And lead us in those
fi - cial flame;	Let our whole soul an
peace - ful love;	And let your Church on
world your home;	De - scend with all your

gra-cious powers,	O come, great Spir - it, come!
paths of life	Where all the right - eous go.
of - f'ring be	To our Re - deem - er's Name.
earth be - come	Blest as the Church a - bove.
gra-cious powers;	O come, great Spir - it, come!

Text: Andrew Reed, 1788-1862, alt.
Tune: GRAEFENBERG, CM; Johann Crüger, 1598-1662

477 Praise the Spirit in Creation

1. Praise the
2. Praise the
3. Praise the
4. Tell of
5. Pray we

Spir - it	in	cre - a - tion,	Breath of	God,	life's or - i-
Spir - it,	close com - pan - ion	Of	our	in -	most thoughts and
Spir - it,	who en - light - ened	Priests and	pro -	phets with	the
how the as - cend - ed	Je - sus	Armed a	peo -	ple for	his
then, O	Lord the	Spir - it,	On our	lives	de - scend in

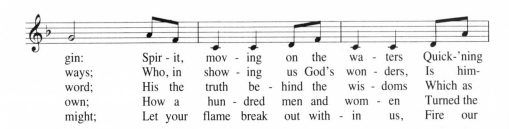

gin:	Spir - it,	mov - ing	on the	wa - ters	Quick-'ning
ways;	Who, in	show - ing	us God's	won - ders,	Is him-
word;	His the	truth be - hind the	wis - doms	Which as
own;	How a	hun - dred	men and	wom - en	Turned the
might;	Let your	flame break	out with - in	us,	Fire our

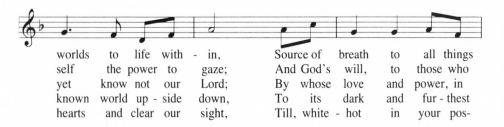

worlds	to	life with - in,	Source of	breath to	all things
self	the power to	gaze;	And God's	will, to	those who
yet	know not our	Lord;	By whose	love and	power, in
known	world up - side down,	To its	dark and	fur - thest
hearts	and clear our	sight,	Till, white - hot	in	your pos-

breath-ing,	Life in whom	all lives be - gin.
lis - ten,	By a still	small voice con - veys.
Je - sus	God him - self	was seen and heard.
cor - ners	By the wind	of heav - en blown.
ses - sion,	We, too, set	the world a - light.

Text: Michael Hewlett, b.1916, alt., © 1975, Oxford University Press
Tune: JULION, 8 7 8 7 8 7 ; David Hurd, b.1950, © 1983, GIA Publications, Inc.

Fire of God, Titanic Spirit 478

1. Fire of God, ti-tan-ic- Spir - it, Burn with-
2. Wind of God, dy-nam-ic Spir - it, Breathe up-
3. Voice of God, pro-phet-ic Spir - it, Speak to

in our hearts to - day; Cleanse our sin — may we ex-
on our hearts to - day; That we may your power in-
ev - 'ry heart to - day To en-cour-age or pro-

hib - it Ho - li - ness in ev - 'ry way:
her - it Hear us, Spir - it, as we pray:
hib - it, Urg-ing ac - tion or de - lay:

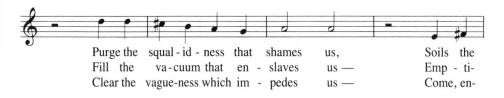

Purge the squal-id-ness that shames us, Soils the
Fill the va-cuum that en - slaves us — Emp-ti-
Clear the vague-ness which im - pedes us — Come, en-

bod - y, taints the soul; And, through Je - sus Christ who
ness of heart and soul; And, through Je - sus Christ who
light-en mind and soul; And, through Je - sus Christ who

claims us, Pu - ri - fy us, make us whole.
saves us, Give us life and make us whole.
leads us, Teach the truth that makes us whole.

Text: Michael Saward, b.1932
Tune: FIRE OF GOD, 8 7 8 7 D; David G. Wilson, b.1940
© 1969, Hope Publishing Co.

479 Veni Creator Spiritus

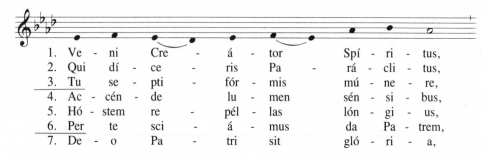

1. Ve - ni Cre - á - tor Spí - ri - tus,
2. Qui dí - ce - ris Pa - rá - cli - tus,
3. Tu se - pti - fór - mis mú - ne - re,
4. Ac - cén - de lu - men sén - si - bus,
5. Hó - stem re - pél - las lón - gi - us,
6. Per te sci - á - mus da Pa - trem,
7. De - o Pa - tri sit gló - ri - a,

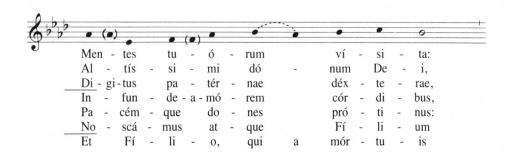

Men - tes tu - ó - rum ví - si - ta:
Al - tís - si - mi dó - num De - i,
Di - gi - tus pa - tér - nae déx - te - rae,
In - fun - de - a - mó - rem cór - di - bus,
Pa - cém - que do - nes pró - ti - nus:
No - scá - mus at - que Fí - li - um
Et Fí - li - o, qui a mór - tu - is

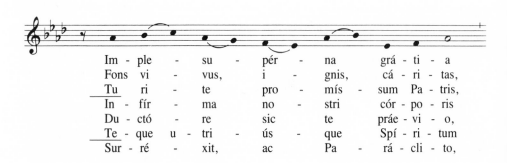

Im - ple - su - pér - na grá - ti - a
Fons vi - vus, i - gnis, cá - ri - tas,
Tu ri - te pro - mís - sum Pa - tris,
In - fír - ma no - stri cór - po - ris
Du - ctó - re sic te práe - vi - o,
Te - que u - tri - ús - que Spí - ri - tum
Sur - ré - xit, ac Pa - rá - cli - to,

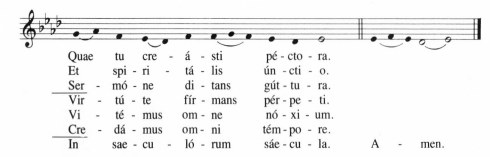

Quae tu cre - á - sti pé - cto - ra.
Et spi - ri - tá - lis ún - cti - o.
Ser - mó - ne di - tans gút - tu - ra.
Vir - tú - te fír - mans pér - pe - ti.
Vi - té - mus om - ne nó - xi - um.
Cre - dá - mus om - ni tém - po - re.
In sae - cu - ló - rum sáe - cu - la. A - men.

Text: Attr. to Rabanus Maurus, 776-856
Tune: VENI CREATOR SPIRITUS, LM; Mode VIII; Acc. by Richard Proulx, b.1937, © 1975, GIA Publications, Inc.

Spirit of God within Me 480

1. Spir - it of God with - in me, Pos-
2. Spir - it of truth with - in me, Pos-
3. Spir - it of love with - in me, Pos-
4. Spir - it of life with - in me, Pos-

sess my hu - man frame; Fan the dull em - bers of my
sess my thought and mind; Light - en a - new the in - ward
sess my hands and heart; Break through the bonds of self - con-
sess this life of mine; Come as the wind of heav - en's

heart, Stir up the liv - ing flame:
eye By Sa - tan ren - dered blind:
cern That seeks to stand a - part:
breath, Come as the fire di - vine!

Strive till that im - age A - dam lost, New
Shine on the words that wis - dom speaks And
Grant me the love that suf - fers long, That
Spir - it of Christ, the liv - ing Lord, Reign

mint - ed and re - stored, In shin - ing splen - dor
grant me pow'r to see The truth made known to
hopes, be - lieves and bears; The love ful - filled in
in this house of clay, Till from its dust with

bright - ly bears The like - ness of the Lord.
all in Christ, And in that truth be free.
sac - ri - fice, That cares as Je - sus cares.
Christ I rise To ev - er - last - ing day.

Text: Timothy Dudley-Smith, b.1926, © 1968, Hope Publishing Co.
Tune: ESCAMBIA, 7 6 8 6 8 6 8 6; Randolph Currie, b.1943, © 1986 GIA Publications, Inc.

481 When God the Spirit Came

1. When God the Spir - it came Up - on his church out-
2. What cour - age, pow'r and grace That youth - ful church dis-
3. They saw God's Word pre - vail, His king - dom still in-
4. Their theme was Christ a - lone, The Lord who lived and
5. So to this pre - sent hour Our task is still the

poured In sound of wind and sign of flame They
played! To those of ev - 'ry tribe and race They
crease, No part of all his pur - pose fail, No
died, Who rose to his e - ter - nal throne At
same, In pen - te - cost - al love and pow'r His

spread his truth a - broad, And filled with the
wit - nessed un - a - fraid, And filled with the
prom-ised bless - ing cease, And filled with the
God the Fa - ther's side; And filled with the
gos - pel to pro - claim, And filled with the

Spir - it Pro - claimed that Christ is Lord.
Spir - it They broke their bread and prayed.
Spir - it Knew love and joy and peace.
Spir - it The church was mul - ti - plied.
Spir - it, Re - joice in Je - sus' Name.

Text: Acts 2; Timothy Dudley-Smith, b.1926, © 1984, Hope Publishing Co.
Tune: VINEYARD HAVEN, 6 6 8 6 6 6; Richard Dirksen, b.1921, © 1974, 1986, Harold Flammer, Inc.

482 Come, Holy Ghost

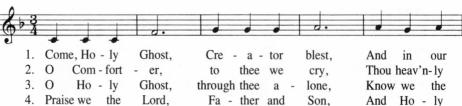

1. Come, Ho - ly Ghost, Cre - a - tor blest, And in our
2. O Com - fort - er, to thee we cry, Thou heav'n-ly
3. O Ho - ly Ghost, through thee a - lone, Know we the
4. Praise we the Lord, Fa - ther and Son, And Ho - ly

hearts take up thy rest; Come with thy grace
gift of God most high; Thou fount of life,
Fa - ther and the Son; Be this our firm
Spir - it with them one; And may the Son

and heav'n - ly aid To fill the hearts which thou hast
and fire of love, And sweet a - noint - ing from a-
un - chang-ing creed, That thou dost from them both pro-
on us be - stow All gifts that from the Spir - it

made, To fill the hearts which thou hast made.
bove, And sweet a - noint - ing from a - bove.
ceed, That thou dost from them both pro - ceed.
flow, All gifts that from the Spir - it flow.

Text: *Veni, Creator Spiritus;* Attr. to Rabanus Maurus, 776-856; Tr. by Edward Caswall, 1814-1878, alt.
Tune: LAMBILLOTTE, LM; with repeat; Louis Lambillotte, SJ, 1796-1855; Harm. by Richard Proulx, b.1937, © 1986, GIA Publications, Inc.

Over the Chaos of the Empty Waters 483

1. O - ver the cha - os of the emp - ty wa - ters Hov - ered the
2. By the same Spir - it we, re - gen - er - at - ed In - to the
3. By the same Spir - it we are called to wor - ship God who cre-

Spir - it, bring-ing forth cre - a - tion; So from the emp - ty
bod - y of our ris - en Sav - ior, Seek through the pow - er
ates, re - deems, and sanc - ti - fies us, Of whom the glo - ry,

tomb the Se - cond Ad - am Is - sued tri - um - phant.
of the new cre - a - tion Life ev - er - last - ing.
in both earth and heav - en, Is man - i - fest - ed.

Text: St. 1, 2, *A Monastic Breviary,* 1976, alt.; © Order of the Holy Cross; St. 3, *The Hymnal 1982*
Tune: BICKFORD, 11 11 11 5; Hank Beebe, b.1926, © 1983

484 O God, Almighty Father

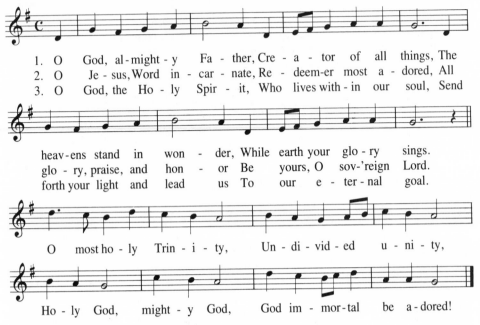

1. O God, al-might-y Fa-ther, Cre-a-tor of all things, The
2. O Je-sus, Word in-car-nate, Re-deem-er most a-dored, All
3. O God, the Ho-ly Spir-it, Who lives with-in our soul, Send

heav-ens stand in won - der, While earth your glo-ry sings.
glo - ry, praise, and hon - or Be yours, O sov-'reign Lord.
forth your light and lead us To our e - ter-nal goal.

O most ho-ly Trin - i - ty, Un - di - vid - ed u - ni - ty,

Ho - ly God, might - y God, God im - mor-tal be a-dored!

Text: *Gott Vater sei gepriesen;* Anon; Tr. by Irvin Udulutsch, OFM Cap., fl.1959, alt. © 1959, The Liturgical Press
Tune: GOTT VATER SEI GEPRIESEN, 76 76 with refrain; *Limburg Gesangbuch,* 1838; Harm. by Healey Willan, 1880-1968, © 1958, Ralph Jusko Publications, Inc.

485 Holy, Holy, Holy! Lord God Almighty

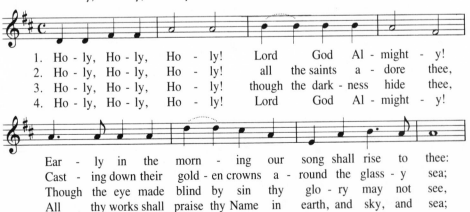

1. Ho - ly, Ho - ly, Ho - ly! Lord God Al - might - y!
2. Ho - ly, Ho - ly, Ho - ly! all the saints a - dore thee,
3. Ho - ly, Ho - ly, Ho - ly! though the dark - ness hide thee,
4. Ho - ly, Ho - ly, Ho - ly! Lord God Al - might - y!

Ear - ly in the morn - ing our song shall rise to thee:
Cast - ing down their gold - en crowns a - round the glass - y sea;
Though the eye made blind by sin thy glo - ry may not see,
All thy works shall praise thy Name in earth, and sky, and sea;

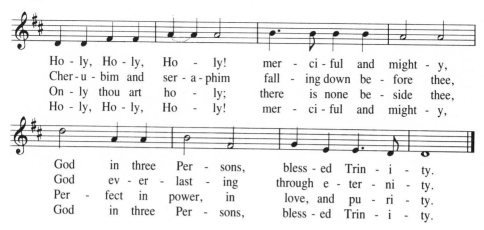

Ho - ly, Ho - ly, Ho - ly! mer - ci - ful and might - y,
Cher - u - bim and ser - a - phim fall - ing down be - fore thee,
On - ly thou art ho - ly; there is none be - side thee,
Ho - ly, Ho - ly, Ho - ly! mer - ci - ful and might - y,

God in three Per - sons, bless - ed Trin - i - ty.
God ev - er - last - ing through e - ter - ni - ty.
Per - fect in power, in love, and pu - ri - ty.
God in three Per - sons, bless - ed Trin - i - ty.

Text: Reginald Heber, 1783-1826, alt.
Tune: NICAEA, 11 12 12 10; John B. Dykes, 1823-1876

God, Whose Almighty Word 486

1. God, whose al - might - y word Cha - os and
2. Sav - ior, you came to give Those who in
3. Spir - it of truth and love, Life - giv - ing,
4. Gra - cious and ho - ly Three, Glo - ri - ous

dark - ness heard, And took their flight:
dark - ness live Heal - ing and sight,
ho - ly dove, Speed on your flight!
Trin - i - ty, Wis - dom, love, might:

Hear us, we hum - bly pray, And where the gos - pel - day
Health to the sick in mind, Sight to the in - ward blind:
Move on the wa - ter's face Bear - ing the lamp of grace
Bound-less as o - cean's tide Roll - ing in full - est pride

Sheds not its glo - rious ray, Let there be light!
Now to all hu - man-kind Let there be light!
And, in earth's dark - est place, Let there be light!
Through the world far and wide, Let there be light!

Text: John Marriott, 1780-1825, alt.
Tune: ITALIAN HYMN, 66 4 666 4; Felice de Giardini, 1716-1796

487 Come, Now Almighty King

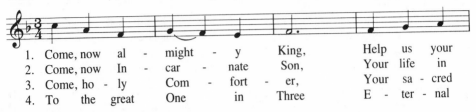

1. Come, now al - might - y King,   Help us your
2. Come, now In - car - nate Son,   Your life in
3. Come, ho - ly Com - fort - er,   Your sa - cred
4. To the great One in Three   E - ter - nal

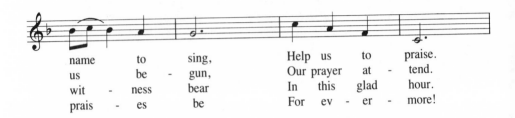

name to sing,   Help us to praise.
us be - gun,   Our prayer at - tend.
wit - ness bear   In this glad hour.
prais - es be   For ev - er - more!

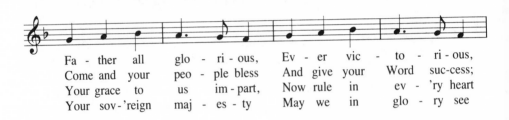

Fa - ther all glo - ri - ous,   Ev - er vic - to - ri - ous,
Come and your peo - ple bless   And give your Word suc-cess;
Your grace to us im - part,   Now rule in ev - 'ry heart
Your sov -'reign maj - es - ty   May we in glo - ry see

Come and reign o - ver us,   An - cient of Days.
Strength-en your right - eous-ness,   Sav - ior and Friend!
Nev - er from us de - part,   Spir - it of Pow'r!
And to e - ter - ni - ty   Love and a - dore!

Text: Anon. c.1757
Tune: ITALIAN HYMN, 66 4 666 4; Felice de Giardini, 1716-1796

Jesus, My Lord, My God, My All 488

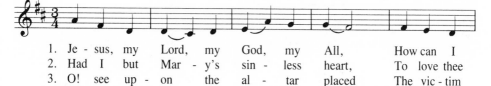

1. Je - sus, my Lord, my God, my All, How can I
2. Had I but Mar - y's sin - less heart, To love thee
3. O! see up - on the al - tar placed The vic - tim

love thee as I ought? And how re - vere this
with, my dear - est King; O! with what bursts of
of di - vin - est love! Let all the earth be-

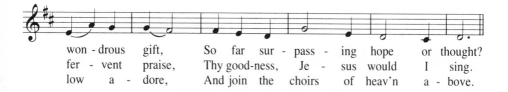

won - drous gift, So far sur - pass - ing hope or thought?
fer - vent praise, Thy good-ness, Je - sus would I sing.
low a - dore, And join the choirs of heav'n a - bove.

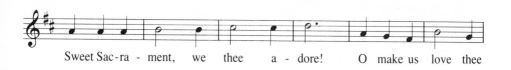

Sweet Sac-ra - ment, we thee a - dore! O make us love thee

more and more! O make us love thee more and more.

Text: St. 1-2, Frederick W. Faber, 1814-1863; St. 3, *Mediator Dei Hymnal*, 1955. © 1955, GIA Publications, Inc.
Tune: SWEET SACRAMENT, LM; with refrain; *Romischkatholisches Gesangbuchlein*, 1826

489 God with Hidden Majesty/Adoro Te Devote

1. God with hid - den maj - es - ty, lies in pres-ence here,
2. All my oth - er sens - es, can - not now per - ceive,
3. God lay stretched up - on the cross, on - ly man could die.
4. Wounds that doubt - ing Thom-as saw I could nev - er see,

1. A - dó - ro te de - vó - te, la - tens Dé - i - tas,
2. Vi - sus, ta - ctus, gus - tus in te fál - li - tur;
3. In cru - ce la - té - bat so - la, Dé - i - tas,
4. Pla - gas, si - cut Tho - mas, non in - tú - e - or

I with deep de - vo - tion my true God re - vere:
But my hear - ing, taught by faith, al - ways will be - lieve:
Here up - on the al - tar God and man both lie;
But I still ac - knowl-edge you my true God to be;

Quae sub his fi - gú - ris ve - re lá - ti - tas:
Sed au - dí - tu so - lo tu - to cré - di - tur:
At hic la - tet si - mul et hu - ma - ni - tas:
De - um ta - men me - um te con - fí - te - or:

Whom this out - ward shape and form se - cret - ly con - tains,
I ac - cept what - ev - er God the Son has said:
This I firm - ly hold as true, this is my be - lief,
Grant that I shall al - ways keep strong in faith and trust,

Ti - bi se cor me - um to - tum súb - ji - cit,
Cre - do quid - quid di - xit De - i Fí - li - us:
Am - bo ta - men cre - dens at - que cón - fi - tens
Fac me ti - bi sem - per ma - gis cré - de - re,

Christ in his di - vin - i - ty man - hood still re - tains.
Those who hear the word of God, by the truth are fed.
And I seek sal - va - tion, like the dy - ing thief.
Guid - ed by my Sav - ior, mer - ci - ful and just.

Qui - a te con - tém - plans to - tum dé - fi - cit,
Nil hoc ver - bo ve - ri - tá - tis ve - ri - us.
Pe - to quod pe - tí - vit la - tro paé - ni - tens.
In te spem ha - bé - re, te di - lí - ge - re.

5. Blest reminder of the death suffered for the world,
Sacrament of living bread, health to every mind,
Let my soul approach you, live within your grace,
Let me taste the perfect joys time shall not efface.

5. *O memoriále mortis Dómini,*
Panis vivus vitam praestans hómini,
Praesta meae menti de te vívere,
Et te illi semper dulce sápere.

6. *Pie pellicáne, Iesu Dómine,*
Me immúndum munda tuo sánguine,
Cuius una stilla salvum fácere,
Tótum múndum quit ab omni scélere.

7. *Iesu, quem velátum nunc aspício,*
Oro fiat illud quod tam sítio:
Ut te reveláta cernens fácie,
Vísu sim beátus tuae glóriae.

Text: Ascr. to Thomas Aquinas, 1227-1274; Tr. by Anthony G. Petti, b. 1932 © 1971, Faber Music Ltd.
Tune: ADORO TE DEVOTE 11 11 11 11; Mode V; Acc. by Richard Proulx, b. 1937 © 1986, GIA Publications, Inc.

490 All You Who Seek a Comfort Sure

1. All you who seek a com-fort sure In sad-ness and dis-tress,
2. Now hear him as he speaks to us Those words for ev-er blest:

What-ev-er sor-row bur-dens you, What-ev-er griefs op-press:
"All you who la-bor, come to me, And I will give you rest."

When Je-sus gave him-self for us And died up-on the tree,
O heart a-dored by saints on high, And hope of sin-ners here,

His heart was pierced for love of us; He died to set us free.
We place our ev-'ry trust in you And lift to you our prayer.

Text: *Quicumque certum quaeritis;* Latin, 18th C.; Tr. by Edward Caswall, 1814-1878, alt.
Tune: KINGSFOLD, CMD; English Traditional; Harm. by Ralph Vaughan Williams, 1872-1958, © Oxford University Press

491 To Christ, the Prince of Peace

1. To Christ, the Prince of peace, And
2. Deep in his heart for us, The
3. O Je-sus, vic-tim blest, What
4. O Fount of end-less life, O

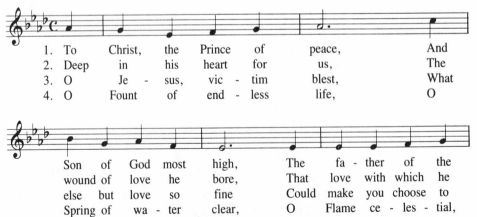

Son of God most high, The fa-ther of the
wound of love he bore, That love with which he
else but love so fine Could make you choose to
Spring of wa-ter clear, O Flame ce-les-tial,

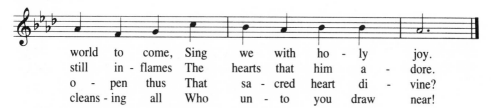

world to come, Sing we with ho - ly joy.
still in - flames The hearts that him a - dore.
o - pen thus That sa - cred heart di - vine?
cleans - ing all Who un - to you draw near!

Text: *Summi parentis filio; Paris Breviary,* 1736; Tr. by Edward Caswall, 1814-1876, alt.
Tune: NARENZA, SM; Liesentritt's *Catholicum Hymnologium Germanicum,* 1584; Adapt. by William H. Havergal, 1793-1870

Jesus Shall Reign 492

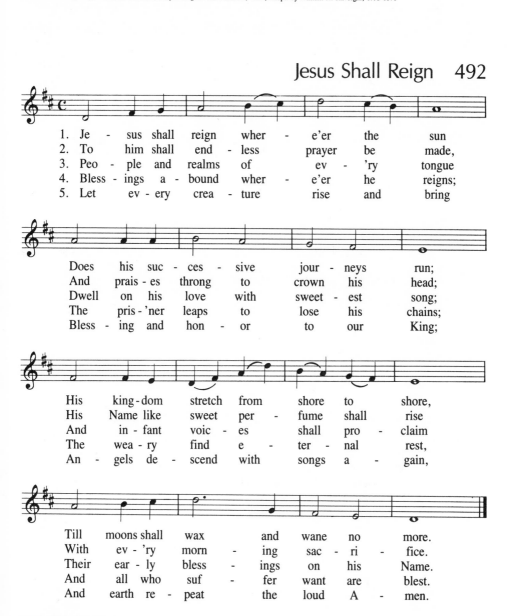

1. Je - sus shall reign wher - e'er the sun
2. To him shall end - less prayer be made,
3. Peo - ple and realms of ev - 'ry tongue
4. Bless - ings a - bound wher - e'er he reigns;
5. Let ev - ery crea - ture rise and bring

Does his suc - ces - sive jour - neys run;
And prais - es throng to crown his head;
Dwell on his love with sweet - est song;
The pris - 'ner leaps to lose his chains;
Bless - ing and hon - or to our King;

His king - dom stretch from shore to shore,
His Name like sweet per - fume shall rise
And in - fant voic - es shall pro - claim
The wea - ry find e - ter - nal rest,
An - gels de - scend with songs a - gain,

Till moons shall wax and wane no more.
With ev - 'ry morn - ing sac - ri - fice.
Their ear - ly bless - ings on his Name.
And all who suf - fer want are blest.
And earth re - peat the loud A - men.

Text: Isaac Watts, 1674-1748, alt.
Tune: DUKE STREET, LM; John Hatton, c.1710-1793

493 Rejoice, the Lord Is King

1. Re - joice, the Lord is King! Your Lord and King a-
2. The Lord, our Sav - ior, reigns, The God of truth and
3. His king - dom can - not fail, He rules o'er earth and
4. Re - joice in glo - rious hope! Our Lord the judge shall

dore! Re - joice, give thanks, and sing, And tri - umph
love; When he had purged our sins, He took his
heav'n; The keys of death and hell Are to our
come And take his ser - vants up To their e-

ev - er - more: Lift up your heart, lift
seat a - bove: Je - sus giv'n:
Je - sus giv'n:
ter - nal home:

up your voice! Re - joice, a - gain I say, re - joice!

Text: Charles Wesley, 1707-1788
Tune: DARWALL'S 148TH, 6 6 6 6 88; John Darwall, 1731-1789; Harm. from *The Hymnal 1940*

494 All Hail the Power of Jesus' Name

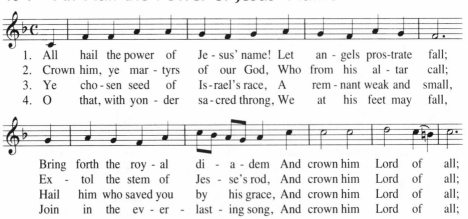

1. All hail the power of Je - sus' name! Let an - gels pros-trate fall;
2. Crown him, ye mar - tyrs of our God, Who from his al - tar call;
3. Ye cho - sen seed of Is - rael's race, A rem - nant weak and small,
4. O that, with yon - der sa - cred throng, We at his feet may fall,

Bring forth the roy - al di - a - dem And crown him Lord of all;
Ex - tol the stem of Jes - se's rod, And crown him Lord of all;
Hail him who saved you by his grace, And crown him Lord of all;
Join in the ev - er - last - ing song, And crown him Lord of all;

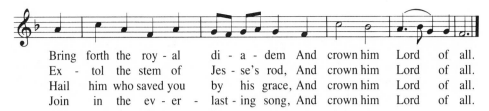

Bring forth the roy - al di - a - dem And crown him Lord of all.
Ex - tol the stem of Jes - se's rod, And crown him Lord of all.
Hail him who saved you by his grace, And crown him Lord of all.
Join in the ev - er - last - ing song, And crown him Lord of all.

Text: Edward Perronet, 1726-1792; Alt. by John Rippon, 1751-1836, alt.
Tune: CORONATION, CM with repeat; Oliver Holden, 1765-1844

All Hail the Power of Jesus' Name   495

1. All hail the pow'r of Je - sus' name! Let an - gels pros - trate
2. Crown him, ye mar - tyrs of our God, Who from his al - tar
3. Ye cho - sen seed of Is - rael's race, A rem - nant weak and
4. O that, with yon - der sa - cred throng, We at his feet may

fall; Bring forth the roy - al di - a - dem, And
call; Ex - tol the stem of Jes - se's rod, And
small, Hail him who saved you by his grace, And
fall, Join in the ev - er - last - ing song, And

crown him Lord of all, And crown him Lord of
crown him Lord of all, And crown him Lord of
crown him Lord of all, And crown him Lord of
crown him Lord of all, And crown him Lord of

all, And crown him Lord of all. Bring
all, And crown him Lord of all. Ex-
all, And crown him Lord of all. Hail
all, And crown him Lord of all. Join

forth the roy - al di - a-dem, And crown him Lord of all.
tol the stem of Jes - se's rod, And crown him Lord of all.
him who saved you by his grace, And crown him Lord of all.
in the ev - er - last - ing song, And crown him Lord of all.

Text: Edward Perronet, 1726-1792; Alt. by John Rippon, 1751-1836, alt .
Tune: DIADEM, CM with repeats; From the *Primitive Baptist Hymn and Tune Book*, 1902; Harm. by Richard Proulx, b.1937, © 1975, GIA Publications, Inc.

496 Crown Him with Many Crowns

1. Crown him with man - y crowns, The Lamb up - on his throne;
2. Crown him the Lord of life, Who tri - umphed o'er the grave,
3. Crown him the Lord of love, Be - hold his hands and side,
4. Crown him the Lord of peace, Whose power a scep - ter sways
5. Crown him the Lord of years, The ris - en Lord sub - lime,

Hark! how the heaven - ly an - them drowns All mu - sic but its own.
And rose vic - to - rious in the strife For those he came to save.
Rich wounds yet vis - i - ble a - bove In beau - ty glo - ri - fied.
From pole to pole, that wars may cease, Ab - sorbed in prayer and praise.
Cre - a - tor of the roll - ing spheres, The Mas - ter of all time.

A - wake, my soul, and sing Of him who set us free,
His glo - ries now we sing, Who died and rose on high,
No an - gel in the sky Can full - y bear that sight,
His reign shall know no end, And round his pierc - ed feet
All hail, Re - deem - er, hail! For you have died for me;

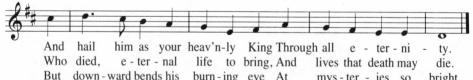

And hail him as your heav'n - ly King Through all e - ter - ni - ty.
Who died, e - ter - nal life to bring, And lives that death may die.
But down - ward bends his burn - ing eye At mys - ter - ies so bright.
Fair flowers of Par - a - dise ex - tend Their fra - grance ev - er sweet.
Your praise and glo - ry shall not fail Through - out e - ter - ni - ty.

Text: Rev. 19:12; St. 1, 3-5, Matthew Bridges, 1800-1894; St. 2, Godfrey Thring, 1823-1903
Tune: DIADEMATA, SMD.; George J. Elvey, 1816-1893

To Jesus Christ, Our Sovereign King 497

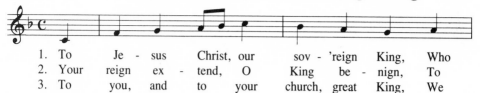

1. To Je - sus Christ, our sov - 'reign King, Who
2. Your reign ex - tend, O King be - nign, To
3. To you, and to your church, great King, We

is the world's sal - va - tion, All praise and hom-age
ev - 'ry land and na - tion; For in your King-dom,
pledge our heart's ob - la - tion; Un - til be - fore your

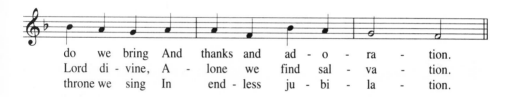

do we bring And thanks and ad - o - ra - tion.
Lord di - vine, A - lone we find sal - va - tion.
throne we sing In end - less ju - bi - la - tion.

Christ Je - sus, Vic - tor! Christ Je - sus, Ru - ler!

Christ Je - sus, Lord and Re - deem - er!

Text: Martin B. Hellrigel, 1891-1981, alt., © 1941, Irene C. Mueller
Tune: ICH GLAUB AN GOTT, 8 7 8 7 with refrain; *Mainz Gesangbuch*, 1870; Harm. by Richard Proulx, b.1937, © 1986, GIA Publications, Inc.

498   He Is King of Kings

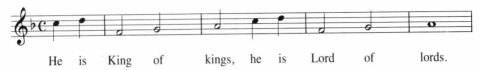

He   is   King   of   kings,   he   is   Lord   of   lords.

Je - sus Christ the   first and   last,   no one works like   him.

Solo:

1. He   built   his   throne   up   in   the   air,
2. He   pitched   his   tents   on   Ca - naan's   ground,

All: *Solo:*

No one   works   like   him.   And   called   his   saints   from
No one   works   like   him.   And   broke   the   Ro - man

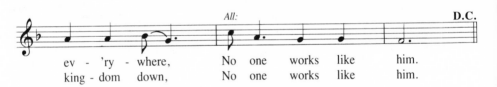

All: **D.C.**

ev - 'ry - where,   No   one   works   like   him.
king - dom   down,   No   one   works   like   him.

Text: Afro-American Spiritual; Ed. by John W. Work, III, 1901-1967
Tune: HE IS KING, Irregular; Afro-American Spiritual; Ed. by John W. Work, III, 1901-1967

At the Name of Jesus 499

1. At the name of Je - sus Ev - 'ry knee shall bow,
2. Hum-bled for a sea - son To re - ceive a name
3. Bore it up tri - umph - ant With its hu - man light,
4. Name him, Chris-tians, name him—Strong your love as death —

Ev - 'ry tongue con - fess him King of glo - ry now;
From the lips of sin - ners Un - to whom he came,
Through all ranks of crea - tures, To the cen - tral height,
But with awe and won - der, And with life - filled breath;

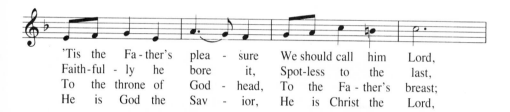

'Tis the Fa - ther's plea - sure We should call him Lord,
Faith-ful - ly he bore it, Spot-less to the last,
To the throne of God - head, To the Fa - ther's breast;
He is God the Sav - ior, He is Christ the Lord,

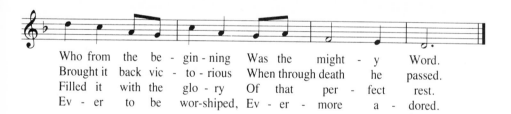

Who from the be - gin - ning Was the might - y Word.
Brought it back vic - to - rious When through death he passed.
Filled it with the glo - ry Of that per - fect rest.
Ev - er to be wor-shiped, Ev - er - more a - dored.

5. In your hearts enthrone him; There let him subdue
   All that is not holy, All that is not true:
   Crown him as your Captain In temptation's hour;
   Let his will enfold you In its light and power.

6. Christians, this Lord Jesus Shall return again,
   With his Father's glory O'er the earth to reign;
   Love and faithful service We his people vow,
   And our hearts confess him King of glory now.

Text: Phil. 2:5-7; Caroline M. Noel, 1817-1877, alt.
Tune: KING'S WESTON, 65 65 D; Ralph Vaughan Williams, 1872-1958, alt., © Oxford University Press

500 Christ Is the King

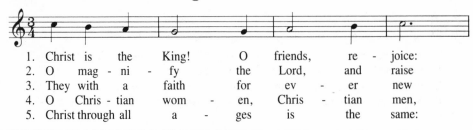

1. Christ is the King! O friends, re - joice:
2. O mag - ni - fy the Lord, and raise
3. They with a faith for ev - er new
4. O Chris - tian wom - en, Chris - tian men,
5. Christ through all a - ges is the same:

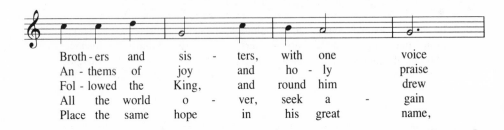

Broth - ers and sis - ters, with one voice
An - thems of joy and ho - ly praise
Fol - lowed the King, and round him drew
All the world o - ver, seek a - gain
Place the same hope in his great name,

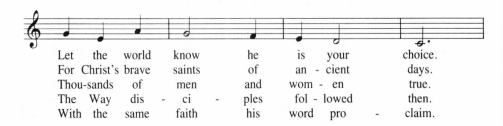

Let the world know he is your choice.
For Christ's brave saints of an - cient days.
Thou-sands of men and wom - en true.
The Way dis - ci - ples fol - lowed then.
With the same faith his word pro - claim.

Al - le - lu - ia, al - le - lu - ia, al - le - lu - ia.

6. Let love's all reconciling might
Your scattered companies unite
In service to the Lord of light.
Alleluia, alleluia, alleluia.

7. So shall God's will on earth be done,
New lamps be lit, new tasks begun,
And the whole Church at last be one.
Alleluia, alleluia, alleluia.

Text: George K. A. Bell, 1883-1958, alt., © Oxford University Press
Tune: GELOBT SEI GOTT, 888 with alleluias; Melchior Vulpius, c.1560-1616

The King of Glory 501

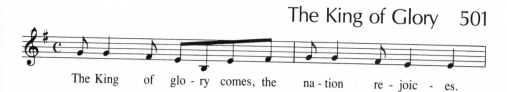

The King   of   glo - ry   comes, the   na - tion   re - joic - es.

O - pen   the   gates   be - fore   him,   lift   up   your   voic - es.

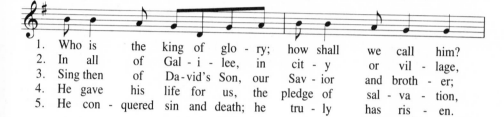

1.	Who is	the	king of	glo - ry;	how shall	we	call	him?
2.	In all	of	Gal - i - lee,	in	cit - y	or	vil - lage,
3.	Sing then	of	Da - vid's Son,	our	Sav - ior	and broth - er;
4.	He gave	his	life for	us,	the	pledge of	sal - va - tion,
5.	He con - quered	sin and death;	he	tru - ly	has	ris - en.

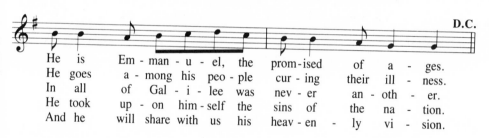

D.C.

He   is   Em - man - u - el,   the   prom - ised   of   a - ges.
He   goes   a - mong his   peo - ple   cur - ing   their   ill - ness.
In   all   of   Gal - i - lee   was   nev - er   an - oth - er.
He   took   up - on   him - self   the   sins   of   the   na - tion.
And   he   will   share with   us   his   heav - en - ly   vi - sion.

Text: Willard F. Jabusch, b.1930, © 1966, 1984
Tune: KING OF GLORY, 12 12 with refrain; Israeli; Harm. by Richard Proulx, b.1937, © 1986, GIA Publications, Inc.

502 I Sing the Mighty Power of God

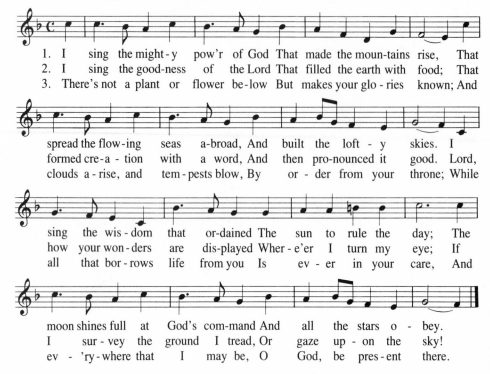

1. I sing the might-y pow'r of God That made the moun-tains rise, That
2. I sing the good-ness of the Lord That filled the earth with food; That
3. There's not a plant or flower be-low But makes your glo-ries known; And

spread the flow-ing seas a-broad, And built the loft-y skies. I
formed cre-a-tion with a word, And then pro-nounced it good. Lord,
clouds a-rise, and tem-pests blow, By or-der from your throne; While

sing the wis-dom that or-dained The sun to rule the day; The
how your won-ders are dis-played Wher-e'er I turn my eye; If
all that bor-rows life from you Is ev-er in your care, And

moon shines full at God's com-mand And all the stars o-bey.
I sur-vey the ground I tread, Or gaze up-on the sky!
ev-'ry-where that I may be, O God, be pres-ent there.

Text: Isaac Watts, 1674-1748, alt.
Tune: MOZART, CMD; Attr. to Wolfgang A. Mozart, 1756-1791

503 Many and Great, O God, Are Your Works

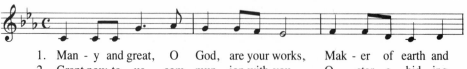

1. Man-y and great, O God, are your works, Mak-er of earth and
2. Grant now to us com-mun-ion with you, O star-a-bid-ing

sky; Your hands have set the heav-ens with stars;
one; Come now to us and dwell with us;

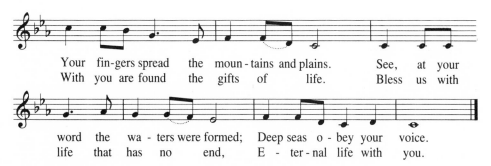

Your fin-gers spread the moun-tains and plains. See, at your
With you are found the gifts of life. Bless us with

word the wa - ters were formed; Deep seas o - bey your voice.
life that has no end, E - ter - nal life with you.

Text: *Wakantanka tuku nitawa;* Dakota Indian Hymn; Para. by Philip Frazier, 1892-1964, alt. © Walton Music Corp.
Tune: LACQUIPARLE, Irregular; *Dakota Odowan,* 1879; Setting by Richard Proulx, b.1937, © 1986, GIA Publications, Inc.

The Works of the Lord Are Created in Wisdom   504

1. The works of the Lord are cre - a - ted in wis - dom!
2. Not e - ven the an - gels have ev - er been grant - ed
3. The sun ev-'ry morn - ing lights up all cre - a - tion,
4. The wind is his breath and the clouds are his sig - nal,
5. The song is un - fin - ished; how shall we com - plete it,

We view the earth's won - ders and call him to mind;
To tell the full sto - ry of na - ture and grace;
The moon marks the rhy - thm of months in their turn;
The rain and the snow are the robes of his choice;
And where find the skill to per - fect all his praise?

We hear what he says in the world we dis - cov - er,
But o - pen to God is all hu - man per - cep - tion,
The glit - ter - ing stars are ar - rayed in God's hon - or,
The storm and the light-ning, his stand - ards and her - alds,
At work in all plac - es, he cares for all peo - ples—

And God shows his glo - ry in all that we find.
The mys - ter - ies of time and the se - crets of space.
A - dorn - ing the years as they cease-less - ly burn.
The crash of the thun - der, the sound of his voice.
How great is the Lord to the end of all days!

Text: Eccles. 42-43; Christopher Idle, b.1938, © 1982, Hope Publishing Co.
Tune: KREMSER, 12 11 12 11; *Neder-landtsch Gedanckclanck,* 1626; Harm. by Edward Kremser, 1838-1914

505 All Things Bright and Beautiful

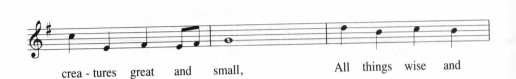

All things bright and beau - ti - ful, All

crea - tures great and small, All things wise and

won - der - ful, The Lord God made them all.

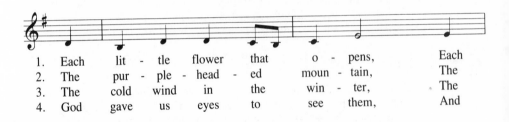

1.	Each	lit - tle	flower	that	o - pens,	Each
2.	The	pur - ple - head - ed			moun - tain,	The
3.	The	cold wind	in	the	win - ter,	The
4.	God	gave us	eyes	to	see them,	And

lit - tle	bird	that	sings,	God made their	glow - ing
riv - er	run - ning		by,	The sun - set,	and the
plea - sant	sum - mer		sun,	The ripe fruits	in the
lips	that we	might	tell	How great is	God Al-

D.C.

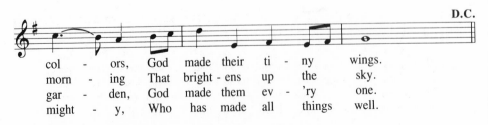

col - ors,	God made their	ti - ny	wings.
morn - ing	That bright - ens	up the	sky.
gar - den,	God made them	ev - 'ry	one.
might - y,	Who has made	all things	well.

Text: Cecil F. Alexander, 1818-1895, alt.
Tune: ROYAL OAK, 7 6 7 6 with refrain; English Melody; Adapted by Martin Shaw, 1875-1958

The Stars Declare His Glory   506

1. The stars de - clare his glo - ry; The
2. The dawn re - turns in splen - dor, The
3. So shine the Lord's com - mand - ments To
4. So or - der too this life of mine, Di-

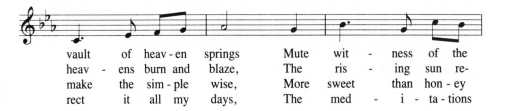

vault of heav - en springs Mute wit - ness of the
heav - ens burn and blaze, The ris - ing sun re-
make the sim - ple wise, More sweet than hon - ey
rect it all my days, The med - i - ta - tions

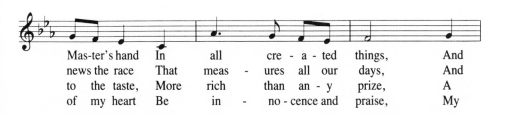

Mas-ter's hand In all cre - a - ted things, And
news the race That meas - ures all our days, And
to the taste, More rich than an - y prize, A
of my heart Be in - no - cence and praise, My

through the si - lenc - es of
writes in fire a - cross the
law of love with - in our
Rock, and my re - deem - ing

space Their sound - less mu - sic sings.
skies God's maj - es - ty and praise.
hearts, A light be - fore our eyes.
Lord, In all my words and ways.

Text: Psalm 19; Timothy Dudley-Smith, b.1926, © 1981, Hope Publishing Co.
Tune: ALDINE, 7 6 8 6 8 6; Richard Proulx, b.1937, © 1986, GIA Publications, Inc.

507 God Is Working His Purpose Out

1. God is work - ing his pur - pose out As
2. From ut - most east to ut - most west, Wher -
3. March we forth in the strength of God, With the
4. All we can do is worth - less toil Un -

year suc - ceeds to year: God is work - ing his
ev - er foot has trod, By the mouth of man - y
ban - ner of Christ un - furled, That the light of the glo - rious
less God bless - es the deed; Vain - ly we hope for the

pur - pose out, And the time is draw - ing near;
mes - sen - gers Goes forth the voice of God;
gos - pel of truth May shine through - out the world:
har - vest - tide Till God gives life to the seed; Yet

Near - er and near - er draws the time, The time that shall sure - ly
Give ear to me, you con - ti - nents, You isles, give ear to
Fight we the fight with sor - row and sin To set their cap - tives
near - er and near - er draws the time, The time that shall sure - ly

be, When the earth shall be filled with the glo - ry of God As the
me, That the earth may be filled with the glo - ry of God As the
free, That the earth may be filled with the glo - ry of God As the
be, When the earth shall be filled with the glo - ry of God As the

1.2.3.   4.

wa - ters cov - er the sea.
wa - ters cov - er the sea.
wa - ters cov - er the sea.
wa - ters cov - er the sea.

Text: Hab. 1:14; Arthur C. Ainger, 1841-1919, alt.
Tune: PURPOSE, Irregular; Martin Shaw, 1875-1958, © Oxford University Press

When Israel Was in Egypt's Land 508

1. When Is - rael was in E - gypt's land,
2. The Lord told Mo - ses what to do,
3. They jour - neyed · on at God's com - mand,
4. Oh, let us all from bond - age flee,

Let my peo - ple go; Op - pressed so hard they
Let my peo - ple go; To lead the chil-dren of
Let my peo - ple go; And came at length to
Let my peo - ple go; And let us all in

could not stand, Let my peo - ple go.
Is - rael through, Let my peo - ple go.
Ca - naan's land, Let my peo - ple go.
Christ be free, Let my peo - ple go.

Go down, Mo - ses, way down in E-gypt's land;

Tell old Phar-aoh to let my peo-ple go.

Text: Afro-American Spiritual
Tune: GO DOWN MOSES, Irregular; Afro-American Spiritual; Harm. from *English Praise*, 1975, © 1975, Oxford University Press

509 Who Can Measure Heaven and Earth

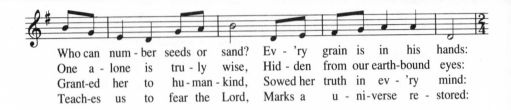

1. Who can meas - ure heav'n and earth? God was pre - sent at their birth;
2. Who can tell what wis - dom brings, First of all cre - a - ted things?
3. Wis-dom in his plans he laid, Plant-ed her in all he made;
4. Wis-dom gives the sur - est wealth, Brings her chil - dren life and health;

Who can num - ber seeds or sand? Ev - 'ry grain is in his hands:
One a - lone is tru - ly wise, Hid - den from our earth-bound eyes:
Grant-ed her to hu - man-kind, Sowed her truth in ev - 'ry mind:
Teach-es us to fear the Lord, Marks a u - ni-verse re - stored:

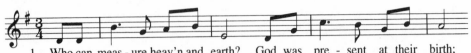

Through cre - a - tion's count-less days Ev - 'ry dawn sings out his praise.
Knowl-edge lies in him a - lone—God, the Lord up - on his throne!
But with rich - est wis - dom blessed Those who love him first and best.
Heav'n and earth she will out - last— Hap - py those who hold her fast!

Text: Eccles. 1; Christopher Idle, b.1938, © 1982, Hope Publishing Co.
Tune: LUCERNA LAUDONIAE, 77 77 77; David Evans, 1874-1948, © Oxford University Press

510 I Want to Walk as a Child of the Light

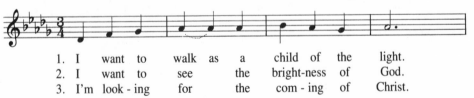

1. I want to walk as a child of the light.
2. I want to see the bright-ness of God.
3. I'm look - ing for the com - ing of Christ.

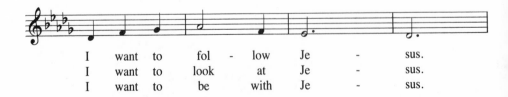

I want to fol - low Je - sus.
I want to look at Je - sus.
I want to be with Je - sus.

God set the stars to give light to the world. The
Clear sun of right-eous-ness shine on my path, And
When we have run with pa-tience the race, We

star of my life is Je - sus.
show me the way to the Fa - ther.
shall know the joy of Je - sus.

In him there is no dark-ness at all. The

night and the day are both a - like. The

Lamb is the light of the cit - y of God.

Shine in my heart, Lord Je - sus.

Text: Eph. 5:8-10; Rev. 21:23; Jn. 12:46; 1 Jn. 1:5; Heb. 12:1; Kathleen Thomerson, b.1934
Tune: HOUSTON, 10 7 10 8 9 9 10 7; Kathleen Thomerson, b.1934
© 1970, 1975, Celebration

511 Thy Strong Word Didst Cleave the Darkness

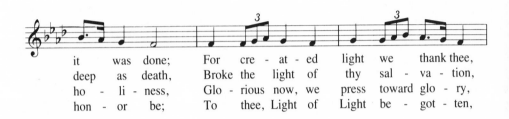

1. Thy strong word didst cleave the dark-ness; At thy speak-ing
2. Lo, on those who dwelt in dark-ness, Dark as night and
3. Thy strong word be - speaks us right-eous; Bright with thine own
4. God the Fa - ther, Light - Cre - a - tor, To thee laud and

it was done; For cre - at - ed light we thank thee,
deep as death, Broke the light of thy sal - va - tion,
ho - li - ness, Glo - rious now, we press toward glo - ry,
hon - or be; To thee, Light of Light be - got - ten,

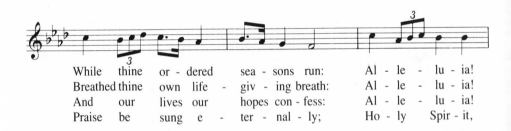

While thine or - dered sea - sons run: Al - le - lu - ia!
Breathed thine own life - giv - ing breath: Al - le - lu - ia!
And our lives our hopes con - fess: Al - le - lu - ia!
Praise be sung e - ter - nal - ly; Ho - ly Spir - it,

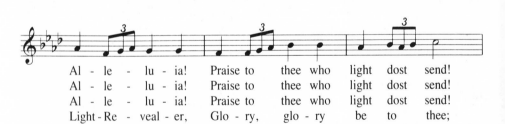

Al - le - lu - ia! Praise to thee who light dost send!
Al - le - lu - ia! Praise to thee who light dost send!
Al - le - lu - ia! Praise to thee who light dost send!
Light - Re - veal - er, Glo - ry, glo - ry be to thee;

Al - le - lu - ia! Al - le - lu - ia! Al - le - lu - ia with-out end!
Al - le - lu - ia! Al - le - lu - ia! Al - le - lu - ia with-out end!
Al - le - lu - ia! Al - le - lu - ia! Al - le - lu - ia with-out end!
Mor - tals, an - gels, now and ev - er Praise the Ho - ly Trin - i - ty!

Text: Martin H. Franzmann, 1907-1976, alt., © 1969, Concordia Publishing House
Tune: EBENEZER, 8 7 8 7 D; Thomas J. Williams, 1869-1944

Immortal, Invisible, God Only Wise   512

1. Im - mor - tal, in - vis - i - ble, God on - ly wise,
2. Un - rest - ing, un - hast - ing, and si - lent as light,
3. Life - giv - ing Cre - a - tor, of both great and small;
4. Great Fa - ther of glo - ry, pure Fa - ther of light,

In light in - ac - ces - si - ble hid from our eyes,
Nor want - ing, nor wast - ing, you rule day and night;
Of all life the mak - er, the true life of all;
Your an - gels a - dor - ing, all veil - ing their sight;

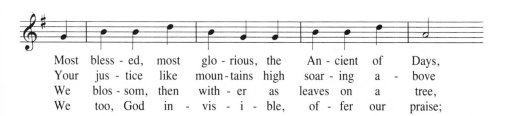

Most bless - ed, most glo - rious, the An - cient of Days,
Your jus - tice like moun - tains high soar - ing a - bove
We blos - som, then with - er as leaves on a tree,
We too, God in - vis - i - ble, of - fer our praise;

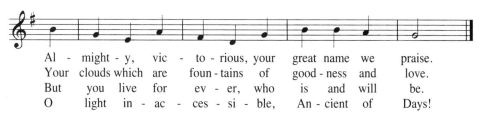

Al - might - y, vic - to - rious, your great name we praise.
Your clouds which are foun - tains of good - ness and love.
But you live for ev - er, who is and will be.
O light in - ac - ces - si - ble, An - cient of Days!

Text: 1 Tim. 1:17; Walter C. Smith, 1824-1908, alt.
Tune: ST DENIO, 11 11 11 11; Roberts' *Canaidau y Cyssegr*, 1839

513 Word of God, Come Down on Earth

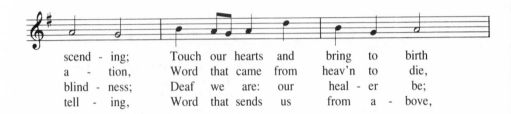

1. Word of God, come down on earth, Liv - ing rain from heav'n de-
2. Word e - ter - nal, throned on high, Word that brought to life cre-
3. Word that caused blind eyes to see, Speak and heal our mor - tal
4. Word that speaks God's ten - der love, One with God be - yond all

scend - ing; Touch our hearts and bring to birth
a - tion, Word that came from heav'n to die,
blind - ness; Deaf we are: our heal - er be;
tell - ing, Word that sends us from a - bove,

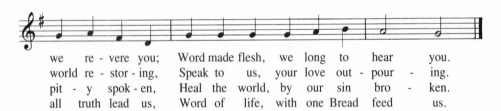

Faith and hope and love un - end - ing. Word al - might - y,
Cru - ci - fied for our sal - va - tion, Sav - ing Word, the
Loose our tongues to tell your kind - ness. Be our Word in
God the Spir - it, with us dwell - ing, Word of truth, to

we re - vere you; Word made flesh, we long to hear you.
world re - stor - ing, Speak to us, your love out - pour - ing.
pit - y spok - en, Heal the world, by our sin bro - ken.
all truth lead us, Word of life, with one Bread feed us.

Text: James Quinn, SJ, b.1919, © 1969
Tune: LIEBSTER JESU, 7 8 7 8 88; Johann R. Ahle, 1625-1673; Harm. by George H. Palmer, 1846-1926

Thanks to God Whose Word Was Spoken 514

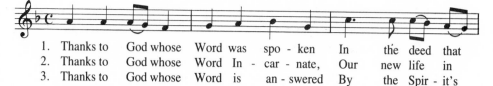

1. Thanks to God whose Word was spo - ken In the deed that
2. Thanks to God whose Word In - car - nate, Our new life in
3. Thanks to God whose Word is an - swered By the Spir - it's

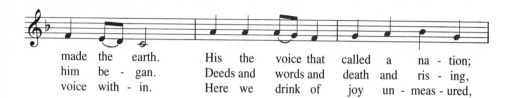

made the earth. His the voice that called a na - tion;
him be - gan. Deeds and words and death and ris - ing,
voice with - in. Here we drink of joy un - meas - ured,

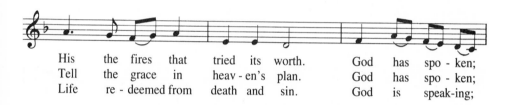

His the fires that tried its worth. God has spo - ken;
Tell the grace in heav - en's plan. God has spo - ken;
Life re - deemed from death and sin. God is speak-ing;

Praise him for his o - pen Word.
Praise him for his o - pen Word.
Praise him for his o - pen Word.

Text: R.T. Brooks, b.1918, © 1954, 1982, Hope Publishing Co.
Tune: WYLDE GREEN, 8 7 8 7 4 7; Peter Cutts, b.1937, © 1966, Hope Publishing Co.

515 His Voice Is in the Thunder, in the Storm

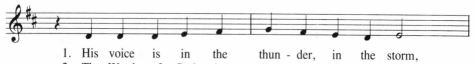

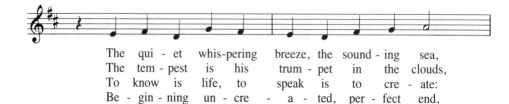

1. His voice is in the thun - der, in the storm,
2. The Word of God be - fore the world be - gan,
3. He is the wis - dom, Mind be - yond all mind;
4. The Lord of speech, the Word of God on earth,
5. Give praise to him, the Christ, the voice of God,

The qui - et whis-pering breeze, the sound - ing sea,
The tem - pest is his trum - pet in the clouds,
To know is life, to speak is to cre - ate:
Be - gin - ning un - cre - a - ted, per - fect end,
The ev - er - last - ing Wis - dom brought to earth,

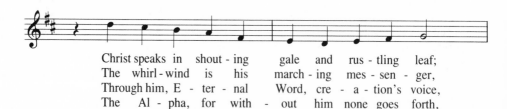

Christ speaks in shout - ing gale and rus - tling leaf;
The whirl - wind is his march - ing mes - sen - ger,
Through him, E - ter - nal Word, cre - a - tion's voice,
The Al - pha, for with - out him none goes forth,
The Lord, the Word, through whom the mute shall speak,

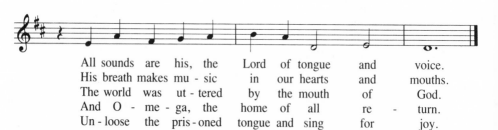

All sounds are his, the Lord of tongue and voice.
His breath makes mu - sic in our hearts and mouths.
The world was ut - tered by the mouth of God.
And O - me - ga, the home of all re - turn.
Un - loose the pris - oned tongue and sing for joy.

Text: Luke Connaughton, 1917-1979, alt., © 1970, Mayhew McCrimmon Ltd.
Tune: FLENTGE, 10 10 10 10; Carl Schalk, b.1929, © 1979

God Has Spoken by His Prophets 516

1. God has spo - ken by his proph - ets, Spo - ken
2. God has spo - ken by Christ Je - sus, Christ, the
3. God is speak - ing by his Spir - it, Speak - ing

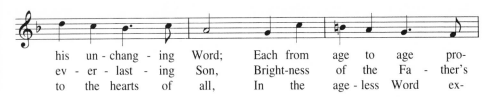

his un - chang - ing Word; Each from age to age pro-
ev - er - last - ing Son, Bright-ness of the Fa - ther's
to the hearts of all, In the age - less Word ex-

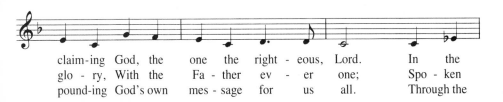

claim-ing God, the one the right - eous, Lord. In the
glo - ry, With the Fa - ther ev - er one; Spo - ken
pound-ing God's own mes - sage for us all. Through the

world's de - spair and tur - moil, One firm
by the Word In - car - nate, God of
rise and fall of na - tions One sure

an - chor holds us fast; God is king, his throne e-
God, be - fore time was; Light of Light, to earth de-
faith yet stand - ing fast; God a - bides, his Word un-

ter - nal; God the first, and God the last.
scend - ing, He re - veals our God to us.
chang - ing; God the first, and God the last.

Text: George W. Briggs, 1875-1959, alt., © 1953, 1981, Hymn Society of America
Tune: RUSTINGTON, 8 7 8 7 D; Charles H. H. Parry, 1848-1918

517 Earth and All Stars

1. Earth and all stars! Loud rush-ing
2. Hail, wind and rain! Loud blow-ing
3. Trum - pet and pipes! Loud clash-ing
4. En - gines and steel! Loud pound-ing

plan - ets Sing to the Lord a new song!
snow - storm Sing to the Lord a new song!
cym - bals Sing to the Lord a new song!
ham - mers Sing to the Lord a new song!

O vic - to - ry! Loud shout - ing ar - my
Flow - ers and trees! Loud rus - tling dry leaves
Harp, lute and lyre! Loud hum - ming cel - los
Lime-stone and beams! Loud build - ing work - ers

Sing to the Lord a new song!

God has done mar - vel-ous things. I too, I

too sing prais - es with a new song!

𝄩 indicates clapping of hands

5. Classrooms and labs! Loud boiling test tubes
Sing to the Lord a new song!
Athlete and band! Loud cheering people
Sing to the Lord a new song!

6. Knowledge and truth! Loud sounding wisdom
Sing to the Lord a new song!
Daughter and son! Loud praying members
Sing to the Lord a new song!

Text: Herbert Brokering, b.1926
Tune: EARTH AND ALL STARS, 4 5 7 D with refrain; Jan Bender, b.1909
© 1968, Augsburg Publishing House.

Glory Be to God in Heaven 518

1. Glo - ry be to God in heav - en, Peace to those
2. On - ly Son of God the Fa - ther, Lamb who takes

who love him well; On the earth let all his
our sin a - way, Now with him in tri - umph

peo - ple Speak his grace, his won - ders tell:
seat - ed— For your mer - cy, Lord, we pray:

Lord, we praise you for your glo - ry, Might - y Fa-
Je - sus Christ, most high and ho - ly, Sav - ior, you

ther, heav-en's king; Hear our joy - ful ad - o-
are God a - lone In the glo - ry of the

ra - tion And ac - cept the thanks we bring.
Fa - ther With the Spir - it: Three in One!

Text: *Gloria in excelsis Deo;* Michael Perry, b.1942, © 1982, Hope Publishing Co.
Tune: LADUE CHAPEL, 8 7 8 7 D; Ronald Arnatt, b.1930, © Walton Music Corp.

Laudate Dominum 519

Lau - da - te Do - mi - num, lau - da - te Do - mi - num

om - nes gen - tes, al - le - lu - ia. al - le - lu - ia.

Tune: Psalm 117, Taizé Community, 1980
Tune: Jacques Berthier, b.1923
© 1980, Les Presses de Taizé

520 All Creatures of Our God and King

1. All crea-tures of our God and King, Lift
2. O rush-ing wind and breez-es soft, O
3. O flow-ing wa-ters, pure and clear, Make
4. Dear moth-er earth, who day by day Un-
5. O ev-'ry one of ten-der heart, For-

up your voice and with us sing: Al - le
clouds that ride the winds a - loft: O
mu - sic for your Lord to hear. O
folds rich bless - ings on our way, O
giv - ing oth - ers, take your part, O

lu - ia! Al - le - lu - ia! O
praise him! Al - le - lu - ia! O
praise him! Al - le - lu - ia! O
praise him! Al - le - lu - ia! The
praise him! Al - le - lu - ia! All

burn - ing sun with gold - en beam And
ris - ing morn, in praise re - joice, O
fire so mas - ter - ful and bright, Pro-
fruits and flow'rs that ver - dant grow, Let
you who pain and sor - row bear, Praise

sil - ver moon with soft - er gleam:
lights of eve - ning, find a voice.
vid - ing us with warmth and light, O
them his praise a - bun - dant show.
God and lay on him your care.

praise him! O praise him! Al - le - lu - ia, al - le-

lu - ia, al - le - lu - ia!

6. And you, most kind and gentle death,
   Waiting to hush our final breath,
   O praise him! Alleluia!
   You lead to heav'n the child of God,
   Where Christ our Lord the way has trod.
   O praise him! O praise him!
   Alleluia, alleluia, alleluia!

7. Let all things their Creator bless,
   And worship him in humbleness,
   O praise him! Alleluia!
   Oh praise the Father, praise the Son,
   And praise the Spirit, Three in One!
   O praise him! O praise him!
   Alleluia, alleluia, alleluia!

Text: *Laudato si, mi Signor:* Francis of Assisi, 1182-1226; Tr. by William H. Draper, 1855-1933, alt., © J. Curwen and Sons
Tune: LASST UNS ERFREUEN, LM with alleluias; *Geistliche Kirchengesänge*, 1623; Harm. by Ralph Vaughan Williams, 1872-1958, © Oxford University Press

From All That Dwell below the Skies   521

1. From all that dwell be - low the skies,
2. E - ter - nal are your mer - cies, Lord;
3. Your loft - y themes, all mor - tals, bring;
4. In ev - ery land be - gin the song;

Let the Cre - a - tor's praise a - rise;
E - ter - nal truth at - tends your word:
In songs of praise di - vine - ly sing;
To ev - ery land the strains be - long;

Let the Re - deem - er's name be sung,
Your praise shall sound from shore to shore,
The great sal - va - tion loud pro - claim,
In cheer - ful sounds all voic - es raise,

Through ev - 'ry land by ev - 'ry tongue.
Till suns shall rise and set no more.
And shout for joy the Sav - ior's name.
And fill the world with loud - est praise.

Text: Psalm 117; St. 1-2; Isaac Watts, 1674-1748; St. 3-4, Anon.
Tune: DUKE STREET, LM; John Hatton, c.1710-1793

522 Heavenly Hosts in Ceaseless Worship

1. Heaven - ly hosts in cease - less wor - ship
2. All cre - a - tion, all re - demp - tion,

"Ho - ly, ho - ly, ho - ly" cry; "He who is, who
Join to sing the Sav - ior's worth; Lamb of God whose

was and will be, God, Al - might - y,
blood has bought us, Kings and priests, to

Lord most high." Praise and hon - or, power and glo - ry,
reign on earth. Wealth and wis - dom, power and glo - ry,

Be to Him who reigns a - lone; We, with all his
Hon - or, might, do - min - ion, praise, Now be his from

hands have fash - ioned, Fall be - fore the Fa - ther's throne.
all his crea - tures And to ev - er - last - ing days.

Text: Rev. 4-5; Timothy Dudley-Smith, b.1926, © 1975, Hope Publishing Co.
Tune: HEAVENLY HOSTS, 8 7 8 7 D; Noel H. Tredinnick, b.1949, © 1973, Hope Publishing Co.

Let All Mortal Flesh Keep Silence   523

1. Let all mor - tal flesh keep si - lence,
2. King of kings, yet born of Mar - y,
3. Rank on rank the host of heav - en
4. At his feet the six - winged ser - aph,

And with fear and trem - bling stand;
As of old on earth he stood,
Spreads its van - guard on the way,
Cher - u - bim with sleep - less eye,

Pon - der noth - ing earth - ly mind - ed,
Lord of lords in hu - man ves - ture,
As the Light of Light de - scend - ing
Veil their fac - es to the Pres - ence,

For with bless - ing in his hand
In the Bo - dy and the Blood
From the realms of end - less day,
As with cease - less voice they cry,

Christ our God to earth de - scend-
He will give to all the faith-
That the pow'rs of hell may van-
"Al - le - lu - ia, al - le - lu-

ing, Our full hom - age to de - mand.
ful His own self for heav'n - ly food.
ish As the dark - ness clears a - way.
ia, Al - le - lu - ia, Lord, most high!"

Text: Σίγησάτω Πᾶσα Σάρξ Βροτεία; Liturgy of St. James 5th C.; Para. by Gerard Moultrie, 1829-1885
Tune: PICARDY, 8 7 8 7 8 7; French, 17th C.; Harm. by Russell Woolen, b.1923

524   Holy God, We Praise Thy Name

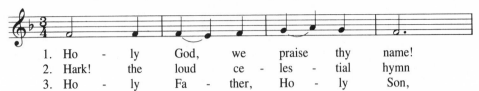

1. Ho - ly God, we praise thy name!
2. Hark! the loud ce - les - tial hymn
3. Ho - ly Fa - ther, Ho - ly Son,

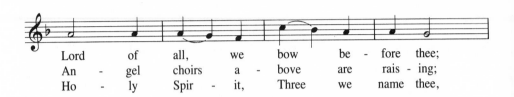

Lord of all, we bow be - fore thee;
An - gel choirs a - bove are rais - ing;
Ho - ly Spir - it, Three we name thee,

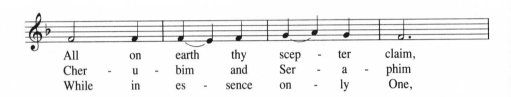

All on earth thy scep - ter claim,
Cher - u - bim and Ser - a - phim
While in es - sence on - ly One,

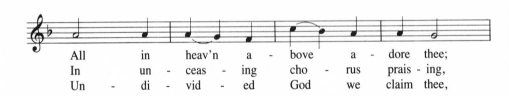

All in heav'n a - bove a - dore thee;
In un - ceas - ing cho - rus prais - ing,
Un - di - vid - ed God we claim thee,

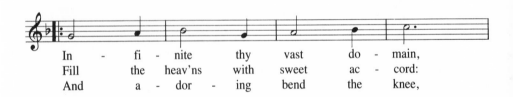

In - fi - nite thy vast do - main,
Fill the heav'ns with sweet ac - cord:
And a - dor - ing bend the knee,

Repeat ad lib

Ev - er - last - ing is thy reign.
Ho - ly, ho - ly, ho - ly Lord!
While we own the mys - ter - y.

Text: *Grosser Gott, wir loben dich;* Ascr. to Ignaz Franz, 1719-1790; Tr. by Clarence Walworth, 1820-1900
Tune: GROSSER GOTT, 7 8 7 8 77; *Katholisches Gesangbuch,* Vienna, c.1774

Joyful, Joyful, We Adore You 525

1. Joy-ful, joy-ful, we a-dore you, God of glo-ry, Lord of love;
2. All your works with joy sur-round you, Earth and heav'n re-flect your rays,
3. Al-ways giv-ing and for-giv-ing, Ev-er bless-ing, ev-er blest,
4. Mor-tals join the might-y cho-rus, Which the morn-ing stars be-gan;

Hearts un-fold like flowers be-fore you, Open-ing to the sun a-bove.
Stars and an-gels sing a-round you, Cen-ter of un-bro-ken praise;
Well-spring of the joy of liv-ing, O-cean depth of hap-py rest!
God's own love is reign-ing o'er us, Join-ing peo-ple hand in hand.

Melt the clouds of sin and sad-ness; Drive the dark of doubt a-way;
Field and for-est, vale and moun-tain, Flow-ery mead-ow, flash-ing sea,
Lov-ing Fa-ther, Christ our broth-er, Let your light up-on us shine;
Ev-er sing-ing, march we on-ward, Vic-tors in the midst of strife;

Giv-er of im-mor-tal glad-ness, Fill us with the light of day!
Chant-ing bird and flow-ing foun-tain, Prais-ing you e-ter-nal-ly!
Teach us how to love each oth-er, Lift us to the joy di-vine.
Joy-ful mu-sic leads us sun-ward In the tri-umph song of life.

Text: Henry van Dyke, 1852-1933, alt., © Charles Scribner's Sons
Tune: HYMN TO JOY, 8 7 8 7 D; Arr. from Ludwig van Beethoven, 1770-1827, by Edward Hodges, 1796-1867

526 Thanks Be to God

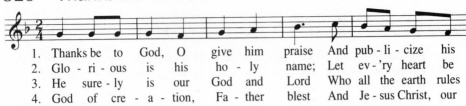

1. Thanks be to God, O give him praise And pub - li - cize his
2. Glo - ri - ous is his ho - ly name; Let ev - 'ry heart be
3. He sure - ly is our God and Lord Who all the earth rules
4. God of cre - a - tion, Fa - ther blest And Je - sus Christ, our

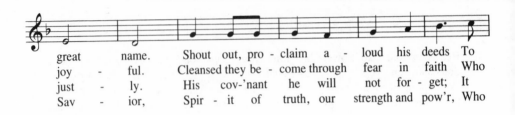

great name. Shout out, pro - claim a - loud his deeds To
joy - ful. Cleansed they be - come through fear in faith Who
just - ly. His cov - 'nant he will not for - get; It
Sav - ior, Spir - it of truth, our strength and pow'r, Who

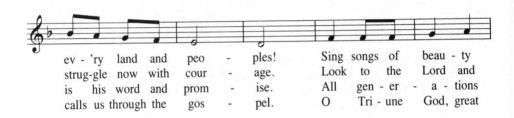

ev - 'ry land and peo - ples! Sing songs of beau - ty
strug - gle now with cour - age. Look to the Lord and
is his word and prom - ise. All gen - er - a - tions
calls us through the gos - pel. O Tri - une God, great

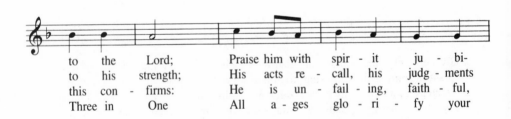

to the Lord; Praise him with spir - it ju - bi -
to his strength; His acts re - call, his judg - ments
this con - firms: He is un - fail - ing, faith - ful,
Three in One All a - ges glo - ri - fy your

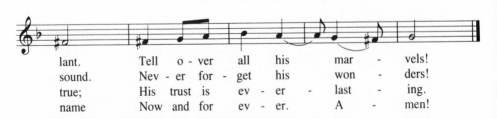

lant. Tell o - ver all his mar - vels!
sound. Nev - er for - get his won - ders!
true; His trust is ev - er - last - ing.
name Now and for ev - er. A - men!

Text: Psalm (104)105; *Danket dem Herren*; Cornelius Becker, 1561-1604; Tr. by Daniel G. Reuning, b.1935, © 1972, GIA Publications, Inc.
Tune: DANKET DEM HERREN, 8 7 8 7 8 8 7; Heinrich Schütz, 1585-1672

All Glory Be to God on High 527

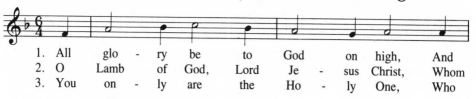

1. All glo - ry be to God on high, And
2. O Lamb of God, Lord Je - sus Christ, Whom
3. You on - ly are the Ho - ly One, Who

peace on earth from heav - en, And God's good-will un-
God the Fa - ther gave us, Who for the world was
came for our sal - va - tion, And on - ly you are

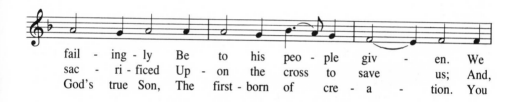

fail - ing-ly Be to his peo - ple giv - en. We
sac - ri - ficed Up - on the cross to save us; And,
God's true Son, The first - born of cre - a - tion. You

bless, we wor - ship you, we raise For your great glo - ry
as you sit at God's right hand, And we for judg - ment
on - ly, Christ, as Lord we own And, with the Spir - it,

thanks and praise, O God, Al - might - y Fa - ther.
there must stand, Have mer - cy, Lord, up - on us.
you a - lone Share in the Fa - ther's glo - ry.

Text: *Allein Gott in der Hoh' sei Ehr' (Gloria in excelsis Deo)*; Nikolaus Decius, c.1485-c.1546; Tr. by F. Bland Tucker, 1895-1984, © 1978, Church Pension Fund
Tune: ALLEIN GOTT IN DER HOH', 8 7 8 7 88 7; Attr. to Nikolaus Decius, c.1485-c.1546; Harm. from Michael Praetorius, 1571-1621

528 Sing Praise to God Who Reigns Above

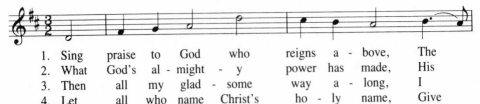

1. Sing praise to God who reigns a - bove, The
2. What God's al - might - y power has made, His
3. Then all my glad - some way a - long, I
4. Let all who name Christ's ho - ly name, Give

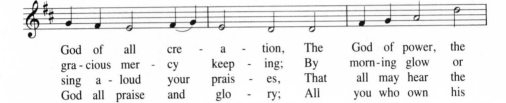

God of all cre - a - tion, The God of power, the
gra - cious mer - cy keep - ing; By morn - ing glow or
sing a - loud your prais - es, That all may hear the
God all praise and glo - ry; All you who own his

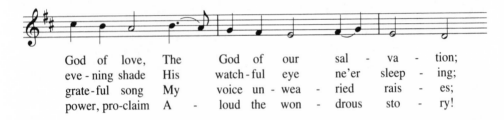

God of love, The God of our sal - va - tion;
eve - ning shade His watch - ful eye ne'er sleep - ing;
grate - ful song My voice un - wea - ried rais - es;
power, pro-claim A - loud the won - drous sto - ry!

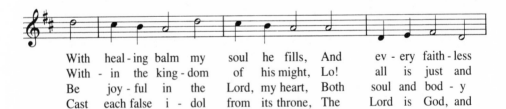

With heal - ing balm my soul he fills, And ev - ery faith - less
With - in the king - dom of his might, Lo! all is just and
Be joy - ful in the Lord, my heart, Both soul and bod - y
Cast each false i - dol from its throne, The Lord is God, and

mur - mur stills: To God all praise and glo - ry.
all is right: To God all praise and glo - ry.
sing your part: To God all praise and glo - ry.
he a - lone: To God all praise and glo - ry.

Text: *Sei Lob und Ehr' dem höchsten Gut;* Johann J. Schütz; 1640-1690; Tr. by Frances E. Cox, 1812-1897
Tune: MIT FREUDEN ZART, 8 7 8 7 88 7; Bohemian Brethren's *Kirchengesange*, 1566

Praise the Lord! You Heavens, Adore Him 529

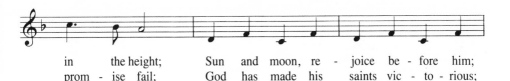

1. Praise the Lord! you heav'ns, a-dore him; Praise him, an-gels,
2. Praise the Lord! for he is glo-rious; Nev-er shall his
3. Wor-ship, hon-or, glo-ry, bless-ing, Lord, we of-fer

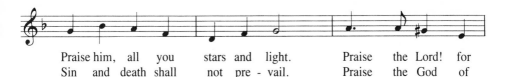

in the height; Sun and moon, re-joice be-fore him;
prom-ise fail; God has made his saints vic-to-rious;
as our gift. Young and old, your praise ex-press-ing,

Praise him, all you stars and light. Praise the Lord! for
Sin and death shall not pre-vail. Praise the God of
Our glad songs to you we lift. All the saints in

he has spo-ken; Worlds his might-y voice o-beyed;
our sal-va-tion! Hosts on high, his pow'r pro-claim;
heav'n a-dore you, We would join their glad ac-claim;

Laws which nev-er shall be bro-ken
Heav'n, and earth, and all cre-a-tion
As your an-gels serve be-fore you,

For their guid-ance he has made.
Praise and glo-ri-fy his name.
So on earth we praise your name.

Text: Psalm 148; St. 1-2, *Foundling Hospital Collection*, 1796; St. 3, Edward Osler, 1798-1863
Tune: HEAVENLY HOSTS, 8 7 8 7 D; Noel H. Tredinnick, b.1949, © 1973, Hope Publishing Co.

530 Praise, My Soul, the King of Heaven

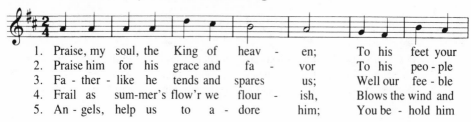

1. Praise, my soul, the King of heav - en; To his feet your
2. Praise him for his grace and fa - vor To his peo - ple
3. Fa - ther - like he tends and spares us; Well our fee - ble
4. Frail as sum-mer's flow'r we flour - ish, Blows the wind and
5. An - gels, help us to a - dore him; You be - hold him

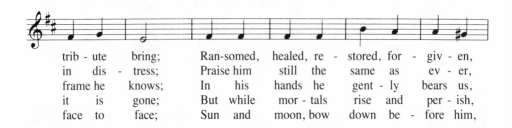

trib - ute bring; Ran-somed, healed, re - stored, for - giv - en,
in dis - tress; Praise him still the same as ev - er,
frame he knows; In his hands he gent - ly bears us,
it is gone; But while mor - tals rise and per - ish,
face to face; Sun and moon, bow down be - fore him,

Ev - er - more his prais - es sing: Al - le - lu - ia!
Slow to chide, and swift to bless: Al - le - lu - ia!
Res - cues us from all our foes. Al - le - lu - ia!
God en - dures un - chang - ing on: Al - le - lu - ia!
Dwell-ers all in time and space: Al - le - lu - ia!

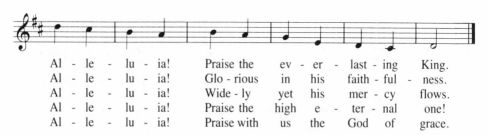

Al - le - lu - ia! Praise the ev - er - last - ing King.
Al - le - lu - ia! Glo - rious in his faith - ful - ness.
Al - le - lu - ia! Wide - ly yet his mer - cy flows.
Al - le - lu - ia! Praise the high e - ter - nal one!
Al - le - lu - ia! Praise with us the God of grace.

Text: Psalm (102)103; Henry F. Lyte, 1793-1847, alt.
Tune: LAUDA ANIMA, 8 7 8 7 8 7; John Goss, 1800-1880

There's a Spirit in the Air 531

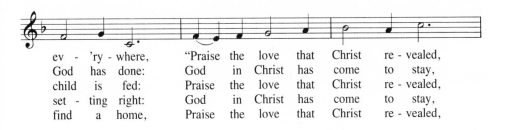

1. There's a spir - it in the air, Tell - ing Chris - tians
2. Lose your shy - ness, find your tongue; Tell the world what
3. When be - liev - ers break the bread, When a hun - gry
4. Still his Spir - it leads the fight, See - ing wrong and
5. When a strang - er's not a - lone, Where the home - less

ev - 'ry - where, "Praise the love that Christ re - vealed,
God has done: God in Christ has come to stay,
child is fed: Praise the love that Christ re - vealed,
set - ting right: God in Christ has come to stay,
find a home, Praise the love that Christ re - vealed,

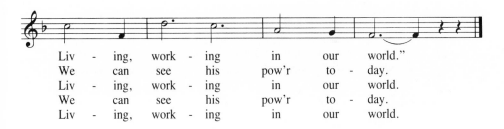

Liv - ing, work - ing in our world."
We can see his pow'r to - day.
Liv - ing, work - ing in our world.
We can see his pow'r to - day.
Liv - ing, work - ing in our world.

6. May his Spirit fill our praise,
   Guide our thoughts and change our ways.
   God in Christ has come to stay,
   We can see his power today.

7. There's a Spirit in the air,
   Calling people ev'rywhere;
   Praise the love that Christ revealed:
   Living, working in our world.

Text: Brian Wren, b.1936
Tune: LAUDS, 77 77; John W. Wilson, b.1905
© 1979, Hope Publishing Co.

532　Sing to the Lord a Joyful Song

1. Sing to the Lord a joy - ful song, Lift up your
2. For life and love, for rest and food, For dai - ly
3. For strength to those who on him wait His truth to
4. For joys un - told, that from a - bove Cheer those who
5. For he is Lord of heav'n and earth, Whom an - gels

hearts, your voic - es raise; To us his gra - cious
help and night - ly care, Sing to the Lord, for
prove, his will to do, Praise we our God, for
love his sweet em - ploy, Sing to our God, for
serve and saints a - dore, The Fa - ther, Son, and

gifts be - long, To him our songs of love and praise.
he is good, And praise his name, for it is fair.
he is great, Trust in his name, for it is true.
he is love, Ex - alt his name, for it is joy.
Spir - it blest, To whom all praise be now con - fessed.

Text: Psalm 145:1-2; John S. B. Monsell, 1811-1875
Tune: GONFALON ROYAL, LM; Percy C. Buck, 1871-1947, © Oxford University Press

533　New Songs of Celebration

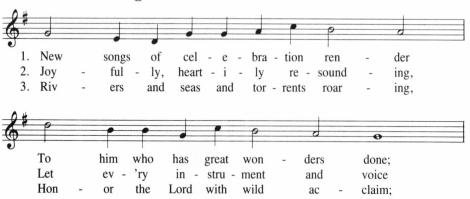

1. New songs of cel - e - bra - tion ren - der
2. Joy - ful - ly, heart - i - ly re - sound - ing,
3. Riv - ers and seas and tor - rents roar - ing,

To him who has great won - ders done;
Let ev - 'ry in - stru - ment and voice
Hon - or the Lord with wild ac - claim;

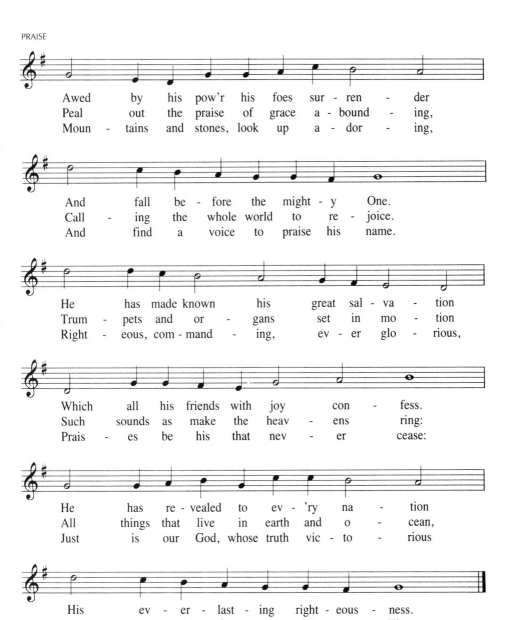

Awed by his pow'r his foes sur - ren - der
Peal out the praise of grace a - bound - ing,
Moun - tains and stones, look up a - dor - ing,

And fall be - fore the might - y One.
Call - ing the whole world to re - joice.
And find a voice to praise his name.

He has made known his great sal - va - tion
Trum - pets and or - gans set in mo - tion
Right - eous, com - mand - ing, ev - er glo - rious,

Which all his friends with joy con - fess.
Such sounds as make the heav - ens ring:
Prais - es be his that nev - er cease:

He has re - vealed to ev - 'ry na - tion
All things that live in earth and o - cean,
Just is our God, whose truth vic - to - rious

His ev - er - last - ing right - eous - ness.
Make mu - sic for your might - y King.
Es - tab - lish - es the world in peace.

Text: Psalm 98; Erik Routley, 1917-1982, © 1974, Hope Publishing Co.
Tune: RENDEZ À DIEU, 9 8 9 8 D; *Genevan Psalter*, 1551; Attr. to Louis Bourgeois, c.1510-1561; Harm. by Erik Routley, 1917-1982, ©1977 Hope Publishing Co.

534 Tell Out, My Soul, the Greatness of the Lord

1. Tell out, my soul, the great-ness of the Lord!
2. Tell out, my soul, the great-ness of his name!
3. Tell out, my soul, the great-ness of his might!
4. Tell out, my soul, the glo - ries of his word!

Un - num - bered bless-ings give my spir - it voice;
Make known his might, the deeds his arm has done;
Pow'rs and do - min-ions lay their glo - ry by;
Firm is his prom - ise, and his mer - cy sure.

Ten - der to me the prom-ise of his word;
His mer - cy sure, from age to age the same;
Proud hearts and stub - born wills are put to flight,
Tell out, my soul, the great-ness of the Lord

In God my Sav - ior shall my heart re - joice.
His ho - ly name—the Lord, the might - y One.
The hun - gry fed, the hum - ble lift - ed high.
To chil - dren's chil - dren and for ev - er - more!

Text: Luke 1:46-55; *Magnificat anima mea;* Timothy Dudley-Smith, b.1926, © 1962, Hope Publishing Co.
Tune: WOODLANDS, 10 10 10 10; Walter Greatorex, 1877-1949, © Oxford University Press

God, We Praise You 535

1. God, we praise you! God, we bless you! God, we
2. True a - pos - tles, faith - ful proph - ets, Saints who
3. Je - sus Christ, the king of glo - ry, Ev - er-
4. Christ, at God's right hand vic - to - rious, You will

name you sov-'reign Lord! Might-y King whom an - gels
set their world a - blaze, Mar - tyrs, once un - known, un-
last - ing Son of God, Hum - ble was your vir - gin
judge the world you made; Lord, in mer - cy help your

wor - ship, Fa - ther, by your church a - dored:
heed - ed, Join one grow - ing song of praise,
moth - er, Hard the lone - ly path you trod:
ser - vants For whose free - dom you have paid:

All cre - a - tion shows your glo - ry, Heav'n and
While your church on earth con - fess - es One ma-
By your cross is sin de - feat - ed, Hell con-
Raise us up from dust to glo - ry, Guard us

earth draw near your throne, Sing-ing "Ho - ly, ho - ly,
jes - tic Trin - i - ty: Fa - ther, Son, and Ho - ly
front - ed face to face, Heav-en o - pened to be-
from all sin to - day; King en - throned a - bove all

ho - ly, Lord of hosts, and God a - lone!"
Spir - it, God, our hope e - ter - nal - ly.
liev - ers, Sin - ners jus - ti - fied by grace.
prais - es, Save your peo - ple, God, we pray.

Text: Based on the *Te Deum*: Christopher Idle, b.1938. © 1982, Hope Publishing Co.
Tune: NETTLETON, 8 7 8 7 D; Wyeth's *Repository of Sacred Music, Pt. II, 1813*

536 Let All the World in Every Corner Sing

Let all the world in ev-'ry cor-ner
Let all the world in ev-'ry cor-ner

sing, My God and King! Let all the world in
sing, My God and King! Let all the world in

ev-'ry cor-ner sing, My God and King! The
ev-'ry cor-ner sing, My God and King! The

heav'ns are not too high, His prais-es there may fly; The
Church with psalms must shout, No door can keep them out; But,

earth is not too low, His prais-es there may grow.
a-bove all the heart Must bear the long-est part.

Let all the world in ev-'ry cor-ner sing, My
Let all the world in ev-'ry cor-ner sing, My

[1.]
God and King.
God and

[2.]
King.   A - men.

Text: George Herbert, 1593-1632
Tune: MAC DOUGALL, 10 4 10 4 66 66 10 4; Calvin Hampton, 1938-1984, © 1975, The Church Pension Fund

The God of Abraham Praise 537

1. The God of A-braham praise, Who reigns en-throned a - bove;
2. He by him-self has sworn: I on his oath de - pend;
3. There dwells the Lord, our King, The Lord, our Right-eous-ness,
4. The God who reigns on high The great arch-an - gels sing,

An - cient of ev - er - last-ing days, And God of love;
I shall, on ea - gle - wings up-borne, To heav'n as - cend:
Tri - umph-ant o'er the world and sin, The Prince of Peace;
And "Ho - ly, Ho - ly, Ho - ly," cry, "Al - might - y King!

To him up - lift your voice, At whose su - preme com - mand
I shall be - hold his face, I shall his power a - dore,
On Zi - on's sa - cred height His king - dom he main - tains,
Who was, and is, the same, For all e - ter - ni - ty,

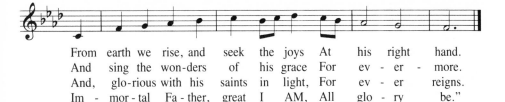

From earth we rise, and seek the joys At his right hand.
And sing the won-ders of his grace For ev - er - more.
And, glo-rious with his saints in light, For ev - er reigns.
Im - mor - tal Fa - ther, great I AM, All glo - ry be."

Text: *Yigdal Elohim Hai;* Ascr. to Daniel ben Judah Dayyan, fl.1400; Para. by Thomas Olivers, 1725-1799. alt.
Tune: LEONI, 6 6 8 4 D; From the *Yigdal;* Transcribed by Meyer Lyon, c.1751-1797

538 Christians, Lift Up Your Hearts

Christians, lift up your hearts, and make this a day of re-joic-ing;

God is our strength and song; glo-ry and praise to his name!

1. This is the house of the Lord, where
3. Praise that his love o-ver-flowed in the
5. Come, Ho-ly Spir-it, to us, who

seek-ers and find-ers are wel-come; En-ter its
hearts of all who re-ceived him, Join-ing to-
live by your pres-ence with-in us, Come to di-

D.C.

gates with your praise, fill all its courts with your song:
geth-er in peace those once di-vid-ed by sin:
rect our course, give us your life and your power:

2. Strong and a-lert in his grace, God's peo-ple are
4. Those who are bur-dened with sin find here the
6. Al-might-y God, send us out to live to your

one in their wor-ship: Kept by his peace they de-
joy of for-give-ness, Lay-ing their sins be-fore
praise and your glo-ry; Yours is the pow'r and the

D.C.

part, read-y for serv-ing their Lord:
Christ, par-don and peace their re-ward:
might, ours be the cour-age and faith:

Text: John E. Bowers, b.1923, alt., © Canon John E. Bowers
Tune: SALVE FESTA DIES, Irregular with refrain; Ralph Vaughan Williams, 1872-1958, © Oxford University Press

Sing Praise to the Lord 539

1. Sing praise to the Lord! praise God in the height;
2. Sing praise to the Lord! praise God up - on earth,
3. Sing praise to the Lord, all things that give sound;
4. Sing praise to the Lord! thanks - giv - ing and song

Re - joice in his word, you an - gels of light;
In tune - ful ac - cord, all you of new birth;
Each ju - bi - lant chord re - ech - o a - round;
To him be out - poured all a - ges a - long;

O heav - ens, a - dore him by whom you were made,
Praise him who has brought you his grace from a - bove,
Loud or - gans, his glo - ry tell forth in deep tone,
For love in cre - a - tion, for heav - en re - stored,

And wor - ship be - fore him in bright - ness ar - rayed.
Praise him who has taught you to sing of his love.
And trum - pets, the sto - ry of what God has done.
For grace of sal - va - tion, sing praise to the Lord!

Text: Psalm 150; Henry W. Baker, 1821-1877, alt.
Tune: LAUDATE DOMINUM, 10 10 11 11; Charles H. H. Parry, 1840-1918

540 Shout for Joy, Loud and Long

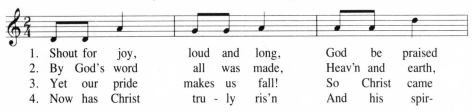

1. Shout for joy, loud and long, God be praised
2. By God's word all was made, Heav'n and earth,
3. Yet our pride makes us fall! So Christ came
4. Now has Christ tru - ly ris'n And his spir-

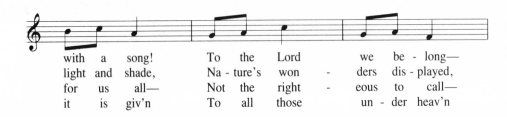

with a song! To the Lord we be - long—
light and shade, Na - ture's won - ders dis - played,
for us all— Not the right - eous to call—
it is giv'n To all those un - der heav'n

Child-ren of our Mak - er, God the great life-
We to rule cre - a - tion From its first foun-
By his cross and pas - sion, Bring - ing us sal-
Who will walk be - side him, Though they once de-

giv - er! Shout for joy, joy, joy! Shout for joy, joy, joy!
da - tion. Shout for joy, joy, joy! Shout for joy, joy, joy!
va - tion! Shout for joy, joy, joy! Shout for joy, joy, joy!
nied him! Shout for joy, joy, joy! Shout for joy, joy, joy!

God is love, God is light, God is ev - er - last - ing!
God is love, God is light, God is ev - er - last - ing!
God is love, God is light, God is ev - er - last - ing!
God is love, God is light, God is ev - er - last - ing!

Text: David Mowbray, b.1938, © 1982, Hope Publishing Co.
Tune: PERSONET HODIE, 666 66 with refrain; *Piae Cantiones*, 1582; Harm. by Richard Proulx, b.1937, © 1978, GIA Publications, Inc.

O God beyond All Praising 541

1. O God be-yond all prais-ing, We wor-ship you to - day
2. Then hear, O gra-cious Sav-ior, Ac - cept the love we bring,

And sing the love a - maz-ing That songs can-not re - pay;
That we who know your fa - vor May serve you as our king;

For we can on - ly won - der At ev - 'ry gift you send,
And wheth - er our to - mor-rows Be filled with good or ill,

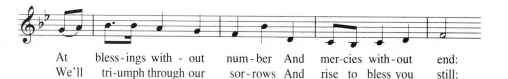

At bless-ings with - out num - ber And mer-cies with-out end:
We'll tri-umph through our sor - rows And rise to bless you still:

We lift our hearts be - fore you And wait up-on your word,
To mar - vel at your beau-ty And glo - ry in your ways,

We hon - or and a - dore you, Our great and might - y Lord.
And make a joy - ful du - ty Our sac - ri - fice of praise.

Text: Michael Perry, b.1942, © 1982, Hope Publishing Co.
Tune: THAXTED, 13 13 13 13 13 13; Gustave Holst, 1874-1934

542 Glory to God in the Highest

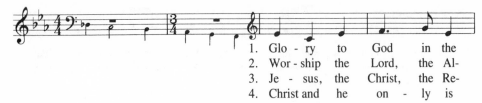

1. Glo - ry to God in the
2. Wor - ship the Lord, the Al-
3. Je - sus, the Christ, the Re-
4. Christ and he on - ly is

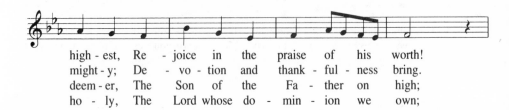

high - est, Re - joice in the praise of his worth!
might - y; De - vo - tion and thank - ful - ness bring.
deem - er, The Son of the Fa - ther on high;
ho - ly, The Lord whose do - min - ion we own;

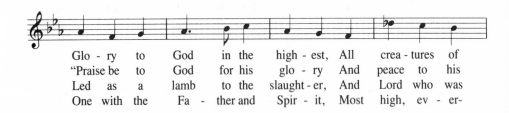

Glo - ry to God in the high - est, All crea - tures of
"Praise be to God for his glo - ry And peace to his
Led as a lamb to the slaught - er, And Lord who was
One with the Fa - ther and Spir - it, Most high, ev - er-

heav - en - ly birth! Glo - ry to God in the
peo - ple," we sing; "Glo - ry to God in the
will - ing to die; God in the heav - en - ly
last - ing, a - lone; Reign-ing e - ter - nal in

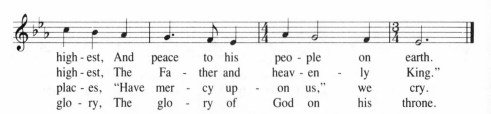

high - est, And peace to his peo - ple on earth.
high - est, The Fa - ther and heav - en - ly King."
plac - es, "Have mer - cy up - on us," we cry.
glo - ry, The glo - ry of God on his throne.

Text: *Gloria in excelsis Deo;* Timothy Dudley-Smith, b.1926, © 1980, Hope Publishing Co.
Tune: RUSSWIN, 8 8 8 8 8 8; Richard Proulx, b.1937, © 1980, GIA Publications, Inc.

Christ Is the World's Light 543

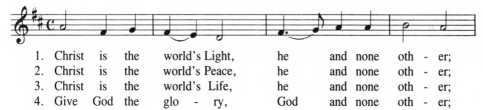

1. Christ is the world's Light, he and none oth - er;
2. Christ is the world's Peace, he and none oth - er;
3. Christ is the world's Life, he and none oth - er;
4. Give God the glo - ry, God and none oth - er;

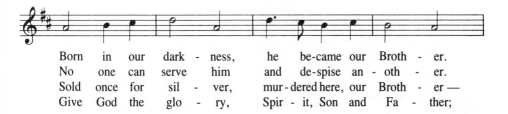

Born in our dark - ness, he be-came our Broth - er.
No one can serve him and de-spise an - oth - er.
Sold once for sil - ver, mur - dered here, our Broth - er —
Give God the glo - ry, Spir - it, Son and Fa - ther;

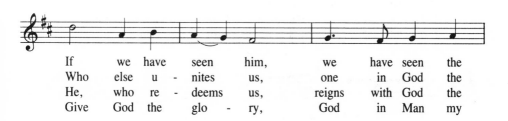

If we have seen him, we have seen the
Who else u - nites us, one in God the
He, who re - deems us, reigns with God the
Give God the glo - ry, God in Man my

Fa - ther: Glo - ry to God on high.
Fa - ther? Glo - ry to God on high.
Fa - ther: Glo - ry to God on high.
broth - er: Glo - ry to God on high.

Text: Fred Pratt Green, b.1903, © 1969, Hope Publishing Co.
Tune: CHRISTE SANCTORUM, 10 11 11 6; *Paris Antiphoner*, 1681

544 Reap Me the Earth

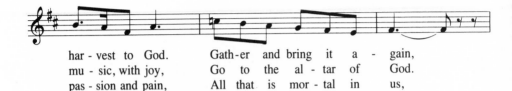

1. Reap me the earth as a
2. Go with your song and your
3. Glad - ness and pit - y and

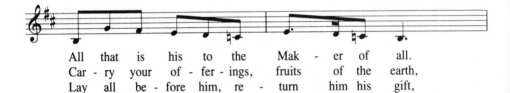

har - vest to God. Gath-er and bring it a - gain,
mu - sic, with joy, Go to the al - tar of God.
pas - sion and pain, All that is mor - tal in us,

All that is his to the Mak - er of all.
Car - ry your of - fer - ings, fruits of the earth,
Lay all be - fore him, re - turn him his gift,

Lift it and of - fer it high:
Work of your la - bor - ing hands:
God, to whom all shall go home:

Bring bread, bring wine, give glo - ry to the Lord.

Whose is the earth but God's, whose is the praise but

his?

Text: Luke Connaughton, 1917-1979, © 1970, Mayhew McCrimmon Ltd.
Tune: BAY HALL, 10 7 10 7 with refrain; Michael Dawney, b.1942, ©

Praise Him 545

1. Praise him, praise him, praise him! pow'rs and dom - i - na-tions,
2. Praise him, praise him, praise him! o - cean depths and wa-ters,
3. Praise him, praise him, praise him! saints of God who fear him:

Praise his Name in glo - rious light, you crea - tures of the day!
El - e-ments of earth and heav'n, your sev - eral prais-es blend.
To the high - est Name of all, con - cert - ed an-thems raise —

Moon and stars ring prais - es through the con-stel - la - tions:
Birds and beasts and cat - tle, Ad - am's sons and daugh-ters,
Is - rael's sons and daugh-ters, ho - ly peo-ple near him,

Lord God, whose word shall nev - er pass a-
Wor - ship the King whose reign shall nev - er
Whom he ex - alts to power and crowns with

way.
end!
praise.

Text: Psalm 148; Michael A. Perry, b.1942
Tune: PRAISE HIM, 4 8 7 6 6 6 10; Norman L. Warren, b.1934
© 1973, Hope Publishing Co.

546 O That I Had a Thousand Voices

1. O that I had a thou - sand voic - es
2. O all you pow'rs that he im - plant - ed,
3. You for - est leaves so green and ten - der
4. All crea - tures that have breath and mo - tion,
5. Cre - a - tor, hum - bly I im - plore you

To praise my God with thou-sand tongues! My heart, which
A - rise, keep si - lence now no more; Put forth the
That dance for joy in sum - mer air, You mead - ow
That throng the earth, the sea, the sky, Come, share with
To lis - ten to my earth - ly song Un - til that

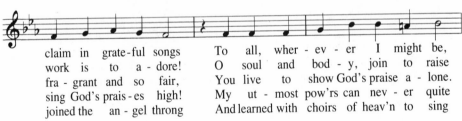

in the Lord re - joic - es, Would then pro-
strength that God has grant - ed! Your no - blest
grass - es, bright and slen - der, You flow'rs so
me my heart's de - vo - tion, Help me to
day when I a - dore you, When I have

claim in grate-ful songs To all, wher - ev - er I might be,
work is to a - dore! O soul and bod - y, join to raise
fra - grant and so fair, You live to show God's praise a - lone.
sing God's prais - es high! My ut - most pow'rs can nev - er quite
joined the an - gel throng And learned with choirs of heav'n to sing

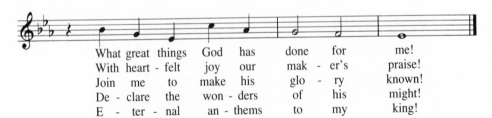

What great things God has done for me!
With heart - felt joy our mak - er's praise!
Join me to make his glo - ry known!
De - clare the won - ders of his might!
E - ter - nal an - thems to my king!

Text: *O dass ich tausend Zungen hätte;* Johann Mentzer, 1658-1734; Tr. *The Lutheran Hymnal,* 1941, alt.
Tune: O DASS ICH TAUSEND ZUNGEN HÄTTE, 9 8 9 8 88; Attr. to Johann B. König, 1691-1758

Praise to the Lord, the Almighty 547

1. Praise to the Lord, the Almighty, the king of creation!
O my soul, praise him, for he is your health and salvation!
Come, all who hear: Brothers and sisters, draw near,
Praise him in glad adoration!

2. Praise to the Lord, above all things so mightily reigning;
Keeping us safe at his side, and so gently sustaining.
Have you not seen All you have needed has been
Met by his gracious ordaining?

3. Praise to the Lord, who shall prosper our work and defend us;
Surely his goodness and mercy shall daily attend us.
Ponder anew What the Almighty can do,
Who with his love will befriend us.

4. Praise to the Lord — O let all that is in us adore him!
All that has life and breath come now with praises before him!
Let the "Amen!" Sound from his people again —
Gladly with praise we adore him!

Text: *Lobe den Herren, den mächtigen König*; Joachim Neander, 1650-1680; Tr. by Catherine Winkworth, 1827-1878, alt.
Tune: LOBE DEN HERREN, 14 14 47 8; Straslund Gesangbuch, 1665; Descant by C.S. Lang, 1891-1971, © 1953, Novello and Co. Ltd.

548 Adoramus Te Domine

(hum)　　　　　　　　A - do - ra-mus te　Do-mi - ne.

Text: *We adore you, Lord;* Taizé Community, 1978
Tune: Jacques Berthier, b.1923
© 1979, Les Presses de Taizé

549 When in Our Music God Is Glorified

1. When in　our　mu - sic God is　glo - ri - fied,
2. How of - ten,　mak - ing mu - sic, we have　found
3. So　has　the　Church in lit - ur - gy and　song,
4. And　did　not　Je - sus sing a　psalm that　night
5. Let　ev - 'ry　in - stru-ment be　tuned for　praise!

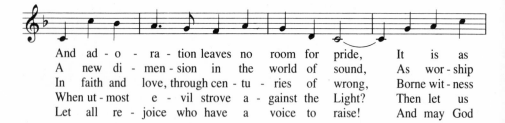

And ad - o - ra - tion leaves no　room for　pride,　It　is　as
A　new di - men - sion in　the　world of　sound,　As wor - ship
In　faith and　love, through cen - tu - ries of　wrong,　Borne wit - ness
When ut - most　e - vil strove a - gainst the　Light?　Then let　us
Let　all　re - joice who have　a　voice to　raise!　And may God

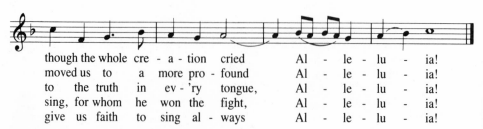

though the whole cre - a - tion　cried　Al - le - lu - ia!
moved us　to　a　more pro - found　Al - le - lu - ia!
to　the truth　in　ev - 'ry　tongue,　Al - le - lu - ia!
sing, for whom　he　won the　fight,　Al - le - lu - ia!
give us faith　to　sing al - ways　Al - le - lu - ia!

Text: Mark 14:26; Fred Pratt Green, b.1903, © 1972, Hope Publishing Co.
Tune: ENGELBERG, 10 10 10 with alleluia; Charles V. Stanford, 1852-1924

Sing a New Song to the Lord   550

1. Sing   a   new   song   to   the   Lord,
2. Now   to   the   ends   of   the   earth
3. Sing   a   new   song   and   re - joice,
4. Join   with   the   hills   and   the   sea

He   to   whom   won - ders   be - long!
See   his   sal - va - tion   is   shown;
Pub - lish   his   prais - es   a - broad!
Thun - ders   of   praise   to   pro - long!

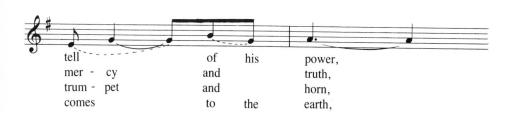

Re - joice   in   his   tri - umph   and
And   still   he   re - mem - bers   his
Let   voic - es   in   cho - rus,   with
In   judge - ment   and   jus - tice   he

tell   of   his   power,
mer - cy   and   truth,
trum - pet   and   horn,
comes   to   the   earth,

O   sing   to   the   Lord   a   new   song!
Un - chang - ing   in   love   to   his   own.
Re - sound   for   the   joy   of   the   Lord!
O   sing   to   the   Lord   a   new   song!

Text: Psalm 98; Timothy Dudley-Smith, b.1926,
Tune: CANTATE DOMINO, Irregular; David G. Wilson, b.1940,
© 1973, Hope Publishing Co.

551 Praise the Lord of Heaven

1. Praise the Lord of heav - en; Praise him in the height!
2. Praise the Lord, you foun - tains Of the depths and seas,
3. Praise him, all you na - tions, Rul - ers and all kings;

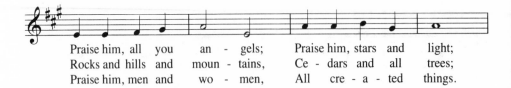

Praise him, all you an - gels; Praise him, stars and light;
Rocks and hills and moun - tains, Ce - dars and all trees;
Praise him, men and wo - men, All cre - a - ted things.

Praise him, earth and wa - ters, Praise him, all you skies;
Praise him, clouds and va - pors, Snow and hail and fire,
Glo - ri - ous and might - y Is his name a - lone;

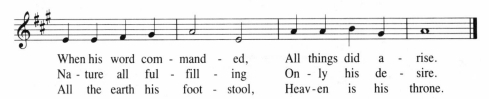

When his word com - mand - ed, All things did a - rise.
Na - ture all ful - fill - ing, On - ly his de - sire.
All the earth his foot - stool, Heav-en is his throne.

Text: Psalm 148; Thomas B. Browne, 1805-1874, alt.
Tune: UNE VAINE CRAINTE, 6 5 6 5 D; French

552 Come, We That Love the Lord

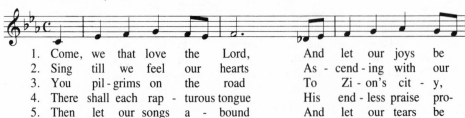

1. Come, we that love the Lord, And let our joys be
2. Sing till we feel our hearts As - cend - ing with our
3. You pil - grims on the road To Zi - on's cit - y,
4. There shall each rap - turous tongue His end - less praise pro-
5. Then let our songs a - bound And let our tears be

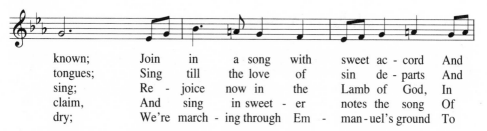

known; Join in a song with sweet ac - cord And
tongues; Sing till the love of sin de - parts And
sing; Re - joice now in the Lamb of God, In
claim, And sing in sweet - er notes the song Of
dry; We're march - ing through Em - man - uel's ground To

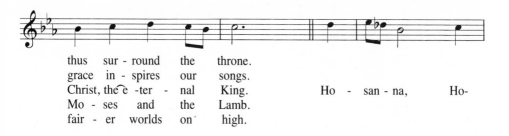

thus sur - round the throne.
grace in - spires our songs.
Christ, the e -ter - nal King. Ho - san - na, Ho-
Mo - ses and the Lamb.
fair - er worlds on high.

san - na, Re - joice, give thanks and sing.

Text: St. 1 & 5, Isaac Watts, 1674-1748; St. 2-4, William Hammond, 1719-1783
Tune: VINEYARD HAVEN, SM with refrain; Richard Dirksen, b.1921, © 1974, 1986 Harold Flammer, Inc.

Canon Magnificat 553

Ⓐ Ma - gni - fi - cat, ma - gni - fi - cat, Ⓑ Ma - gni - fi - cat a - ni - ma

me - a Do - mi - num. Ⓒ Ma - gni - fi - cat, ma - gni - fi - cat,

Ⓓ Ma - gni - fi - cat a - ni - ma me - a!

Text: Luke 1:46, My soul magnifies the Lord; Taizé Community, 1978
Tune: Jacques Berthier, b.1923
© 1979, Les Presses de Taizé

554 Sing Alleluia, Praise the Lord

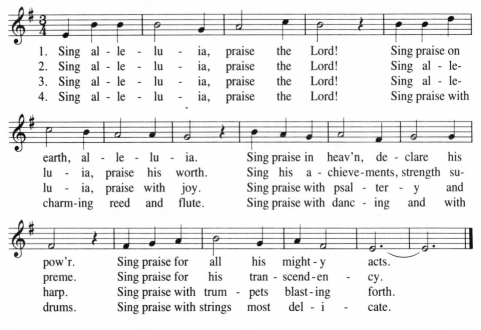

1. Sing al - le - lu - ia, praise the Lord! Sing praise on
2. Sing al - le - lu - ia, praise the Lord! Sing al - le-
3. Sing al - le - lu - ia, praise the Lord! Sing al - le-
4. Sing al - le - lu - ia, praise the Lord! Sing praise with

earth, al - le - lu - ia. Sing praise in heav'n, de - clare his
lu - ia, praise his worth. Sing his a - chieve-ments, strength su-
lu - ia, praise with joy. Sing praise with psal - ter - y and
charm-ing reed and flute. Sing praise with danc - ing and with

pow'r. Sing praise for all his might - y acts.
preme. Sing praise for his tran - scend-en - cy.
harp. Sing praise with trum - pets blast-ing forth.
drums. Sing praise with strings most del - i - cate.

5. Sing alleluia, praise the Lord!
Sing alleluia, cymbals clash.
Sing alleluia, cymbals ring.
Sing all that breathe, alleluia!

6. Sing alleluia, praise the Lord!
All ages glorify his name.
Father and Son and Spirit, one;
Now and for evermore. Amen!

Text: Psalm 150 *Lobt Gott in seinem Heiligtum;* Cornelius Becker, 1561-1604; Tr. by Daniel G. Reuning, b.1935, © 1972, GIA Publications, Inc.
Tune: LOBT GOTT IN SEINEM HEILIGTUM, LM; Heinrich Schütz, 1585-1672

555 Jubilate Deo

Canon - *2 voices*

Ju - bi - la - te De - o om - nis ter - ra.

Ser - vi - te Do - mi - no in lae - ti - ti - a.

Al - le - lu - ia, al - le - lu - ia, in lae - ti - ti - a.

Al - le - lu - ia, al - le - lu - ia, in lae - ti - ti - a!

Text: Psalm 100, *Rejoice in God, all the earth. Serve the Lord with gladness;* Taizé Community, 1978
Tune: Jacques Berthier, b.1923
© 1979, Les Presses de Taizé

Lord of Our Growing Years 556

1. Lord of our grow - ing years,   With us from in - fan - cy,
2. Lord of our strong - est years,   Stretch-ing our youth - ful pow'rs,
3. Lord of our mid - dle years,   Giv - er of stead - fast - ness,
4. Lord of our old - er years,   Steep though the road may be,
5. Lord of our clos - ing years,   Al - ways your prom - ise stands;

Laugh-ter and quick-dried tears,   Fresh-ness and en - er - gy:
Lov - ers and pi - o - neers   When all the world seems ours:
Cour - age that per - se - veres   When there is small suc - cess:
Rid us of fool - ish fears,   Bring us se - ren - i - ty:
Hold us when death ap - pears,   Safe - ly with - in your hands:

Your grace sur - rounds us all our days—
Your grace sur - rounds us all our days—
Your grace sur - rounds us all our days—
Your grace sur - rounds us all our days—
Your grace sur - rounds us all our days—

For all your gifts we bring our praise.
For all your gifts we bring our praise.
For all your gifts we bring our praise.
For all your gifts we bring our praise.
For all your gifts we bring our praise.

Text: David Mowbray, b.1938, © 1982, Hope Publishing Co.
Tune: LITTLE CORNARD, 6 6 6 6 88; Martin Shaw, 1875-1958, © J. Curwen and Sons

557 For the Beauty of the Earth

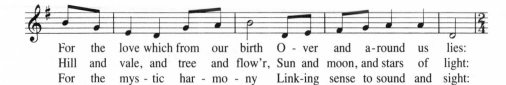

1. For the beau - ty of the earth, For the glo - ry of the skies,
2. For the beau - ty of each hour Of the day and of the night,
3. For the joy of ear and eye, For the heart and mind's de - light,
4. For the joy of hu-man love, Broth-er, sis - ter, par - ent, child,

For the love which from our birth O - ver and a-round us lies:
Hill and vale, and tree and flow'r, Sun and moon, and stars of light:
For the mys - tic har - mo - ny Link-ing sense to sound and sight:
Friends on earth, and friends a - bove; For all gen - tle thoughts and mild:

Lord of all, to you we raise This our hymn of grate - ful praise.

5. For your church, that evermore
Lifts its holy hands above,
Off'ring up on ev'ry shore
Its pure sacrifice of love:
Lord of all, to you we raise
This our hymn of grateful praise.

6. For, yourself, best Gift Divine!
To this world so freely giv'n;
Word Incarnate, God's design,
Peace on earth and joy in heav'n:
Lord of all, to you we raise
This our hymn of grateful praise.

Text: Folliot S. Pierpont, 1835-1917
Tune: LUCERNA LAUDONIAE, 7 7 7 7 77; David Evans, 1874-1948, © Oxford University Press

Father, We Thank Thee, Who Hast Planted 558

1. Fa - ther, we thank thee, who hast plant - ed Thy ho - ly
2. Watch o'er thy Church, O Lord, in mer - cy, Save it from

Name with - in our hearts. Knowl-edge and faith and life im-
e - vil, guard it still, Per - fect it in thy love, u-

mor - tal Je - sus, thy Son, to us im - parts.
nite it, Cleansed and con-formed un - to thy will.

Thou, Lord, didst make all for thy plea - sure, Didst give us
As grain, once scat - ter'd on the hill - sides, Was in this

food for all our days, Giv - ing in Christ the Bread
bro - ken bread made one, So from all lands thy Church

e - ter - nal; Thine is the power, be thine the praise.
be gath - er'd In - to thy king - dom by thy Son.

Text: From the *Didache*, c.110; Tr. by F. Bland Tucker, 1895-1984, alt., © 1940, The Church Pension Fund
Tune: RENDEZ À DIEU, 9 8 9 8 D; *Genevan Psalter*, 1551; Attr. to Louis Bourgeois, c.1510-1561

559 Let All Things Now Living

1. Let all things now liv - ing A song of thanks - giv - ing
2. His law he en - forc - es, The stars in their cours - es,

To God our Cre - a - tor tri - um - phant - ly raise;
The sun in its or - bit o - be - dient - ly shine,

Who fash-ioned and made us, Pro - tect - ed and stayed us,
The hills and the moun-tains, The riv - ers and foun - tains,

By guid - ing us on to the end of our days.
The depths of the o - cean pro - claim God di - vine.

God's ban - ners are o'er us, Pure light goes be - fore us,
We, too, should be voic - ing Our love and re - joic - ing

A pil - lar of fire shin - ing forth in the night:
With glad ad - o - ra - tion, a song let us raise:

Till shad - ows have van - ished And dark - ness is ban - ished,
Till all things now liv - ing U - nite in thanks - giv - ing,

As for - ward we trav - el from light in - to Light.
To God in the high - est, ho - san - na and praise.

Text: Katherine K. Davis, 1892-1980, © 1939, E.C. Schirmer Music Co.
Tune: ASH GROVE, 66 11 66 11 D; Welsh; Harm. by Gerald H. Knight, 1908-1979, © The Royal School of Church Music

Now Thank We All Our God 560

1. Now thank we all our God With hearts and hands and voic - es,
2. O may this gra - cious God Through all our life be near us,
3. All praise and thanks to God The Fa - ther now be giv - en,

Who won-drous things has done, In whom his world re - joic - es;
With ev - er joy - ful hearts And bless - ed peace to cheer us;
The Son, and Spir - it blest, Who reigns in high - est heav - en,

Who, from our moth - ers' arms, Hath blessed us on our way
Pre - serve us in his grace, And guide us in dis - tress,
E - ter - nal, Tri - une God, Whom earth and heav'n a - dore;

With count-less gifts of love, And still is ours to - day.
And free us from all sin, Till heav - en we pos - sess.
For thus it was, is now, And shall be ev - er - more.

Text: *Nun danket alle Gott;* Martin Rinkart, 1586-1649; Tr. by Catherine Winkworth, 1827-1878, alt.
Tune: NUN DANKET, 6 7 6 7 6 6 6 6; Johann Crüger, 1598-1662; Harm. by A. Gregory Murray, OSB, b.1905

561 Confitemini Domino

Con-fi - te - mi - ni Do-mi - no quo - ni - am bo - nus.

Con-fi - te - mi - ni Do-mi - no, Al - le - lu - ia!

Text: Psalm 137, *Give thanks to the Lord for he is good;* Taizé Community, 1982
Tune: Jacques Berthier, b.1923
© 1982, Les Presses de Taizé

562 For the Fruits of This Creation

1. For the fruits of this cre - a - tion, Thanks be to
2. In the just re - ward of la - bor, God's will is
3. For the har - vests of the Spir - it, Thanks be to

God; For the gifts to ev - 'ry na - tion,
done; In the help we give our neigh - bor,
God; For the good we all in - her - it,

Thanks be to God; For the plow - ing,
God's will is done; In our world - wide
Thanks be to God; For the won - ders

sow - ing, reap - ing, Si - lent growth while we are sleep - ing,
task of car - ing For the hun - gry and de - spair - ing,
that as - tound us, For the truths that still con - found us,

Fu - ture needs in earth's safe keep - ing, Thanks be to God.
In the har - vests we are shar - ing, God's will is done.
Most of all, that love has found us, Thanks be to God.

Text: Fred Pratt Green, b.1903. © 1970, Hope Publishing Co.
Tune: EAST ACKLAM, 8 4 8 4 888 4; Francis Jackson, b.1917, ©

God, Omnipotent, Eternal 563

1. God, om - nip - o - tent, e - ter - nal,
2. In that dis - tant, wild be - gin - ning
3. "Si - lence this in - de - cent danc - ing,"
4. Lord, for - give us; Lord, re - store us,
5. Teach us to de - light in jus - tice,

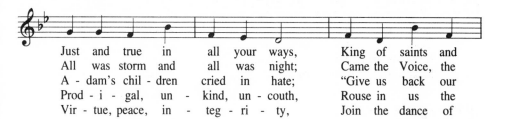

Just and true in all your ways, King of saints and
All was storm and all was night; Came the Voice, the
A - dam's chil - dren cried in hate; "Give us back our
Prod - i - gal, un - kind, un - couth, Rouse in us the
Vir - tue, peace, in - teg - ri - ty, Join the dance of

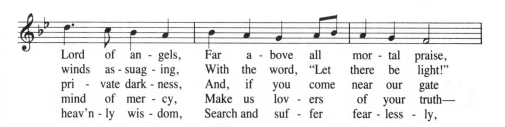

Lord of an - gels, Far a - bove all mor - tal praise,
winds as - suag - ing, With the word, "Let there be light!"
pri - vate dark - ness, And, if you come near our gate
mind of mer - cy, Make us lov - ers of your truth—
heav'n - ly wis - dom, Search and suf - fer fear - less - ly,

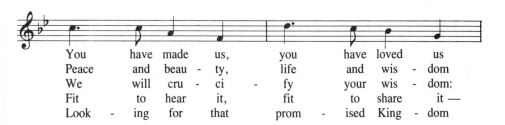

You have made us, you have loved us
Peace and beau - ty, life and wis - dom
We will cru - ci - fy your wis - dom:
Fit to hear it, fit to share it —
Look - ing for that prom - ised King - dom

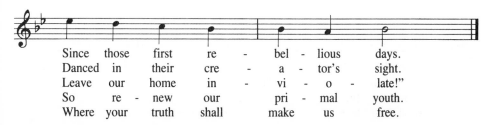

Since those first re - bel - lious days.
Danced in their cre - a - tor's sight.
Leave our home in - vi - o - late!"
So re - new our pri - mal youth.
Where your truth shall make us free.

Text: Erik Routley, 1917-1982, © 1979, Hope Publishing Co.
Tune: REGENT SQUARE, 8 7 8 7 8 7; Henry T. Smart, 1813-1879

564 Jesus, Come! For We Invite You

1. Je - sus, come! for we in - vite you,
2. Je - sus, come! trans - form our pleas - ures,
3. Je - sus, come! in new cre - a - tion,
4. Je - sus, come! sur - prise our dull - ness,

Guest and mas - ter, friend and Lord;
Guide us in - to paths un - known;
Heav'n brought near in power di - vine;
Make us will - ing to re - ceive

Now as once at Ca - na's wed - ding,
Bring your gifts, com - mand your ser - vants,
Give your un - ex - pect - ed glo - ry
More than we can yet i - mag - ine,

Speak, and let us hear your word:
Let us trust in you a - lone:
Chang - ing wa - ter in - to wine:
All the best you have to give:

Lead us through our need or doubt - ing,
Though your hand may work in se - cret,
Rouse the faith of your dis - ci - ples —
Let us find your hid - den rich - es,

Hope be born and joy re - stored.
All shall see what you have done.
Come, our first and great - est Sign!
Taste your love, be - lieve, and live!

Text: John 2; Christopher Idle, b.1938, © 1982, Hope Publishing Co.
Tune: BEST GIFT, 8 7 8 7 8 7; Ronald F. Krisman, b.1946, © 1986, GIA Publications, Inc.

Hope of the World   565

1. Hope of the world, O Christ of great com - pas - sion:
2. Hope of the world, God's gift from high - est heav - en,
3. Hope of the world, a - foot on dust - y high - ways,
4. Hope of the world, who by your cross did save us
5. Hope of the world, O Christ, o'er death vic - to - rious,

Speak to our fear - ful hearts by con - flict rent.
Bring - ing to hun - gry souls the bread of life:
Show - ing to wan - d'ring souls the path of light:
From death and dark de - spair, from sin and guilt:
Who by this sign did con - quer grief and pain:

Save us, your peo - ple, from con - sum - ing pas - sion,
Still let your Spir - it un - to us be giv - en
Walk now be - side us lest the tempt - ing by - ways
We ren - der back the love your mer - cy gave us;
We would be faith - ful to your gos - pel glo - rious;

Who by our own false hopes and aims are spent.
To heal earth's wounds and end our bit - ter strife.
Lure us a - way from you to end - less night.
Take now our lives and use them as you will.
You are our Lord! And you for ev - er reign!

Text: Georgia Harkness, 1891-1974, alt., © 1954, 1982, Hymn Society of America
Tune: DONNE SECOURS, 11 10 11 10; *Genevan Psalter,* 1551; Harm. by Claude Goudimel, c.1505-1572

566 Come to Us, Creative Spirit

1. Come to us, cre - a - tive Spir - it, In our
2. Po - et, paint - er, mu - sic - mak - er, All your
3. Word from God e - ter - nal spring - ing, Fill our
4. In all plac - es and for ev - er Glo - ry

Fa - ther's house; Ev - 'ry hu - man tal - ent hal - low,
trea - sures bring; Crafts-man, ac - tor, grace-ful danc - er,
minds, we pray; And in all ar - tis - tic vi - sion
be ex - pressed To the Son, with God the Fa - ther

Hid - den skills a - rouse, That with- in your earth - ly
Make your of - fer - ing; Join your hands in cel - e-
Give in - teg - ri - ty: May the flame with - in us
And the Spir - it blessed: In our wor - ship and our

tem - ple, Wise and sim - ple, may re - joice.
bra - tion: Let cre - a - tion shout and sing!
burn - ing Kin - dle yearn - ing day by day.
liv - ing Keep us striv - ing for the best.

Text: David Mowbray, b.1938, © Stainer and Bell Publications
Tune: CASTLEWOOD, 8 5 8 5 84 3; Richard Proulx, b.1937, © 1986, GIA Publications, Inc.

567 God Be in My Head

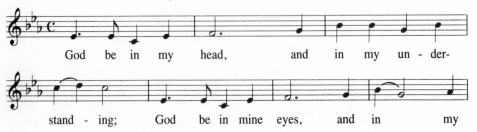

God be in my head, and in my un - der-

stand - ing; God be in mine eyes, and in my

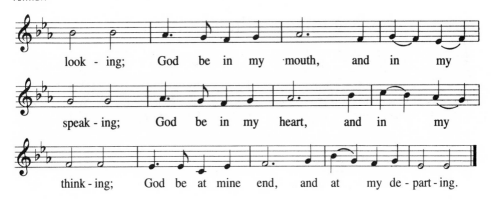

look - ing; God be in my mouth, and in my

speak - ing; God be in my heart, and in my

think - ing; God be at mine end, and at my de - part - ing.

Text: *Sarum Primer,* 1514
Tune: FIELD, Irregular; Keith Landis, b.1922; Harm. Jeffrey Rickard, b.1942, © 1986, Praise Publications

Lord of All Hopefulness 568

1. Lord of all hope - ful - ness, Lord of all joy,
2. Lord of all ea - ger - ness, Lord of all faith,
3. Lord of all kind - li - ness, Lord of all grace,
4. Lord of all gen - tle - ness, Lord of all calm,

Whose trust, e - ver child - like, no cares can de - stroy,
Whose strong hands were skilled at the plane and the lathe,
Your hands swift to wel - come, your arms to em - brace,
Whose voice is con - tent - ment, whose pres - ence is balm,

Be there at our wak - ing, and give us, we pray,
Be there at our la - bors, and give us, we pray,
Be there at our hom - ing, and give us, we pray,
Be there at our sleep - ing, and give us, we pray,

Your bliss in our hearts, Lord, at the break of the day.
Your strength in our hearts, Lord, at the noon of the day.
Your love in our hearts, Lord, at the eve of the day.
Your peace in our hearts, Lord, at the end of the day.

Text: Jan Struther, 1901-1953, © Oxford University Press
Tune: SLANE, 10 11 11 12; Gaelic; Harm. by Erik Routely, 1917-1982, © 1985, Hope Publishing Co.

569 Come, My Way, My Truth, My Life

1. Come, my Way, my Truth, my Life: Such a
2. Come, my Light, my Feast, my Strength: Such a
3. Come, my Joy, my Love, my Heart: Such a

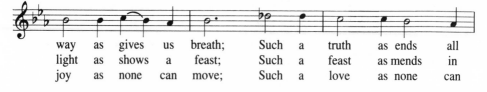

way as gives us breath; Such a truth as ends all
light as shows a feast; Such a feast as mends in
joy as none can move; Such a love as none can

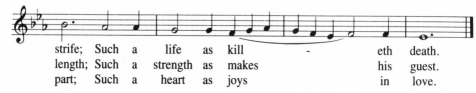

strife; Such a life as kill - eth death.
length; Such a strength as makes his guest.
part; Such a heart as joys in love.

Text: George Herbert, 1593-1632
Tune: THE CALL, 7 7 7 7; Ralph Vaughan Williams, 1872-1958, © Stainer and Bell Publications

570 Our Father, by Whose Name

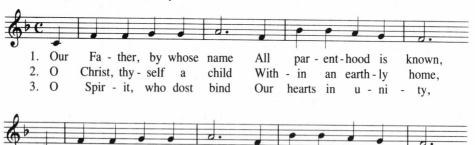

1. Our Fa - ther, by whose name All par - ent-hood is known,
2. O Christ, thy - self a child With - in an earth - ly home,
3. O Spir - it, who dost bind Our hearts in u - ni - ty,

Who dost in love pro - claim Each fam - i - ly thine own.
With heart still un - de - filed, Thou didst to man - hood come;
And teach - est us to find The love from self set free,

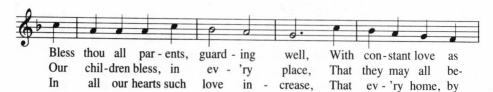

Bless thou all par - ents, guard - ing well, With con - stant love as
Our chil - dren bless, in ev - 'ry place, That they may all be-
In all our hearts such love in - crease, That ev - 'ry home, by

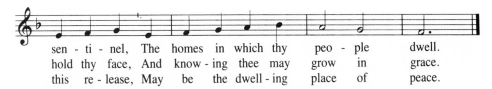

sen - ti - nel, The homes in which thy peo - ple dwell.
hold thy face, And know - ing thee may grow in grace.
this re - lease, May be the dwell - ing place of peace.

Text: F. Bland Tucker, 1895-1984, alt., © 1941, The Church Pension Fund
Tune: RHOSYMEDRE, 6 6 6 6 888; John Edwards, 1806-1885

Faith of Our Fathers 571

1. Faith of our fa - thers! liv - ing still In spite of dun-geon,
2. Our fa- thers, chained in pris - ons dark, Were still in heart and
3. Faith of our fa - thers! faith and pray'r Shall win all na - tions
4. Faith of our fa - thers! we will love Both friend and foe in

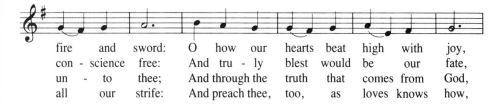

fire and sword: O how our hearts beat high with joy,
con - science free: And tru - ly blest would be our fate,
un - to thee; And through the truth that comes from God,
all our strife: And preach thee, too, as loves knows how,

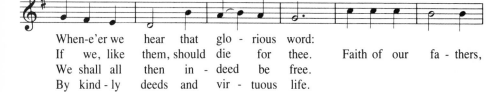

When-e'er we hear that glo - rious word:
If we, like them, should die for thee. Faith of our fa - thers,
We shall all then in - deed be free.
By kind - ly deeds and vir - tuous life.

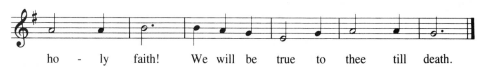

ho - ly faith! We will be true to thee till death.

Text: Frederick W. Faber, 1814-1863, alt.
Tune: ST. CATHERINE, LM with refrain; Henry F. Hemy, 1818-1888; Adapt. by James G. Walton, 1821-1905

572 We Walk by Faith

1. We walk by faith, and not by sight; No gra - cious words we hear From him who spoke as none e'er spoke; But we be - lieve him near.

2. We may not touch his hands and side, Nor fol - low where he trod; But in his prom - ise we re - joice, And cry, "My Lord and God!"

3. Help then, O Lord, our un - be - lief; And may our faith a - bound, To call on you when you are near, And seek where you are found:

4. That, when our life of faith is done, In realms of clear - er light We may be - hold you as you are, With full and end - less sight.

Text: Henry Alford, 1810-1871, alt.
Tune: DUNLAP'S CREEK, CM; Samuel McFarland, fl. 1816; Harm. by Richard Proulx, b.1937, © 1986, GIA Publications, Inc.

573 He Comes to Us as One Unknown

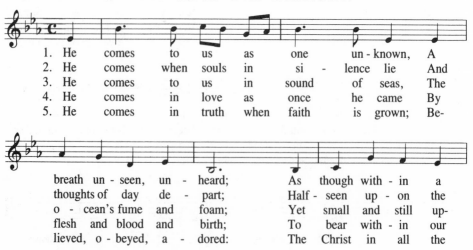

1. He comes to us as one un - known, A breath un - seen, un - heard; As though with - in a

2. He comes when souls in si - lence lie, And thoughts of day de - part; Half - seen up - on the

3. He comes to us in sound of seas, The o - cean's fume and foam; Yet small and still up-

4. He comes in love as once he came By flesh and blood and birth; To bear with - in our

5. He comes in truth when faith is grown; Be - lieved, o - beyed, a - dored: The Christ in all the

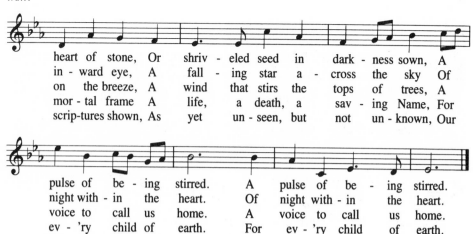

heart of stone, Or shriv - eled seed in dark - ness sown, A
in - ward eye, A fall - ing star a - cross the sky Of
on the breeze, A wind that stirs the tops of trees, A
mor - tal frame A life, a death, a sav - ing Name, For
scrip-tures shown, As yet un - seen, but not un - known, Our

pulse of be - ing stirred. A pulse of be - ing stirred.
night with - in the heart. Of night with - in the heart.
voice to call us home. A voice to call us home.
ev - 'ry child of earth. For ev - 'ry child of earth.
Sav - ior and our Lord. Our Sav - ior and our Lord.

Text: Timothy Dudley-Smith, b.1926, © 1984, Hope Publishing Co.
Tune: REPTON, 8 6 88 6 with repeat; Charles H. H. Parry, 1848-1918

A Single Unmatched Stone 574

1. A sin - gle un-matched stone The build - ers hurled a-
2. A sin - gle faith - ful act That healed a man once
3. A sin - gle deed or word Of truth or peace or

side Holds up the church a - lone Its
lame The tem - ple priests at - tacked For
grace Not seen be - fore or heard Is

cor - ner-stone and pride. The sym - me - try the
bear-ing Je - sus' name. The right-eous heart, the
dif - fi - cult to face. Help us, O God, by

build - ers planned Was al - tered by an - oth - er's hand.
rig - id mind To God's new work were deaf and blind.
faith to see What seems a threat may set us free.

Text: Acts 4:5-12; Thomas H. Troeger, b.1945
Tune: UNMATCHED STONE, 6 6 6 6 88; Carol Doran, b.1936
© 1985, Oxford University Press, Inc.

575 God Is Our Fortress and Our Rock

1. God is our for-tress and our rock, Our might-y
2. Our hope is fixed on Christ a - lone, The Man, of
3. The word of God will not be slow While de - mon

help in dan - ger; He shields us from the bat-tle's
God's own choos - ing; With-out him noth-ing can be
hordes sur - round us, Though e - vil strike its cruel-est

shock And thwarts the de - vil's an - ger: For still the
won And fight-ing must be los - ing: So let the
blow And death and hell con - found us: For e - ven

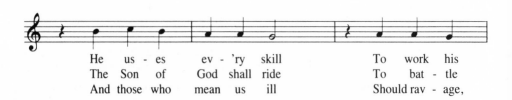

prince of night Pro - longs his e - vil fight;
pow'rs ac - cursed Come on and do their worst,
if dis - tress Should take all we pos - sess,

He us - es ev - 'ry skill To work his
The Son of God shall ride To bat - tle
And those who mean us ill Should rav - age,

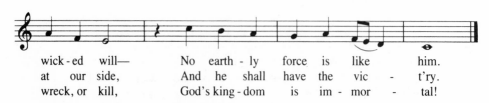

wick - ed will— No earth - ly force is like him.
at our side, And he shall have the vic - t'ry.
wreck, or kill, God's king - dom is im - mor - tal!

Text: Psalm (45)46; *Ein' feste Burg ist unser Gott;* Martin Luther, 1483-1546; Tr. by Michael Perry, b.1942, © 1982, Hope Publishing Co.
Tune: EIN' FESTE BURG, 8 7 8 7 66 66 7; Martin Luther, 1483-1546; Harm. by J.S. Bach, 1685-1750

God Is Our Fortress and Our Rock 576

1. God is our for-tress and our rock, Our might-y
2. Our hope is fixed on Christ a-lone, The Man, of
3. The word of God will not be slow While de-mon

help in dan - ger; He shields us from the bat - tle's
God's own choos - ing; With-out him noth-ing can be
hordes sur-round us, Though e - vil strike its cruel - est

shock And thwarts the dev - il's an - ger:
won And fight - ing must be los - ing:
blow And death and hell con - found us:

For still the prince of night
So let the pow'rs ac - cursed
For e - ven if dis - tress

Pro - longs his e - vil fight; He us - es ev - 'ry skill
Come on and do their worst, The Son of God shall ride
Should take all we pos - sess, And those who mean us ill

To work his wick - ed will
To bat - tle at our side,
Should rav - age, wreck, or kill,

No earth - ly force is like him.
And he shall have the vic - t'ry.
God's king - dom is im - mor - tal!

Text: Psalm (45)46; *Ein' fest Burg ist unser Gott;* Martin Luther, 1483-1546; Tr. by Michael Perry, b.1942, © 1982, Hope Publishing Co.
Tune: EIN' FESTE BURG, 8 7 8 7 66 66 7; Martin Luther, 1483-1546; Harm. based on Hans Leo Hassler, 1564-1612

577 By Gracious Powers

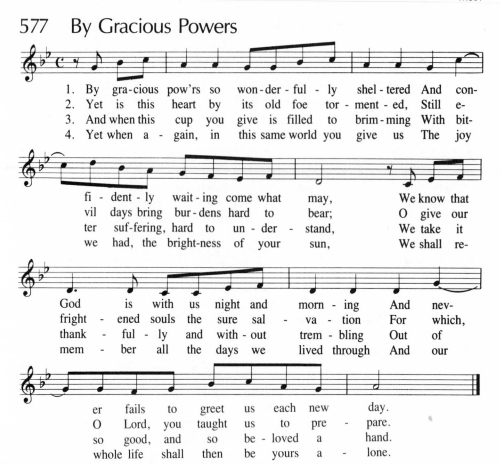

1. By gra-cious pow'rs so won-der-ful-ly shel-tered And con-
2. Yet is this heart by its old foe tor-ment-ed, Still e-
3. And when this cup you give is filled to brim-ming With bit-
4. Yet when a-gain, in this same world you give us The joy

fi-dent-ly wait-ing come what may, We know that
vil days bring bur-dens hard to bear; O give our
ter suf-fering, hard to un-der-stand, We take it
we had, the bright-ness of your sun, We shall re-

God is with us night and morn-ing And nev-
fright-ened souls the sure sal-va-tion For which,
thank-ful-ly and with-out trem-bling Out of
mem-ber all the days we lived through And our

er fails to greet us each new day.
O Lord, you taught us to pre-pare.
so good, and so be-loved a hand.
whole life shall then be yours a-lone.

Text: *Von guten Mächten;* Dietrich Bonhoeffer, 1906-1945; Tr. by Fred Pratt Green, b.1903, © 1974, Hope Publishing Co.
Tune: LE CÉNACLE, 11 10 11 10; Joseph Gelineau, SJ, b.1920, © SEFIM

God Spoke to Our Father Abraham   578

1. God spoke to our fa-ther A-bra-ham,
2. "We car-ry the wood, the fire, the knife,
3. A voice in the bra-zen wil-der-ness,
4. With wood on his shoul-der walked the boy,
5. His mem-o-ry, sealed in bread, in wine,

De-mand-ing death for I-saac the sin-less,
But where is found the vic-tim, my fa-ther,
The her-ald's voice, as bright as a trum-pet:
O-be-dient, bowed and meek to his fa-ther:
For strength and sav-ing, marks us dis-ci-ples;

Re-hears-ing the day when he would send
The lamb to be slain and of-fered up?"
"Look, there is the Lamb, the Lamb of God,
The Christ lifts his load, the wood of death,
In char-i-ty one, to set us free,

His on-ly Son to die for the world.
"O here, my son, for you are the lamb."
Whose death de-stroys the sin of the world!"
Sub-ject-ed to his Fa-ther's com-mand.
To lift our load, to crown us with life.

He res-cued his ser-vants who trust-ed in him:
He res-cued his ser-vants who trust-ed in him:
He res-cued his ser-vants who trust-ed in him:
He res-cued his ser-vants who trust-ed in him:
He res-cued his ser-vants who trust-ed in him:

From blood and from drown-ing he saved them.
From blood and from drown-ing he saved them.
From blood and from drown-ing he saved them.
From blood and from drown-ing he saved them.
From blood and from drown-ing he saved them.

Text: Gen. 22; Luke Connaughton, 1917-1979, © 1970, Mayhew McCrimmon Ltd.
Tune: SACRIFICE, 9 10 9 9 with refrain; John Schiavone, b.1947, © 1986, GIA Publications, Inc.

579 O God, Our Help in Ages Past

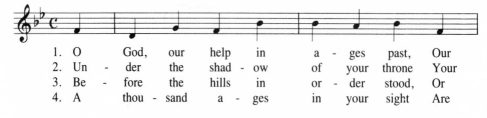

1. O God, our help in a - ges past, Our
2. Un - der the shad - ow of your throne Your
3. Be - fore the hills in or - der stood, Or
4. A thou - sand a - ges in your sight Are

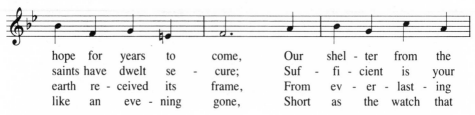

hope for years to come, Our shel - ter from the
saints have dwelt se - cure; Suf - fi - cient is your
earth re - ceived its frame, From ev - er - last - ing
like an eve - ning gone, Short as the watch that

storm - y blast, And our e - ter - nal home.
arm a - lone, And our de - fense is sure.
you are God, To end - less years the same.
ends the night Be - fore the ris - ing sun.

5. Time, like an ever-rolling stream,
   Soon bears us all away;
   We fly forgotten, as a dream
   Dies at the op'ning day.

6. O God, our help in ages past,
   Our hope for years to come,
   Still be our guard while troubles last,
   And our eternal home.

Text: Psalm (89)90; Isaac Watts, 1674-1748
Tune: ST. ANNE, CM; Attr. to William Croft, 1678-1727; Harm. composite from 18th C. versions

580 Seek Ye First the Kingdom of God

1. Seek ye first the king - dom of God and his right - eous-
2. Ask, and it shall be giv-en un - to you, seek, and ye shall

ness, and all these things shall be add - ed un - to you;
find, knock, and the door shall be o-pened un - to you;

2.

Al - le - lu, al - le - lu - ia. Al - le-
lu - ia, al - le - lu - ia, al - le-
lu - ia, al - le - lu, al - le - lu - ia.

Text: Mt. 6:33, 7:7; St. 1, adapt. by Karen Lafferty, b.1948; St. 2, anon.
Tune: SEEK YE FIRST, Irregular; Karen Lafferty, b.1948
© 1972, Maranatha! Music

God Is My Great Desire 581

1. God is my great de - sire, His face I seek the first;
2. God is my true de - light, My rich - est feast his praise,
3. God is my strong de - fense In ev - 'ry e - vil hour;

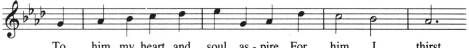

To him my heart and soul as - pire, For him I thirst.
Through si - lent watch - es of the night, Through all my days.
In him I face with con - fi - dence The temp - ter's power.

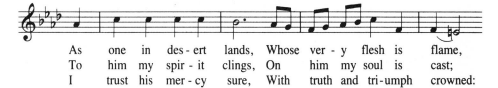

As one in des - ert lands, Whose ver - y flesh is flame,
To him my spir - it clings, On him my soul is cast;
I trust his mer - cy sure, With truth and tri - umph crowned:

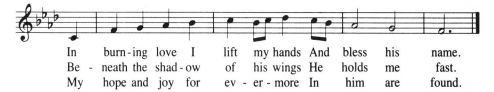

In burn - ing love I lift my hands And bless his name.
Be - neath the shad - ow of his wings He holds me fast.
My hope and joy for ev - er - more In him are found.

Text: Psalm 63; Timothy Dudley-Smith, b.1926. © 1984, Hope Publishing Co.
Tune: LEONI, 6 6 8 4 D; From the *Yigdal*; Transcribed by Meyer Lyon, c.1751-1797

582 This World, My God, Is Held within Your Hand

1. This world, my God, is held with - in your hand,
2. From youth - ful con - fi - dence to care - ful age,

Though we for - get your love and stead - fast might
Help us each one to be your lov - ing friend,

And in the chang - ing day un - cer - tain stand,
Re - ward - ed by the faith - ful ser - vant's wage,

Dis - turbed by morn - ing, and a - fraid of night.
God in Three Per - sons, reign - ing with - out end.

Text: Hamish Swanston, © 1971, Faber Music Ltd.
Tune: SURSUM CORDA, 10 10 10 10; Alfred M. Smith, 1879-1971, © Mrs. Alfred M. Smith

583 Amazing Grace

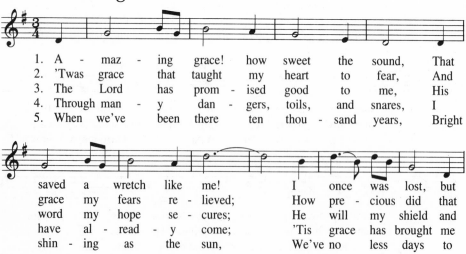

1. A - maz - ing grace! how sweet the sound, That
2. 'Twas grace that taught my heart to fear, And
3. The Lord has prom - ised good to me, His
4. Through man - y dan - gers, toils, and snares, I
5. When we've been there ten thou - sand years, Bright

saved a wretch like me! I once was lost, but
grace my fears re - lieved; How pre - cious did that
word my hope se - cures; He will my shield and
have al - read - y come; 'Tis grace has brought me
shin - ing as the sun, We've no less days to

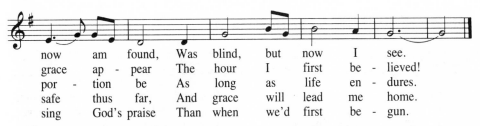

now   am   found,   Was   blind,   but   now   I   see.
grace   ap - pear   The   hour   I   first   be - lieved!
por   - tion be   As   long   as   life   en - dures.
safe   thus far,   And   grace   will   lead   me   home.
sing   God's praise   Than   when   we'd   first   be - gun.

Text: St. 1-4, John Newton, 1725-1807; St. 5, Ascr. to John Rees, fl.1859
Tune: NEW BRITAIN, CM; *Virginia Harmony,* 1831; Harm. by John Barnard, b.1948, © 1982, Hope Publishing Co.

Surely It Is God Who Saves Me 584

1. Sure - ly   it   is   God   who
2. Make his   deeds known   to   the

saves me; Trust-ing   him,   I   shall   not   fear.   For   the
peo - ples; Tell out   his   ex - alt - ed   Name.   Praise the

Lord   de - fends and   shields   me   And   his   sav - ing help   is
Lord,   who   has done   great things; All   his   works his might   pro-

near.   So   re - joice   as   you draw   wa - ter   From sal-
claim.   Zi - on,   lift   your voice in   sing - ing;   For with

va - tion's liv - ing   spring;   In   the   day   of   your de-
you has come   to   dwell,   In   your   ver - y   midst, the

liv - 'rance   Thank the   Lord, his   mer - cies   sing.
great   and   Ho - ly   One   of   Is - ra - el.

Text: Is. 12:1-6; Carl P. Daw, Jr., b.1944, © 1982
Tune: RAQUEL, 8 7 8 7 D; Skinner Chávez-Melo, b.1944, ©

585 How Firm a Foundation

1. How firm a foun - da - tion, you saints of the Lord,
2. "Fear not, I am with you, O be not dis - mayed,
3. "When through the deep wa - ters I call you to go,
4. "The soul that on Je - sus still leans for re - pose,

Is laid for your faith in his ex - cel - lent Word!
For I am your God, and will still give you aid;
The riv - ers of woe shall not you o - ver - flow;
I will not, I will not de - sert to its foes;

What more can he say than to you he has said,
I'll strength - en you, help you, and cause you to stand,
For I will be with you, your trou - bles to bless,
That soul, though all hell should en - deav - or to shake,

To you who for ref - uge to Je - sus have fled?
Up - held by my right - eous, om - nip - o - tent hand.
And sanc - ti - fy to you, your deep - est dis - tress.
I'll nev - er, no nev - er, no nev - er for - sake!"

Text: 2 Peter 1:4; "K" in Rippon's *A Selection of Hymns*, 1787
Tune: FOUNDATION, 11 11 11 11; Funk's *Compilation of Genuine Church Music*, 1832; Harm. by Richard Proulx, b.1937, © 1975, GIA Publications, Inc.

586 Awake, O Sleeper, Rise from Death

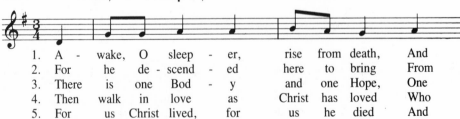

1. A - wake, O sleep - er, rise from death, And
2. For he de - scend - ed here to bring From
3. There is one Bod - y and one Hope, One
4. Then walk in love as Christ has loved Who
5. For us Christ lived, for us he died And

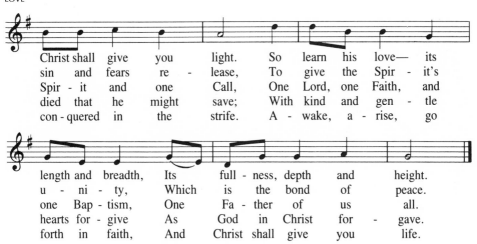

Christ shall	give	you	light.	So	learn	his	love—	its
sin and	fears	re -	lease,	To	give	the	Spir -	it's
Spir - it	and	one	Call,	One	Lord,	one	Faith,	and
died that	he	might	save;	With	kind	and	gen -	tle
con - quered	in	the	strife.	A -	wake,	a - rise,		go

length and	breadth,	Its	full - ness,	depth	and		height.
u - ni -	ty,	Which	is	the	bond	of	peace.
one Bap -	tism,	One	Fa - ther	of	us		all.
hearts for -	give	As	God	in	Christ	for -	gave.
forth in	faith,	And	Christ	shall	give	you	life.

Text: Eph. 3-5; F. Bland Tucker, 1895-1984, alt., © 1980, Augsburg Publishing House
Tune: AZMON, CM; Carl G. Gläser, 1784-1829; Harm. by Lowell Mason, 1792-1872

Morning Glory, Starlit Sky   587

1.	Morn - ing	glo -	ry,	star - lit	sky,		Soar - ing
2.	O - pen	are	the	gifts of	God,		Gifts of
3.	Love that	gives,	gives	ev - er	more,		Gives with
4.	Drained is	love	in	mak - ing	full,		Bound in

mu -	sic,	schol - ars'	truth,	Flight of	swal - lows,	au - tumn
love	to	mind and	sense;	Hid - den	is	love's	ag - o-
zeal,	with	ea - ger	hands,	Spares not,	keeps	not,	all out-
set -	ting	oth - ers	free,	Poor in	mak - ing	man - y

leaves,	Mem-ory's	trea - sure,	grace	of	youth:
ny,	Love's en -	deav - or,	love's	ex -	pense.
pours,	Ven - tures	all,	its	all	ex - pends.
rich,	Weak in	giv - ing	pow'r	to	be.

5. Therefore he who shows us God
   Helpless hangs upon the tree;
   And the nails and crown of thorns
   Tell of what God's love must be.

6. Here is God: no monarch he,
   Throned in easy state to reign;
   Here is God, whose arms of love
   Aching, spent, the world sustain.

Text: W. H. Vanstone, b.1923. © J.W. Shore
Tune: BINGHAM, 7 7 7 7; Dorothy Sheets, b.1915. ©

588 Love Divine, All Loves Excelling

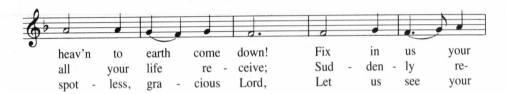

1. Love di - vine, all loves ex - cel - ling, Joy of
2. Come, al - might - y to de - liv - er, Let us
3. Fin - ish then your new cre - a - tion, Pure and

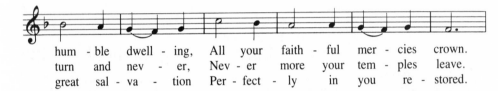

heav'n to earth come down! Fix in us your
all your life re - ceive; Sud - den - ly re -
spot - less, gra - cious Lord, Let us see your

hum - ble dwell - ing, All your faith - ful mer - cies crown.
turn and nev - er, Nev - er more your tem - ples leave.
great sal - va - tion Per - fect - ly in you re - stored.

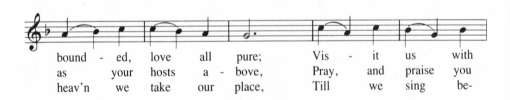

Je - sus, source of all com - pas - sion, Love un -
Lord, we would be al - ways bless - ing, Serve you
Changed from glo - ry in - to glo - ry, Till in

bound - ed, love all pure; Vis - it us with
as your hosts a - bove, Pray, and praise you
heav'n we take our place, Till we sing be -

your sal - va - tion, Let your love in us en - dure.
with - out ceas - ing, Glo - ry in your pre - cious love.
fore the al - might - y Lost in won - der, love and praise.

Text: Charles Wesley, 1707-1788, alt.
Tune: HYFRYDOL, 8 7 8 7 D; Rowland H. Prichard, 1811-1887

Not for Tongues of Heaven's Angels 589

1. Not for tongues of heav-en's an - gels, Not for
2. Love is hum - ble, love is gen - tle, Love is
3. Nev - er jeal - ous, nev - er self - ish, Love will
4. Soon will fade the word of wis - dom, Faith and

wis - dom to dis - cern, Not for faith that mas - ters
ten - der, true and kind; Love is gra - cious, ev - er-
not re - joice in wrong; Nev - er boast - ful nor re-
hope be one day past: When we see our Sav - ior

moun - tains— For this bet - ter gift we yearn:
pa - tient, Gen - er - ous of heart and mind—
sent - ful, Love be - lieves and suf - fers long—
clear - ly Love it is a - lone will last—

May love be ours, O Lord.
May love be ours, O Lord.
May love be ours, O Lord.
May love be ours, O Lord.

Text: 1 Cor. 13; Timothy Dudley-Smith, b.1926. © 1985, Hope Publishing Co.
Tune: BRIDEGROOM, 8 7 8 7 6; Peter Cutts, b.1937. © 1969, Hope Publishing Co.

590 This Is My Will

1. "This is my will, my one com - mand, That love should
2. "No great - er love that one can have Than that one
3. "I call you now no long - er slaves; No slave knows
4. "You chose not me, but I chose you, That you should
5. "All that you ask my Fa - ther dear For my name's

dwell a - mong you all. This is my will, that
die to save one's friends. You are my friends if
all the mas - ter does. I call you friends, for
go and bear much fruit. I chose you out that
sake you shall re - ceive. This is my will, my

you should love As I have shown that I love you.
you o - bey What I com - mand that you should do.
all I hear My Fa - ther say you hear from me.
you in me Should bear much fruit that will a - bide."
one com - mand, That love should dwell in each, in all."

Text: James Quinn, SJ, b.1919, © 1969
Tune: SUANTRAI, LM; Gaelic; Harm. by T.H. Weaving, © Estate of T.H. Weaving

591 O for a Heart to Praise My God

1. O for a heart to praise my God, A heart from
2. A heart, re - signed, sub - mis - sive, meek, My great Re-
3. A hum - ble, low - ly, con - trite heart, Be - liev - ing,
4. A heart in ev - 'ry thought re-newed, A heart whose
5. Your na - ture, gra - cious Lord, im - part; Come quick - ly

sin set free, A heart that al - ways
deem - er's throne, Where on - ly Christ is
true, and clean: Which nei - ther life nor
love en - dures; So per - fect, right, and
from a - bove, Write your new name up-

feels your blood / So free - ly / shed / for / me.
heard to speak, / Where Je - sus / reigns / a - lone:
death can part / From Him that / dwells / with - in:
pure, and good, / A cop - y, / Lord, / of / yours.
on my heart, / Your new, best / name / of / love.

Text: Psalm (50)51; Charles Wesley, 1707-1788, alt.
Tune: O FOR A HEART, CM; Malcolm Williamson, b.1943, © 1971, Josef Weinberger Ltd.

God Is Unique and One   592

1. God is u - nique and one: / Mak - er, sus - tain - er, Lord!
2. Love came to earth in Christ, / Our com - mon life to share,
3. The Ho - ly Spir - it moves / Peo - ple to trace God's plan,
4. He shall for ev - er reign, / Rul - er of time and space,

Pat - terns of life were spun / By God's cre - a - tive
Choos - ing to be the least, / Will - ing a cross to
This in - spi - ra - tion proves / More than the mind can
God in the midst of life, / Seen in the hu - man

word. / Of God's in - ten - tion, / love and
bear. / He died, he rose, that / we might
span. / Each lis - tening heart is / led to
face. / We give ex - pres - sion to / our

care / We are with grow - ing / trust a - ware.
live / And all our love, re - spond - ing, give.
find / The will of God for hu - man - kind.
creed / By love in thought, in word and deed.

Text: Fred Kaan, b.1929, alt., © 1968, Hope Publishing Co.
Tune: LITTLE CORNARD, 6 6 6 6 88; Martin Shaw, 1875-1958, © J. Curwen and Sons

593 I Sought the Lord

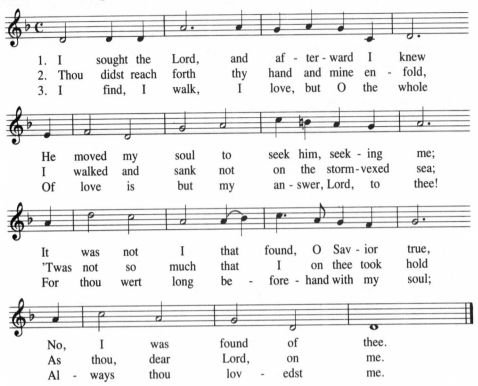

1. I sought the Lord, and af-ter-ward I knew
2. Thou didst reach forth thy hand and mine en - fold,
3. I find, I walk, I love, but O the whole

He moved my soul to seek him, seek - ing me;
I walked and sank not on the storm-vexed sea;
Of love is but my an - swer, Lord, to thee!

It was not I that found, O Sav - ior true,
'Twas not so much that I on thee took hold
For thou wert long be - fore - hand with my soul;

No, I was found of thee.
As thou, dear Lord, on me.
Al - ways thou lov - edst me.

Text: Mt. 14:22-32; Anon. c.1878
Tune: FAITH, 10 10 10 6; J. Harold Moyer, b.1927, © 1969, Faith and Life Press

594 Christian, Do You Hear the Lord

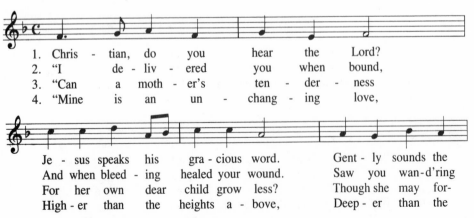

1. Chris - tian, do you hear the Lord?
2. "I de - liv - ered you when bound,
3. "Can a moth - er's ten - der - ness
4. "Mine is an un - chang - ing love,

Je - sus speaks his gra - cious word. Gent - ly sounds the
And when bleed - ing healed your wound. Saw you wan-d'ring
For her own dear child grow less? Though she may for-
High - er than the heights a - bove, Deep - er than the

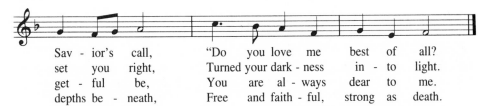

Sav - ior's call,
set you right,
get - ful be,
depths be - neath,

"Do you love me best of all?
Turned your dark - ness in - to light.
You are al - ways dear to me.
Free and faith - ful, strong as death.

5. "You shall see my glory soon,
When the work of grace is done;
Crowned with splendor you shall be:
Christian, come and follow me!"

6. Lord, it is my chief complaint
That my love is weak and faint;
Yet I love you, and adore—
O for grace to love you more!

Text: William Cowper, 1731-1800, alt., © 1982, Hope Publishing Co.
Tune: ORIENTIS PARTIBUS, 77 77; Pierre de Corbiel, d.1222

There's a Wideness in God's Mercy 595

1. There's a wide-ness in God's mer-cy Like the wide - ness of the sea;
2. For the love of God is broad-er Than the meas - ures of our mind,
3. Trou- .bled souls, why will you scat-ter Like a crowd of fright-ened sheep?

There's a kind-ness in God's jus-tice Which is more than lib - er - ty.
And the heart of the E - ter-nal Is most won - der - ful - ly kind.
Fool- ish hearts, why will you wan-der From a love so true and deep?

There is plen - ti - ful re - demp-tion In the blood that has been shed;
If our love were but more sim - ple We should take him at his word,
There is wel-come for the sin - ner And more grac - es for the good;

There is joy for all the mem-bers In the sor - rows of the Head.
And our lives would be thanks-giv-ing For the good - ness of our Lord.
There is mer - cy with the Sav - ior, There is heal - ing in his blood.

Text: Frederick W. Faber, 1814-1863, alt.
Tune: IN BABILONE, 8 7 8 7 D; Oude en Nieuwe Hollanste Boerenlities, c.1710

596   There's a Wideness in God's Mercy

1. There's a wide - ness in God's mer-
2. For the love of God is broad-
3. Trou-bled souls, why will you scat-

cy   Like the wide - ness of the sea;
er   Than the meas - ures of our mind,
ter   Like a crowd of fright - ened sheep?

There's a kind - ness in God's jus-
And the heart of the E - ter-
Fool-ish hearts, why will you wan-

tice   Which is more than lib - er - ty.
nal   Is most won - der - ful - ly kind.
der   From a love so true and deep?

There is plen - ti - ful re-demp - tion
If our love were but more sim - ple
There is wel - come for the sin - ner

In the blood that has been shed;   There is joy for
We should take him at his word,   And our lives would
And more grac-es for the good;   There is mer - cy

all the mem - bers   In the sor-rows of the Head.
be thanks-giv - ing   For the good-ness of our Lord.
with the Sav - ior,   There is heal-ing in his blood.

after last stanza - optional

A - men.

Text: Frederick W. Faber, 1814-1863, alt.
Tune: ST. HELENA, 8 7 8 7 D; Calvin Hampton, 1938-1984, © 1977, GIA Publications, Inc.

A Spendthrift Lover Is the Lord   597

1. A spend-thrift lov-er is the Lord Who nev-er counts the cost Or asks if heav-en can af-ford To woo a world that's lost.
2. Still more is spent in blood and tears To win the hu-man heart, To o-ver-come the vio-lent fears That drive the world a-part.
3. How shall we love this heart-strong God Who gives us ev-'ry-thing, Whose ways to us are strange and odd, What can we give or bring?

Our lov-er toss-es coins of gold A-cross the mid-night skies And stokes the sun a-gainst the cold To warm us when we rise.
Be-hold the bruised and thorn-crowned face Of one who bears our scars And emp-ties out the wealth of grace That's hint-ed by the stars.
Ac-cept-ance of the match-less gift Is gift e-nough to give. The ver-y act will shake and shift The way we love and live.

Text: Jn. 3:14-21; Thomas Troeger, b.1945
Tune: SPENDTHRIFT LOVER, CMD; Carol Doran, b.1936. © 1983, Thomas H. Troeger and Carol Doran

598 Where True Love and Charity Are Found / Ubi Caritas

Where true love and char-i-ty are found, God is al-ways there.
U - bi cá - ri - tas et a - mor De - us i - bi est.

1. Since the love of Christ has brought us all to-geth-er,
2. There-fore when we gath-er as one in Christ Je - sus,
3. Bring us with your saints to be - hold your great beau - ty,
1. *Con - gre - gá - vit nos in u - num Chri - sti a - mor.*
2. *Si - mul er - go cum in u - num con - gre - gá - mur:*
3. *Si - mul quo - que cum be - á - tis vi - de - á - mus.*

Let us all re - joice and be glad, now and al - ways.
Let our love en - fold each race, creed, ev - 'ry per - son.
There to see you, Christ our God, throned in great glo - ry;
Ex - sul - té - mus et in ip - so iu - cun - dé - mur.
Ne nos men - te di - vi - dá - mur, ca - ve - á - mus.
Glo - ri - án - ter vul - tum tu - um, Chri - ste De - us:

Let ev - 'ry one love the Lord God, the liv - ing God;
Let en - vy, di - vi - sion and strife cease a - mong us;
There to pos - sess heav-en's peace and joy, your truth and love,
Ti - me - á - mus et a - me - mus De - um vi - vum.
Ces - sent iúr - gi - a ma - líg - na, ces - sent li - tes.
Gáu - di - um, quod est im - mén - sum at - que pro - bum.

D.C.

And with sin - cere hearts let us love each oth - er now.
May Christ our Lord dwell a - mong us in ev - 'ry heart.
For end - less a - ges of a - ges, world with - out end.
Et ex cor - de di - li - gá - mus nos sin - cé - ro.
Et in mé - di - o no - stri sit Chri - stus De - us.
Sáe - cu - la per in - fi - ní - ta sae - cu - ló - rum.

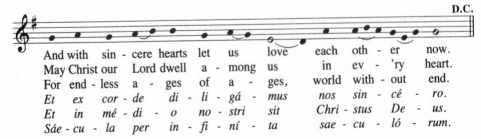

Text: Latin, 9th C.; Tr. by Richard Proulx, b.1937, © 1975, 1986, GIA Publications, Inc.
Tune: UBI CARITAS, 12 12 12 12 with refrain; Mode VI; Acc. by Richard Proulx, b.1937, © 1986, GIA Publications, Inc.

Love Is His Word 599

1. Love is his word, love is his way. Feast-ing with all,
2. Love is his way, love is his mark. Shar-ing his last
3. Love is his mark, love is his sign. Bread for our strength,
4. Love is his sign, love is his news. "Do this," he said,
5. Love is his news, love is his name. We are his own,

fast - ing a - lone, Liv - ing and dy - ing,
Pass - o - ver feast. Guest at his ta - ble,
wine for our joy. "This is my bod - y,
"lest you for - get All my deep sor - row,
cho - sen and called, Fam - i - ly, breth - ren,

ris - ing a - gain. Love, on - ly love, is his way.
host to the Twelve, Love, on - ly love, is his mark.
this is my blood." Love, on - ly love, is his sign.
all my dear blood." Love, on - ly love, is his news.
cous-ins and kin. Love, on - ly love, is his name.

Rich - er than gold is the love of my Lord,

bet - ter than splen-dor and wealth. Rich - er than gold is the

love of my Lord, bet - ter than splen-dor and wealth.

6. Love is his name, love is his law.
   Hear his command, all who are his:
   "Love one another, I have loved you."
   Love, only love, is his law.

7. Love is his law, love is his word:
   Love of the Lord, Father and Word.
   Love of the Spirit, God ev'ry one.
   Love, only love, is his word.

Text: Luke Connaughton, 1917-1979. © 1970 Mayhew McCrimmon Ltd.
Tune: JULINORMA, 4 4 8 5 4 7; Robert M. Hutmacher, OFM, b.1948, © 1986, GIA Publications, Inc.

600 What Wondrous Love Is This

1. What won-drous love is this, O my soul, O my soul?
2. To God and to the Lamb I will sing, I will sing;
3. And when from death I'm free, I'll sing on, I'll sing on;

What won-drous love is this, O my soul?
To God and to the Lamb, I will sing;
And when from death I'm free, I'll sing on;

What won-drous love is this that caused the Lord of bliss
To God and to the Lamb who is the great I Am,
And when from death I'm free, I'll sing and joy-ful be,

To bear the dread-ful curse for my soul, for my soul;
While mil-lions join the theme, I will sing, I will sing;
And through e-ter-ni-ty I'll sing on, I'll sing on!

To bear the dread-ful curse for my soul?
While mil-lions join the theme, I will sing.
And through e-ter-ni-ty, I'll sing on.

Text: Alexander Means, 1801-1853
Tune: WONDROUS LOVE, 12 9 12 12 9; *Southern Harmony*, 1835; Harm. from *Cantate Domino*, 1980, © 1980, World Council of Churches

601 Beloved, Let Us Love

1. Be - lov - ed, let us love: for love is of God;
2. Be - lov - ed, let us love: for those who love,
3. Be - lov - ed, let us love: for love is rest,
4. Be - lov - ed, let us love: for love is light,
5. Be - lov - ed, let us love: for on - ly thus

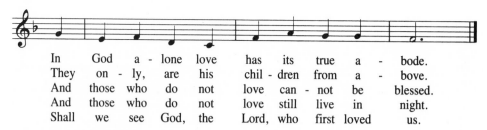

In God a - lone love has its true a - bode.
They on - ly, are his chil - dren from a - bove.
And those who do not love can - not be blessed.
And those who do not love still live in night.
Shall we see God, the Lord, who first loved us.

Text: 1 Jn. 4, 7; Horatius Bonar, 1808-1889
Tune: SONG 46, 10 10; Orlando Gibbons, 1583-1625

Lord of All Nations, Grant Me Grace   602

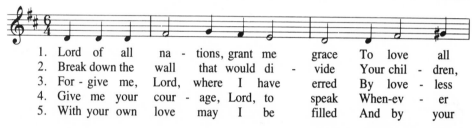

1. Lord of all na - tions, grant me grace To love all
2. Break down the wall that would di - vide Your chil - dren,
3. For - give me, Lord, where I have erred By love - less
4. Give me your cour - age, Lord, to speak When-ev - er
5. With your own love may I be filled And by your

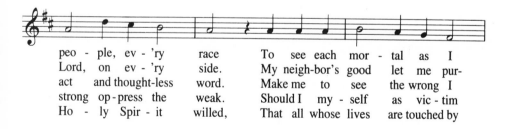

peo - ple, ev - 'ry race To see each mor - tal as I
Lord, on ev - 'ry side. My neigh-bor's good let me pur-
act and thought-less word. Make me to see the wrong I
strong op - press the weak. Should I my - self as vic - tim
Ho - ly Spir - it willed, That all whose lives are touched by

ought, My kin - dred, whom your love has bought.
sue, Let Chris - tian love bind warm and true.
do Will cru - ci - fy my Lord a - new.
live, Re - mem - b'ring you, may I for - give.
mine, May know your heal - ing touch di - vine.

Text: Phil. 2:1-18; Olive W. Spannaus, b.1916, © 1969, Concordia Publishing House
Tune: BEATUS VIR, LM; Slovak; Harm. by Richard Hillert, b.1923, © 1969, Concordia Publishing House

603 This Is My Commandment

This is my com - mand-ment, that you love one an-
oth - er as I have loved you.

1. Greater love has no one than this, than to
2. No longer do I call you servants, but
3. You did not choose me, but
4. What- ever you ask in my name the

lay down one's life for one's friends. You are my
I have called you friends; for the servant does not
I have cho - sen you, that you should bear
Fa - ther will give to you. This I com -

2 D.C.

friends if you do what I com - mand you.
know what the mas - ter is doing.
fruit and that your fruit should a - bide.
mand you, To love one an - other.

Text: John 15:12-17; Revised Standard Version, alt., © Division of Education and Ministry, NCCC
Tune: OF LOVE DIVINE, Irregular; Erik Routley, 1917-1982, © 1974, Novello and Co. Ltd.

604 Ubi Caritas

U - bi ca - ri - tas et a - mor,

u - bi ca - ri - tas De - us i - bi est.

Text: 1 Cor. 13: 2-8, *Where charity and love are found, God is there.* Taizé Community, 1978
Tune: Jacques Berthier, b.1923
© 1979, Les Presses de Taizé

O Jesus, Joy of Loving Hearts   605

1. O Je - sus, joy of lov - ing hearts, The fount of
2. We taste in you our liv - ing bread, And long to
3. For you our rest - less spir - its yearn Wher - e'er our
4. O Je - sus, ev - er with us stay; Make all our

life and our true light, We seek the peace your
feast up - on you still; We drink of you, the
chang - ing lot is cast; Glad, when your pres - ence
mo - ments calm and bright; O chase the night of

love im - parts, And stand re - joic - ing in your sight.
foun - tain - head, Our thirst - ing souls to quench and fill.
we dis - cern, Blest, when our faith can hold you fast.
sin a - way, Shed o'er the world your ho - ly light.

Text: *Jesu, delcedo cordium;* Attr. to Bernard of Clairvaux, 1091-1153; Para. by Ray Palmer, 1808-1887, alt.
Tune: WAREHAM, LM; William Knapp, 1698-1768

606 My Shepherd Will Supply My Need

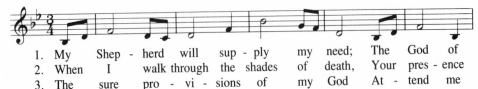

1. My Shep - herd will sup - ply my need; The God of
2. When I walk through the shades of death, Your pres - ence
3. The sure pro - vi - sions of my God At - tend me

love su - preme; In pas - tures green you
is my stay; One word of your sup-
all my days; O may your house be

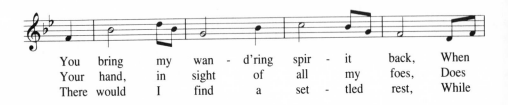

make me feed, Be - side the liv - ing stream.
port - ing breath Drives all my fears a - way.
my a - bode, And all my work be praise!

You bring my wan - d'ring spir - it back, When
Your hand, in sight of all my foes, Does
There would I find a set - tled rest, While

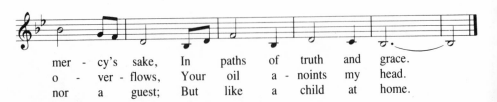

I for - sake your ways; And lead me for your
still my ta - ble spread; My cup with bless - ings
oth - ers go and come, No more a stran - ger

mer - cy's sake, In paths of truth and grace.
o - ver - flows, Your oil a - noints my head.
nor a guest; But like a child at home.

Text: Psalm (22)23; Isaac Watts, 1674-1748, alt.
Tune: RESIGNATION, CMD; Funk's *Compilation of Genuine Church Music*, 1832; Harm. by Richard Proulx, b.1937. © 1975, GIA Publications, Inc.

I Heard the Voice of Jesus Say   607

1. I heard the voice of Je - sus say, "Come
2. I heard the voice of Je - sus say, "Be -
3. I heard the voice of Je - sus say, "I

un - to me and rest; Lay down, O wear - y
hold, I free - ly give The liv - ing wa - ter;
am this dark world's light; Look un - to me, your

one, lay down Your head up - on my breast."
thirst - y one, Stoop down, and drink, and live."
morn shall rise, And all your day be bright."

I came to Je - sus as I was, So
I came to Je - sus, and I drank Of
I looked to Je - sus, and I found In

wea - ry worn and sad; I found in him a
that life - giv - ing stream; My thirst was quenched, my
him my star, my sun; And in that light of

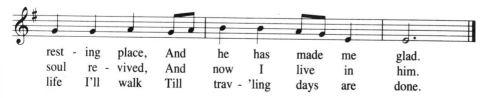

rest - ing place, And he has made me glad.
soul re - vived, And now I live in him.
life I'll walk Till trav - 'ling days are done.

Text: Horatius Bonar, 1808-1889
Tune: KINGSFOLD, CMD; English; Harm. by Ralph Vaughan Williams, 1872-1958, © Oxford University Press

608 There Is a Balm in Gilead

There is a balm in Gil - e - ad To make the wound - ed whole, There is a balm in Gil - e - ad To heal the sin - sick soul.

1. Some - times I feel dis - cour - aged And think my work's in vain, But then the Ho - ly Spir - it Re - vives my soul a - gain.
2. If you can - not preach like Pe - ter, If you can - not pray like Paul, You can tell the love of Je - sus, And say, "He died for all!"
3. Don't ev - er feel dis - cour - aged, For Je - sus is your friend; And if you lack for knowl-edge He'll ne'er re - fuse to lend.

D.C.

Text: Jer. 8:22, Afro-American Spiritual
Tune: BALM IN GILEAD, Irregular; Afro-American Spiritual; Harm. by David Hurd, b.1950, © 1985, GIA Publications, Inc.

609 The King of Love My Shepherd Is

1. The King of love my shep - herd is, Whose
2. Where streams of liv - ing wa - ter flow My
3. Con - fused and fool - ish oft I strayed, But
4. In death's dark vale I fear no ill With

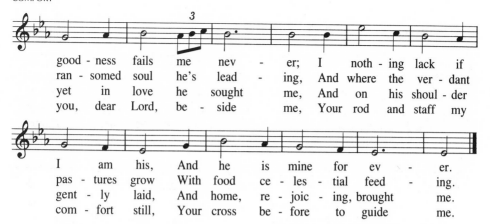

good - ness fails me nev - er; I noth - ing lack if
ran - somed soul he's lead - ing, And where the ver - dant
yet in love he sought me, And on his shoul - der
you, dear Lord, be - side me, Your rod and staff my

I am his, And he is mine for ev - er.
pas - tures grow With food ce - les - tial feed - ing.
gent - ly laid, And home, re - joic - ing, brought me.
com - fort still, Your cross be - fore to guide me.

5. You spread a table in my sight;
   Your saving grace bestowing;
   And O what transport of delight
   From your pure chalice flowing!

6. And so through all the length of days
   Your goodness fails me never;
   Good Shepherd, may I sing your praise
   Within your house for ever.

Text: Psalm (22)23; Henry W. Baker, 1821-1877, alt.
Tune: ST. COLUMBA, 8 7 8 7; Gaelic; Harm. by A. Gregory Murray, OSB, b.1905, ©

How Good the Name of Jesus Sounds   610

1. How good the name of Je - sus sounds To
2. It makes the wound - ed spir - it whole, And
3. Blest Name! the rock on which we build, Our
4. O Je - sus, Shep - herd, Guard - ian, Friend, Our

all be - liev - ing ears! It soothes our sor - rows,
calms the trou - bled mind; His man - na for each
shield and rest - ing place, Our nev - er - fail - ing
Proph - et, Priest and King, Our Lord, our Life, our

heals our wounds, And drives a - way our fears.
hun - gry soul, The lost and wear - y find.
com - fort, filled With bless - ings of his grace.
Way, our End, Ac - cept the praise we bring.

Text: John Newton, 1725-1807, alt.
Tune: ST. PETER, CM; Alexander R. Reinagle, 1799-1877

611 Jesus, Lead the Way

1. Je - sus, lead the way Through our life's long day, When at
2. Je - sus be our light, In the midst of night, Let not
3. When in deep - est grief, Strength-en our be - lief. When temp-
4. Je - sus, still lead on 'Til our rest be won: If you

times the way is cheer - less, Help us fol - low, calm and
faith - less fear o'er - take us, Let not faith and hope for-
ta - tions come al - lur - ing, Make us pa - tient and en-
lead us through rough plac - es, Grant us your re - deem - ing

fear - less; Guide us by your hand To the prom-ised land.
sake us; May we feel you near As we wor - ship here.
dur - ing; Lord we seek your grace In this ho - ly place.
grac - es. When our course is o'er, O - pen heav-en's door.

Text: *Jesu, geh voran;* Nicholas L. von Zinzendorf, 1700-1760; Tr. by Jane Borthwick, 1813-1897, alt.
Tune: ROCHELLE, 55 88 55; Adam Drese, 1620-1701; Harm. alt.

612 The Living God My Shepherd Is

1. The liv - ing God my shep - herd is, I know no
2. You lead me where cool wa - ters flow By rip - pling
3. I noth - ing fear; for you, O Lord, Are with me
4. And so through all the length of days, Your mer - cy

care or need. You guide me where rich pas - tures grow,
stream and rill, Where I may taste the springs of life,
night and day, In - tent, with shep-herd's staff and rod,
waits on me, At last with - in my Fa - ther's house

A - long the ver - dant mead, Where ev - 'ry day, by
My thirst - ing spir - it fill; You near me bide and
To guide me when I stray, And in the fold you
Your glo - ry I shall see; You ev - er - more will

pleas - ant way, My hun - g'ring soul may feed.
home - ward guide My va - grant heart and will.
will up - hold My faint - ing heart al - ways.
I a - dore Through all e - ter - ni - ty.

Text: Psalm 23; J. Driscoll, SJ, 1946, © Peter Janson-Smith
Tune: BROTHER JAMES' AIR, 8 6 8 6 8 6; J. L. Macbeth Bain, c.1840-1925; Harm. by Gordon P. Jacob, 1895-1984, © Campbell, Thompson and
McLaughlin, Ltd.

The Lord, the Lord, the Lord Is My Shepherd   613

1. The Lord, the Lord, the Lord is my shep - herd, The
2. He brings me rest in green, green pas - tures, He
3. My fear is gone for he is with me, His

Lord, the Lord, the Lord is my shep - herd, The
leads me to the still, still wa - ters, He
rod and staff bring com - fort sure; His

Lord, the Lord, the Lord is my shep - herd, The
guides me a - long his own right way, The
good - ness and mer - cy shall fol - low me, The

Lord is my shep-herd and I shall not want.
Lord is my shep-herd and I shall not want.
Lord is my shep-herd and I shall not want.

Text: Afro-American Spiritual
Tune: THE LORD IS MY SHEPHERD, Irregular; Afro-American Spiritual; Harm. by Austin C. Lovelace, b.1919, © 1986, GIA Publications, Inc.

614 When Jesus Came Preaching the Kingdom of God

1. When Je - sus came preach - ing the King - dom of God With the
2. Since Je - sus came preach - ing the King - dom of God, What a
3. Still Je - sus comes preach - ing the King - dom of God In a

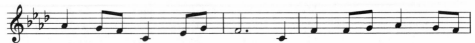

love that has pow'r to per - suade, The sick were made whole, both in
change in our lives he has made! How man - y have shared in the
world that is sick and a - fraid; His gos - pel has spread like the

bod - y and soul, And e - ven the de - mons o - beyed.
joy of their Lord, In self - giv - ing have loved and o - beyed!
leav - en in bread By the love that has a pow'r to per - suade.

But he need - ed a few he could trust to be true, To
But let none of us doubt what re - li - gion's a - bout, Or by
So let none of us swerve from our mis - sion to serve, That has

share in his work from the start: When Je - sus came preach-ing the
what it is shamed and be - trayed: Do just - ly, love mer - cy, walk
made us his Church from the start, May Je - sus, the light of the

King - dom of God, God's gift to the hum - ble of heart.
hum - bly with God, Is the rule of life Je - sus o - beyed.
world, send us out In the strength of the hum - ble of heart.

Text: Fred Pratt Green, b.1903, © 1974, Hope Publishing Co.
Tune: SAMANTHRA, 11 8 11 8 D; *Southern Harmony*, 1835; Harm. by Austin C. Lovelace, b.1919, © 1986, GIA Publications, Inc.

The Kingdom of God 615

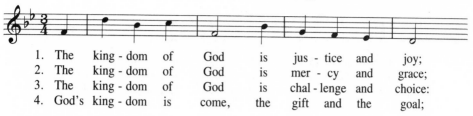

1. The king - dom of God is jus - tice and joy;
2. The king - dom of God is mer - cy and grace;
3. The king - dom of God is chal - lenge and choice:
4. God's king - dom is come, the gift and the goal;

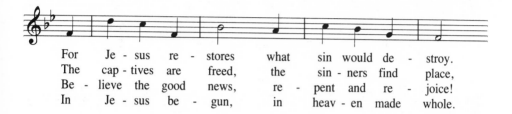

For Je - sus re - stores what sin would de - stroy.
The cap - tives are freed, the sin - ners find place,
Be - lieve the good news, re - pent and re - joice!
In Je - sus be - gun, in heav - en made whole.

God's pow - er and glo - ry in Je - sus we know;
The out - cast are wel - comed God's ban - quet to share;
God's love for us sin - ners brought Christ to his cross;
The heirs of the king - dom shall an - swer his call;

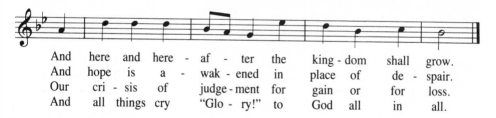

And here and here - af - ter the king - dom shall grow.
And hope is a - wak - ened in place of de - spair.
Our cri - sis of judge - ment for gain or for loss.
And all things cry "Glo - ry!" to God all in all.

Text: Bryn A. Rees, b.1911, © Mrs. M. Rees
Tune: LAUDATE DOMINUM, 10 10 11 11; Charles H. H. Parry, 1848-1918

616 Christ's Church Shall Glory in His Power

1. Christ's church shall glo - ry in his pow'r
2. Christ's peo - ple serve his way - ward world
3. Christ's liv - ing lamp shall bright - ly burn,

And grow to his per - fec - tion;
To whom he seems a stran - ger;
And to our earth - ly cit - y

He is our rock, our might - y tow'r
He knows its wel - come from of old,
For - got - ten beau - ty shall re - turn,

Our life, our res - ur - rec - tion:
He shares our joy, our dan - ger:
And pu - ri - ty and pit - y:

So by his skill - ful hand The church of
So strong, and yet so weak, The church of
To give the op - pressed their right The church of

Christ shall stand; The mas - ter - build - er's plan
Christ shall speak; His cross our great - est need,
Christ shall fight; And though the years seem long

He works, as he be - gan,
His word the vi - tal seed
He is our strength and song,

And soon will crown with splen - dor.
That brings a fruit - ful har - vest.
And he is our sal - va - tion.

Text: Christopher Idle, b.1938, © 1982, Hope Publishing Co.
Tune: EIN' FESTE BURG, 8 7 8 7 66 66 7; Martin Luther, 1483-1546; Harm. by J.S. Bach, 1685-1750

Christ Is Made the Sure Foundation 617

1. Christ is made the sure foun - da - tion, Christ the head and
2. To this tem - ple where we call you, Come, O Lord of
3. Grant, we pray, to all your peo - ple, All the grace they

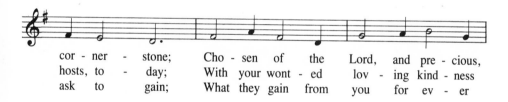

cor - ner - stone; Cho - sen of the Lord, and pre - cious,
hosts, to - day; With your wont - ed lov - ing kind - ness
ask to gain; What they gain from you for ev - er

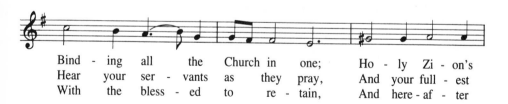

Bind - ing all the Church in one; Ho - ly Zi - on's
Hear your ser - vants as they pray, And your full - est
With the bless - ed to re - tain, And here - af - ter

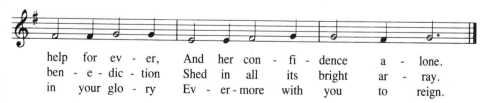

help for ev - er, And her con - fi - dence a - lone.
ben - e - dic - tion Shed in all its bright ar - ray.
in your glo - ry Ev - er - more with you to reign.

Text: *Angularis fundamentum;* 11th C.; Tr. by John M. Neale, 1818-1866, alt.
Tune: WESTMINSTER ABBEY, 8 7 8 7 8 7; Adapted from an anthem of Henry Purcell, 1659-1695

618 O Christ the Great Foundation

1. O Christ the great foun - da - tion On which your peo - ple stand
2. Bap - tized in one con - fes - sion, One church in all the earth,
3. Where ty - rants' hold is tight - ened, Where strong de - vour the weak,
4. This is the mo - ment glo - rious When he who once was dead

To preach your true sal - va - tion In ev - 'ry age and land:
We bear our Lord's im - pres - sion, The sign of sec - ond birth:
Where in - no - cents are fright - ened The right-eous fear to speak,
Shall lead his church vic - to - rious, Their cham-pion and their head.

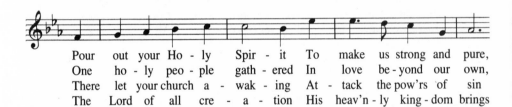

Pour out your Ho - ly Spir - it To make us strong and pure,
One ho - ly peo - ple gath - ered In love be - yond our own,
There let your church a - wak - ing At - tack the pow'rs of sin
The Lord of all cre - a - tion His heav'n - ly king - dom brings

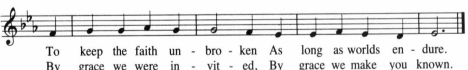

To keep the faith un - bro - ken As long as worlds en - dure.
By grace we were in - vit - ed, By grace we make you known.
And, all their ram - parts break - ing, With you the vic - tory win.
The fi - nal con - sum - ma - tion, The glo - ry of all things.

Text: Timothy T'ingfang Lew, 1891-1947, alt., © Christian Conference of Asia
Tune: AURELIA, 7 6 7 6 D; Samuel S. Wesley, 1810-1876

Glorious in Majesty 619

1. Glo - ri - ous in maj - es - ty, ho - ly in his prais - es,
2. Vic - to - ry he won for us, free - ing us from dark - ness,
3. One in love, as fam - i - ly, liv - ing with each oth - er,

Je - sus, our Sav - ior and our King.
dy - ing and ris - ing from the dead.
glad - ly we share each oth - er's pain.

Born a man, yet God of old, let us all a - dore him:
Liv - ing with the Fa - ther now, yet he is a - mong us:
Yet he will not leave us so, soon he is re - turn - ing,

filled with his Spir - it, let us sing.
we are the bod - y, he the head.
tak - ing us back with him to reign.

Liv - ing is to love him, serv - ing him to know his free - dom.

Come a - long with us to join the praise of Je - sus.

Come to Je - sus now, Go to live his word re - joic - ing.

Text: Jeff Cothran, fl.1972
Tune: SHIBBOLET BASADEH, 7 6 8 D with refrain; Jewish; Harm. by Jeff Cothran, fl.1972
© 1972, GIA Publications, Inc.

620 O Blessed Are the Poor in Spirit

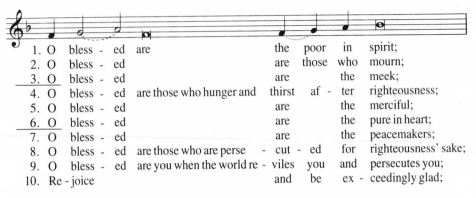

1. O bless - ed are · · · · · the poor in spirit;
2. O bless - ed · · · · · · are those who mourn;
3. O bless - ed · · · · · · are the meek;
4. O bless - ed are those who hunger and thirst af - ter righteousness;
5. O bless - ed · · · · · · are the merciful;
6. O bless - ed · · · · · · are the pure in heart;
7. O bless - ed · · · · · · are the peacemakers;
8. O bless - ed are those who are perse - cut - ed for righteousness' sake;
9. O bless - ed are you when the world re - viles you and persecutes you;
10. Re - joice · · · · · · and be ex - ceedingly glad;

1. for theirs is the kingdom of heav - en.
2. for they shall be com - fort - ed.
3. for they shall in - her - it the earth.
4. for they shall be sat - is - fied.
5. for they shall obtain mer - cy.
6. for they shall see God.
7. for they shall be called the chil - dren of God.
8. for theirs is the kingdom of heav - en.
9. and utters all manner of evil against you falsely for my sake.
10. for great is your reward in heav - en.

Text: Matt. 5:3-12; *The Beatitudes*
Tune: KONTAKION, Irregular; Byzantine/Slavonic Chant, Adapt. by Richard Proulx, b.1937. © 1985, GIA Publications, Inc.

621 All Who Love and Serve Your City

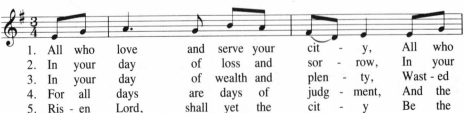

1. All who love and serve your cit - y, All who
2. In your day of loss and sor - row, In your
3. In your day of wealth and plen - ty, Wast - ed
4. For all days are days of judg - ment, And the
5. Ris - en Lord, shall yet the cit - y Be the

bear	its	dai - ly	stress,	All who	cry	for peace	and
day	of	help-less	strife,	Hon - or,	peace,	and love	re-
work	and	wast - ed	play,	Call to	mind	the word	of
Lord	is	wait - ing	still,	Draw-ing	near	his friends	who
cit -	y	of de -	spair?	Come to -	day,	our judge,	our

jus -	tice,	All who	curse	and all who	bless.
treat -	ing,	Seek the	Lord,	who is your	life.
Je -	sus,	"Work on	yet	while it is	day."
spurn	him,	Of - f'ring	peace	from Cal - v'ry's	hill.
glo -	ry;	Be its	name	"The Lord is	there!"

Text: Erik Routley, 1917-1982, © Galliard Publications
Tune: BIRABUS, 8 7 8 7; Peter Cutts, b.1937, © 1969, Hope Publishing Co.

Where Temple Offerings Are Made 622

1.	Where Tem-ple of - fer - ings	are made,	And know - ing	he	must
2.	Some of - fer sil - ver,	oth - ers gold,	Some what they	can	af-
3.	Name-less as shad - ows	on a wall	The poor - er	come	and
4.	A wid - ow, pass - ing	by, who scarce	Can scrape e - nough	to
5.	How deep - ly moved he	is by this,	He leaves us	in	no

die,	Our Mas - ter, rest - ing	in the shade,
ford;	Some give, in or - der	to with-hold,
go;	It is as if he	knows them all,
live,	She finds two pen - nies	in her purse,
doubt:	And he him - self will	die for us,

Watch-es	the	world	go	by.
And some	to	gain	re -	ward.
As on - ly	God	can		know.
Gives all	that	she	can	give.
Be - fore	the	week	is	out.

Text: Mk. 12:41-44; Fred Pratt Green, b.1903, © 1982, Hope Publishing Co.
Tune: O FOR A HEART, CM; Malcolm Williamson, b.1943, © 1971, Josef Weinberger Ltd.

623 We Are Your People

1. We are your peo - ple: Lord, by your
2. How can we dem-on-strate Your love and
3. Called to por - tray you, Help us to
4. Glad of tra - di - tion, Help us to

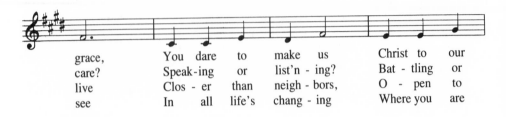

grace, You dare to make us Christ to our
care? Speak-ing or list'n - ing? Bat - tling or
live Clos - er than neigh - bors, O - pen to
see In all life's chang - ing Where you are

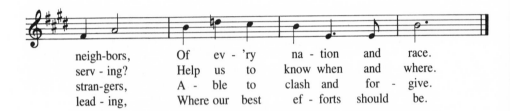

neigh-bors, Of ev - 'ry na - tion and race.
serv - ing? Help us to know when and where.
stran-gers, A - ble to clash and for - give.
lead - ing, Where our best ef - forts should be.

5. Joined in community,
   Breaking your bread,
May we discover
Gifts in each other,
   Willing to lead and be led.

6. Lord, as we minister
   In diff'rent ways,
May all we're doing
Show that you're living,
   Meeting your love with our praise.

Text: Brian Wren, b.1936, © 1975, Hope Publishing Co.
Tune: WHITFIELD, 5 4 5 5 7; John W. Wilson, b.1905, © 1980, Hope Publishing Co.

624 What Does the Lord Require

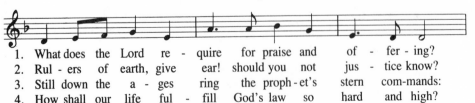

1. What does the Lord re - quire for praise and of - fer - ing?
2. Rul - ers of earth, give ear! should you not jus - tice know?
3. Still down the a - ges ring the proph - et's stern com-mands:
4. How shall our life ful - fill God's law so hard and high?

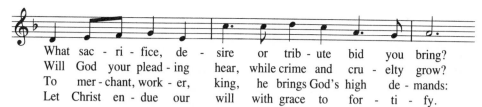

What sac - ri - fice, de - sire or trib - ute bid you bring?
Will God your plead - ing hear, while crime and cru - elty grow?
To mer - chant, work - er, king, he brings God's high de - mands:
Let Christ en - due our will with grace to for - ti - fy.

Do just - ly; Love mer - cy; Walk hum-bly with your God.
Do just - ly; Love mer - cy; Walk hum-bly with your God.
Do just - ly; Love mer - cy; Walk hum-bly with your God.
Then just - ly, In mer - cy, We'll hum-bly walk with God.

Text: Micah 6:6-8; Albert F. Bayly. 1901-1984, alt., © Oxford University Press
Tune: SHARPTHORNE, 6 6 6 6 33 6; Erik Routley, 1917-1982, © 1969, Hope Publishing Co.

Now Let Us from This Table Rise 625

1. Now let us from this ta - ble rise Re - newed in
2. With minds a - lert, up - held by grace, To spread the
3. To fill each hu - man house with love, It is the
4. Then grant us cour - age, car - ing God, To choose a-

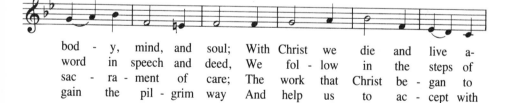

bod - y, mind, and soul; With Christ we die and live a-
word in speech and deed, We fol - low in the steps of
sac - ra - ment of care; The work that Christ be - gan to
gain the pil - grim way And help us to ac - cept with

gain, His self - less love has made us whole.
Christ, At one with us in hope and need.
do We hum - bly pledge our - selves to share.
joy The chal - lenge of to - mor - row's day.

Text: Fred Kaan, b.1929. © 1968, Hope Publishing Co.
Tune: DEUS TUORUM MILITUM, LM; Grenoble Antiphoner, 1753; Harm. by Basil Harwood, 1859-1949, © Executors of the late Dr. Basil Harwood

626 The Church of Christ in Every Age

1. The Church of Christ in ev - 'ry age Be - set by
2. A - cross the world, a - cross the street, The vic - tims
3. Then let the ser - vant Church a - rise, A car - ing
4. For he a - lone, whose blood was shed, Can cure the
5. We have no mis - sion but to serve In full o-

change but Spir - it led, Must claim and test its her - it-
of in - jus - tice cry For shel - ter and for bread to
Church that longs to be A part - ner in Christ's sac - ri-
fe - ver in our blood, And teach us how to share our
be - dience to our Lord: To care for all, with - out re-

age And keep on ris - ing from the dead.
eat, And nev - er live un - til they die.
fice, And clothed in Christ's hu - man - i - ty.
bread And feed the starv - ing mul - ti - tude.
serve, And spread his lib - er - at - ing Word.

Text: Fred Pratt Green, b.1903, © 1971, Hope Publishing Co.
Tune: DUNEDIN, LM; Vernon Griffiths, 1894-1985, © 1971, Faber Music Ltd.

627 Forth in the Peace of Christ

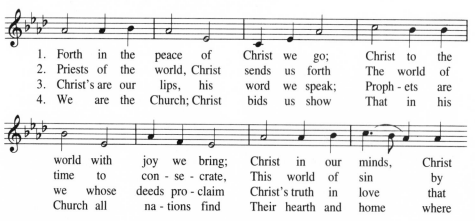

1. Forth in the peace of Christ we go; Christ to the
2. Priests of the world, Christ sends us forth The world of
3. Christ's are our lips, his word we speak; Proph - ets are
4. We are the Church; Christ bids us show That in his

world with joy we bring; Christ in our minds, Christ
time to con - se - crate, This world of sin by
we whose deeds pro - claim Christ's truth in love that
Church all na - tions find Their hearth and home where

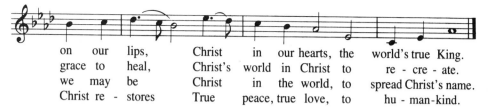

on our lips,	Christ	in our hearts, the	world's true King.
grace to heal,	Christ's	world in Christ to	re - cre - ate.
we may be	Christ	in the world, to	spread Christ's name.
Christ re - stores	True	peace, true love, to	hu - man-kind.

Text: James Quinn, SJ, b.1919, © 1969
Tune: LLEDROD, LM; Welsh; *Caniadan y Cyssegr,* 1839

Go Make of All Disciples   628

1. "Go make of all dis - ci - ples": We hear the
2. "Go make of all dis - ci - ples": Bap - tiz - ing
3. "Go make of all dis - ci - ples": We at your
4. "Go make of all dis - ci - ples": We wel - come

call, O Lord, That comes from you, our Fa - ther,
in the name Of Fa - ther, Son, and Spir - it—
feet would stay Un - til each life's vo - ca - tion
your com - mand; "Lo, I am with you al - ways":

In your e - ter - nal Word. In - spire our ways of
From age to age the same. We call each new dis -
Ac - cents your ho - ly way. We cul - ti - vate the
We take your guid - ing hand. The task looms large be -

learn - ing Through earn - est, fer - vent prayer, And let our
ci - ple To fol - low you, O Lord, Re - deem - ing
na - ture God plants in ev - 'ry heart, Re - veal - ing
fore us— We fol - low with - out fear. In heav'n and

dai - ly liv - ing Re - veal you ev - 'ry - where.
soul and bod - y By wa - ter and the Word.
in our wit - ness The Mas - ter Teach-er's art.
earth your pow - er Shall bring God's king - dom here.

Text: Matt. 28:19-20; Leon M. Adkins, b.1896, alt., © 1955,1964, Abingdon Press
Tune: ELLECOMBE, 76 76 D; *Gesangbuch der Herzogl,* Wirtemberg, 1784

629 How Shall They Hear the Word of God

1. How shall they hear the word of God Un - less the
2. How shall they call to God for help Un - less they
3. How shall the gos - pel be pro - claimed If her - alds

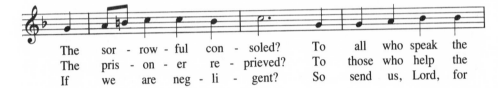

truth is told? How shall the sin - ful be set free,
have be - lieved? How shall the poor be giv - en hope,
are not sent? How shall the world find peace at last

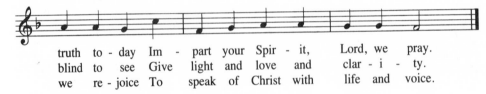

The sor - row - ful con - soled? To all who speak the
The pris - on - er re - prieved? To those who help the
If we are neg - li - gent? So send us, Lord, for

truth to - day Im - part your Spir - it, Lord, we pray.
blind to see Give light and love and clar - i - ty.
we re - joice To speak of Christ with life and voice.

Text: Michael Perry, b.1942, © 1980, Hope Publishing Co.
Tune: AUCH JETZT MACHT GOTT, 8 6 8 6 88; Koch's *Choralbuch*, 1816

Lord, Whose Love in Humble Service 630

1. Lord, whose love in hum - ble ser - vice Bore the
2. Still your chil - dren wan - der home - less; Still the
3. As we wor - ship, grant us vi - sion, Till your
4. Called from wor - ship in - to ser - vice Forth in

weight of hu - man need, Who did on the
hun - gry cry for bread; Still the cap - tives
love's re - veal - ing light, Till the height and
your great name we go, To the child, the

Cross for - sak - en, Show us mer - cy's per - fect deed;
long for free - dom; Still in grief we mourn our dead.
depth and great - ness Dawns up - on our hu - man sight:
youth, the a - ged, Love in liv - ing deeds to show;

We, your ser - vants, bring the wor - ship Not of
As, O Lord, your deep com - pas - sion Healed the
Mak - ing known the needs and bur - dens Your com-
Hope and health, good - will and com - fort, Coun - sel,

voice a - lone, but heart: Con - se - crat - ing
sick and freed the soul, Use the love your
pas - sion bids us bear, Stir - ring us to
aid, and peace we give That your chil - dren,

to your pur - pose Ev - 'ry gift which you im - part.
Spir - it kin - dles Still to save and make us whole.
faith - ful ser - vice. Your a - bun - dant life to share.
Lord, in free - dom, May your mer - cy know and live.

Text: Albert F. Bayly, 1901-1984, © Oxford University Press
Tune: IN BABILONE 8 7 8 7 D; *Oude en Nieuwe Hollanse Boerenlities*, c.1710

631 God, Whose Giving Knows No Ending

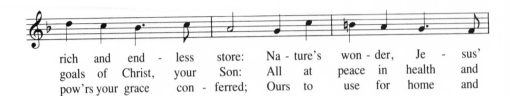

1. God, whose giv-ing knows no end-ing, From your
2. Skills and time are ours for press-ing Toward the
3. Trea-sure, too, you have en-trust-ed, Gain through

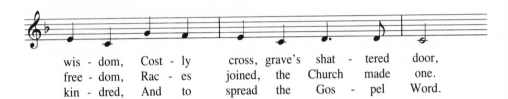

rich and end-less store: Na-ture's won-der, Je-sus'
goals of Christ, your Son: All at peace in health and
pow'rs your grace con-ferred; Ours to use for home and

wis-dom, Cost-ly cross, grave's shat-tered door,
free-dom, Rac-es joined, the Church made one.
kin-dred, And to spread the Gos-pel Word.

Gift-ed by you, we turn to you, Of-f'ring
Now di-rect our dai-ly la-bor, Lest we
O-pen wide our hands in shar-ing, As we

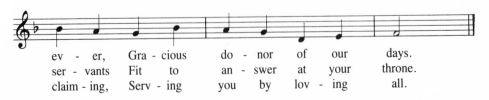

up our-selves in praise; Thank-ful song shall rise for-
strive for self a-lone; Born with tal-ents, make us
heed Christ's age-less call, Heal-ing, teach-ing, and re-

ev-er, Gra-cious do-nor of our days.
ser-vants Fit to an-swer at your throne.
claim-ing, Serv-ing you by lov-ing all.

Text: Robert L. Edwards, b.1915, © 1961, Hymn Society of America
Tune: RUSTINGTON, 8 7 8 7 D; Charles H. H. Parry, 1848-1918

Those Who Love and Those Who Labor   632

1. Those who love and those who la - bor Fol - low in the way of Christ;
2. Where the man - y work to - geth - er, They with Christ him - self a - bide,
3. Let the seek - er nev - er fal - ter Till the truth is found a - far

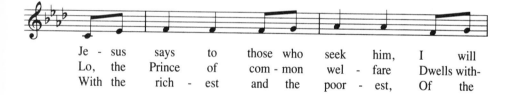

Thus the first dis - ci - ples found him, Thus the gift of love suf - ficed.
But the lone - ly work - ers al - so Find him ev - er at their side.
With the wis - dom of the a - ges Un - der - neath a gi - ant star,

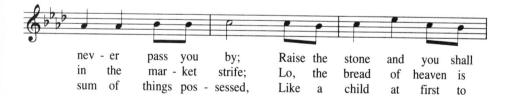

Je - sus says to those who seek him, I will nev - er pass you by;
Lo, the Prince of com - mon wel - fare Dwells with - in the mar - ket strife;
With the rich - est and the poor - est, Of the sum of things pos - sessed,

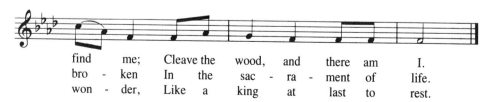

Raise the stone and you shall find me; Cleave the wood, and there am I.
Lo, the bread of heaven is bro - ken In the sac - ra - ment of life.
Like a child at first to won - der, Like a king at last to rest.

Text: Geoffrey Dearmer, b.1893, © Oxford University Press
Tune: DOMHNACH TRIONOIDE, 8 7 8 7 D; Gaelic; Harm. by Richard Proulx, b.1937, © 1975, GIA Publications, Inc.

633 Two Fishermen

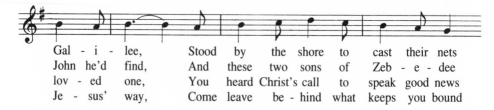

1. Two fish - er - men, who lived a - long The Sea of
2. And as he walked a - long the shore 'Twas James and
3. O Si - mon Pe - ter, An - drew, James And John be -
4. And you, good Chris - tians, one and all Who'd fol - low

Gal - i - lee, Stood by the shore to cast their nets
John he'd find, And these two sons of Zeb - e - dee
lov - ed one, You heard Christ's call to speak good news
Je - sus' way, Come leave be - hind what keeps you bound

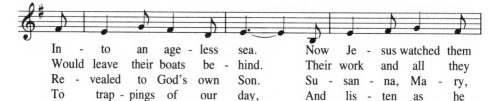

In - to an age - less sea. Now Je - sus watched them
Would leave their boats be - hind. Their work and all they
Re - vealed to God's own Son. Su - san - na, Ma - ry,
To trap - pings of our day, And lis - ten as he

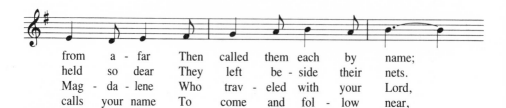

from a - far Then called them each by name;
held so dear They left be - side their nets.
Mag - da - lene Who trav - eled with your Lord,
calls your name To come and fol - low near,

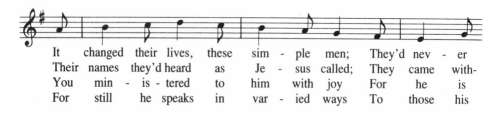

It changed their lives, these sim - ple men; They'd nev - er
Their names they'd heard as Je - sus called; They came with -
You min - is - tered to him with joy For he is
For still he speaks in var - ied ways To those his

be the same. Leave all things you have And
out re - gret. Leave all things you have And
God a - dored. Leave all things you have And
call will hear. Leave all things you have And

come and fol - low me, And come and fol - low me.
come and fol - low me, And come and fol - low me.
come and fol - low me, And come and fol - low me.
come and fol - low me, And come and fol - low me.

Text: Suzanne Toolan, SM, b.1927, © 1986, GIA Publications, Inc.
Tune: LEAVE ALL THINGS, CMD with refrain; Suzanne Toolan, SM, b.1927, © 1970, GIA Publications, Inc.

Take Up Your Cross 634

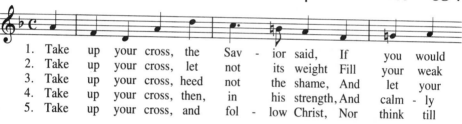

1. Take up your cross, the Sav - ior said, If you would
2. Take up your cross, let not its weight Fill your weak
3. Take up your cross, heed not the shame, And let your
4. Take up your cross, then, in his strength, And calm - ly
5. Take up your cross, and fol - low Christ, Nor think till

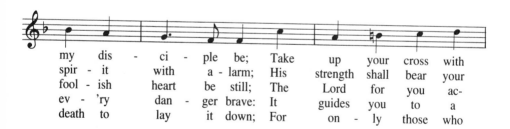

my dis - ci - ple be; Take up your cross with
spir - it with a - larm; His strength shall bear your
fool - ish heart be still; The Lord for you ac-
ev - 'ry dan - ger brave: It guides you to a
death to lay it down; For on - ly those who

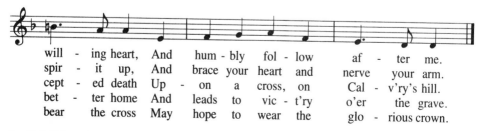

will - ing heart, And hum - bly fol - low af - ter me.
spir - it up, And brace your heart and nerve your arm.
cept - ed death Up - on a cross, on Cal - v'ry's hill.
bet - ter home And leads to vic - t'ry o'er the grave.
bear the cross May hope to wear the glo - rious crown.

Text: Charles W. Everest, 1814-1877, alt.
Tune: O JESU, MI DULCISSIME, LM; *Clausener Gesangbuch*, 1655

635 Weary of All Trumpeting

1. Wea - ry of all trum - pet - ing, Wea - ry of all kill - ing,
2. Bless - ed Sav - ior, low - ly Lord, Ser - vant King, your dy - ing
3. To the tri - umph of your cross Sum - mon all the liv - ing;

Wea - ry of all songs that sing Prom - ise, non - ful - fill - ing,
Asked us sheathe the fool - ish sword, Asked us cease de - ny - ing.
Sum - mon us to live by loss, Gain - ing all by giv - ing.

We would raise, O Christ, one song: We would join in sing - ing
Trum - pet with your Spir - it's breath Through each height and hol - low:
Suff'r - ing all, that we may see Tri - umph in sur - ren - der;

That great mu - sic pure and strong, Where - with heav'n is ring - ing.
In - to your self - giv - ing death, Call us all to fol - low.
Leav - ing all, that we may be Part - ners in your splen - dor.

Text: Martin Franzmann, 1907-1976, © Chantry Music Press
Tune: DISTLER, 7 6 7 6 D; Hugo Distler, 1908-1942, © Chantry Music Press; Harm. by Richard Proulx, b.1937, ©1975, GIA Publications, Inc.

636 I Danced in the Morning

1. I danced in the
2. I danced for the
3. I danced on the
4. I danced on a
5. They cut me

morn - ing when the world was be - gun, And I danced in the
scribe and the phar - i - see, But they would - n't
Sab - bath and I cured the lame: The ho - ly peo - ple
Fri - day when the sky turned black; It's hard to
down and I leap up high; I am the

moon and the stars and the sun, And I
dance, and they would - n't fol - low me; I
said it was a shame. They
dance with the dev - il on your back. They
life that - 'll nev - er, nev - er die; I'll

came down from heav - en and I danced on the earth;
danced for the fish - er - men, for James and John;
whipped and they stripped and they hung me high,
bur - ied my bod - y and they thought I'd gone;
live in you if you'll live in me:

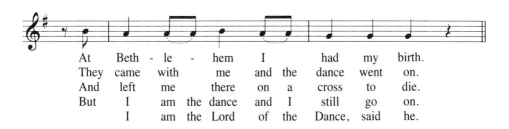

At Beth - le - hem I had my birth.
They came with me and the dance went on.
And left me there on a cross to die.
But I am the dance and I still go on.
I am the Lord of the Dance, said he.

Dance then wher - ev - er you may be; I am the Lord of the

Dance, said he, And I'll lead you all, wher - ev - er you may be,

And I'll lead you all in the dance, said he. dance, said he.

Text: Sydney Carter, b.1915. © Galliard Publications
Tune: SHAKER SONG. Irregular; American Shaker; Harm. by Sydney Carter, b.1915. © Galliard Publications

637 It Shocked Them That the Master Did Not Fast

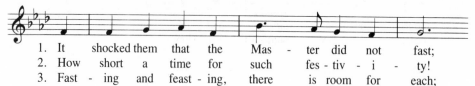

1. It shocked them that the Mas - ter did not fast;
2. How short a time for such fes - tiv - i - ty!
3. Fast - ing and feast - ing, there is room for each;

But Je - sus wit - ti - ly de - fends
Soon they must mourn a Bride - groom slain,
But, Lord, let not our fast - ing strip

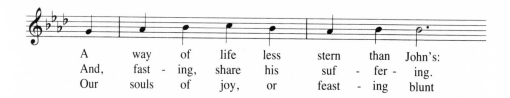

A way of life less stern than John's:
And, fast - ing, share his suf - fer - ing.
Our souls of joy, or feast - ing blunt

Fast - ing would ill be - come the Bride-groom's friends.
Then, one mo - men - tous morn - ing, feast a - gain!
The dis - ci - plines of our dis - ci - ple - ship.

Text: Fred Pratt Green, b.1903. © 1982, Hope Publishing Co.
Tune: MINTWOOD, 10 8 8 10; James J. Chepponis, b.1956. © 1986, GIA Publications, Inc.

Your Love, O God, Has All the World Created   638

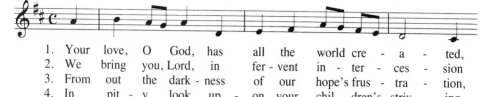

1. Your love, O God, has all the world cre - a - ted,
2. We bring you, Lord, in fer - vent in - ter - ces - sion
3. From out the dark - ness of our hope's frus - tra - tion,
4. In pit - y look up - on your chil - dren's striv - ing
5. In - spire your church, mid earth's dis - cord - ant voic - es,

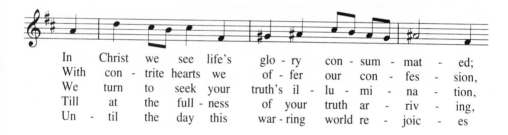

And led your peo - ple to this pre - sent hour;
The chil - dren of your world-wide fam - i - ly:
From all the bro - ken i - dols of our pride,
In dai - ly strug - gles to be un - der - stood,
To preach the gos - pel of its Lord a - bove,

In Christ we see life's glo - ry con - sum - mat - ed;
With con - trite hearts we of - fer our con - fes - sion,
We turn to seek your truth's il - lu - mi - na - tion,
Till at the full - ness of your truth ar - riv - ing,
Un - til the day this war - ring world re - joic - es

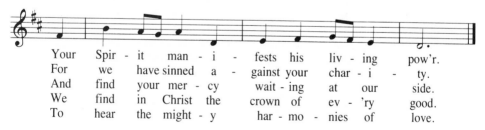

Your Spir - it man - i - fests his liv - ing pow'r.
For we have sinned a - gainst your char - i - ty.
And find your mer - cy wait - ing at our side.
We find in Christ the crown of ev - 'ry good.
To hear the might - y har - mo - nies of love.

Text: Albert F. Bayly, 1901-1984, alt.
Tune: NORTHBROOK, 11 10 11 10; Reginald S. Thatcher, 1888-1957. © Oxford University Press

639 Come, Let Us Love the Unborn Generations

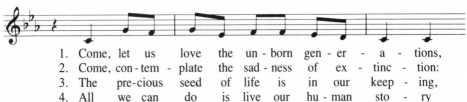

1. Come, let us love the un - born gen - er - a - tions,
2. Come, con - tem - plate the sad - ness of ex - tinc - tion:
3. The pre - cious seed of life is in our keep - ing,
4. All we can do is live our hu - man sto - ry
5. We can - not sti - fle knowl-edge or in - ven - tion.

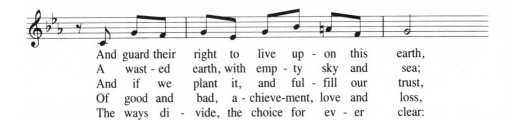

And guard their right to live up - on this earth,
A wast - ed earth, with emp - ty sky and sea;
And if we plant it, and ful - fill our trust,
Of good and bad, a - chieve-ment, love and loss,
The ways di - vide, the choice for ev - er clear:

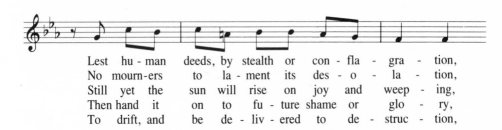

Lest hu - man deeds, by stealth or con - fla - gra - tion,
No mourn-ers to la - ment its des - o - la - tion,
Still yet the sun will rise on joy and weep - ing,
Then hand it on to fu - ture shame or glo - ry,
To drift, and be de - liv - ered to de - struc - tion,

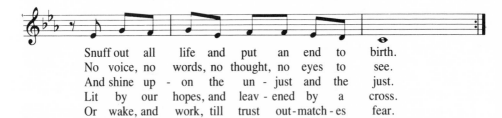

Snuff out all life and put an end to birth.
No voice, no words, no thought, no eyes to see.
And shine up - on the un - just and the just.
Lit by our hopes, and leav - ened by a cross.
Or wake, and work, till trust out - match - es fear.

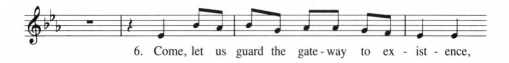

6. Come, let us guard the gate - way to ex - ist - ence,

That thou-sands yet may stand where we have stood.

Give thanks for life, and prais-ing our per-sist-ence,

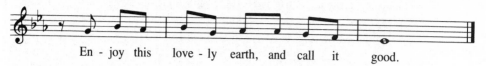

En - joy this love - ly earth, and call it good.

Text: Brian Wren, b.1936, © 1983, Hope Publishing Co.
Tune: LIFE ON EARTH, 11 10 11 10; Robert Leaf, b.1936, © 1986, GIA Publications, Inc.

God, Whose Purpose Is to Kindle 640

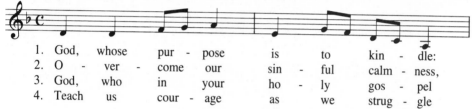

1. God, whose pur - pose is to kin - dle:
2. O - ver - come our sin - ful calm - ness,
3. God, who in your ho - ly gos - pel
4. Teach us cour - age as we strug - gle

Now ig - nite us with your fire; While the earth a-
Stir us with your sav - ing name; Bap - tize with your
Wills that all should tru - ly live, Make us sense our
In all lib - er - at - ing strife; Lift the small - ness

waits your burn - ing, With your pas - sion us in - spire.
fi - ery Spir - it, Crown our lives with tongues of flame.
share of fail - ure, Our tran - quil - li - ty for - give.
of our vi - sion By your own a - bun - dant life.

5. God, who still a sword delivers
   Rather than a placid peace,
   With your sharpened word disturb us,
   From complacency release!

6. Save us now from satisfaction,
   When we privately are free,
   Yet are undisturbed in spirit
   By our neighbor's misery.

Text: Luke 12:49; David E. Trueblood, b.1900, © 1967, David Elton Trueblood
Tune: LIBERTY, 8 7 8 7; American; Harm. by Donald R. Riddle, b.1930, © 1975, Broadman Press

641 Lift Every Voice and Sing

1. Lift ev-'ry voice and sing, Till earth and heav-en ring,
2. Ston-y the road we trod, Bit-ter the chas-t'ning rod,
3. God of our wea-ry years, God of our si-lent tears,

Ring with the har-mo-nies of lib-er-ty;
Felt in the days when hope un-born had died;
Thou who hast brought us thus far on the way;

Let our re-joic-ing rise High as the lis-t'ning skies,
Yet with a stead-y beat, Have not our wear-y feet
Thou who hast by thy might, Led us in-to the light,

Let it re-sound loud as the roll-ing sea.
Come to the place for which our peo-ple sighed?
Keep us for ev-er in the path, we pray.

Sing a song full of the faith that the dark past has taught us,
We have come o-ver a way that with tears has been wa-tered,
Lest our feet stray from the plac-es, our God, where we met thee,

Sing a song full of the hope that the pres-ent has brought
We have come, tread-ing our path thro' the blood of the slaugh-
Lest our hearts, drunk with the wine of the world, we for-get

us; Fac-ing the ris-ing sun Of our new day be-
tered; Out from the gloom-y past, Till now we stand at
thee; Shad-owed be-neath thy hand, May we for ev-er

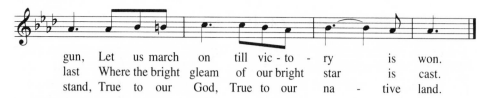

gun, Let us march on till vic - to - ry is won.
last Where the bright gleam of our bright star is cast.
stand, True to our God, True to our na - tive land.

Text: James W. Johnson, 1871-1938
Tune: ANTHEM, 66 10 66 10 14 14 66 10; J. Rosamund Johnson, 1873-1954
© Edward B. Marks

O God, Empower Us 642

1. O God, em - pow - er us to stem The ha - treds that di -
2. When neigh - bors feel dis - tress or grieve, Or sick - ness takes its
3. Though cold sus - pi - cion meet our warmth, We love at your com -

vide. En - a - ble us to bring an end To
toll, En - a - ble us to feel their pain, The
mand; And though not al - ways un - der - stood, We

ghast - ly wars of pride. Let our ex - am - ple
bet - ter to con - sole. And when our neigh - bor's
pray to un - der - stand. En - a - ble us to

point the way, That feuds be not pro - longed. Let us for -
path is dark And heav - y with de - spair, Help us to
sti - fle greed For thanks or gain, dear Lord, And live that

give, as you for - gave, When we have suf - fered wrong.
lift the Gos - pel's light And show true Chris - tian care.
sac - ri - fi - cial life Which is its own re - ward.

Text: Lee M. Baldwin, 1906-1982, ©
Tune: LLANGLOFFAN, CMD; Welsh

643 For the Healing of the Nations

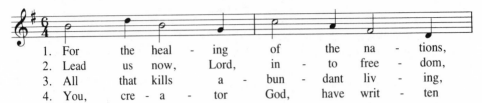

1. For the heal - ing of the na - tions,
2. Lead us now, Lord, in - to free - dom,
3. All that kills a - bun - dant liv - ing,
4. You, cre - a - tor God, have writ - ten

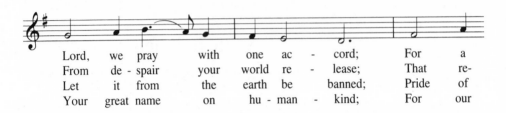

Lord, we pray with one ac - cord; For a
From de - spair your world re - lease; That re-
Let it from the earth be banned; Pride of
Your great name on hu - man - kind; For our

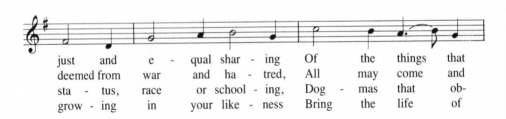

just and e - qual shar - ing Of the things that
deemed from war and ha - tred, All may come and
sta - tus, race or school - ing, Dog - mas that ob-
grow - ing in your like - ness Bring the life of

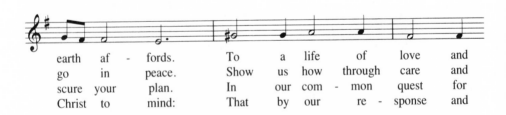

earth af - fords. To a life of love and
go in peace. Show us how through care and
scure your plan. In our com - mon quest for
Christ to mind: That by our re - sponse and

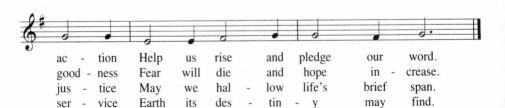

ac - tion Help us rise and pledge our word.
good - ness Fear will die and hope in - crease.
jus - tice May we hal - low life's brief span.
ser - vice Earth its des - tin - y may find.

Text: Fred Kaan, b.1929, alt., © 1968, Hope Publishing Co.
Tune: WESTMINSTER ABBEY, 8 7 8 7 8 7; Adapted from an anthem of Henry Purcell, c.1659-1695

Said Judas to Mary 644

1. Said Ju-das to Mar-y, "Now what will you do With your
2. "Oh Mar-y, O Mar-y, O think of the poor. This
3. "To-mor-row, to-mor-row, I'll think of the poor; To-
4. Said Je-sus to Mar-y, "Your love is so deep To-

oint-ment so rich and so rare?" "I'll pour it all o-ver the
oint-ment, it could have been sold; And think of the blan-kets and
mor-row," she said, "not to-day; For dear-er than all of the
day, you may do as you will. To-mor-row, you say, I am

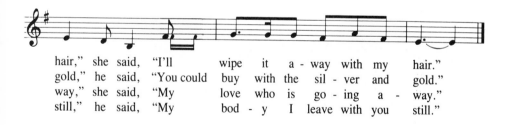

feet of the Lord, And I'll wipe it a-way with my
think of the bread You could buy with the sil-ver and
poor in the world Is my love who is go-ing a-
go-ing a-way, But my bod-y I leave with you

hair," she said, "I'll wipe it a-way with my hair."
gold," he said, "You could buy with the sil-ver and gold."
way," she said, "My love who is go-ing a-way."
still," he said, "My bod-y I leave with you still."

5. "The poor of the world are my body," he said,
   "To the end of the world they shall be.
   The bread and the blankets you give to the poor
   You'll know you have given to me," he said,
   "You'll know you have given to me."

6. "My body will hang on the cross of the world
   Tomorrow," he said, "not today.
   And Martha and Mary will find me again
   And wash all my sorrow away," he said,
   "And wash all my sorrow away."

Text: Sydney Carter, b.1915
Tune: JUDAS AND MARY, Irregular; Sydney Carter, b.1915
© Galliard Publications

645　With Jesus for Hero

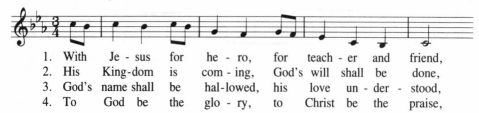

1. With Je - sus for he - ro, for teach - er and friend,
2. His King-dom is com - ing, God's will shall be done,
3. God's name shall be hal-lowed, his love un - der - stood,
4. To God be the glo - ry, to Christ be the praise,

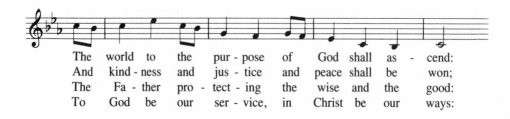

The world to the pur - pose of God shall as - cend:
And kind - ness and jus - tice and peace shall be won;
The Fa - ther pro - tect - ing the wise and the good:
To God be our ser - vice, in Christ be our ways:

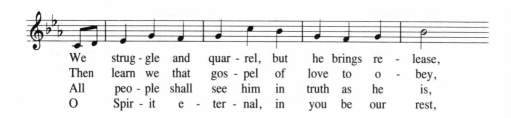

We strug - gle and quar - rel, but he brings re - lease,
Then learn we that gos - pel of love to o - bey,
All peo - ple shall see him in truth as he is,
O Spir - it e - ter - nal, in you be our rest,

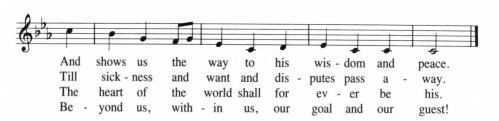

And shows us the way to his wis - dom and peace.
Till sick - ness and want and dis - putes pass a - way.
The heart of the world shall for ev - er be his.
Be - yond us, with - in us, our goal and our guest!

Text: Percy Dearmer, 1867-1936, © Oxford University Press
Tune: SIOBÁN NI LAOGHAIRE, 11 11　11 11; Gaelic; Harm. by Richard Proulx, b.1937, © 1975, GIA Publications, Inc.

O Jesus Christ, May Grateful Hymns Be Rising   646

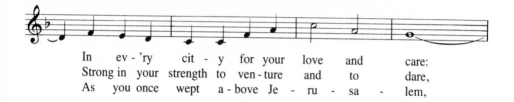

1. O Je - sus Christ,   may grate - ful hymns be   ris - ing
2. Grant us new cour - age,   sac - ri - fi - cial,   hum - ble,
3. Show us your Spir - it,   brood - ing o'er each   cit - y

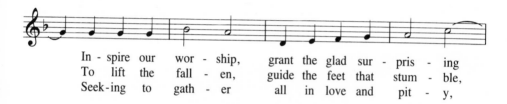

In ev - 'ry   cit - y   for your   love   and   care:
Strong in your strength to ven - ture   and   to   dare,
As   you once   wept   a - bove Je - ru - sa - lem,

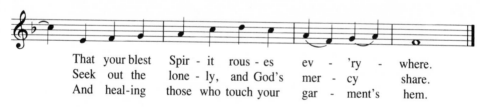

In - spire our   wor - ship,   grant the glad   sur - pris - ing
To   lift   the   fall - en,   guide the feet that   stum - ble,
Seek - ing   to   gath - er   all   in   love and   pit - y,

That your blest   Spir - it   rous - es   ev - 'ry - where.
Seek   out the   lone - ly,   and God's   mer - cy   share.
And   heal - ing   those who touch your   gar - ment's   hem.

Text: Bradford G. Webster, b.1898, © 1954, 1982, Hymn Society of America
Tune: CHARTERHOUSE, 11 10 11 10; David Evans, 1874-1948, © 1927, Oxford University Press

647 Now Join We to Praise the Creator

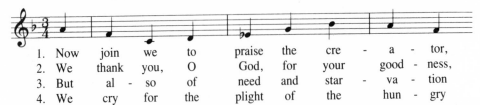

1. Now join we to praise the cre - a - tor,
2. We thank you, O God, for your good - ness,
3. But al - so of need and star - va - tion
4. We cry for the plight of the hun - gry

Our voic - es in wor - ship and song;
For the joy and a - bun - dance of crops,
We sing with con - cern and de - spair,
While har - vests are left on the field,

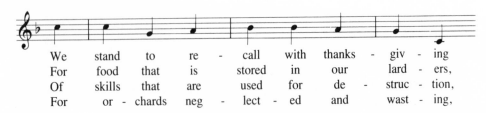

We stand to re - call with thanks - giv - ing
For food that is stored in our lard - ers,
Of skills that are used for de - struc - tion,
For or - chards neg - lect - ed and wast - ing,

That to God all sea - sons be - long.
For all we can buy in the shops.
Of land that is burnt and laid bare.
For pro - duce from mar - kets with - held.

5. The song grows in depth and in wideness:
   The earth and its people are one.
   There can be no thanks without giving,
   No words without deeds that are done.

6. Then teach us, O Lord of the harvest,
   To be humble in all that we claim;
   To share what we have with the nations,
   To care for the world in your name.

Text: Fred Kaan, b.1929, © 1968, Hope Publishing Co.
Tune: HARVEST, 9 8 9 8; Geoffrey Laycock, b.1927, © 1971, Faber Music Ltd.

God, Who Stretched the Spangled Heavens 648

1. God, who stretched the span - gled heav - ens
2. Proud - ly rise our mod - ern cit - ies,
3. We have ven - tured worlds un - dreamed of
4. As each far ho - ri - zon beck - ons,

In - fi - nite in time and place, Flung the suns in
State - ly build - ings, row on row; Yet their win - dows,
Since the child - hood of our race; Known the ec - sta-
May it chal - lenge us a - new, Chil - dren of cre-

burn - ing ra - diance Through the si - lent fields of space;
blank, un - feel - ing, Stare on can - yoned streets be - low,
sy of wing - ing Through un - trav - eled realms of space;
a - tive pur - pose, Serv - ing oth - ers, hon - oring you.

We, your chil - dren, in your like - ness,
Where the lone - ly drift un - no - ticed
Probed the se - crets of the at - om,
May our dreams prove rich with prom - ise,

Share in - ven - tive pow'rs with you; Great Cre - a - tor,
In the cit - y's ebb and flow, Lost to pur - pose
Yield-ing un - i - mag - ined power, Fac - ing us with
Each en - deav - or, well be - gun: Great Cre - a - tor,

still cre - a - ting, Show us what we yet may do.
and to mean - ing, Scarce-ly car - ing where they go.
life's de - struc - tion Or our most tri - um - phant hour.
give us guid - ance Till our goals and yours are one.

Text: Catherine Cameron, b.1927, © 1967, Hope Publishing Co.
Tune: HOLY MANNA, 8 7 8 7 D; William Moore, fl.1830; Harm. by Charles Anders, b.1929, © 1969, Contemporary Worship I: Hymns

649 Jesus, Shepherd of Our Souls

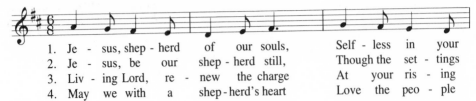

1. Je - sus, shep - herd of our souls, Self - less in your
2. Je - sus, be our shep - herd still, Though the set - tings
3. Liv - ing Lord, re - new the charge At your ris - ing
4. May we with a shep - herd's heart Love the peo - ple

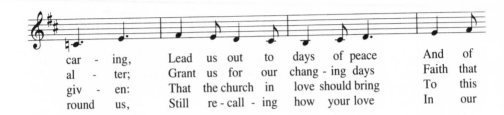

car - ing, Lead us out to days of peace And of
al - ter; Grant us for our chang - ing days Faith that
giv - en: That the church in love should bring To this
round us, Still re - call - ing how your love In our

thought-ful shar - ing. Free our life from ill and war;
will not fal - ter. Bless us in our mod - ern scene
earth your heav - en. Give us in - sight, show us how
stray - ing found us. Keep us, Lord, in hum - ble ways;

What is good in us re - store.
Of com-put - er and ma - chine.
Life is here the task is now.
Lead us clear - ly all our days.

Text: Fred Kaan, b.1929, © 1968, Hope Publishing Co.
Tune: GOOD SHEPHERD, 7 6 7 6 77; Alexander Peloquin, b.1918, © 1975, GIA Publications, Inc.

650 O God of Every Nation

1. O God of ev - 'ry na - tion,
2. (From) search for wealth and pow - er
3. (Lord,) strength - en all who la - bor
4. (Keep) bright in us the vi - sion

Of ev - 'ry race and land,
And scorn of truth and right,
That we may find re - lease
Of days when wars shall cease,

Re-
From
From
When

deem your whole cre - a - tion With your al - might - y
trust in bombs that show - er De - struc-tion through the
fear of rat - tling sa - ber, From dread of war's in-
ha - tred and di - vi - sion Give way to love and

hand;
night,
crease;
peace,

Where hate and fear di - vide us
From pride of race and sta - tion
When hope and cour-age fal - ter,
Till dawns the morn-ing glo - rious

And bit - ter threats are hurled,
And blind - ness to your way,
Your still small voice be heard;
When Christ a - lone shall reign

In
De-
With
And

love and mer - cy guide us And heal our strife - torn
liv - er ev - 'ry na - tion, E - ter - nal God, we
faith that none can al - ter, Up - hold us by your
he shall rule vic - to - rious O'er all the world's do-

1.,2.,3.

world.
pray.
word.
main.

4.

From
Lord,
Keep

A - men.

Text: William W. Reid, b.1923, alt., © 1958, Hymn Society of America
Tune: PIKE, 7 6 7 6 D; Calvin Hampton, 1938-1984, © 1975, GIA Publications, Inc.

651 Great God, Our Source and Lord of Space

1. Great God, our source and Lord of space, O
2. Great God of fire, in - car - nate flame, Through
3. Lord of the at - om, we praise your might, Ex -

Force of all by whose sheer pow'r The pri - mal
Christ in whom your love has burned And burns the
pressed in ter - ri - fy - ing light; Be - fore us

fires that flared and raged Were struck, blazed on, and
way for our dark pace On cos - mic routes with-
rise the flames as pyres, Or bursts of love—they

still are made: O save us, Lord, at this fierce
in us turned: Lead us be - yond a - tom - ic
blind our sight. Help us, our Lord, O help us

hour From threat - 'ning fires that we have laid.
night; Guide, Lord, in hope our bro - ken race.
see New forms of peace through suf - f'ring fires.

Text: George Utech, b.1931, ©
Tune: SALVA NOS, 8 8 8 8 8 8; John Schiavone, b.1947, © 1986, GIA Publications, Inc.

652 O God of Love, O King of Peace

1. O God of love, O King of peace, Make
2. Whom shall we trust but you, O Lord? Where
3. Where saints and an - gels dwell a - bove, All

4.

wars through-out	the	world	to	cease;	Our	vio - lent	ways	help
rest but	on	your	faith - ful	word?	None	ev - er	called	on
hearts are	joined	in	ho - ly	love;	O	bind	us	in	that

us	con - tain;	Give	peace,	O	God,	give	peace	a - gain!
you	in	vain;	Give	peace,	O	God,	give	peace	a - gain!
heav'n-ly	chain;	Give	peace,	O	God,	give	peace	a - gain!

Text: Henry W. Baker, 1821-1877
Tune: TALLIS' CANON, LM; Thomas Tallis, d.1585

Let There Be Light 653

1. Let there be light,
2. O - pen our lips,
3. Per - ish the sword,
4. Hal - low our love,

Let	all	the	na - tions	ga -	ther,	Let	there	be	un - der-
O - pen	our	minds	to	pon -	der,	O -	pen	the	door	of
Per - ish	the	an -	gry	judge - ment,	Per -	ish	the	bombs	and
Hal - low	the	deaths	of	mar -	tyrs,	Hal -	low	their	ho -	ly

stand - ing,	Let	them	be	face	to	face;
con -	cord	O -	pen - ing	in -	to	grace;
hun -	ger,	Per - ish	the	fight	for	gain;
free -	dom,	Hal - low - ed	be	your	name;

5. Your kingdom come,
   Your spirit turn to language,
   Your people speak together,
   Your spirit never fade;

6. Let there be light,
   Open our hearts to wonder,
   Perish the way of terror,
   Hallow the world God made.

Text: Frances W. Davis, b.1936, © American Peace Society
Tune: SPRAGUE, 4 7 7 6; David Hurd, b.1950, © 1985, GIA Publications, Inc.

654　O Day of Peace

1. O day of peace that dim - ly
2. Then shall the wolf dwell with the

shines Through all our hopes and prayers and dreams, Guide us to
lamb Nor shall the fierce de - vour the small; As beasts and

jus - tice, truth and love; De - liv-ered from our self - ish
cat - tle calm - ly graze, A lit - tle child shall lead them

schemes. May swords of hate fall from our hands, Our hearts from
all. Then en - e - mies shall learn to love, All crea - tures

en - vy find re - lease, Till by God's grace our war - ring
find their true ac - cord; The hope of peace shall be ful-

world Shall see Christ's prom - ised reign of peace.
filled, For all the earth shall know the Lord.

Text: Carl P. Daw, Jr., b.1944, © 1982, Carl P. Daw, Jr.
Tune: JERUSALEM, LMD; Charles H. H. Parry, 1848-1918, © Roberton Publications; Harm. by Richard Proulx, b.1937, © 1986, GIA Publications, Inc.

Father, Lord of All Creation 655

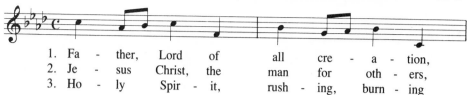

1. Fa - ther, Lord of all cre - a - tion,
2. Je - sus Christ, the man for oth - ers,
3. Ho - ly Spir - it, rush - ing, burn - ing

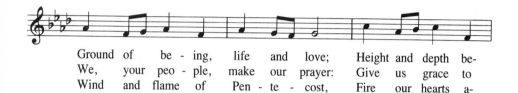

Ground of be - ing, life and love; Height and depth be-
We, your peo - ple, make our prayer: Give us grace to
Wind and flame of Pen - te - cost, Fire our hearts a-

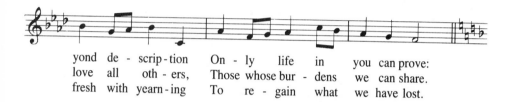

yond de - scrip - tion On - ly life in you can prove:
love all oth - ers, Those whose bur - dens we can share.
fresh with yearn - ing To re - gain what we have lost.

You are mor - tal life's de - pen - dence:
Where your name binds us to - geth - er
May your love u - nite our ac - tion,

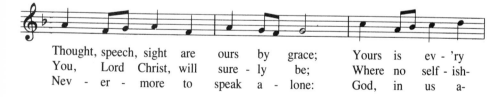

Thought, speech, sight are ours by grace; Yours is ev - 'ry
You, Lord Christ, will sure - ly be; Where no self - ish-
Nev - er - more to speak a - lone: God, in us a-

hour's ex - ist - ence, Sov - ereign Lord of time and space.
ness can sev - er, There your love we all may see.
bol - ish fac - tion, God, through us your love make known.

Text: Steward Cross, b.1928, ©
Tune: GENEVA, 8 7 8 7 D; George H. Day, 1883-1966, © 1942, The Church Pension Fund

656 Help Us Accept Each Other

1. Help us ac-cept each oth - er As Christ ac-cept-ed us;
2. Teach us, O Lord, your les - sons, As in our dai - ly life
3. Let your ac-cept-ance change us, So that we may be moved
4. Lord, for to-day's en - coun - ters With all who are in need,

Teach us as sis - ter, broth - er, Each per - son to em - brace.
We strug-gle to be hu - man And search for hope and faith.
In liv - ing sit-u - a - tions To do the truth in love;
Who hun - ger for ac - cept - ance, For right-eous-ness and bread,

Be pres - ent, Lord, a - mong us, And bring us to be - lieve
Teach us to care for peo - ple, For all, not just for some;
To prac-tice your ac - cept - ance, Un - til we know by heart
We need new eyes for see - ing, New hands for hold - ing on;

We are our-selves ac - cept - ed And meant to love and live.
To love them as we find them, Or, as they may be - come.
The ta - ble of for - give - ness And laugh-ter's heal - ing art.
Re - new us with your Spir - it; Lord, free us, make us one!

Text: Jn. 15:12; Fred Kaan, b.1929, © 1975, Hope Publishing Co.
Tune: KING'S LYNN, 7 6 7 6 D; English; Harm. by Ralph Vaughan Williams 1872-1958, © Oxford University Press

There Is One Lord   657

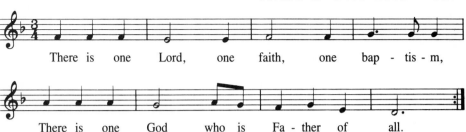

There is one Lord, one faith, one bap - tis - m,

There is one God who is Fa - ther of all.

Text: Eph. 4, Taizé Community, 1984
Tune: Jacques Berthier, b.1923
© 1984, Les Presses de Taizé

Lord Christ, the Father's Mighty Son   658

1. Lord Christ, the Fa - ther's might - y Son,
2. To make us one your prayers were said,
3. Lord Christ, for - give us, make us new!
4. We will not ques - tion or re - fuse

Whose work up - on the cross was done To
To make us one you broke the bread For
What our de - signs could nev - er do Your
The way you work, the means you choose, The

give and re - ceive, Make all our scat - tered
all to re - ceive; Its piec - es scat - ter
love can a - chieve. Our prayers, our work, we
pat - tern you weave; But rec - on - cile our

church-es one, That the world may be - lieve.
us in - stead: How can oth - ers be - lieve?
bring to you; That the world may be - lieve.
war - ring views, That the world may be - lieve.

Text: Brian Wren, b.1936
Tune: HAMPTON POYLE, 88 5 8 6; Peter Cutts, b.1937
© 1968, Hope Publishing Co.

659 In Christ There Is No East or West

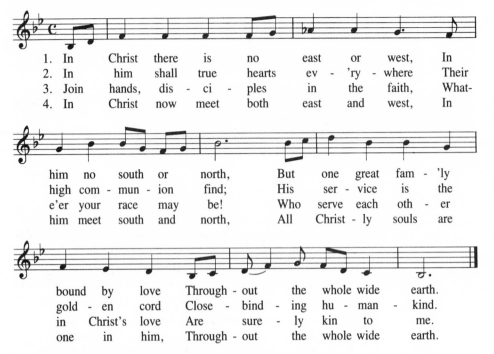

1. In Christ there is no east or west, In
2. In him shall true hearts ev - 'ry - where Their
3. Join hands, dis - ci - ples in the faith, What-
4. In Christ now meet both east and west, In

him no south or north, But one great fam - 'ly
high com - mun - ion find; His ser - vice is the
e'er your race may be! Who serve each oth - er
him meet south and north, All Christ - ly souls are

bound by love Through - out the whole wide earth.
gold - en cord Close - bind - ing hu - man - kind.
in Christ's love Are sure - ly kin to me.
one in him, Through - out the whole wide earth.

Text: Gal. 3:28; John Oxenham, 1852-1941, © American Tract Society
Tune: MC KEE, CM; Afro-American; Adapted by Harry T. Burleigh, 1866-1949

660 Peace with the Father

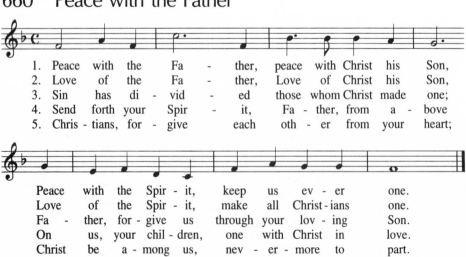

1. Peace with the Fa - ther, peace with Christ his Son,
2. Love of the Fa - ther, Love of Christ his Son,
3. Sin has di - vid - ed those whom Christ made one;
4. Send forth your Spir - it, Fa - ther, from a - bove
5. Chris - tians, for - give each oth - er from your heart;

Peace with the Spir - it, keep us ev - er one.
Love of the Spir - it, make all Christ - ians one.
Fa - ther, for - give us through your lov - ing Son.
On us, your chil - dren, one with Christ in love.
Christ be a - mong us, nev - er - more to part.

Text: James Quinn, SJ, b.1919, © 1969
Tune: SONG 46, 10 10; Orlando Gibbons, 1583-1625

Is This a Day of New Beginnings 661

1. Is this a day of new be - gin - nings,
2. How can the sea - sons of a plan - et
3. Yet thro' the life and death of Je - sus
4. Then let us with the Spir - it's dar - ing,
5. So let us gath - er 'round the ta - ble

Time to re - mem - ber and move on,
Mind - less - ly spin - ning 'round its sun
Love's might - y Spir - it, now as then,
Step from the past and leave be - hind
To taste and share what love can do.

Time to be - lieve what love is bring - ing,
With just a hu - man name and num - ber
Can make for us a world of dif - f'rence
Its dis - ap - point - ment, guilt, and griev - ing,
This is a day of new be - gin - nings—

Lay - ing to rest the pain that's gone?
Say that some new thing has be - gun?
As faith and hope are born a - gain.
Seek - ing new paths, and sure to find.
Our God is mak - ing all things new.

Text: Brian Wren, b.1936, © 1983, Hope Publishing Co.
Tune: STEEPLE BELLS, 9 8 9 8; Normal L. Warren, b.1934, © 1982, Hope Publishing Co.

662 On This Day, the First of Days

1. On this day, the first of days,
2. On this day the e - ter - nal Son
3. Word - made - flesh, all prais - es be!
4. Ho - ly Spir - it, you im - part
5. God, the bless - ed Three in One,

God our Mak - er's name we praise;
O - ver death his tri - umph won;
You from sin have set us free;
Gifts of love to ev - 'ry heart;
May your ho - ly will be done;

Who, cre - a - tion's
On this day the
And with you we
Give us light and
In your word our

Lord and Spring, Did the world from dark - ness bring.
Spir - it came With its gifts of liv - ing flame.
die and rise Un - to God in sac - ri - fice.
grace, we pray, Fill our hearts this ho - ly day.
souls are free, As we praise the Trin - i - ty.

Text: *Die parente temporum; Le Mans Breviary,* 1748; Tr. by Henry W. Baker, 1821-1877
Tune: LÜBECK, 77 77; *Freylinghausen's Gesangbuch,* 1704

663 This Is the Day When Light Was First Created

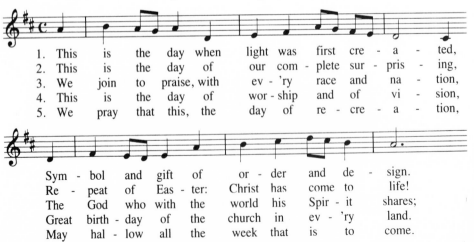

1. This is the day when light was first cre - a - ted,
2. This is the day of our com - plete sur - pris - ing,
3. We join to praise, with ev - 'ry race and na - tion,
4. This is the day of wor - ship and of vi - sion,
5. We pray that this, the day of re - cre - a - tion,

Sym - bol and gift of or - der and de - sign.
Re - peat of Eas - ter: Christ has come to life!
The God who with the world his Spir - it shares;
Great birth - day of the church in ev - 'ry land.
May hal - low all the week that is to come.

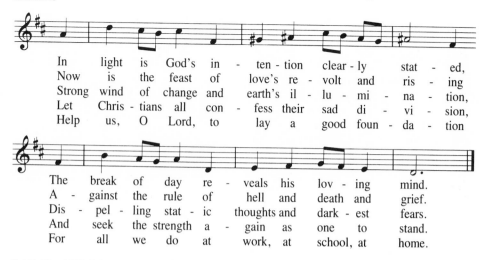

In light is God's in - ten - tion clear - ly stat - ed,
Now is the feast of love's re - volt and ris - ing
Strong wind of change and earth's il - lu - mi - na - tion,
Let Chris - tians all con - fess their sad di - vi - sion,
Help us, O Lord, to lay a good foun - da - tion

The break of day re - veals his lov - ing mind.
A - gainst the rule of hell and death and grief.
Dis - pel - ling stat - ic thoughts and dark - est fears.
And seek the strength a - gain as one to stand.
For all we do at work, at school, at home.

Text: Fred Kaan, b.1929, © 1968, Hope Publishing Co.
Tune: NORTHBROOK, 11 10 11 10; Reginald S. Thatcher, 1888-1957, © Oxford University Press

Come, Rejoice before Your Maker   664

1. Come, re - joice be - fore your Mak - er
2. Know for cer - tain, our Cre - a - tor
3. Come with grate - ful hearts be - fore him,
4. For the Lord our God is gra - cious

All you peo - ples of the earth; Serve the Lord your
Is the true and on - ly God; We are his, for
En - ter now his courts with praise; Show your thank - ful-
Ev - er - last - ing in his love, And to ev - 'ry

God with glad - ness, Come be - fore him with a song!
he has made us— We are sheep with - in his fold.
ness to - wards him, Give due hon - or to his name.
gen - er - a - tion His great faith - ful - ness en - dures.

Text: Psalm 100; Michael Baughen, b.1930
Tune: JUBILATE DEO, 8 7 8 7; Noel H. Tredinnick, b.1949
© 1973, Hope Publishing Co.

665 Gather Us In

1. Here in this place, new light is stream-ing,
2. We are the young— our lives are a mys-t'ry,
3. Here we will take the wine and the wa-ter,
4. Not in the dark of build-ings con-fin-ing,

Now is the dark-ness van-ished a-way,
We are the old— who yearn for your face,
Here we will take the bread of new birth,
Not in some heav-en, light years a-way, But

See, in this space, our fears and our dream-ings,
We have been sung through-out all of his-t'ry,
Here you shall call your sons and your daugh-ters,
here in this place, the new light is shin-ing,

Brought here to you in the light of this
Called to be light to the whole hu-man
Call us a-new to be salt for the
Now is the King-dom, now is the

day. Gath-er us in— the
race. Gath-er us in— the
earth. Give us to drink the
day. Gath-er us in— and

lost and for-sak-en, Gath-er us in— the
rich and the haugh-ty, Gath-er us in— the
wine of com-pas-sion, Give us to eat the
hold us for ev-er, Gath-er us in— and

blind and the lame; Call to us now, and
proud and the strong; Give us a heart so
bread that is you; Nour - ish us well, and
make us your own; Gath - er us in— all

we shall a - wak - en, We shall a - rise at the
meek and so low - ly, Give us the cour - age to
teach us to fash - ion, Lives that are ho - ly and
peo - ples to - geth - er, Fire of love in our

sound of our name.
en - ter the song.
hearts that are true.
flesh and our bone.

Text: Marty Haugen, b.1950
Tune: GATHER US IN, 10 9 10 10 D (slightly irreg.); Marty Haugen, b.1950
© 1982, GIA Publications, Inc.

666 Only-begotten, Word of God Eternal

1. On - ly - be - got - ten, Word of God e-
2. Ho - ly this tem - ple where our Lord is
3. Lord, we be - seech you, as we throng your
4. God in Three Per - sons, Fa - ther ev - er-

ter - nal, Lord of cre - a - tion, mer - ci - ful and
dwell - ing, This is none oth - er than the gate of
tem - ple, By your past bless - ings, by your pres - ent
liv - ing, Son co - e - ter - nal, ev - er - bless - ed

might - y, Hear now your ser - vants, when their tune - ful
heav - en; Stran - gers and pil - grims, seek - ing homes e-
boun - ty, Smile on your chil - dren, and with ten - der
Spir - it, Yours be the glo - ry, praise and ad - or-

voic - es Rise to your pres - ence.
ter - nal, Pass through its por - tals.
mer - cy Hear our pe - ti - tions.
a - tion, Now and for ev - er.

Text: *Christe cunctorum dominator alme*; Latin, 9th C.; Tr. by Maxwell J. Blacker, 1822-1888
Tune: ISTE CONFESSOR 11 11 11 5; Rouen Church Melody; Harm. by Carl Schalk, b.1929, © 1969, Concordia Publishing House

God Is Here! As We His People 667

1. God is here! As we his peo-ple, Meet to
2. Here are sym-bols to re-mind us Of our
3. Here our chil-dren find a wel-come In the
4. Lord of all, of church and king-dom, In an

of - fer praise and prayer, May we find in ful - ler
life - long need of grace; Here are ta - ble, font and
Shep - herd's flock and fold; Here, as bread and wine are
age of change and doubt, Keep us faith - ful to the

meas-ure What it is in Christ we share:
pul - pit, Here the cross has cen - tral place:
tak - en, Christ sus - tains us as of old:
gos - pel, Help us work your pur - pose out:

Here, as in the world a - round us, All our
Here in hon - es - ty of preach - ing, Here in
Here the ser - vants of the Ser - vant Seek in
Here, in this day's ded - i - ca - tion, All we

var - ied skills and arts Wait the com - ing
si - lence as in speech, Here in new - ness
wor - ship to ex - plore What it means in
have to give, re - ceive; We who can - not

of his Spir - it In - to o - pen minds and hearts.
and re - new - al God the Spir - it comes to each.
dai - ly liv - ing To be - lieve and to a - dore.
live with - out you, We a - dore you! We be - lieve!

Text: Fred Pratt Green, b.1903, © 1979, Hope Publishing Co.
Tune: ABBOT'S LEIGH, 8 7 8 7 D; Cyril V. Taylor, b.1907, © 1942, 1970, Hope Publishing Co.; Suggested alternate tune IN BABILONE

668 Now the Silence

Now the si-lence, Now the peace, Now the

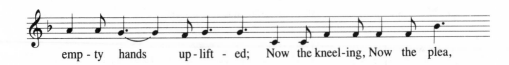

emp-ty hands up-lift-ed; Now the kneel-ing, Now the plea,

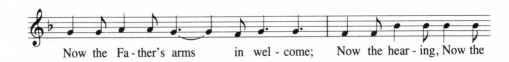

Now the Fa-ther's arms in wel-come; Now the hear-ing, Now the

pow'r, Now the ves-sel brimmed for pour-ing; Now the bod-y,

Now the blood, Now the joy-ful cel - e-bra-tion;

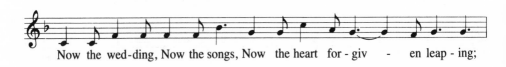

Now the wed-ding, Now the songs, Now the heart for-giv - en leap-ing;

Now the Spir-it's vis-i-ta-tion, Now the Son's e-piph-a-ny,

Now the Fa-ther's bless-ing. Now. Now. Now.

Text: Jaroslav J. Vajda, b.1919
Tune: NOW, 4 3 8 4 3 8 D with refrain; Carl Schalk, b.1929
© 1969, Hope Publishing Co.

All People That on Earth Do Dwell   669

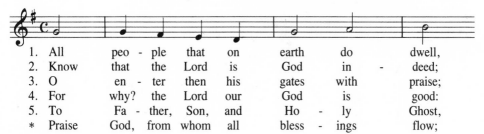

1. All peo - ple that on earth do dwell,
2. Know that the Lord is God in - deed;
3. O en - ter then his gates with praise;
4. For why? the Lord our God is good:
5. To Fa - ther, Son, and Ho - ly Ghost,
* Praise God, from whom all bless - ings flow;

Sing to the Lord with cheer - ful voice;
With - out our aid he did us make;
Ap - proach with joy his courts un - to;
His mer - cy is for ev - er sure;
The God whom heaven and earth a - dore,
Praise Him, all crea - tures here be - low;

Him serve with mirth, his praise forth tell,
We are his folk, he does us feed,
Praise, laud, and bless his Name al - ways,
His truth at all times firm - ly stood,
From us and from the an - gel host
Praise Him a - bove, you heav'n - ly host:

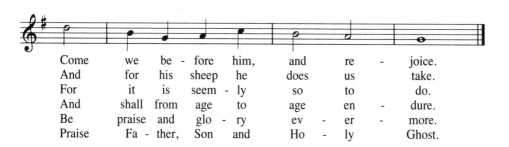

Come we be - fore him, and re - joice.
And for his sheep he does us take.
For it is seem - ly so to do.
And shall from age to age en - dure.
Be praise and glo - ry ev - er - more.
Praise Fa - ther, Son and Ho - ly Ghost.

*May be sung alone or as an alternate to stanza 5.

Text: Psalm (99)100; William Kethe, d. c.1593; Doxology, Thomas Ken, 1637-1711
Tune: OLD HUNDREDTH, LM; Louis Bourgeois, c.1510-1561; alt. harm. by John Dowland, 1562-1626

670 All People That on Earth Do Dwell

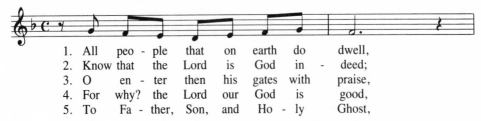

1. All peo - ple that on earth do dwell,
2. Know that the Lord is God in - deed;
3. O en - ter then his gates with praise,
4. For why? the Lord our God is good,
5. To Fa - ther, Son, and Ho - ly Ghost,

Sing to the Lord with cheer - ful voice:
With - out our aid he did us make:
Ap - proach with joy his courts un - to;
His mer - cy is for ev - er sure;
The God whom heav'n and earth a - dore;

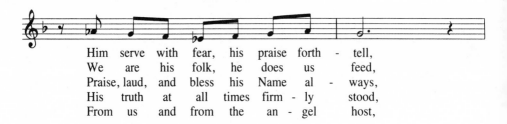

Him serve with fear, his praise forth - tell,
We are his folk, he does us feed,
Praise, laud, and bless his Name al - ways,
His truth at all times firm - ly stood,
From us and from the an - gel host,

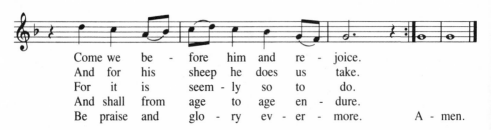

Come we be - fore him and re - joice.
And for his sheep he does us take.
For it is seem - ly so to do.
And shall from age to age en - dure.
Be praise and glo - ry ev - er - more. A - men.

Text: Psalm 100; William Kethe, d. c.1593
Tune: DE TAR, LM; Calvin Hampton,. 1938-1984, © 1973, Concordia Publishing House

I Sing As I Arise Today 671

1. I sing as I a - rise to - day! I
2. The word of God to be my speech, The
3. Al - le - lu - ia, al - le - lu - ia, Al-

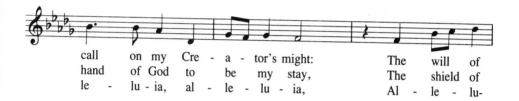

call on my Cre - a - tor's might: The will of
hand of God to be my stay, The shield of
le - lu - ia, al - le - lu - ia, Al - le - lu-

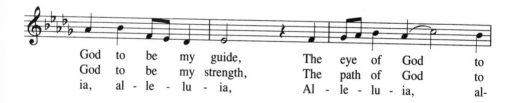

God to be my guide, The eye of God to
God to be my strength, The path of God to
ia, al - le - lu - ia, Al - le - lu - ia, al-

be my sight,
be my way.
le - lu - ia.

Text: Ascr. to St. Patrick, 372-466; Tr. Anonymous
Tune: KING, LM; David Hurd, b.1950, © 1983, GIA Publications, Inc.

672 How Beautiful the Morning and the Day

1. How beau-ti-ful the morn-ing and the day; My
2. How glo-ri-ous the morn-ing and the day; My
3. How boun-ti-ful the bless-ings that he brings Of
4. How mer-ci-ful the work-ings of God's grace; A-
5. How bar-ren was my life be-fore he came Sup-

heart a-bounds with mu-sic, My lips can on-ly
heart is still and lis-tens, My soul be-gins to
peace and joy and rap-ture That make my spir-it
rous-ing faith and ac-tion My soul would nev-er
ply-ing love and heal-ing; I live now to ac-

say How beau-ti-ful the morn-ing and the day.
pray To God who is the glo-ry of the day.
sing: How boun-ti-ful the bless-ings that he brings.
face With-out such match-less mer-cy and such grace.
claim The maj-es-ty and won-der of God's Name.

Text: Owen D. Barker, 1899-1974, alt.
Tune: ST. OWEN, 10 7 6 10; Sherrell Prebble, b.1951
© 1975, Celebration

673 This Day God Gives Me

1. This day God gives me Strength of high heav-en,
2. This day God sends me Strength as my guard-ian,
3. God's way is my way, God's shield is round me,
4. Ris-ing, I thank you, Might-y and strong One,

Sun and moon shin-ing, Flame in my hearth,
Might to up-hold me, Wis-dom as guide.
God's host de-fends me, Sav-ing from ill.
King of cre-a-tion, Giv-er of rest,

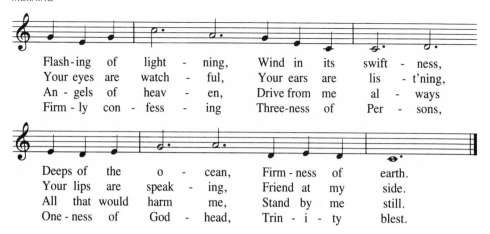

Flash-ing of light - ning, Wind in its swift - ness,
Your eyes are watch - ful, Your ears are lis - t'ning,
An - gels of heav - en, Drive from me al - ways
Firm - ly con - fess - ing Three-ness of Per - sons,

Deeps of the o - cean, Firm - ness of earth.
Your lips are speak - ing, Friend at my side.
All that would harm me, Stand by me still.
One - ness of God - head, Trin - i - ty blest.

Text: Ascr. to St. Patrick, 372-466; Adapted by James Quinn, SJ, b.1919, © 1969
Tune: BUNESSAN 5 5 5 4 D; Gaelic; Harm. by A. Gregory Murray, OSB, b.1905, ©

Morning Has Broken 674

Use previous tune

1. Morning has broken
   Like the first morning,
   Blackbird has spoken
   Like the first bird.
   Praise for the singing!
   Praise for the morning!
   Praise for them, springing
   Fresh from the Word!

2. Sweet the rain's new fall
   Sunlit from heaven,
   Like the first dewfall
   On the first grass.
   Praise for the sweetness
   Of the wet garden,
   Sprung in completeness
   Where his feet pass.

3. Mine is the sunlight!
   Mine is the morning
   Born of the one light
   Eden saw play!
   Praise with elation,
   Praise ev'ry morning,
   God's re-creation
   Of the new day!

Text: Eleanor Farjeon, 1881-1965, © David Higham Assoc. Ltd.

675   When Morning Gilds the Skies

1. When morn - ing gilds the skies, My heart, a - wak - ing, cries,
2. To God, the Word, on high The hosts of an - gels cry:
3. Let earth's wide cir - cle round In joy - ful notes re - sound:
4. Be this while life is mine My can - ti - cle di - vine:

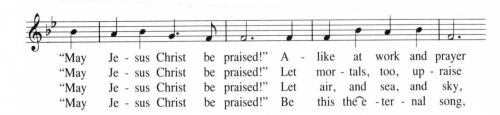

"May Je - sus Christ be praised!" A - like at work and prayer
"May Je - sus Christ be praised!" Let mor - tals, too, up - raise
"May Je - sus Christ be praised!" Let air, and sea, and sky,
"May Je - sus Christ be praised!" Be this thee - ter - nal song,

To Je - sus I re - pair: "May Je - sus Christ be praised!"
Their voice in hymns of praise: "May Je - sus Christ be praised!"
From depth to height, re - ply: "May Je - sus Christ be praised!"
Through all the a - ges long: "May Je - sus Christ be praised!"

Text: *Wach ich früh Morgens auf; Katholiches Gesangbuch,* 1828; Tr. by Edward Caswall, 1814-1878
Tune: LAUDES DOMINI, 66 6 D; Joseph Barnby, 1838-1896

Nunc Dimittis 676

Nunc di - mit - tis ser-vum tu - um Do -mi - ne,   se-

cun - dum ver-bum tu - um in pa - ce.   Nunc di-

Text: Luke 2:29, *Now, Lord, let your servant go in peace according to your promise;* Taizé Community, 1980
Tune: Jacques Berthier, b.1923
© 1980, Les Presses de Taizé

Day Is Done 677

1. Day   is   done, but   love   un-fail - ing   Dwells ev - er   here;
2. Dark   de-scends, but light un-end - ing   Shines through our night;
3. Eyes   will close, but   you   un-sleep - ing Watch   by   our   side;

Shad - ows fall, but   hope, pre-vail - ing, Calms ev - 'ry   fear.
You   are with   us,   ev - er lend - ing   New   strength to   sight:
Death may come, in love's safe keep - ing   Still   we   a - bide.

God, our Mak - er,   none for-sak - ing,   Take our hearts, of Love's own
One in love, your   truth con-fess - ing,   One in hope of   heav - en's
God of love, all   e - vil quell-ing,   Sin for-giv - ing, fear dis-

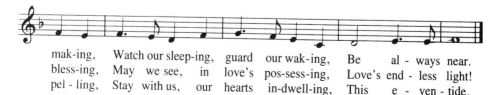

mak-ing, Watch our sleep-ing, guard our wak-ing, Be al - ways near.
bless-ing, May we see, in   love's pos-sess-ing, Love's end - less light!
pel - ling, Stay with us, our hearts in-dwell-ing, This e - ven - tide.

Text: James Quinn, SJ, b.1919, © 1969
Tune: AR HYD Y NOS, 8 4 8 4 888 4; Welsh

678 The Day You Gave Us, Lord, Is Ended

1. The day you gave us, Lord, is end-ed, The dark-ness
2. We thank you that your Church, un-sleep-ing While earth rolls
3. A-cross each con-ti-nent and is-land As dawn leads
4. The sun that bids us rest is wak-ing Your friends be-
5. So be it, Lord; your throne shall nev-er, Like earth's proud

falls at your be-hest; To you our morn-ing
on-ward in-to light, Through all the world its
on an-oth-er day, The voice of prayer is
neath the west-ern sky, And hour by hour fresh
em-pires, pass a-way: Your king-dom stands, and

hymns as-cend-ed, Your praise shall sanc-ti-fy our rest.
watch is keep-ing, And rests not now by day or night.
nev-er si-lent, Nor dies the strain of praise a-way.
lips are mak-ing Your won-drous do-ings heard on high.
grows for ev-er, Till all your crea-tures own your sway.

Text: John Ellerton, 1826-1893, alt.
Tune: ST. CLEMENT, 9 8 9 8; Clement C. Scholefield, 1839-1904

679 O Gladsome Light

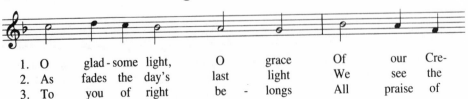

1. O glad-some light, O grace Of our Cre-
2. As fades the day's last light, We see the
3. To you of right be-longs All praise of

a - tor's face, The e - ter - nal splen - dor wear - ing:
lamps of night, Our com - mon hymn out - pour - ing,
ho - ly songs, O Son of God, Life - giv - er;

Ce - les - tial, ho - ly blest, Our Sav - ior
O God of might un - known, You, the in-
You, there - fore, O Most High, The world does

Je - sus Christ, Joy - ful in your ap - pear - ing!
car - nate Son, And Spir - it blest a - dor - ing.
glo - ri - fy And shall ex - alt for ev - er.

Text: Φωσ Ἱλαρον; Greek, c.200; Tr. Robert S. Bridges, 1844-1930
Tune: NUNC DIMITTIS 66 7 66 7; *Genevan Psalter,* 1549; Harm. by Claude Goudimel, c.1505-1572

We Praise You, Father 680

1. We praise you, Fa - ther, for your gift Of dusk and
2. With - in your hands we rest se - cure; In qui - et
3. Your glo - ry may we ev - er seek In rest, as

night - fall o - ver earth, Fore-shad - ow - ing the
sleep our strength re - new; Yet give your peo - ple
in ac - tiv - i - ty, Un - til its full - ness

mys - ter - y Of death that leads to end - less day.
hearts that wake In love to you, un - sleep - ing Lord.
is re - vealed, O Source of life, O Trin - i - ty.

Text: Benedictine Nuns of St. Mary's Abbey, West Malling, Kent, ©
Tune: WERNER, LM; Anthony Werner, fl.1863

681 Christ, Mighty Savior

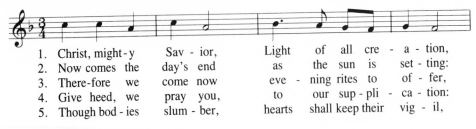

1. Christ, might-y Sav - ior, Light of all cre - a - tion,
2. Now comes the day's end as the sun is set - ting:
3. There-fore we come now eve - ning rites to of - fer,
4. Give heed, we pray you, to our sup - pli - ca - tion:
5. Though bod - ies slum - ber, hearts shall keep their vig - il,

You make the day - time ra - diant with the sun - light
Mir - ror of day-break, pledge of res - ur - rec - tion;
Joy - ful - ly chant - ing ho - ly hymns to praise you,
That you may grant us par - don for of - fens - es,
For ev - er rest - ing in the peace of Je - sus,

And to the night give glit - ter - ing a - dorn-ment,
While in the heav - ens choirs of stars ap - pear - ing
With all cre - a - tion join - ing hearts and voic - es
Strength for our weak hearts, rest for ach - ing bod - ies,
In light or dark - ness wor - ship - ing our Sav - ior

Stars in the heav - ens.
Hal - low the night - fall.
Sing - ing your glo - ry.
Sooth - ing the wea - ry.
Now and for ev - er.

Text: *Christe, lux mundi;* Mozarabic Rite, 10th C.; Tr. by Alan G. McDougall, 1895-1964 Rev. by Anne K. LeCroy, b.1930, and others, ©
Tune: MIGHTY SAVIOR, 11 11 11 5; David Hurd, b.1950. © 1985, GIA Publications, Inc.

Praise and Thanksgiving 682

1. Praise and thanks - giv - ing, Fa - ther, we of - fer,
2. Lord, bless the la - bor We bring to serve you,
3. Fa - ther, pro - vid - ing Food for your chil - dren,
4. Then will your bless - ing Reach ev - 'ry peo - ple,

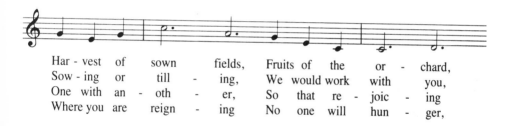

For all things liv - ing You have made good.
That with our neigh - bor We may be fed.
Your wis - dom guid - ing Teach-es us share
Free - ly con - fess - ing Your gra - cious hand.

Har - vest of sown fields, Fruits of the or - chard,
Sow - ing or till - ing, We would work with you,
One with an - oth - er, So that re - joic - ing
Where you are reign - ing No one will hun - ger,

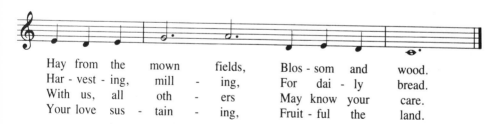

Hay from the mown fields, Blos - som and wood.
Har - vest - ing, mill - ing, For dai - ly bread.
With us, all oth - ers May know your care.
Your love sus - tain - ing Fruit - ful the land.

Text: Albert F. Bayly, 1901-1984, © Oxford University Press
Tune: BUNESSAN, 5 5 5 4 D; Gaelic; Harm. by A. Gregory Murray, OSB, b.1905, ©

683 God, Whose Farm Is All Creation

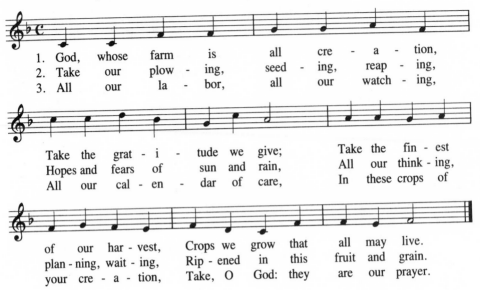

1. God, whose farm is all cre - a - tion,
   Take the grat - i - tude we give;
   of our har - vest, Crops we grow that all may live.
2. Take our plow - ing, seed - ing, reap - ing,
   Hopes and fears of sun and rain,
   plan - ning, wait - ing, Rip - ened in this fruit and grain.
3. All our la - bor, all our watch - ing,
   All our cal - en - dar of care,
   your cre - a - tion, Take, O God: they are our prayer.

Take the fin - est
All our think - ing,
In these crops of

Text: John Arlott, b.1914, © The Old Sun
Tune: STUTTGART, 8 7 8 7; Christian F. Witt, 1660-1716; Harm. by Kenneth D. Smith, b.1928, © National Christian Education Council

684 He Walks among the Golden Lamps

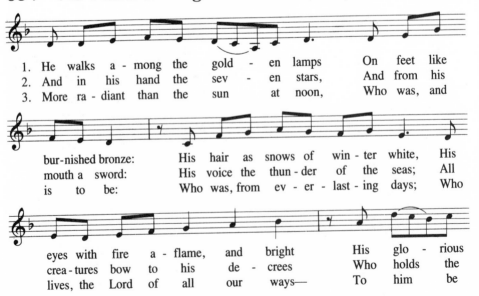

1. He walks a - mong the gold - en lamps
   On feet like
   bur-nished bronze: His hair as snows of win - ter white, His
   eyes with fire a - flame, and bright His glo - rious
2. And in his hand the sev - en stars,
   And from his
   mouth a sword: His voice the thun - der of the seas; All
   crea - tures bow to his de - crees Who holds the
3. More ra - diant than the sun at noon,
   Who was, and
   is to be: Who was, from ev - er - last - ing days; Who
   lives, the Lord of all our ways— To him be

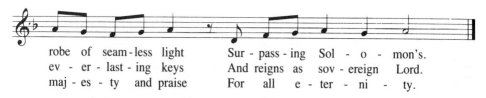

robe of seam-less light   Sur - pass-ing Sol - o - mon's.
ev - er - last-ing keys   And reigns as sov - ereign Lord.
maj - es - ty and praise   For all e - ter - ni - ty.

Text: Rev. 1:12-18; Timothy Dudley-Smith, b.1926, © 1973, Hope Publishing Co.
Tune: REVELATION, 8 6 888 6; Robert LeBlanc, b.1948, © 1986, GIA Publications, Inc.

O Holy City, Seen of John   685

1. O Ho - ly Cit - y, seen of John, Where Christ, the
2. O shame to us who rest con - tent While lust and
3. Give us, O God, the strength to build The Cit - y
4. Al - read - y in the mind of God That Cit - y

Lamb, does reign, With - in those four - square walls shall
greed for gain In street and shop and ten - e -
that has stood Too long a dream, whose laws are
ris - es fair: Lo, how its splen - dor chal - leng-

come No night, nor need, nor pain, And where the
ment Wring gold from hu - man pain, And bit - ter
love, Whose ways, the com - mon good, And where the
es The souls that great - ly dare: Yea, bids us

tears are wiped from eyes That shall not weep a - gain.
lips in blind de - spair Cry, "Christ has died in vain."
shin - ing sun be - comes God's grace for hu - man good.
seize the whole of life And build its glo - ry there.

Text: Rev.21; W. Russell Bowie, 1882-1969, © Harper and Row
Tune: MORNING SONG, 8 6 8 6 8 6; Kentucky Harmony, 1816; Harm. by C. Winfred Douglas, 1867-1944, © 1940, The Church Pension Fund

686 Mine Eyes Have Seen the Glory

1. Mine eyes have seen the glo - ry of the com - ing of the
2. I have seen him in the watch - fires of a hun - dred cir - cling
3. He has sound - ed forth the trum - pet that shall nev - er call re-
4. In the beau - ty of the lil - ies Christ was born a - cross the

Lord; He is tram - pling out the vin - tage where the grapes of wrath are
camps; They have build - ed him an al - tar in the eve - ning dews and
treat; He is sift - ing out all hu - man hearts be - fore his judg - ment
sea, With a glo - ry in his bos - om that trans - fig - ures you and

stored; He hath loosed the fate - ful light - ning of his ter - ri - ble swift
damps; I can read the right - eous sen - tence by the dim and flar - ing
seat; O be swift, my soul, to an - swer him; be ju - bi - lant, my
me; As he died to make us ho - ly, let us die that all be

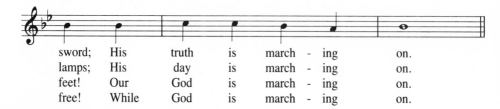

sword; His truth is march - ing on.
lamps; His day is march - ing on.
feet! Our God is march - ing on.
free! While God is march - ing on.

Glo - ry! Glo - ry! Hal - le - lu - jah! Glo - ry!

Glo - ry! Hal - le - lu - jah! Glo - ry! Glo - ry! Hal - le-

lu - jah! His truth is march - ing on.

Text: Julia W. Howe, 1819-1910
Tune: BATTLE HYMN OF THE REPUBLIC, 15 15 15 6 with refrain; Attr. to William Steffe, d.1911

Now the Day of the Lord Is at Hand 687

1. Now the day of the Lord is at hand, at hand;
2. Who would sigh for an old lost age of gold,

Its storms roll up the sky;
While the Lord of a - ges is here?

The na - tions sleep starv - ing on heaps of gold; All
True hearts then will leap at the trum - pet of God, And

dream - ers toss and sigh; The night is dark - est be-
those who suf - fer can dare. Each age of gold was an

fore the morn; When pain is great - est the
iron age too, And the meek - est of saints may find

child is born, For the day of the Lord is at
work to do For the day of the Lord is at

hand, at hand, The day of the Lord is at hand.
hand, at hand, The day of the Lord is at hand.

Text: Based on Charles Kingsley, 1819-1875, by Richard Proulx, b.1937
Tune: REMEMBER THE POOR, Irregular; Gaelic; Alt. and harm. by Richard Proulx, b.1937, © 1986, GIA Publications, Inc.

688 A Multitude Comes from the East and the West

1. A mul - ti - tude comes from the east and the west
2. O God, let us hear when our shep - herd shall call
3. All trials shall be like a dream that is past;
4. The heav - ens shall ring with an an - them more grand

To sit at the feast of sal - va - tion
In ac - cents per - sua - sive and ten - der,
For - got - ten all trou - ble and mourn - ing.
Than ev - er on earth was re - cord - ed;

With A - bra - ham, I - saac, and Ja - cob, the blest,
That while there is time we make haste, one and all,
All ques - tions and doubts have been an - swered at last,
The blest of the Lord shall re - ceive at his hand

O - bey - ing the Lord's in - vi - ta - tion.
And find him, our might - y de - fend - er.
When ris - es the light of that morn - ing.
The crown to the vic - tors a - ward - ed.

Text: *Der Mange skal komme fra Öst og fra Vest;* Magnus B. Landstad, 1802-1880; Tr. by Peer O. Strömme, 1856-1951, adapt.
Tune: CONSUMMATION, 11 9 11 9; Robert LeBlanc, b.1948, © 1986, GIA Publications, Inc.

689 O the Beautiful Treasures

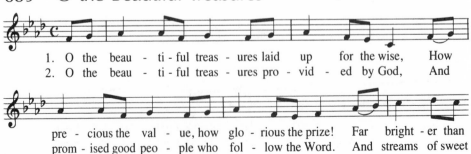

1. O the beau - ti - ful treas - ures laid up for the wise, How
2. O the beau - ti - ful treas - ures pro - vid - ed by God, And

pre - cious the val - ue, how glo - rious the prize! Far bright - er than
prom - ised good peo - ple who fol - low the Word. And streams of sweet

dia - monds on princ - es' brow, And rich - er than roy - al - ty
mer - cy shall bring them home, To rest from the sor - row-ful

can be - stow. O the beau - ti - ful treas - ures laid up for the wise.
paths they roam. O the beau - ti - ful treas - ures pro - vid - ed by God.

Text: Shaker
Tune: BEAUTIFUL TREASURES, 12 11 10 10 12; American Shaker Melody, 1849; Harm. by Richard Proulx, b.1937, © 1986, GIA Publications, Inc.

Jerusalem, My Happy Home 690

1. Je - ru - sa - lem, my hap - py home, When
2. Your saints are crowned with glo - ry great; They
3. There Da - vid stands with harp in hand As
4. Our La - dy sings Mag - nif - i - cat With

shall I with you be? When shall my sor - rows
see God face to face; They tri - umph still, they
mas - ter of the choir: Ten thou - sand times that
tune sur - pass - ing sweet; And all the vir - gins

have an end? Your joys when shall I see?
still re - joice: In that most ho - ly place.
we were blest That might this mu - sic hear.
join the song While sit - ting at her feet.

5. There Magdalene has left her tears,
And cheerfully does sing
With blessed saints, whose harmony
In ev'ry street does ring.

6. Jerusalem, Jerusalem,
God grant that I may see
Your endless joy, and of the same
Partaker ever be!

Text: Joseph Bromehead, 1747-1826, alt.
Tune: LAND OF REST, CM; American; Harm. by Richard Proulx, b.1937, © 1975, GIA Publications, Inc.

691 Lord, Bid Your Servant Go in Peace

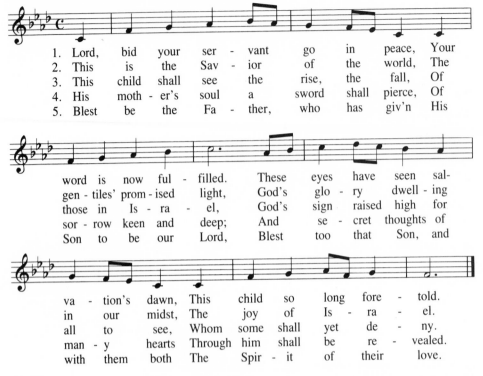

1. Lord, bid your ser - vant go in peace, Your
2. This is the Sav - ior of the world, The
3. This child shall see the rise, the fall, Of
4. His moth - er's soul a sword shall pierce, Of
5. Blest be the Fa - ther, who has giv'n His

word is now ful - filled. These eyes have seen sal-
gen - tiles' prom - ised light, God's glo - ry dwell - ing
those in Is - ra - el, God's sign raised high for
sor - row keen and deep; And se - cret thoughts of
Son to be our Lord, Blest too that Son, and

va - tion's dawn, This child so long fore - told.
in our midst, The joy of Is - ra - el.
all to see, Whom some shall yet de - ny.
man - y hearts Through him shall be re - vealed.
with them both The Spir - it of their love.

Text: Lk. 2:29-32, 34-35; *Nunc dimittis*; James Quinn, SJ, b.1919, alt., © 1969
Tune: MORNING SONG, CM; Wyeth's *Repository of Sacred Music*, 1813; Harm. by Richard Proulx, b.1937, © 1975, GIA Publications, Inc.

692 Hail to the Lord Who Comes

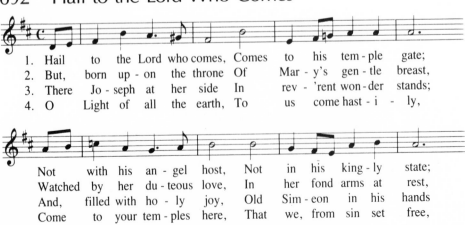

1. Hail to the Lord who comes, Comes to his tem - ple gate;
2. But, born up - on the throne Of Mar - y's gen - tle breast,
3. There Jo - seph at her side In rev - 'rent won - der stands;
4. O Light of all the earth, To us come hast - i - ly,

Not with his an - gel host, Not in his king - ly state;
Watched by her du - teous love, In her fond arms at rest,
And, filled with ho - ly joy, Old Sim - eon in his hands
Come to your tem - ples here, That we, from sin set free,

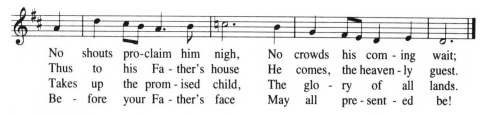

No   shouts pro-claim him nigh,   No   crowds his com - ing   wait;
Thus to   his Fa - ther's house   He   comes, the heaven - ly guest.
Takes up   the prom - ised child, The glo - ry of   all   lands.
Be - fore   your Fa - ther's face   May all   pre - sent - ed   be!

Text: John Ellerton, 1826-1893, alt.
Tune: PRESENTATION, 6 6 6 6 6 6; Sean Duggan, OSB, b.1954, © 1986, GIA Publications, Inc.

Joseph, Be Our Guide and Pattern   693

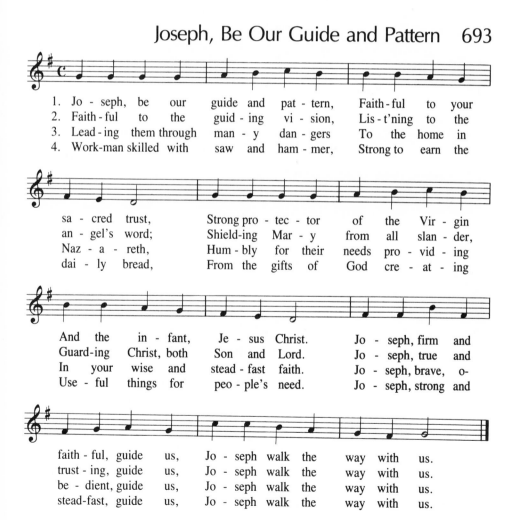

1. Jo - seph, be   our   guide and pat - tern,   Faith - ful to   your
2. Faith - ful to   the   guid - ing vi - sion,   Lis - t'ning to   the
3. Lead - ing them through man - y   dan - gers   To   the   home in
4. Work-man skilled with   saw   and ham - mer,   Strong to   earn the

sa - cred trust,   Strong pro - tec - tor of   the   Vir - gin
an - gel's word;   Shield - ing Mar - y   from   all   slan - der,
Naz - a - reth,   Hum - bly   for   their   needs pro - vid - ing
dai - ly   bread,   From the   gifts of   God   cre - at - ing

And   the   in - fant, Je - sus Christ.   Jo - seph, firm and
Guard-ing Christ, both Son   and Lord.   Jo - seph, true and
In   your   wise and stead - fast faith.   Jo - seph, brave, o-
Use - ful things for peo - ple's need.   Jo - seph, strong and

faith - ful, guide us,   Jo - seph walk the   way with us.
trust - ing, guide us,   Jo - seph walk the   way with us.
be - dient, guide us,   Jo - seph walk the   way with us.
stead-fast, guide us,   Jo - seph walk the   way with us.

Text: Muriel Newton-White, b.1928, © 1972, Canadian Catholic Conference
Tune: ORIEL, 8 7 8 7 8 7; Ett's *Cantica Sacra*, 1840

694 Come Now, and Praise the Humble Saint

1. Come now, and praise the hum - ble saint Of Da - vid's house and line, The car - pen - ter whose life ful - filled Our gra - cious God's de - sign.
2. The Ar - chi - tect's high mir - a - cles He saw, and what was done, The Vir - gin's spouse, the guard - ian of Great Da - vid's great - er Son.
3. For him there was no glo - ry here, No crown or mar - tyr's fame, For him there was the pa - tient life Of faith and hum - ble name.
4. But now with - in the Fa - ther's grace Where saints and an - gel's throng, Be - side his spouse, be - fore the Son, He joins the heav'n - ly song.

Text: G. W. Williams, b.1922, © 1979, Hymn Society of America
Tune: LAND OF REST, CM; American; Harm. by Richard Proulx, b.1937, © 1975, GIA Publications, Inc.

695 The Angel Gabriel from Heaven Came

1. The an - gel Ga - bri - el from heav - en came, His wings as drift - ed snow, his eyes as flame; "All
2. "For know a bless - ed Moth - er you shall be, All gen - er - a - tions praise con - tin - ual - ly, Your
3. Then gen - tle Mar - y meek - ly bowed her head, "To me be as it pleas - es God," she said, "My
4. Of her, Em-man - u - el, the Christ was born In Beth - le - hem, all on a Christ - mas morn, And

hail," said he, "O low - ly maid - en Mar - y, Most
Son shall be Em - man - u - el, by seers fore - told." Most
soul shall laud and mag - ni - fy his ho - ly name." Most
Chris-tian folk through-out the world will ev - er say Most

high - ly fa - vored la - dy," Glo - ri - a!

Text: Sabine Baring-Gould, 1834-1924
Tune: GABRIEL'S MESSAGE, 10 10 12 10; Basque Carol; Harm. by Charles E. Pettman, 1865-1943
© 1961, H. Freeman and Co.

Praise We the Lord This Day   696

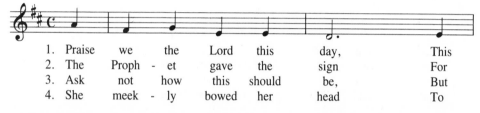

1. Praise we the Lord this day, This
2. The Proph - et gave the sign For
3. Ask not how this should be, But
4. She meek - ly bowed her head To

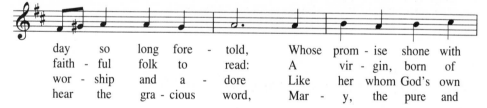

day so long fore - told, Whose prom - ise shone with
faith - ful folk to read: A vir - gin, born of
wor - ship and a - dore Like her whom God's own
hear the gra - cious word, Mar - y, the pure and

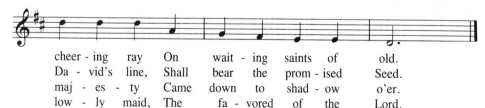

cheer - ing ray On wait - ing saints of old.
Da - vid's line, Shall bear the prom - ised Seed.
maj - es - ty Came down to shad - ow o'er.
low - ly maid, The fa - vored of the Lord.

5. Blesséd shall be her name
  In all the Church on earth
  Through whom that wondrous mercy came,
  The incarnate Savior's birth.

6. O Christ, the Virgin's Son,
  We praise you and adore,
  You are with God the Father One
  And Spirit evermore.

Text: Matt. 1:23; *Hymns for the Festivals and Saints' Days*, 1846
Tune: SWABIA, SM; Johann M. Spiess, 1715-1772

697 When Jesus Came to Jordan

1. When Je - sus came to Jor - dan To
2. He came to share re - pen - tance With
3. He came to share temp - ta - tion, Our
4. So when the Dove de - scend - ed On

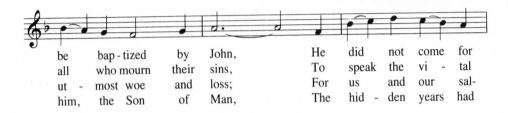

be bap - tized by John, He did not come for
all who mourn their sins, To speak the vi - tal
ut - most woe and loss; For us and our sal-
him, the Son of Man, The hid - den years had

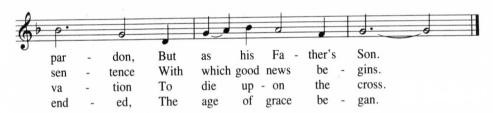

par - don, But as his Fa - ther's Son.
sen - tence With which good news be - gins.
va - tion To die up - on the cross.
end - ed, The age of grace be - gan.

Text: Fred Pratt Green, b.1903, © 1980, Hope Publishing Co.
Tune: DE EERSTEN ZIJN DE LAATSTEN, 7 6 7 6; Frits Mehrtens, 1922-1975, © Boekencentrum

698 The Great Forerunner of the Morn

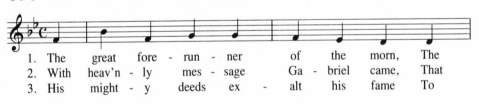

1. The great fore - run - ner of the morn, The
2. With heav'n - ly mes - sage Ga - briel came, That
3. His might - y deeds ex - alt his fame To

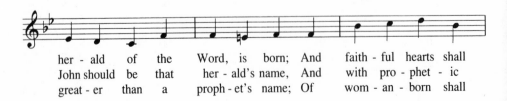

her - ald of the Word, is born; And faith - ful hearts shall
John should be that her - ald's name, And with pro - phet - ic
great - er than a proph - et's name; Of wom - an - born shall

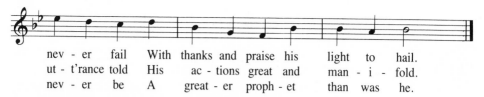

nev - er   fail   With   thanks and   praise his   light   to   hail.
ut - t'rance told   His   ac - tions great and   man - i -   fold.
nev - er   be   A   great - er   proph - et   than   was   he.

Text: *Praecursor altus luminis;* Venerable Bede, 673-735; Tr. by John M. Neale, 1818-1866, alt.
Tune: WINCHESTER NEW, LM; Ádapt. from *Musikalisches Handbuch,* Hamburg, 1690

Two Noble Saints   699

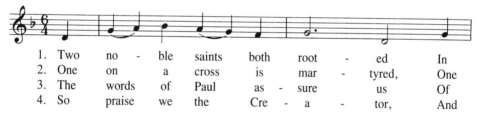

1. Two   no - ble   saints   both   root - ed   In
2. One   on   a   cross   is   mar - tyred,   One
3. The   words   of   Paul   as - sure   us   Of
4. So   praise   we   the   Cre - a - tor,   And

faith   and   ho - ly   love,   By   hope   of   God   u-
by   the sword   is   slain;   Both   tri - umph   in   their
Christ's re - deem - ing   word;   The   works   of   Pe - ter
praise   we Christ   the   Son,   Who   with   the   Ho - ly

nit - ed   They   reach   to heaven   a - bove.
dy - ing,   Both   glo - rious saint - hood   gain.
show   us   How   we   may serve   the   Lord.
Spir - it,   Now   reign, blest Three   in   One.

Text: Based on *Decora lux aeternitatis auream,* by Anne K. LeCroy, b.1930, ©
Tune: DE EERSTEN ZIJN DE LAASTEN, 7 6 7 6 Fritis Mehrtens, 1922-1975, © Boekencentrum

700 'Tis Good, Lord, to Be Here

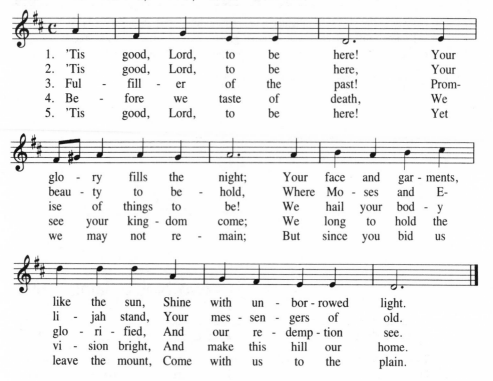

1. 'Tis good, Lord, to be here! Your
2. 'Tis good, Lord, to be here, Your
3. Ful - fill - er of the past! Prom-
4. Be - fore we taste of death, We
5. 'Tis good, Lord, to be here! Yet

glo - ry fills the night; Your face and gar - ments,
beau - ty to be - hold, Where Mo - ses and E-
ise of things to be! We hail your bod - y
see your king - dom come; We long to hold the
we may not re - main; But since you bid us

like the sun, Shine with un - bor - rowed light.
li - jah stand, Your mes - sen - gers of old.
glo - ri - fied, And our re - demp - tion see.
vi - sion bright, And make this hill our home.
leave the mount, Come with us to the plain.

Text: Lk. 9:32-33; Joseph A. Robinson, 1858-1933, alt., © Esme. D. E. Bird
Tune: SWABIA, SM; Johann M. Speiss, 1715-1772; Adapt. by William H. Havergal, 1793-1870

701 Christ upon the Mountain Peak

1. Christ up - on the moun - tain peak Stands a - lone in
2. Trem - bling at his feet we saw Mo - ses and E-
3. Swift the cloud of glo - ry came: God pro - claim - ing
4. This is God's be - lov - ed Son! Law and proph - ets

glo - ry blaz - ing; Let us, if we dare to speak,
li - jah speak - ing. All the proph - ets and the law
in the thun - der Je - sus as his Son by name!
fade be - fore him; First and last and on - ly One,

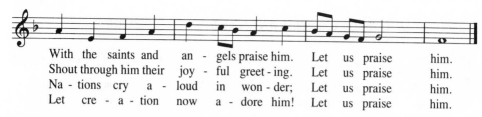

With the saints and an - gels praise him. Let us praise him.
Shout through him their joy - ful greet - ing. Let us praise him.
Na - tions cry a - loud in won - der; Let us praise him.
Let cre - a - tion now a - dore him! Let us praise him.

Text: Brian Wren, b.1936; © 1977, Hope Publishing Co.
Tune: MOWSLEY, 7 8 7 8 4; Cyril V. Taylor, b.1907; © 1985, Hope Publishing Co.

Hail, Holy Queen Enthroned Above 702

1. Hail, ho - ly Queen en - throned a - bove, O Ma-
2. The cause of joy to all be - low, O Ma-
3. O gen - tle, lov - ing, ho - ly one, O Ma-

ri - a. Hail, Queen of mer - cy and of love,
ri - a. The spring through which all grac - es flow,
ri - a. The God of light be - came your Son,

O Ma - ri - a. Tri - umph, all ye Cher - u - bim,
O Ma - ri - a. An - gels, all your prais - es bring,
O Ma - ri - a. Tri - umph, all ye Cher - u - bim,

Sing with us, ye Ser - a - phim, Heav'n and earth re - sound the
Earth and heav - en, with us sing, All cre - a - tion ech - o-
Sing with us, ye Ser - a - phim, Heav'n and earth re - sound the

hymn: Sal - ve, Sal - ve, Sal - ve, Re - gi - na.
ing: Sal - ve, Sal - ve, Sal - ve, Re - gi - na.
hymn: Sal - ve, Sal - ve, Sal - ve, Re - gi - na.

Text: Salve, Regina, mater misericordia; c.1080; Tr. Roman Hymnal, 1884; St. 2-3, adapt. by M. Owen Lee, CSB, b.1930
Tune: SALVE REGINA COELITUM, 8 4 8 4 777 4 5; Choralmelodien zum Heiligen Gesänge, 1808; Harm. by Healey Willan, 1880-1968, © Willis
Music Co.

703 Hail, Queen of Heaven/Salve, Regina

Hail, Queen of Heav - en, hail, our Moth - er com - pas - sion - ate,
Sal - ve, Re - gí - na, ma - ter mi - se - ri - cór - di - ae:

True life and com - fort and our hope, we greet you!
Vi - ta, dul - cé - do et spes no - stra sal - ve.

To you we ex - iles, chil - dren of Eve, raise our voic - es.
Ad te cla - má - mus, éx - su - les fí - li - i He - vae.

We send up sighs to you, as mourn - ing and weep - ing,
Ad te sus - pi - rá - mus, ge - mén - tes et flen - tes

we pass through this vale of sor - row. Then turn to us,
in hac la - cri - má - rum val - le. E - ia er - go,

O most gra - cious Wom - an, those eyes of yours, so full of
ad - vo - cá - ta no - stra, il - los tu - os mi - se - ri-

love and ten - der - ness, so full of pit - y.
cór - des ó - cu - los ad nos con - vér - te.

And grant us af - ter these, our days of lone - ly
Et Je - sum, be - ne - dí - ctum fru - ctum ven - tris

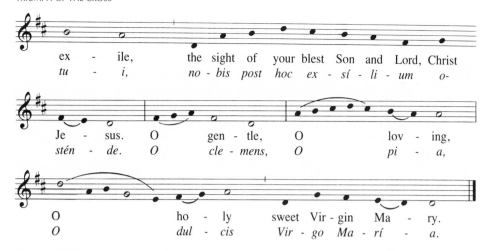

ex - ile, the sight of your blest Son and Lord, Christ
tu - i, *no - bis post hoc ex - sí - li - um o-*

Je - sus. O gen - tle, O lov - ing,
stén - de. *O* *cle - mens,* *O* *pi - a,*

O ho - ly sweet Vir - gin Ma - ry.
O *dul - cis* *Vir - go Ma - rí - a.*

Text: Latin, c.1080; Tr. by John C. Selner, SS, b.1904, © 1954, GIA Publications, Inc.
Tune: SALVE REGINA, Irregular; Mode V; Acc. by Gerard Farrell, OSB, b.1919, © 1986, GIA Publications, Inc.

Lift High the Cross 704

Lift high the cross, the love of Christ pro - claim till

all the world a - dore his sa - cred name.

1. Come, Chris - tians, fol - low where the Mas - ter trod, our
2. Led on their way by this tri - um - phant sign, the
3. Each new - born fol - l'wer of the Cru - ci - fied bears
4. O Lord, once lift - ed on the glo - rious tree, your
5. So shall our song of tri - umph ev - er be: praise

D.C.

King vic - to - rious, Christ, the Son of God.
hosts of God in con - quering ranks com - bine.
on the brow the seal of him who died.
death has bought us life e - ter - nal - ly.
to the Cru - ci - fied for vic - to - ry!

Text: 1 Cor. 1:18; George W. Kitchen, 1827-1912, and Michael R. Newbolt, 1874-1956, alt.
Tune: CRUCIFER, 10 10 with refrain; Sydney H. Nicholson, 1875-1947
© 1978, Hope Publishing Co.

705 For All the Saints

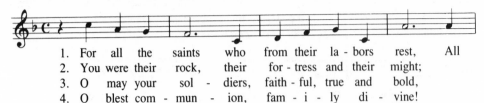

1. For all the saints who from their la - bors rest, All
2. You were their rock, their for - tress and their might;
3. O may your sol - diers, faith - ful, true and bold,
4. O blest com - mun - ion, fam - i - ly di - vine!

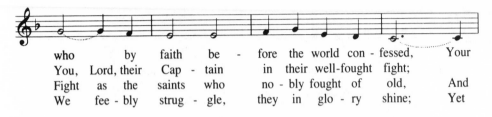

who by faith be - fore the world con - fessed, Your
You, Lord, their Cap - tain in their well-fought fight;
Fight as the saints who no - bly fought of old, And
We fee - bly strug - gle, they in glo - ry shine; Yet

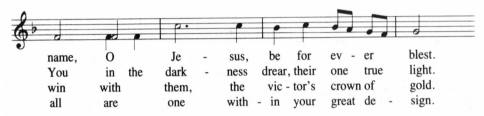

name, O Je - sus, be for ev - er blest.
You in the dark - ness drear, their one true light.
win with them, the vic - tor's crown of gold.
all are one with - in your great de - sign.

Al - le - lu - ia! Al - le - lu - ia!

5. And when the strife is fierce, the warfare long,
   Steals on the ear the distant triumph song,
   And hearts are brave again, and arms are strong.

6. The golden evening brightens in the west;
   Soon, soon to faithful warriors comes their rest;
   Sweet is the calm of paradise the blest.

7. But then there breaks a yet more glorious day:
   The saints triumphant rise in bright array;
   The King of glory passes on his way.

8. From earth's wide bounds, from ocean's farthest coast,
   Through gates of pearl streams in the countless host,
   Singing to Father, Son, and Holy Ghost:

Text: William W. How, 1823-1897
Tune: SINE NOMINE, 10 10 10 with alleluias; Ralph Vaughan Williams, 1872-1958, © Oxford University Press

By All Your Saints Still Striving 706

1. By all your saints still striv - ing, For all your saints at rest,
*2. A - pos - tles, proph - ets, mar - tyrs, And all the no - ble throng
3. Then let us praise the Fa - ther And wor - ship God the Son

Your ho - ly Name, O Je - sus, For ev - er - more be blessed.
Who wear the spot - less rai - ment And raise the cease - less song:
And sing to God the Spir - it, E - ter - nal Three in One,

You rose, our King vic - to - rious, That they might wear the crown
For them and those whose wit - ness Is on - ly known to you
Till all the ran - somed num - ber Who stand be - fore the throne,

And ev - er shine in splen - dor Re - flect - ed from your throne.
By walk - ing in their foot - steps We give you praise a - new.
A - scribe all pow'r and glo - ry And praise to God a - lone.

Text: Based on Horatio Nelson, 1823-1913, by Jerry D. Godwin, b.1944, © 1985, The Church Pension Fund
Tune: ST. THEODULPH, 7 6 7 6 D; Melchior Teschner, 1584-1635

*This stanza may be replaced by an appropriate stanza taken from the following pages.

January 25: Conversion of Paul

Praise for the light from heaven
  And for the voice of awe:
Praise for the glorious vision
  The persecutor saw.
O Lord, for Paul's conversion,
  We bless your Name today.
Come shine within our darkness
  And guide us in the Way.

February 22: Chair of Peter

We praise you, Lord, for Peter,
  So eager and so bold:
Thrice falling, yet repentant,
  Thrice charged to feed your fold.
Lord, make your pastors faithful
  To guard your flock from harm
And hold them when they waver
  With your almighty arm.

March 19: Joseph, Husband of Mary

All praise, O God, for Joseph,
   The guardian of your Son,
Who saved him from King Herod,
   When safety there was none.
He taught the trade of builder,
   When they to Naz'reth came,
And Joseph's love made "Father"
   To be, for Christ, God's name.

March 25: Annunciation of Our Lord

We sing with joy of Mary
   Whose heart with awe was stirred
When, youthful and unready,
   She heard the angel's word;
Yet she her voice upraises
   God's glory to proclaim,
As once for our salvation
   Your mother she became.

April 25: Mark

For Mark, O Lord, we praise you,
   The weak by grace made strong:
His witness in his Gospel
   Becomes victorious song.
May we, in all our weakness,
   Receive your power divine,
And all, as faithful branches,
   Grow strong in you, the Vine.

May 3: Philip and James

We praise you, Lord, for Philip,
   Blest guide to Greek and Jew,
And for young James the faithful,
   Who heard and followed you,
O grant us grace to know you,
   The victor in the strife,
That we with all your servants
   May wear the crown of life.

May 14: Matthias

For one in place of Judas,
   The apostles sought God's choice:
The lot fell to Matthias
   For whom we now rejoice.
May we like true apostles
   Your holy Church defend,
And not betray our calling
   But serve you to the end.

June 11: Barnabas

For Barnabas we praise you,
   Who kept your law of love
And, leaving earthly treasures,
   Sought riches from above.
O Christ, our Lord and Savior,
   Let gifts of grace descend,
That your true consolation
   May through the world extend.

June 24: Birth of John the Baptist

All praise for John the Baptist,
   Forerunner of the Word,
Our true Elijah, making
   A highway for the Lord.
The last and greatest prophet,
   He saw the dawning ray
Of light that grows in splendor
   Until the perfect day.

June 29: Peter and Paul

We praise you for Saint Peter;
   We praise you for Saint Paul.
They taught both Jew and Gentile
   That Christ is all in all.
To cross and sword they yielded
   And saw the kingdom come:
O God, your two apostles
   Won life through martyrdom.

July 3: Thomas

All praise, O Lord, for Thomas
   Whose short-lived doubtings prove
Your perfect twofold nature,
   The depth of your true love.
To all who live with questions
   A steadfast faith afford;
And grant us grace to know you,
   Made flesh, yet God and Lord.

July 22: Mary Magdalene

All praise for Mary Magdalene,
   Whose wholeness was restored
By you, her faithful Master,
   Her Savior and her Lord.
On Easter morning early,
   A word from you sufficed:
Her faith was first to see you,
   Her Lord, the risen Christ.

July 25: James

O Lord, for James, we praise you,
　Who fell to Herod's sword.
He drank the cup of suff'ring
　And thus fulfilled your word.
Lord, curb our vain impatience
　For glory and for fame,
Equip us for such suff'rings
　As glorify your Name.

August 24: Bartholomew

Praised for your blest apostle
　Surnamed Bartholomew;
We know not his achievements
　But know that he was true,
For he at the Ascension
　Was an apostle still.
May we discern your presence
　And seek, like him, your will.

September 21: Matthew

We praise you, Lord, for Matthew,
　Whose gospel words declare
That, worldly gain forsaking,
　Your path of life we share.
From all unrighteous mammon,
　O raise our eyes anew,
That we, whate'er our station
　May rise and follow you.

October 18: Luke

For Luke, beloved physician,
　All praise; whose Gospel shows
The healer of the nations,
　The one who shares our woes.
Your wine and oil, O Savior,
　Upon our spirits pour,
And with true balm of Gilead
　Anoint us evermore.

October 28: Simon and Jude

Praise, Lord, for your apostles,
　Saint Simon and Saint Jude.
One love, one hope impelled them
　To tread the way, renewed.
May we with zeal as earnest
　The faith of Christ maintain,
Be bound in love together,
　And life eternal gain.

November 30: Andrew

All praise, O Lord, for Andrew,
　The first to follow you;
He witnessed to his brother,
　"This is Messiah true."
You called him from his fishing
　Upon Lake Galilee;
He rose to meet your challenge,
　"Leave all and follow me."

December 26: Stephen

All praise, O Lord, for Stephen
　Who, martyred, saw you stand
To help in time of torment,
　To plead at God's right hand.
Like you, our suff'ring Savior,
　His enemies he blessed,
With "Lord, receive my spirit,"
　His faith, in death, confessed.

December 27: John

For John, your loved disciple,
　Exiled to Patmos' shore,
And for his faithful record,
　We praise you evermore;
Praise for the mystic vision
　His words to us unfold.
Instill in us his longing,
　Your glory to behold.

December 28: Holy Innocents

Praise for your infant martyrs,
　Whom your mysterious love
Called early from life's conflicts
　To share your peace above.
O Rachel, cease your weeping;
　They're free from pain and cares.
Lord, grant us crowns as brilliant
　And lives as pure as theirs.

707 Ye Watchers and Ye Holy Ones

1. Ye watch - ers and ye ho - ly ones,
2. O high - er than the cher - u - bim,
3. Re - spond, ye souls in end - less rest,
4. O friends, in glad - ness let us sing,

Bright ser - aphs, cher - u - bim, and thrones,
More glo - rious than the ser - a - phim,
Ye pa - tri - archs and proph - ets blest,
Su - per - nal an - thems ech - o - ing,

Raise the glad strain, Al - le - lu - ia!
Lead their prais - es, Al - le - lu - ia!
Al - le - lu - ia, Al - le - lu - ia!
Al - le - lu - ia, Al - le - lu - ia!

Cry out, do - min - ions, prince - doms, powers,
O bear - er of the e - ter - nal Word,
Ye ho - ly Twelve, ye mar - tyrs strong,
To God the Fa - ther, God the Son,

Vir - tues, arch - an - gels, an - gels' choirs,
Most gra - cious, mag - ni - fy the Lord,
All saints tri - um - phant, raise in song,
And God the Spir - it, Three in One,

Al - le - lu - ia, Al - le - lu - ia, Al - le - lu - ia,

Al - le - lu - ia, Al - le - lu - ia!

Text: John A. Riley, 1858-1945, © Oxford University Press
Tune: LASST UNS ERFREUEN, LM with alleluias; *Geistliche Kirchengesänge*, Cologne, 1623; Harm. by Ralph Vaughan Williams, 1872-1958, © Oxford University Press

Immaculate Mary 708

1. Im - ma - cu - late Mar - y, your prais - es we sing;
2. Pre - des - tined for Christ by e - ter - nal de - cree,
3. To you by an an - gel, the Lord God made known
4. Most blest of all wom - en, you heard and be - lieved,
5. The an - gels re - joiced when you brought forth God's Son;

You reign now in splen - dor with Je - sus our King.
God willed you both vir - gin and moth - er to be.
The grace of the Spir - it, the gift of the Son.
Most blest in the fruit of your womb then con - ceived.
Your joy is the joy of all a - ges to come.

A - ve, A - ve, A - ve, Ma - ri - a.

A - ve, A - ve, Ma - ri - a.

6. Your child is the Savior, all hope lies in him:
He gives us new life and redeems us from sin.

7. In glory for ever now close to your Son,
All ages will praise you for all God has done.

Text: St. 1, Jeremiah Cummings, 1814-1866, alt.; St. 2-7, Brian Foley, b.1919, © 1971, Faber Music Ltd.
Tune: LOURDES HYMN, 11 11 with refrain; Grenoble, 1882

709 What Is This Place

1. What is this place where we are meet-ing? On-ly a
2. Words from a - far, stars that are fall-ing, Sparks that are
3. And we ac-cept bread at his ta-ble, Bro-ken and

house, the earth its floor, Walls and a roof shel-ter-ing
sown in us like seed. Names for our God, dreams, signs, and
shared, a liv-ing sign. Here in this world, dy-ing and

peo-ple, Win-dows for light, an o - pen door.
won-ders Sent from the past are all we need.
liv-ing, We are each oth-er's bread and wine.

Yet it be-comes a bod - y that lives When we are
We in this place re - mem - ber and speak A - gain what
This is the place where we can re-ceive What we need

gath-ered here, And know our God is near.
we have heard: God's free re - deem-ing word.
to in - crease: God's jus - tice and God's peace.

Text: *Zomaar een dak boven wat hoofden*; Huub Oosterhuis, b.1933; Tr. by David Smith, b.1933. © 1984, TEAM Publications
Tune: KOMT NU MET ZANG, 9 8 9 8 9 66; Valerius' *Neder-landtsche gedenck-klanck*, 1626; Harm. by Adrian Engels, b.1906

710 How Blessed Is This Place

1. How bless - ed is this place, O Lord, Where you are
2. Here let your sa - cred fire of old De - scend to
3. Here let your wear - y one find rest, The trou - bled
4. Here your an - gel - ic spir - its send Their sol - emn

wor - shiped and a - dored; In faith we here an
kin - dle spir - its cold; And may our prayers, when
heart, your com - fort blest, The guilt - y one, a
praise with ours to blend, And grant the vi - sion,

al - tar raise To your great glo - ry, God of praise.
here we bend, Like in - cense sweet to you as - cend.
sure re - treat, The sin - ner, par - don at your feet.
in - ly giv'n, Of this your house, the gate of heav'n.

Text: Ernest E. Ryden, 1886-1981, alt., © Sts. 1-3, Lutheran Church in America, © St. 4, 1958, Service Book and Hymnal
Tune: O WALY WALY, LM; English; Harm. by Martin West, b.1929, © 1983, Hope Publishing Co.

Mary, How Lovely the Light of Your Glory   711

1. Mar - y, how love - ly the light of your glo - ry,
2. Blest of all wom - en, both Vir - gin and Moth - er,
3. Pray for us, plead for us, ex - iles in dark - ness,

From Da - vid's house, roy - al daugh - ter you come,
Fa - vored in grace for the Son whom you bore,
Pray with us, pray - ing to Christ in our needs;

Ho - li - er, high - er than an - gels in heav - en,
Christ is your Son whom all peo - ples must wor - ship,
All pow'r is giv - en him here and in heav - en,

Ho - li - est, high - est through all God has done.
Christ is your Son whom all an - gels a - dore.
Christ ev - er lives for us and in - ter - cedes.

Text: Brian Foley, b.1919
Tune: CHANCE, 11 10 11 10; Colin Mawby, b.1936
© 1971, Faber Music Ltd.

712 O Sanctissima

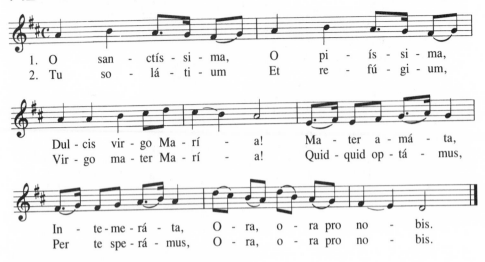

1. O san - ctís - si - ma, O pi - ís - si - ma,
2. Tu so - lá - ti - um Et re - fú - gi - um,

Dul - cis vir - go Ma - rí - a! Ma - ter a - má - ta,
Vir - go ma - ter Ma - rí - a! Quid - quid op - tá - mus,

In - te - me - rá - ta, O - ra, o - ra pro no - bis.
Per te spe - rá - mus, O - ra, o - ra pro no - bis.

Text: St. 1, *Stimmen der Völker in Liedern*, 1807; St. 2, *Arundel Hymnal*, 1902
Tune: O DU FRÖLICHE, 55 7 55 7; Tattersall's *Improved Psalmody*, 1794

713 Ave Maria

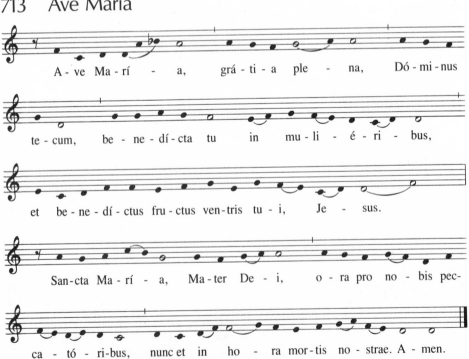

A - ve Ma - rí - a, grá - ti - a ple - na, Dó - mi - nus

te - cum, be - ne - dí - cta tu in mu - li - é - ri - bus,

et be - ne - dí - ctus fru - ctus ven - tris tu - i, Je - sus.

San - cta Ma - rí - a, Ma - ter De - i, o - ra pro no - bis pec -

ca - tó - ri - bus, nunc et in ho - ra mor - tis no - strae. A - men.

Text: Lk. 1:29; Latin, 13th C.
Tune: AVE MARIA, Irregular; Mode I; Acc. by Robert LeBlanc, b.1948, © 1986, GIA Publications, Inc.

Sing We of the Blessed Mother 714

1. Sing we of the bless - ed Moth - er
2. Sing we, too, of Mar - y's sor - rows,
3. Sing a - gain the joys of Mar - y
4. Sing the great - est joy of Mar - y

Who re - ceived the an - gel's word, And o - be - dient
Of the sword that pierced her through, When be - neath the
When she saw the ris - en Lord, And in prayer with
When on earth her work was done, And the Lord of

to the sum - mons Bore in love the in - fant Lord;
cross of Je - sus She his weight of suf - f'ring knew,
Christ's a - pos - tles, Wait - ed on his prom - ised word:
all cre - a - tion Brought her to his heav'n - ly home:

Sing we of the joys of Mar - y
Looked up - on her Son and Sav - ior
From on high the blaz - ing glo - ry
Vir - gin Moth - er, Mar - y bless - ed,

At whose breast that child was fed Who is Son of
Reign-ing from the aw - ful tree, Saw the price of
Of the Spir - it's pres - ence came, Heav'n-ly breath of
Raised on high and crowned with grace, May your Son, the

God e - ter - nal And the ev - er - last - ing Bread.
our re - demp-tion Paid to set the sin - ner free.
God's own be - ing, To - kened in the wind and flame.
world's re - deem - er, Grant us all to see his face.

Text: George B. Timms, b.1910, © 1975, Oxford University Press
Tune: OMNE DIE, 8 7 8 7 D; *Trier Gesängebuch*, 1695

715 Let Us with Joy Our Voices Raise

1. Let us with joy our voic - es raise In
2. O Strength of all the strong, God's Son, Through
3. Praise God, Cre - a - tor, God the Son, And

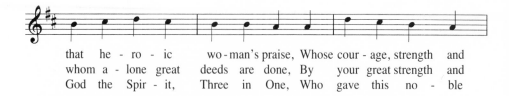

that he - ro - ic wo - man's praise, Whose cour - age, strength and
whom a - lone great deeds are done, By your great strength and
God the Spir - it, Three in One, Who gave this no - ble

ho - ly fame Have giv - en her an hon - ored name.
through her prayer May we bear wit - ness ev - 'ry - where.
wo - man grace A life of vir - tue to em - brace.

Text: *Fortem virili pectore;* Silvio Antoniano, 1540-1603; Tr. and St. 3 by Roger Nachtwey, b.1930, alt., © 1965, FEL Publications, Ltd.
Tune: EISENACH, LM; Johann H. Schein, 1586-1630; Harm. by J.S. Bach, 1685-1750

716 Let All on Earth Their Voices Raise

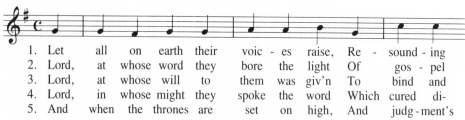

1. Let all on earth their voic - es raise, Re - sound - ing
2. Lord, at whose word they bore the light Of gos - pel
3. Lord, at whose will to them was giv'n To bind and
4. Lord, in whose might they spoke the word Which cured di-
5. And when the thrones are set on high, And judg - ment's

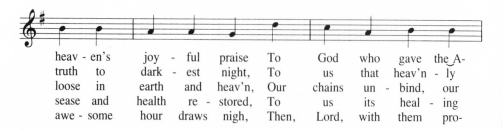

heav - en's joy - ful praise To God who gave the A-
truth to dark - est night, To us that heav'n - ly
loose in earth and heav'n, Our chains un - bind, our
sease and health re - stored, To us its heal - ing
awe - some hour draws nigh, Then, Lord, with them pro-

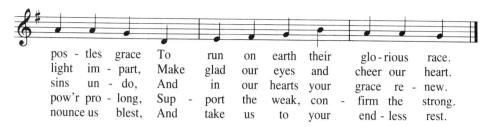

pos - tles grace To run on earth their glo - rious race.
light im - part, Make glad our eyes and cheer our heart.
sins un - do, And in our hearts your grace re - new.
pow'r pro - long, Sup - port the weak, con - firm the strong.
nounce us blest, And take us to your end - less rest.

Text: *Exsultet orbis gaudiis;* Latin, 10th C.; Tr. by Richard Mant, 1776-1848, alt.
Tune: TALLIS' CANON, LM; Thomas Tallis, c.1505-1585

This Is the Feast Day of the Lord's True Witness 717

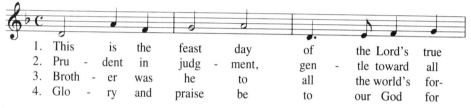

1. This is the feast day of the Lord's true
2. Pru - dent in judg - ment, gen - tle toward all
3. Broth - er was he to all the world's for-
4. Glo - ry and praise be to our God for

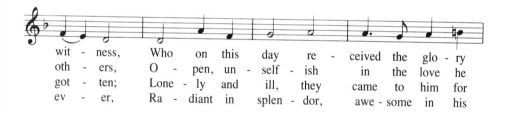

wit - ness, Who on this day re - ceived the glo - ry
oth - ers, O - pen, un - self - ish in the love he
got - ten; Lone - ly and ill, they came to him for
ev - er, Ra - diant in splen - dor, awe - some in his

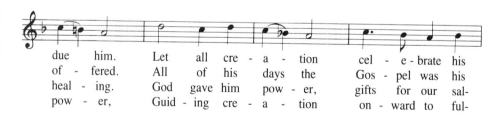

due him. Let all cre - a - tion cel - e - brate his
of - fered. All of his days the Gos - pel was his
heal - ing. God gave him pow - er, gifts for our sal-
pow - er, Guid - ing cre - a - tion on - ward to ful-

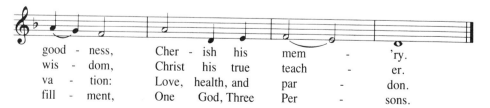

good - ness, Cher - ish his mem - 'ry.
wis - dom, Christ his true teach - er.
va - tion: Love, health, and par - don.
fill - ment, One God, Three Per - sons.

Text: *Iste confessor Domini, colentes;* Latin, 8th C.; Tr. by Peter J. Scagnelli, b.1949, ©
Tune: ISTE CONFESSOR, 11 11 11 5; Rouen Church Melody; Harm. by Carl Schalk, b.1929, © 1969, Condordia Publishing House

718 Blessed Feasts of Blessed Martyrs

1. Bless-ed feasts of bless-ed mar-tyrs, Ho-ly wom-en,
2. Faith pre-vail-ing, hope un-fail-ing, Lov-ing Christ with
3. There-fore, all that reign in glo-ry, Strong and sure with

ho-ly men, With our love and ad-mi-ra-tion, Greet we
sin-gle heart, Thus they, glo-rious and vic-to-rious, Brave-ly
Christ on high, Join to ours your sup-pli-ca-tion When be-

your re-turn a-gain. Wor-thy deeds are theirs, and won-ders,
bore the mar-tyr's part, By con-tempt of ev-'ry an-guish,
fore him we draw nigh, Pray-ing that, this life com-plet-ed,

Wor-thy of the name they bore; We, with joy-ful
By un-yield-ing bat-tle done; Vic-tors at the
All its fleet-ing mo-ments past, By his grace we

praise and sing-ing, Hon-or them for ev-er-more.
last, they tri-umph, With the host of an-gels one.
may be wor-thy Of e-ter-nal bliss at last.

Text: *O beata beatorum;* Latin, 12th C.; Tr. by John M. Neale, 1818-1866, alt.
Tune: IN BABILONE, 8 7 8 7 D; *Oude en Nieuwe Hollanste Boerenlities,* c.1710

719 Around the Throne a Glorious Band

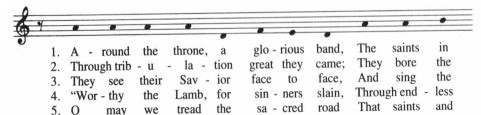

1. A-round the throne, a glo-rious band, The saints in
2. Through trib-u-la-tion great they came; They bore the
3. They see their Sav-ior face to face, And sing the
4. "Wor-thy the Lamb, for sin-ners slain, Through end-less
5. O may we tread the sa-cred road That saints and

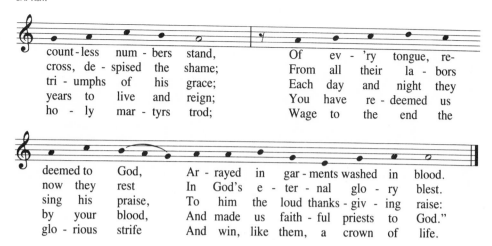

count - less num - bers stand,
cross, de - spised the shame;
tri - umphs of his grace;
years to live and reign;
ho - ly mar - tyrs trod;

Of ev - 'ry tongue, re-
From all their la - bors
Each day and night they
You have re - deemed us
Wage to the end the

deemed to God,
now they rest
sing his praise,
by your blood,
glo - rious strife

Ar - rayed in gar - ments washed in blood.
In God's e - ter - nal glo - ry blest.
To him the loud thanks - giv - ing raise:
And made us faith - ful priests to God."
And win, like them, a crown of life.

Text: Rowland Hill, 1744-1833
Tune: JESU DULCIS MEMORIA, LM; Model I; Acc. by Richard Proulx, b.1937, © 1975, GIA Publications, Inc.

Baptized in Water   720

1. Bap - tized in wa - ter, Sealed by the Spir - it,
2. Bap - tized in wa - ter, Sealed by the Spir - it,
3. Bap - tized in wa - ter, Sealed by the Spir - it,

Cleansed by the blood of Christ our King:
Dead in the tomb with Christ our King:
Marked with the sign of Christ our King:

Heirs of sal - va - tion, Trust - ing his prom - ise,
One with his ris - ing, Freed and for - giv - en,
Born of one Fa - ther, We are his chil - dren,

Faith - ful - ly now God's praise we sing.
Thank - ful - ly now God's praise we sing.
Joy - ful - ly now God's praise we sing.

Text: Michael A. Saward, b.1932, © 1982, Hope Publishing Co.
Tune: BUNESSAN, 5 5 8 D; Gaelic; Harm. by A. Gregory Murray, OSB, b.1905, ©

721 We Know That Christ Is Raised

1. We know that Christ is raised and dies no more. Em - braced by death, he broke its fear - ful hold, And our de - spair he turned to blaz - ing joy. Al - le - lu - ia!
2. We share by wa - ter in his sav - ing death. Re - born, we share with him an East - er life As liv - ing mem - bers of our Sav - ior Christ. Al - le - lu - ia!
3. The Fa - ther's splen - dor clothes the Son with life. The Spir - it's fis - sion shakes the Church of God. Bap - tized, we live with God the Three in One. Al - le - lu - ia!
4. A new cre - a - tion comes to life and grows As Christ's new bod - y takes on flesh and blood. The u - ni - verse re - stored and whole will sing: Al - le - lu - ia!

Text: Rom. 6:4,9; John B. Geyer, b.1932, ©
Tune: ENGELBERG, 10 10 10 with alleluia; Charles V. Stanford, 1852-1924

722 This Is the Spirit's Entry Now

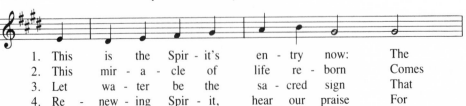

1. This is the Spir - it's en - try now: The
2. This mir - a - cle of life re - born Comes
3. Let wa - ter be the sa - cred sign That
4. Re - new - ing Spir - it, hear our praise For

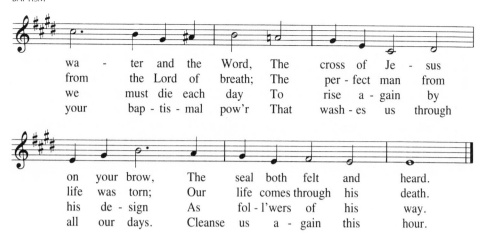

wa - ter and the Word, The cross of Je - sus
from the Lord of breath; The per - fect man from
we must die each day To rise a - gain by
your bap - tis - mal pow'r That wash - es us through

on your brow, The seal both felt and heard.
life was torn; Our life comes through his death.
his de - sign As fol - l'wers of his way.
all our days. Cleanse us a - gain this hour.

Text: Thomas E. Herbranson, b.1933, alt., © 1978
Tune: PERRY, CM; Leo Sowerby, 1895-1968, © 1964, Abingdon Press

Come and Let Us Drink of That New River 723

1. Come and let us drink of that new riv - er,
2. Now the world has bright il - lu - mi - na - tion,
3. Yes - ter - day with you in bur - ial ly - ing,

Not from bar - ren rock di - vine - ly poured,
Heav - en and all things up - on the earth:
Now with you in tri - umph I a - rise,

But the fount of life that springs for ev - er
Ris - en is the God of all cre - a - tion,
Yes - ter - day the part - ner of your dy - ing,

From the sa - cred bod - y of our Lord.
Christ the Lord who gave cre - a - tion birth.
Raise me with you far be - yond the skies.

Text: Δεῦτε Πόμα Πίωμεν; John of Damascus, c.675-746; Tr. by John M. Neale, 1818-1866, adapt. by Anthony G. Petti, 1932-1985, © 1971, Faber
Music Ltd.
Tune: NEW RIVER 10 9 10 9; Kenneth D. Smith, b.1928

724 God Sends Us His Spirit

1. God sends us his Spir - it to be-friend and help us.
2. Dark-ened roads are clear - er, heav - y bur - dens light - er,
3. Now we are God's peo - ple, bond - ed by God's pres - ence,

Re - cre - ate and guide us, Spir - it - Friend.
When we're walk - ing with our Spir - it - Friend.
A - gents of God's pur - pose, Spir - it - Friend.

Spir - it who en - liv - ens, sanc - ti - fies, en - light - ens,
Now we need not fear the pow - ers of the dark - ness.
Lead us for - ward ev - er, slip - ping back-ward nev - er,

Sets us free, is now our Spir - it - Friend.
None can o - ver - come our Spir - it - Friend.
To your re - made world, our Spir - it - Friend.

Sung three times after each stanza. Hand claps

Spir - it of our Mak - er, Spir - it - Friend.
Spir - it of our Je - su, Spir - it - Friend.
Spir - it of God's peo - ple, Spir - it - Friend.

Text: Tom Colvin, b.1925
Tune: NATOMAH, 12 9 12 9 with refrain; Gonja Folk Song; Adapt. by Tom Colvin, b.1925
© 1969, Hope Publishing Co.

725 O Breathe on Me, O Breath of God

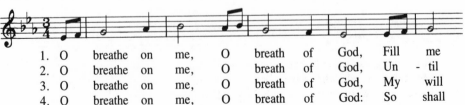

1. O breathe on me, O breath of God, Fill me
2. O breathe on me, O breath of God, Un - til
3. O breathe on me, O breath of God, My will
4. O breathe on me, O breath of God: So shall

with	life	a -	new,	That	I	may	love	the
my	heart	is	pure;	Un -	til	my	will	is
to	yours	in -	cline,	Un -	til	this	self -	ish
I	nev -	er	die,	But	live	with	you	the

things	you	love,	And	do	what	you	would	do.
one	with	yours,	To	do	and	to	en -	dure.
part	of	me	Glows with	your	fire	di -	vine.
per -	fect	life	Of	your	e -	ter -	ni -	ty.

Text: Edwin Hatch, 1835-1889
Tune: ST. COLUMBA, CM; Gaelic; Harm. by A. Gregory Murray, OSB, b.1905, ©

I Come with Joy to Meet My Lord   726

1.	I	come	with	joy	to	meet	my	Lord,	For-
2.	I	come	with	Chris - tians	far	and	near	To
3.	As	Christ	breaks	bread	and	bids	us	share	Each
4.	And	thus	with	joy	we	meet	our	Lord.	His
5.	To - geth -	er	met,	to - geth -	er	bound,	We'll

giv -	en,	loved,	and	free,	In	awe	and	won - der
find,	as	all	are	fed,	The	new	com - mu - ni-
proud	di - vi -	sion	ends.	The	love	that	made	us
pres -	ence,	al -	ways	near,	Is	in	such	friend - ship
go	our	dif -	f'rent	ways,	And	as	his	peo - ple

to	re - call	His	life	laid	down	for	me.
ty	of	love	In	Christ's	com - mu -	nion	bread.
makes	us	one,	And	strang -	ers	now	are	friends.
bet -	ter	known;	We	see	and	praise	him	here.
in	the	world,	We'll	live	and	speak	his	praise.

Text: Brian Wren, b.1936, © 1971, Hope Publishing Co.
Tune: LAND OF REST, CM; American; Harm. by Annabel M. Buchanan, b.1888, © 1938, 1966, J. Fisher and Bro.

727 Let Us Break Bread Together

1. Let us break bread to-geth-er on our knees;
2. Let us drink wine to-geth-er on our knees;
3. Let us praise God to-geth-er on our knees;

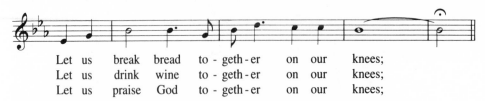

Let us break bread to-geth-er on our knees;
Let us drink wine to-geth-er on our knees;
Let us praise God to-geth-er on our knees;

When I fall on my knees, With my face to the ris-ing

sun, O Lord, have mer-cy on me.

Text: American Folk Hymn
Tune: LET US BREAK BREAD, 10 10 6 8 7; American Folk Hymn; Harm. by David Hurd, b.1950, © 1986, GIA Publications, Inc.

728 Shepherd of Souls

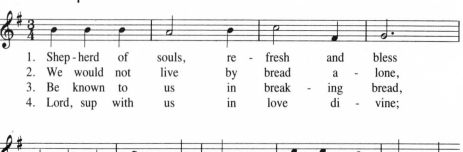

1. Shep-herd of souls, re-fresh and bless
2. We would not live by bread a-lone,
3. Be known to us in break-ing bread,
4. Lord, sup with us in love di-vine;

Your cho-sen pil-grim flock With man-na in the
But by your word of grace, In strength of which we
But do not then de-part; Sav-ior, a-bide with
Your Bod-y and your Blood, That liv-ing bread, that

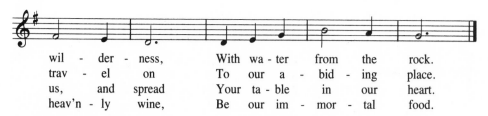

wil - der - ness, With wa - ter from the rock.
trav - el on To our a - bid - ing place.
us, and spread Your ta - ble in our heart.
heav'n - ly wine, Be our im - mor - tal food.

Text: James Montgomery, 1771-1854, alt.
Tune: ST. AGNES, CM; John B. Dykes, 1823-1876; Harm. by Richard Proulx, b.1937; © 1986, GIA Publications, Inc.

O Food of Exiles Lowly 729

1. O Food of ex - iles low - ly, O Bread of
2. O cleans - ing wa - ter, stream - ing From Je - sus'
3. O Lord, we kneel be - fore you And fer - vent-

an gels ho - ly, O Man - na from on high! We
side re - deem - ing All those of A - dam's race! O
ly a - dore you, All hid be - neath this bread. But

hun - ger for your bless - ing, All good in you pos-
quench-ing foun - tain flow - ing, Our ev - 'ry want be-
make to us this prom - ise: To see you in your

sess - ing, With fa - vor hear our heart's out - cry.
stow - ing, O come and fill our souls with grace.
full - ness, The sa - cred bo - dy's mys - tic head.

Text: *O esca viatorum; Mainz Gesangbuch,* 1661; Tr. by M. Owen Lee, CSB, b.1930
Tune: INNSBRUCK, 77 6 77 8; Heinrich Isaak, c.1460-c.1527; Harm. by J.S. Bach, 1685-1750

730 Ave Verum

A - ve ve-rum Cor-pus na-tum de Ma-rí-a Vír-gi-ne:

Ve - re pas-sum im-mo-lá-tum in cru-ce pro hó-mi-ne:

Cu-jus la-tus per-fo-rá-tum flu-xit a - qua et

sán-gui-ne: Es-to no-bis prae-gu-stá-tum mor-tis

in ex-á-mi-ne. O Je-su dul-cis! O Je-

su pi-e! O Je-su fi-li Ma-rí-ae.

Text: Ascr. to Innocent VI, d.1362
Tune: AVE VERUM, Irregular; Mode VI; Acc. by Robert LeBlanc, b.1948, © 1986, GIA Publications, Inc.

731 Draw Us in the Spirit's Tether

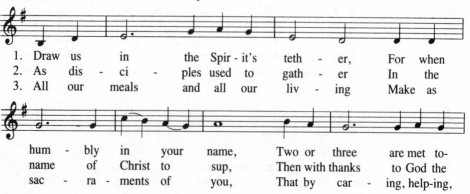

1. Draw us in the Spir-it's teth - er, For when
2. As dis - ci - ples used to gath - er In the
3. All our meals and all our liv - ing Make as

hum - bly in your name, Two or three are met to-
name of Christ to sup, Then with thanks to God the
sac - ra - ments of you, That by car - ing, help-ing,

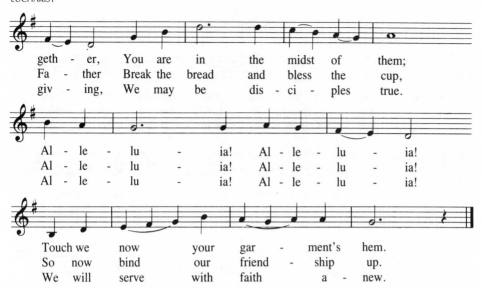

geth - er,   You are   in   the   midst   of   them;
Fa - ther   Break the bread   and   bless   the   cup,
giv - ing,   We may be   dis - ci - ples   true.

Al - le - lu - ia!   Al - le - lu - ia!
Al - le - lu - ia!   Al - le - lu - ia!
Al - le - lu - ia!   Al - le - lu - ia!

Touch we   now   your   gar - ment's hem.
So now   bind   our   friend - ship up.
We will   serve   with   faith   a - new.

Text: Percy Dearmer, 1867-1936, alt., © Oxford University Press
Tune: UNION SEMINARY, 8 7 8 7 44 7; Harold Friedell, 1905-1958, © 1957, H.W. Gray Co., Inc.; Harm. by Jet Turner, 1928-1984, © Christian Board
    of Education

Draw Near and Take the Body of Your Lord   732

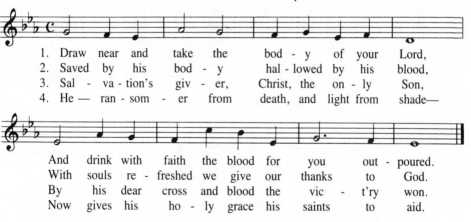

1. Draw near and   take the   bod - y   of your   Lord,
2. Saved by his   bod - y   hal - lowed by his   blood,
3. Sal - va - tion's giv - er,   Christ, the   on - ly   Son,
4. He — ran - som - er from   death, and light from   shade—

And drink with faith   the blood for   you   out - poured.
With souls re - freshed we   give our   thanks   to   God.
By   his   dear cross   and blood the   vic - t'ry   won.
Now gives his   ho - ly grace his   saints   to   aid.

5. Let us approach
    with faithful hearts sincere,
And take the pledges
    of salvation here.

6. The Lord in this world
    rules his saints, and shields,
To all believers
    life eternal yields:

7. With heav'nly bread makes
    those who hunger whole,
Gives living waters
    to the thirsting soul.

8. Before your presence, Lord,
    all people bow.
In this your feast of love
    be with us now.

Text: *Sancti, venite, Christe corpus sumite;* Latin, 7th C.; Tr. by John M. Neale, 1818-1866, alt.
Tune: COENA DOMINI, 10 10; Arthur S. Sullivan, 1842-1900

733   At That First Eucharist

1. At that first Eu - cha - rist be - fore you died,
2. For all your church, O Lord, we in - ter - cede;
3. We pray for those who wan - der from the fold;

O Lord, you prayed that all be one in you;
O make our lack of char - i - ty to cease;
O bring them back, Good Shep - herd of the sheep,

At this our Eu - cha - rist a - gain pre - side,
Draw us the near - er each to each we plead,
Back to the faith which saints be - lieved of old,

And in our hearts your law of love re - new.
By draw - ing all to you, O Prince of Peace.
Back to the Church which still that faith does keep.

Thus may we all one Bread, one Bod - y be;

Through this blest Sac - ra - ment of U - ni - ty.

Text: William H. Turton, 1859-1938, alt.
Tune: UNDE ET MEMORES, 10 10 10 10 with refrain; William H. Monk, 1823-1889, alt.

734   Eat This Bread

Eat this bread, drink this cup, come to me and

nev - er be hun - gry. Eat this bread, drink this cup,

trust in me and you will not thirst.

Text: John 6; Adapted by Robert J. Batastini, b.1942 and the Taizé Community, 1984
Tune: Jacques Berthier, b.1923
© 1984, Les Presses de Taizé

I Received the Living God 735

I re - ceived the liv - ing God, and my

heart is full of joy. I re - ceived the liv - ing

God, and my heart is full of joy.

1. He has said: I am the Bread Knead - ed
2. He has said: I am the Way, And my
3. He has said: I am the Truth; If you
4. He has said: I am the Life Far from

long to give you life; You who will par-
Fa - ther longs for you; So I come to
fol - low close to me, You will know me
whom no thing can grow, But re - ceive this

D.C.

take of me Need not ev - er fear to die.
bring you home To be one with him a - new.
in your heart, And my word shall make you free.
liv - ing bread, And my Spir - it you shall know.

Text: Anonymous
Tune: LIVING GOD, 7 7 7 7 with refrain; Anonymous; Harm. by Richard Proulx, b.1937, © 1986, GIA Publications, Inc.

736 You Satisfy the Hungry Heart

You sat - is - fy the hun - gry heart With

gift of fin - est wheat; Come give to us, O

sav - ing Lord, The bread of life to eat.

1. As when the shep - herd calls his sheep, They
2. With joy - ful lips we sing to you Our
3. Is not the cup we bless and share The
4. The mys - t'ry of your pres-ence, Lord, No
5. You give your - self to us, O Lord; Then

know and heed his voice; So when you call your
praise and grat - i - tude, That you should count us
blood of Christ out - poured? Do not one cup, one
mor - tal tongue can tell: Whom all the world can-
self - less let us be, To serve each oth - er

D.C.

fam - 'ly, Lord, We fol - low and re - joice.
wor - thy, Lord, To share this heav'n - ly food.
loaf, de - clare Our one - ness in the Lord?
not con - tain Comes in our hearts to dwell.
in your name In truth and char - i - ty.

Text: Omer Westendorf, b.1916
Tune: BICENTENNIAL, CM with refrain; Robert E. Kreutz, b.1922
© 1977, Archdiocese of Philadelphia

Alleluia! Sing to Jesus   737

1. Al - le - lu - ia! sing to Je - sus! His the
2. Al - le - lu - ia! not as or - phans Are we
3. Al - le - lu - ia! Bread of An - gels, Here on
4. Al - le - lu - ia! King e - ter - nal, You the

scep - ter, his the throne; Al - le - lu - ia!
left in sor - row now; Al - le - lu - ia!
earth our food, our stay! Al - le - lu - ia!
Lord of lords we own; Al - le - lu - ia!

his the tri - umph, His the vic - to - ry a - lone;
he is near us, Faith be - lieves, nor ques - tions how:
here the sin - ful Flee to you from day to day:
born of Mar - y, Earth your foot - stool, heav'n your throne:

Hark! the songs of peace - ful Zi - on Thun - der
Though the cloud from sight re - ceived him, When the
In - ter - ces - sor, friend of sin - ners, Earth's re-
You, with - in the veil, have en - tered, Robed in

like a might - y flood; Je - sus out of
for - ty days were o'er, Shall our hearts for-
deem - er, plead for me, Where the songs of
flesh, our great high priest; Here on earth both

ev - 'ry na - tion Has re - deemed us by his blood.
get his prom - ise, "I am with you ev - er - more"?
all the sin - less Sweep a - cross the crys - tal sea.
priest and vic - tim In the eu - cha - ris - tic feast.

Text: Rev. 5:9; William C. Dix, 1837-1898
Tune: HYFRYDOL, 8 7 8 7 D; Rowland H. Prichard, 1811-1887

738   I Am the Bread of Life

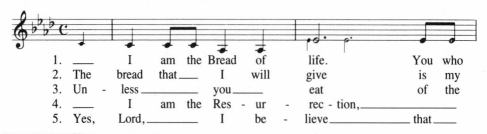

1. ___ I am the Bread of life. You who
2. The bread that___ I will give is my
3. Un - less___ you___ eat of the
4. ___ I am the Res - ur - rec - tion,___
5. Yes, Lord,___ I be - lieve___ that___

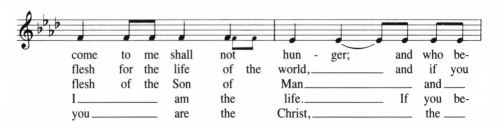

come to me shall not hun - ger; and who be-
flesh for the life of the world,___ and if you
flesh of the Son of Man___ and___
I___ am the life.___ If you be-
you___ are the Christ,___ the ___

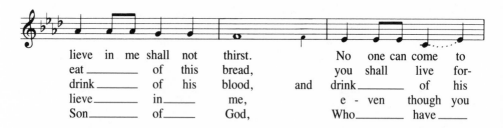

lieve in me shall not thirst. No one can come to
eat___ of this bread, you shall live for-
drink___ of his blood, and drink___ of his
lieve___ in___ me, e - ven though you
Son___ of___ God, Who___ have___

me un - less the Fa - ther beck - ons.
ev - er,___ you shall live for ev - er.
blood, you shall not have life with - in you.
die,___ you shall live for ev - er.
come in - to___ the___ world.___

And I will raise you up, and I will raise you

up, and I will raise you up on the last day.

Text: John 6; Suzanne Toolan, SM, b.1927
Tune: BREAD OF LIFE, Irregular with refrain; Suzanne Toolan, SM, b.1927, © 1966, GIA Publications, Inc.
© 1970, GIA Publications, Inc.

Lord of the Living 739

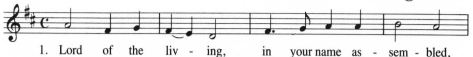

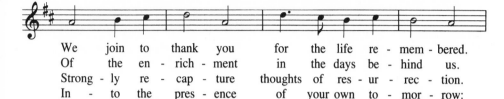

1. Lord of the liv - ing, in your name as - sem - bled,
2. Help us to treas - ure all that will re - mind us
3. May we, when - ev - er tempt - ed to de - jec - tion,
4. Lord, you can lift us from the grave of sor - row

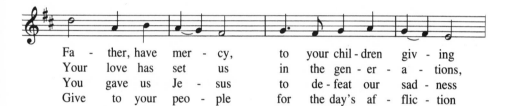

We join to thank you for the life re - mem - bered.
Of the en - rich - ment in the days be - hind us.
Strong - ly re - cap - ture thoughts of res - ur - rec - tion.
In - to the pres - ence of your own to - mor - row:

Fa - ther, have mer - cy, to your chil - dren giv - ing
Your love has set us in the gen - er - a - tions,
You gave us Je - sus to de - feat our sad - ness
Give to your peo - ple for the day's af - flic - tion

Hope in be - liev - ing.
God of cre - a - tion.
With East - er glad - ness.
Your ben - e - dic - tion.

Text: Fred Kaan, b.1929, © 1968, Hope Publishing Co.
Tune: CHRISTE SANCTORUM, 11 11 11 5; *Paris Antiphoner,* 1681

740 O Lord, You Died That All Might Live

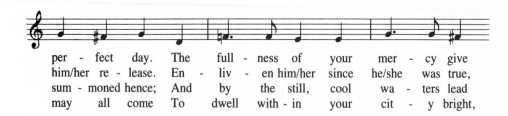

1. O Lord, you died that all might live And rise to see the
2. Lord, bless our friend who died in you, As you have giv - en
3. In your green, pleas - ant pas - tures feed The sheep that you have
4. Di - rect us with your arm of might, That with our friend we

per - fect day. The full - ness of your mer - cy give
him/her re - lease. En - liv - en him/her since he/she was true,
sum - moned hence; And by the still, cool wa - ters lead
may all come To dwell with - in your cit - y bright,

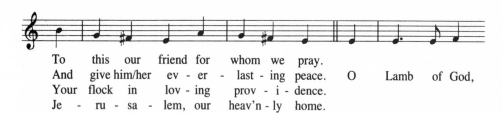

To this our friend for whom we pray.
And give him/her ev - er - last - ing peace. O Lamb of God,
Your flock in lov - ing prov - i - dence.
Je - ru - sa - lem, our heav'n - ly home.

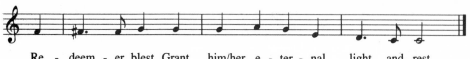

Re - deem - er blest, Grant him/her e - ter - nal light and rest.

Text: Richard F. Littledale, 1833-1890, alt.
Tune: MELITA, LM, with refrain; John B. Dykes, 1823-1876

741 Let Saints on Earth in Concert Sing

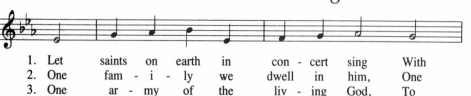

1. Let saints on earth in con - cert sing With
2. One fam - i - ly we dwell in him, One
3. One ar - my of the liv - ing God, To
4. E'en now by faith we join our hands With
5. Je - sus, be now our con - stant guide; Then,

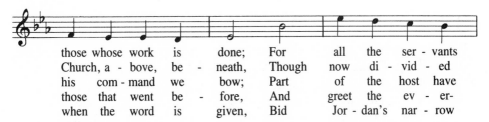

those whose work	is	done;	For	all	the	ser - vants
Church, a - bove,	be -	neath,	Though	now	di - vid - ed
his com - mand	we	bow;	Part	of	the	host have
those that went	be -	fore,	And	greet	the	ev - er-
when the word	is	given,	Bid	Jor - dan's	nar - row

of	our	King	In	heav'n and	earth	are	one.
by	the	stream,	The	nar - row	stream	of	death.
crossed the	flood,	And	part	are	cross - ing	now.
liv - ing	bands	On	the	e - ter - nal	shore.
stream di -	vide,	And	bring	us	safe	to	heaven.

Text: Charles Wesley, 1707-1788
Tune: DUNDEE, CM; *Scottish Psalter, 1615*

May the Grace of Christ Our Savior 742

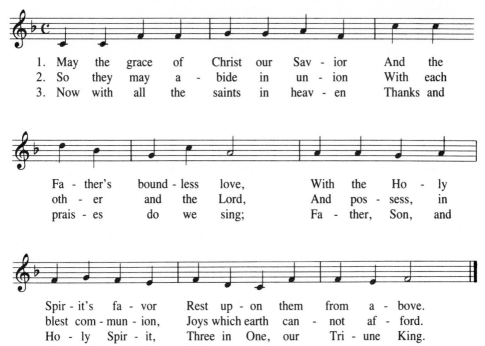

1. May the grace of Christ our Sav - ior And the
2. So they may a - bide in un - ion With each
3. Now with all the saints in heav - en Thanks and

Fa - ther's bound - less love, With the Ho - ly
oth - er and the Lord, And pos - sess, in
prais - es do we sing; Fa - ther, Son, and

Spir - it's fa - vor Rest up - on them from a - bove.
blest com - mun - ion, Joys which earth can - not af - ford.
Ho - ly Spir - it, Three in One, our Tri - une King.

Text: 2 Cor. 13-14; St. 1-2, John Newton, 1725-1807; St. 3, Adapt. by Carroll T. Andrews, b.1918, © 1971, GIA Publications, Inc.
Tune: STUTTGART, 8 7 8 7; Christian F. Witt, 1660-1716; Harm. by Kenneth D. Smith, b.1928, © National Christian Education Council

743 Within Your House, O God, Today

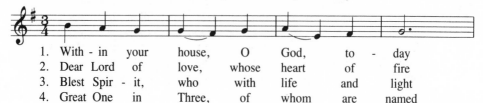

1. With - in your house, O God, to - day
2. Dear Lord of love, whose heart of fire
3. Blest Spir - it, who with life and light
4. Great One in Three, of whom are named

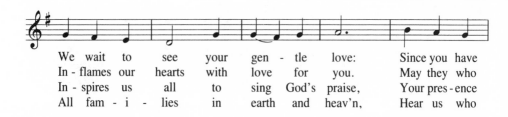

We wait to see your gen - tle love: Since you have
In - flames our hearts with love for you. May they who
In - spires us all to sing God's praise, Your pres - ence
All fam - i - lies in earth and heav'n, Hear us who

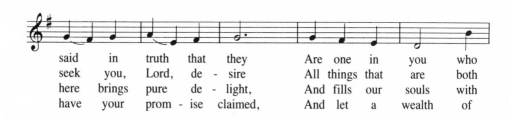

said in truth that they Are one in you who
seek you, Lord, de - sire All things that are both
here brings pure de - light, And fills our souls with
have your prom - ise claimed, And let a wealth of

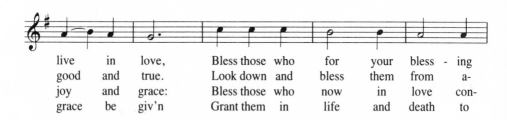

live in love, Bless those who for your bless - ing
good and true. Look down and bless them from a-
joy and grace: Bless those who now in love con-
grace be giv'n Grant them in life and death to

wait; Their love ac - cept and con - se - crate.
bove, And keep their hearts a - light with love.
sent; Cre - a - tor, crown your sac - ra - ment.
be Both joined in you e - ter - nal - ly.

Text: Robert H. Benson, 1871-1914, alt.
Tune: ST. CATHERINE, 8 8 8 8 88; Henry F. Hemy, 1818-1888; Adapt. by James G. Walton, 1821-1905

O Father, All-creating   744

1. O Fa - ther, all - cre - a - ting, Whose wis - dom, love, and pow'r
2. With good wine, Lord, at Ca - na The wed - ding feast you blessed.
3. O Spir - it of the Fa - ther, Breathe on them from a - bove,
4. Un - less you build it, Fa - ther, The house is built in vain;

First bound two lives to - geth - er In E - den's pri - mal hour,
Grant al - so these your pres - ence, And be their dear - est guest.
So might - y in your pure - ness, So ten - der in your love
Un - less you, Sav - ior, bless it, The joy will turn to pain.

To - day to these your chil - dren Your ear - liest gifts re - new:
Their store of earth - ly glad - ness Trans - form to heav'n - ly wine,
That, guard - ed by your pres - ence And kept from strife and sin,
But noth - ing breaks a mar - riage Of hearts in you made one;

A home by you made hap - py, A love by you kept true.
And teach them, in the test - ing, To know the gift di - vine.
Their hearts may sense your guid - ance And know you dwell with - in.
The love your Spir - it hal - lows Is end - less love be - gun.

Text: John Ellerton, 1826-1893, alt.
Tune: AURELIA, 7 6 7 6 D; Samuel S. Wesley, 1810-1876

sing to front

745 When Love Is Found

1. When love is found and hope comes home, Sing and be
2. When love has flow'red in trust and care, Build both each
3. When love is tried as loved-ones change, Hold still to
4. When love is torn and trust be - trayed, Pray strength to
5. Praise God for love, praise God for life, In age or

glad that two are one. When love ex - plodes and
day that love may dare To reach be - yond home's
hope though all seems strange, Till ease re - turns and
love till tor - ments fade, Till lov - ers keep no
youth, in hus - band, wife. Lift up your hearts let

fills the sky, Praise God and share our Mak - er's joy.
warmth and light, To serve and strive for truth and right.
love grows wise Through list - 'ning ears and o - pened eyes.
score of wrong But hear through pain love's East - er song.
love be fed Through death and life in bro - ken bread.

Text: Brian Wren, b.1936, © 1983, Hope Publishing Co.
Tune: O WALY WALY, LM; English; Harm. by Martin West, b.1929, © 1983, Hope Publishing Co.

746 Great God of Mercy

1. Great God of mer - cy, God of con - so-
2. Je - sus Re - deem - er, Lord of all cre-
3. Joy - giv - ing Spir - it, be our light in
4. God in three per - sons, Trin - i - ty e-

la - tion, Look on your peo - ple, gath - ered here to
a - tion, Come as our Sav - ior, Je - sus, friend of
dark - ness, Come to be - friend us, help us bear our
ter - nal, Come to re - new us, fill your Church with

praise you: Pit - y our weak - ness, come in pow'r to
sin - ners: Grant us for - give - ness, lift our down-cast
bur - dens: Give us true cour - age, breathe your peace a-
glo - ry: Grant us your heal - ing, pledge of res - ur-

aid us, Source of all bless - ing.
spir - it, Heal us and save us.
round us, Stay with us al - ways.
rec - tion, Fore - taste of heav - en.

Text: James Quinn, SJ, b.1919, © 1980, ICEL
Tune: HERZLIEBSTER JESU, 11 11 11 5; Johann Crüger, 1598-1662

O Christ, the Healer 747

1. O Christ, the heal - er, we have come To pray for
2. From ev - 'ry ail - ment flesh en - dures Our bod - ies
3. How strong, O Lord, are our de - sires, How weak our
4. In con - flicts that de - stroy our health We re - cog-
5. Grant that we all, made one in faith, In your com-

health, to plead for friends. How can we fail to
clam - or to be freed; Yet in our hearts we
knowl-edge of our - selves! Re - lease in us those
nize the world's di - sease; Our com - mon life de-
mun - i - ty may find The whole - ness that, en-

be re - stored, When reached by love that nev - er ends?
would con - fess That whole - ness is our deep - est need.
heal - ing truths Un - con - scious pride re - sists or shelves.
clares our ills: Is there no cure, O Christ, for these?
rich - ing us, Shall reach the whole of hu - man - kind.

Text: Fred Pratt Green, b.1903, © 1969, Hope Publishing Co.
Tune: ERHALT UNS HERR, LM; Klug's *Geistliche Lieder*, 1543; Harm. by J.S. Bach, 1685-1750

748 O Son of God, in Galilee

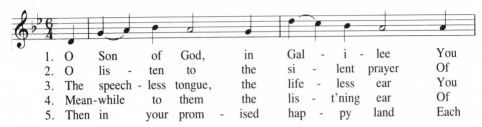

1. O Son of God, in Gal - i - lee You
2. O lis - ten to the si - lent prayer Of
3. The speech - less tongue, the life - less ear You
4. Mean-while to them the lis - t'ning ear Of
5. Then in your prom - ised hap - py land Each

made the deaf to hear, The mute to speak, the
your af - flict - ed ones. O bid them cast on
can re - store, O Lord; Your "Eph - phe - tha," O
stead - fast faith im - part, And let your word bring
loss will prove a gain; All mys - t'ries we shall

blind to see; O bless - ed Lord, be near.
you their care; Your grace to them make known.
Sav - ior dear, Can in - stant help af - ford.
light and cheer To ev - 'ry trou - bled heart.
un - der - stand, For you will make them plain.

Text: Anna Hoppe, 1889-1941, alt., © Lutheran Church in America
Tune: LEWIS-TOWN, CM; William Billings, 1746-1800; Harm. by Donald A. Busarow, b.1934, © 1978, *Lutheran Book of Worship*

749 He Healed the Darkness of My Mind

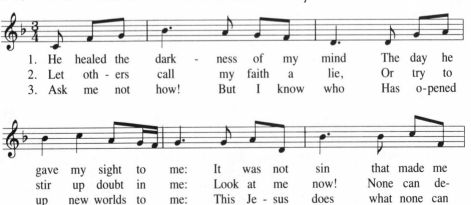

1. He healed the dark - ness of my mind The day he
2. Let oth - ers call my faith a lie, Or try to
3. Ask me not how! But I know who Has o-pened

gave my sight to me: It was not sin that made me
stir up doubt in me: Look at me now! None can de -
up new worlds to me: This Je - sus does what none can

blind: It   was   no   sin - ner   made   me   see.
ny   I   once was   blind   and   now   I   see!
do—   I   once was   blind, and   now   I   see.

Text: John 9; Fred Pratt Green, b.1903, © 1982, Hope Publishing Co.
Tune: DUNEDIN, LM; Vernon Griffiths, 1894-1985, © 1971, Faber Music Ltd.

Your Hands, O Lord, in Days of Old   750

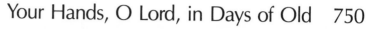

1. Your   hands,   O   Lord,   in   days   of   old   Were strong   to   heal   and
2. And   then   your touch brought   life   and health,   Gave speech, and strength, and
3. O   be   our might - y   heal - er   still,   O   Lord   of   life   and

save;   They   tri - umphed o - ver   pain   and death,   Fought
sight;   And   youth   re - newed and   health   re - stored,   Claimed
death;   Re - store   and strength - en,   soothe   and bless,   With

dark - ness   and   the   grave.   To   you   they went,   the
you,   the   Lord   of   light: And   so,   O   Lord,   be
your   al - might - y   breath: On   hands   that work   and

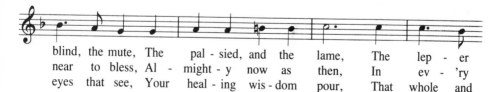

blind, the mute,   The   pal - sied, and   the   lame,   The   lep - er
near   to   bless,   Al - might - y   now   as   then,   In   ev - 'ry
eyes   that see,   Your   heal - ing   wis - dom   pour,   That   whole   and

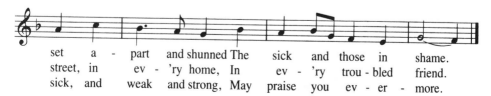

set   a - part   and shunned The   sick   and those   in   shame.
street,   in   ev - 'ry   home,   In   ev - 'ry   trou - bled   friend.
sick,   and   weak   and strong,   May   praise   you   ev - er - more.

Text: Mt. 145:35-36; Edward H. Plumtre, 1821-1891, alt., © 1986, GIA Publicaions, Inc.
Tune: MOZART, CMD; Adapt. from Wolfgang A. Mozart, 1756-1791

751 Silence! Frenzied, Unclean Spirit

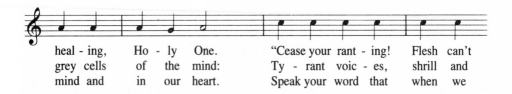

1. "Si - lence! fren - zied, un - clean spir - it," Cried God's
2. Lord, the de - mons still are thriv - ing In the
3. Si - lence, Lord, the un - clean spir - it In our

heal - ing, Ho - ly One. "Cease your rant - ing! Flesh can't
grey cells of the mind: Ty - rant voic - es, shrill and
mind and in our heart. Speak your word that when we

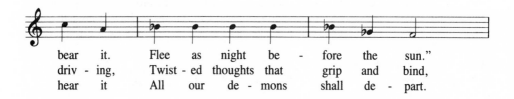

bear it. Flee as night be - fore the sun."
driv - ing, Twist - ed thoughts that grip and bind,
hear it All our de - mons shall de - part.

At Christ's voice the de - mon trem - bled, From its
Doubts that stir the heart to pan - ic, Fears dis-
Clear our thought and calm our feel - ing. Still the

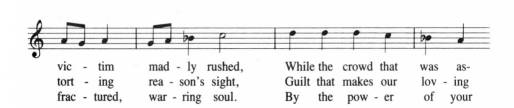

vic - tim mad - ly rushed, While the crowd that was as-
tort - ing rea - son's sight, Guilt that makes our lov - ing
frac - tured, war - ring soul. By the pow - er of your

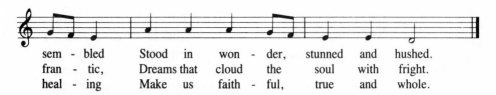

sem - bled Stood in won - der, stunned and hushed.
fran - tic, Dreams that cloud the soul with fright.
heal - ing Make us faith - ful, true and whole.

Text: Mk. 1:23-28; Thomas Troeger, b.1945
Tune: AUTHORITY, 8 7 8 7 D; Carol Doran, b.1936; (Suggested alternate tune: GENEVA)
© 1985, Oxford University Press, Inc.

The Master Came to Bring Good News   752

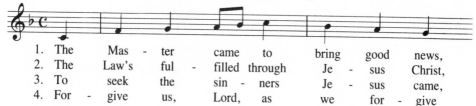

1. The Mas - ter came to bring good news,
2. The Law's ful - filled through Je - sus Christ,
3. To seek the sin - ners Je - sus came,
4. For - give us, Lord, as we for - give

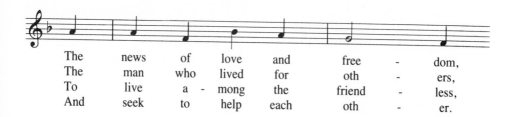

The news of love and free - dom,
The man who lived for oth - ers,
To live a - mong the friend - less,
And seek to help each oth - er.

To heal the sick and seek the poor,
The law of Christ is: Serve in love
To show them love that they might share
For - give us, Lord, and we shall live

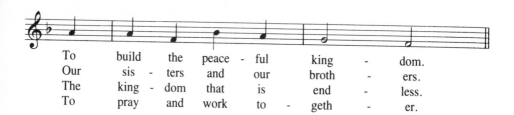

To build the peace - ful king - dom.
Our sis - ters and our broth - ers.
The king - dom that is end - less.
To pray and work to - geth - er.

Fa - ther, for - give us! Through Je - sus hear us!

As we for - give one an - oth - er!

Text: Ralph Finn, b.1941, © 1965, GIA Publications, Inc.
Tune: ICH GLAUB AN GOTT, 8 7 8 7 with refrain; *Mainz Gesanbuch*, 1870; Harm. by Richard Proulx, b.1937, © 1986, GIA Publications, Inc.

753 Have Mercy, Lord, on Us

1. Have mer-cy, Lord, on us, For you are ev-er kind;
2. Lord, wash a-way our guilt, And cleanse us from our sin;
3. The joy your grace can give, Let us a-gain ob-tain,

Though we have sinned be-fore you, Lord, Your mer-cy let us find.
For we con-fess our wrongs, and see How great our guilt has been.
And may your Spir-it's firm sup-port Our spir-its then sus-tain.

Text: Psalm 51; Nahum Tate, 1652-1715, and Nicholas Brady, 1659-1726, alt.
Tune: SOUTHWELL, SM; Damon's *Psalmes*, 1579

754 Forgive Our Sins

1. "For - give our sins as we for - give," You
2. How can your par - don reach and bless The
3. In blaz - ing light your Cross re - veals The
4. Lord, cleanse the depths with - in our souls And

taught us, Lord, to pray, But you a - lone can
un - for - giv - ing heart That broods on wrongs and
truth we dim - ly knew: What triv - ial debts are
bid re - sent - ment cease. Then, bound to all in

grant us grace To live the words we say.
will not let Old bit - ter-ness de - part?
owed to us, How great our debt to you!
bonds of love, Our lives will spread your peace.

Text: Rosamund Herklots, b.1905, © Oxford University Press
Tune: DETROIT, CM; Supplement to *Kentucky Harmony*, 1820; Harm. by Gerald H. Knight, 1908-1979, © The Royal School of Church Music

Our Father, We Have Wandered 755

1. Our Fa - ther, we have wan - dered And
2. And now at length dis - cern - ing The
3. O Lord of all the liv - ing, Both

hid - den from your face; In fool - ish-
e - vil that we do, Be - hold us,
ban - ished and re - stored, Com - pas - sion-

ness have squan - dered Your leg - a - cy of
Lord, re - turn - ing With hope and trust to
ate, for - giv - ing And ev - er car - ing

grace. But now, in ex - ile dwell - ing,
you. In haste you come to meet us,
Lord, Grant now that our trans - gress - ing,

We rise with fear and shame, As dis - tant
And home re - joic - ing bring, In glad - ness
Our faith - less - ness may cease. Stretch out your

but com - pell - ing, We hear you call our name.
there to greet us With calf and robe and ring.
hand in bless - ing, In par - don and in peace.

Text: Kevin Nichols, b.1929, © 1980, ICEL
Tune: PASSION CHORALE, 7 6 7 6 D; Hans Leo Hassler, 1564-1612; Harm. by J.S. Bach, 1685-1750

756 Come, You Sinners, Poor and Needy

1. Come, you sin - ners, poor and need - y, Weak and
2. Come, you thirst - y, come, and wel - come, God's free
3. Come, you wea - ry, heav - y lad - en, Lost and

wound-ed, sick and sore, Je - sus, Son of God, will
boun - ty glo - ri - fy; True be - lief and true re -
ru - ined by the fall; If you tar - ry till you're

save you, Full of pit - y, love, and pow'r.
pent - ance, Ev - 'ry grace that brings you nigh.
bet - ter, You will nev - er come at all.

I will a - rise and go to Je - sus, He will em-

brace me in his arms; In the arms of my dear

Sav - ior; O there are ten thou - sand charms.

Text: Joseph Hart, 1712-1768, alt.
Tune: RESTORATION, 8 7 8 7 with refrain; American; Harm. by George Mims, b.1938, © 1979, Church of the Redeemer, Houston

757 O Saving Victim/O Salutaris

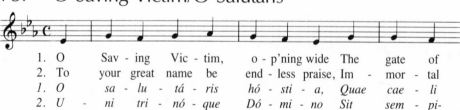

1. O Sav - ing Vic - tim, o - p'ning wide The gate of
2. To your great name be end - less praise, Im - mor - tal
1. O sa - lu - tá - ris hó - sti - a, Quae cae - li
2. U - ni tri - nó - que Dó - mi - no Sit sem - pi-

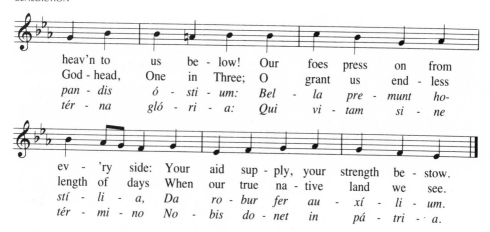

heav'n to   us   be - low! Our   foes   press   on   from
God - head,   One   in   Three;   O   grant   us   end - less
pan - dis   ó - sti - um: Bel - la   pre - munt   ho-
tér - na   gló - ri - a: Qui   vi - tam   si - ne

ev - 'ry   side: Your   aid   sup - ply, your   strength be - stow.
length of   days When our   true   na - tive   land   we   see.
stí - li - a,   Da   ro - bur fer   au - xí - li - um.
tér - mi - no No - bis do - net   in   pá - tri - a.

Text: Thomas Aquinas, 1227-1275; Tr. by Edward Caswall, 1814-1878, alt.
Tune: DUGUET, LM; Dieu donne Duguet, d.1767

Come Adore/Tantum Ergo   758

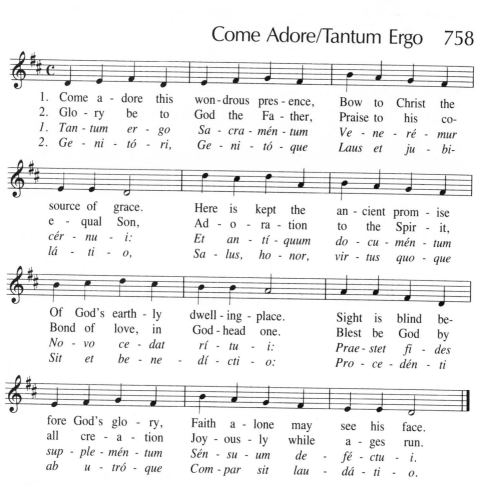

1. Come a - dore this won - drous pres - ence, Bow to Christ the
2. Glo - ry be to God the Fa - ther, Praise to his co-
1. Tan - tum er - go Sa - cra - mén - tum Ve - ne - ré - mur
2. Ge - ni - tó - ri, Ge - ni - tó - que Laus et ju - bi-

source of grace. Here is kept the an - cient prom - ise
e - qual Son, Ad - o - ra - tion to the Spir - it,
cér - nu - i: Et an - tí - quum do - cu - mén - tum
lá - ti - o, Sa - lus, ho - nor, vir - tus quo - que

Of God's earth - ly dwell - ing - place. Sight is blind be-
Bond of love, in God - head one. Blest be God by
No - vo ce - dat rí - tu - i: Prae - stet fi - des
Sit et be - ne - dí - cti - o: Pro - ce - dén - ti

fore God's glo - ry, Faith a - lone may see his face.
all cre - a - tion Joy - ous - ly while a - ges run.
sup - ple - mén - tum Sén - su - um de - fé - ctu - i.
ab u - tró - que Com - par sit lau - dá - ti - o.

Text: Thomas Aquinas, 1227-1274; Tr. by James Quinn, SJ, b.1919, © 1969
Tune: ST. THOMAS, 8 7 8 7 8 7; John F. Wade, 1711-1786

759 Come, Ye Thankful People, Come

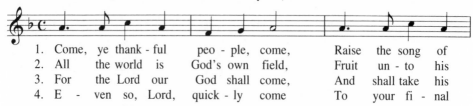

1. Come, ye thank - ful peo - ple, come, Raise the song of
2. All the world is God's own field, Fruit un - to his
3. For the Lord our God shall come, And shall take his
4. E - ven so, Lord, quick - ly come To your fi - nal

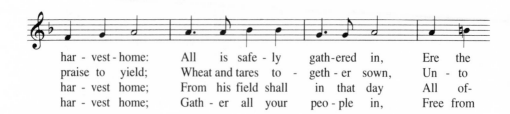

har - vest - home: All is safe - ly gath-ered in, Ere the
praise to yield; Wheat and tares to - geth - er sown, Un - to
har - vest home; From his field shall in that day All of-
har - vest home; Gath - er all your peo - ple in, Free from

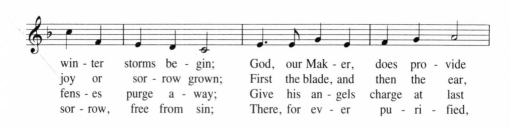

win - ter storms be - gin; God, our Mak - er, does pro - vide
joy or sor - row grown; First the blade, and then the ear,
fens - es purge a - way; Give his an - gels charge at last
sor - row, free from sin; There, for ev - er pu - ri - fied,

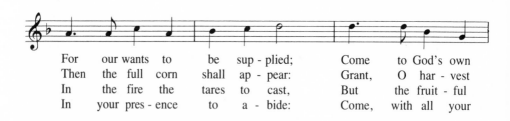

For our wants to be sup - plied; Come to God's own
Then the full corn shall ap - pear: Grant, O har - vest
In the fire the tares to cast, But the fruit - ful
In your pres - ence to a - bide: Come, with all your

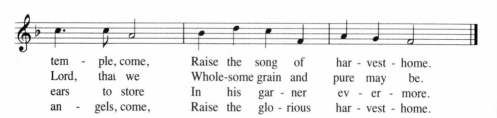

tem - ple, come, Raise the song of har - vest - home.
Lord, that we Whole-some grain and pure may be.
ears to store In his gar - ner ev - er - more.
an - gels, come, Raise the glo - rious har - vest - home.

Text: Henry Alford, 1810-1871, alt.
Tune: ST. GEORGE'S WINDSOR, 77 77 D; George J. Elvey, 1816-1893; Harm. by Richard Proulx, b.1937. © 1986, GIA Publications, Inc.

We Gather Together 760

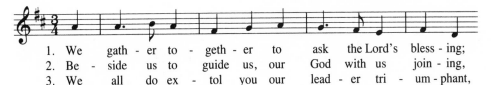

1. We gath - er to - geth - er to ask the Lord's bless - ing;
2. Be - side us to guide us, our God with us join - ing,
3. We all do ex - tol you our lead - er tri - um - phant,

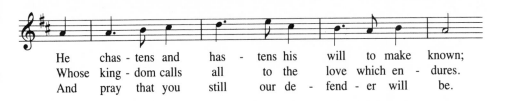

He chas - tens and has - tens his will to make known;
Whose king - dom calls all to the love which en - dures.
And pray that you still our de - fend - er will be.

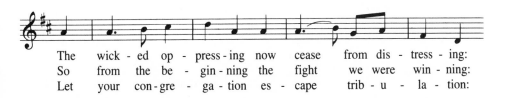

The wick - ed op - press - ing now cease from dis - tress - ing:
So from the be - gin - ning the fight we were win - ning:
Let your con - gre - ga - tion es - cape trib - u - la - tion:

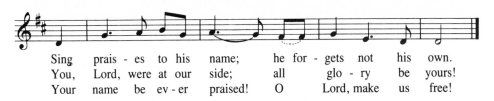

Sing prais - es to his name; he for - gets not his own.
You, Lord, were at our side; all glo - ry be yours!
Your name be ev - er praised! O Lord, make us free!

Text: *Wilt heden nu treden;* Tr. by Theodore Baker, 1851-1934, alt., © J. Curwen and Sons
Tune: KREMSER, 12 11 12 11; *Neder-landtsch Gedenckclanck,* 1626; Harm. by Edward Kremser, 1838-1914

761 Star-Spangled Banner

1. O say can you see by the dawn's ear - ly light,
2. On the shore, dim - ly seen thro' the mists of the deep,
3. O thus be it ev - er when free - men shall stand

What so proud - ly we hailed at the twi-light's last gleam-ing,
Where the foe's haugh-ty host in dead si - lence re - pos - es,
Be - tween their loved homes and the war's des - o - la - tion!

Whose broad stripes and bright stars, through the per - il - ous fight,
What is that which the breeze, o'er the tow - er - ing steep,
Blest with vic - t'ry and peace, may the heav'n - res - cued land

O'er the ram - parts we watched, were so gal - lant - ly stream-ing?
As it fit - ful - ly blows half con - ceals, half dis - clos - es?
Praise the Pow'r that hath made and pre - served us a na - tion!

And the rock - ets' red glare, the bombs burst - ing in air,
Now it catch - es the gleam of the morn-ing's first beam,
Then con - quer we must, when our cause it is just,

Gave proof through the night that our flag was still there.
In full glo - ry re - flect - ed now shined on the stream,
And this be our mot - to, "In God is our trust."

O say does that Star-Spang - led Ban - ner yet wave
'Tis the Star-Spang - led Ban - ner O long may it wave
And the Star-Spang - led Ban - ner in tri - umph shall wave

O'er the land of the free and the home of the brave?
O'er the land of the free and the home of the brave!
O'er the land of the free and the home of the brave!

Text: Francis S. Key, 1779-1843
Tune: STAR SPANGLED BANNER, Irregular; John S. Smith, 1750-1836

My Country, 'Tis of Thee   762

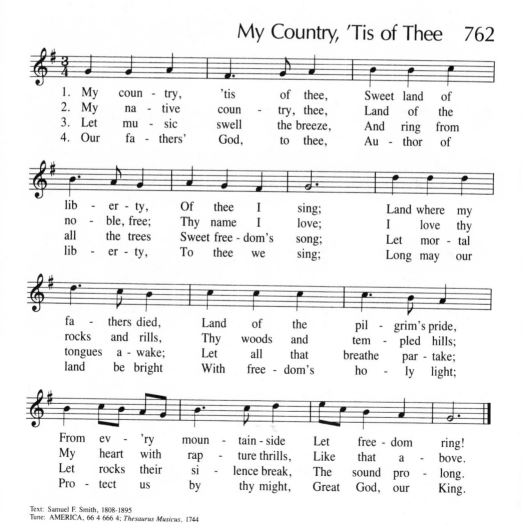

1. My coun - try, 'tis of thee, Sweet land of
2. My na - tive coun - try, thee, Land of the
3. Let mu - sic swell the breeze, And ring from
4. Our fa - thers' God, to thee, Au - thor of

lib - er - ty, Of thee I sing; Land where my
no - ble, free; Thy name I love; I love thy
all the trees Sweet free - dom's song; Let mor - tal
lib - er - ty, To thee we sing; Long may our

fa - thers died, Land of the pil - grim's pride,
rocks and rills, Thy woods and tem - pled hills;
tongues a - wake; Let all that breathe par - take;
land be bright With free - dom's ho - ly light;

From ev - 'ry moun - tain - side Let free - dom ring!
My heart with rap - ture thrills, Like that a - bove.
Let rocks their si - lence break, The sound pro - long.
Pro - tect us by thy might, Great God, our King.

Text: Samuel F. Smith, 1808-1895
Tune: AMERICA, 66 4 666 4; *Thesaurus Musicus*, 1744

763 America the Beautiful

1. O beau - ti - ful for spa - cious skies, For am - ber
2. O beau - ti - ful for pil - grim feet, Whose stern, im-
3. O beau - ti - ful for he - roes proved In lib - er-
4. O beau - ti - ful for pa - triot dream That sees be-

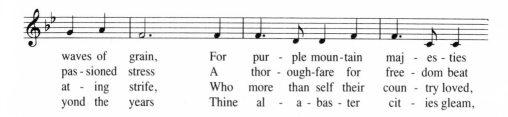

waves of grain, For pur - ple moun-tain maj - es - ties
pas - sioned stress A thor - ough-fare for free - dom beat
at - ing strife, Who more than self their coun - try loved,
yond the years Thine al - a - bas - ter cit - ies gleam,

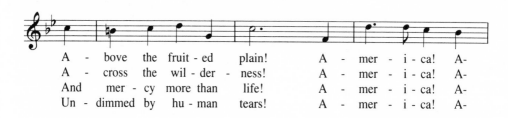

A - bove the fruit - ed plain! A - mer - i - ca! A-
A - cross the wil - der - ness! A - mer - i - ca! A-
And mer - cy more than life! A - mer - i - ca! A-
Un - dimmed by hu - man tears! A - mer - i - ca! A-

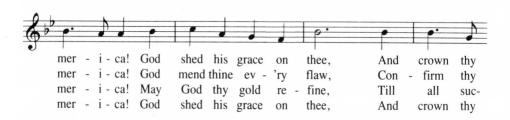

mer - i - ca! God shed his grace on thee, And crown thy
mer - i - ca! God mend thine ev - 'ry flaw, Con - firm thy
mer - i - ca! May God thy gold re - fine, Till all suc-
mer - i - ca! God shed his grace on thee, And crown thy

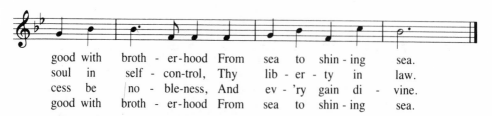

good with broth - er-hood From sea to shin - ing sea.
soul in self - con-trol, Thy lib - er - ty in law.
cess be no - ble-ness, And ev - 'ry gain di - vine.
good with broth - er-hood From sea to shin - ing sea.

Text: Katherine L. Bates, 1859-1929
Tune: MATERNA, CMD; Samuel A. Ward, 1848-1903

God of Our Fathers   764

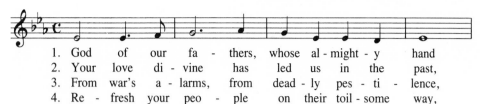

1. God of our fa - thers, whose al - might - y hand
2. Your love di - vine has led us in the past,
3. From war's a - larms, from dead - ly pes - ti - lence,
4. Re - fresh your peo - ple on their toil - some way,

Leads forth in beau - ty all the star - ry band
In this free land by you our lot is cast;
Your might - y arm our ev - er sure de - fense;
Lead us from night to nev - er - end - ing day;

Of shin - ing worlds in splen-dor through the skies,
Be our strong rul - er, guar-dian, guide, and stay,
Your true re - li - gion in our hearts in - crease,
Fill all our lives with heav'n-born love and grace,

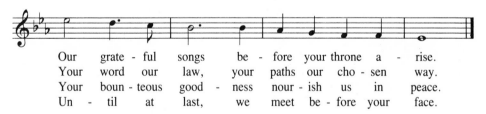

Our grate - ful songs be - fore your throne a - rise.
Your word our law, your paths our cho - sen way.
Your boun - teous good - ness nour - ish us in peace.
Un - til at last, we meet be - fore your face.

Text: Daniel C. Roberts, 1841-1907
Tune: NATIONAL HYMN, 10 10   10 10; George W. Warren, 1828-1902

Advent/Christmas

765 In various ways and various places the churches have marked the days around the winter solstice (adapting when possible in the southern hemisphere when December and January surround the summer solstice). Christians have quite naturally kept from their former religions and traditions all manner of customs and rituals, giving these a home around the many-faceted celebration of the Word-made-flesh, the manifestation of God-with-us.

The present Roman calendar has a period of three to four weeks before December 25. This is called Advent and it is filled with beautiful scriptures, songs, prayers and gestures. These have no single focus but abound with images: of God's promise and human longing, of the beauty in both darkness and light, of the earth's sorrows and its fullness, of the goodness and mystery of time. The spirit of the church's Advent is in the silence and song that arise from constant attention to the human condition.

At Christmas this spirit blossoms in acclamation: the stories of nativity and epiphany, of Mary and of the Innocents, of Jesus baptized and of water become wine. Until well into January the songs and sights and smells of Christmas surround the church not with sentimental fantasies but with everyday faith in a gracious God. The festivals of the Christmas season bear their own reflection of what is proclaimed on every Sunday of the year and in every baptism: our lives are caught up now in Jesus who was born of the virgin Mary, who suffered, died and has been raised.

The lectionary of Advent/Christmas is the foundation of these winter days. These scriptures, read and pondered year after year, turn the Christian and the church toward that peace and glory we name but do not yet know.

FIRST SUNDAY OF ADVENT / A

READING I

Isaiah 2, 1-5 / 1

RESPONSORIAL PSALM

Psalm (121)122, 1-2.3-4.4-5.6-7.8-9 / 1

I re-joiced when I heard them say: let us go to the house of the Lord.

I rejoiced when I heard them say:
"Let us go to God's house."
And now our feet are standing
within your gates, O Jerusalem. ℞.

Jerusalem is built as a city
strongly compact.
It is there that the tribes go up,
the tribes of the Lord. ℞.

For Israel's law it is,
there to praise the Lord's name.
There were set the thrones of judgment
of the house of David. ℞.

For the peace of Jerusalem pray:
"Peace be to your homes!
May peace reign in your walls,
in your palaces, peace!" ℞.

For love of my brethren and friends
I say: "Peace upon you!"
For love of the house of the Lord
I will ask for your good. ℞.

READING II

Romans 13, 11-14 / 1

GOSPEL

Matthew 24, 37-44 / 1

767 FIRST SUNDAY OF ADVENT / B

READING I   *Isaiah 63, 16-17.19; 64, 2-7 / 2*

RESPONSORIAL PSALM   *Psalm (79)80, 2-3.15-16.18-19 / 2*

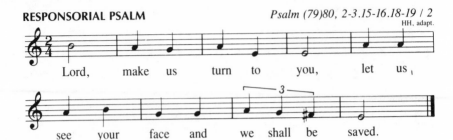

O shepherd of Israel, hear us,
shine forth from your cherubim throne.
O Lord, rouse up your might,
O Lord, come to our help. ℟.

God of hosts, turn again, we implore,
look down from heaven and see.
Visit this vine and protect it,
the vine your right hand has planted. ℟.

May your hand be on the man you have
    chosen,
the man you have given your strength.
And we shall never forsake you again;
give us life that we may call upon your
    name. ℟.

READING II   *1 Corinthians 1, 3-9 / 2*

GOSPEL   *Mark 13, 33-37 / 2*

768 FIRST SUNDAY OF ADVENT / C

READING I   *Jeremiah 33, 14-16 / 3*

RESPONSORIAL PSALM   *Psalm (24)25, 4-5.8-9.10.14 / 3*

Lord, make me know your ways.
Lord, teach me your paths.
Make me walk in your truth, and
    teach me,
for you are God my savior.
In you I hope all day long. ℟.

The Lord is good and upright.
He shows the path to those who
    stray,
he guides the humble in the right
    path,
he teaches his way to the poor. ℟.

His ways are faithfulness and love
for those who keep his covenant and
    will.
The Lord's friendship is for those
    who revere him;
to them he reveals his covenant. ℞.

READING II   *1 Thessalonians 3, 12-4, 2 / 3*

GOSPEL   *Luke 21, 25-28, 34-36 / 3*

SECOND SUNDAY OF ADVENT / A   769

READING I   *Isaiah 11, 1-10 / 4*

RESPONSORIAL PSALM   *Psalm (71)72, 1-2.7-8.12-13.17 / 4*

Jus - tice shall flour - ish in his time, and full - ness of peace for ev - er.

O God, give your judgment to the
    king,
to a king's son your justice,
that he may judge your people in
    justice
and your poor in right judgment. ℞.

In his days justice shall flourish
and peace till the moon fails.
He shall rule from sea to sea,
from the Great River to earth's
    bounds. ℞.

For he shall save the
    poor when they cry
and the needy who are helpless.
He will have pity on the weak
and save the lives of the poor. ℞.

May his name be blessed for ever
and endure like the sun.
Every tribe shall be blessed in him,
all nations bless his name. ℞.

READING II   *Romans 15, 4-9 / 4*

GOSPEL   *Matthew 3, 1-12 / 4*

770 SECOND SUNDAY OF ADVENT / B

READING I   *Isaiah 40, 1-5.9-11 / 5*

RESPONSORIAL PSALM   *Psalm (84)85, 9-10.11-12.13-14 / 5*

Lord, let us see your kind-ness, and grant us your sal - va-tion.

I will hear what the Lord God has to
  say,
a voice that speaks of peace,
peace for his people and his friends
and those who turn to him in their
  hearts.
His help is near for those who fear him
and his glory will dwell in our land. ℟.

Mercy and faithfulness have met;
justice and peace have embraced.
Faithfulness shall spring from the earth
and justice look down from heaven. ℟.

The Lord will make us prosper
and our earth shall yield its fruit.
Justice shall march before him
and peace shall follow his steps. ℟.

READING II   *2 Peter 3, 8-14 / 5*

GOSPEL   *Mark 1, 1-8 / 5*

771 SECOND SUNDAY OF ADVENT / C

READING I   *Baruch 5, 1-9 / 6*

RESPONSORIAL PSALM   *Psalm (125)126, 1-2.2-3.4-5.6 / 6*

The Lord has done great things for us;

we are filled with joy, we are filled with joy.

When the Lord delivered Zion from
  bondage,
it seemed like a dream.
Then was our mouth filled with
  laughter,
on our lips there were songs. ℟.

The heathens themselves said: "What
  marvels
the Lord worked for them!"
What marvels the Lord worked for
  us!
Indeed we were glad. ℟.

Deliver us, O Lord, from our bondage
as streams in dry land.
Those who are sowing in tears
will sing when they reap. ℞.

They go out, they go out, full of tears,
carrying seed for the sowing;
they come back, they come back, full
of song,
carrying their sheaves. ℞.

READING II   *Philippians 1, 4-6.8-11 / 6*

GOSPEL   *Luke 3, 1-6 / 6*

THIRD SUNDAY OF ADVENT / A   772

READING I   *Isaiah 35, 1-6.10 / 7*

RESPONSORIAL PSALM   *Psalm (145)146, 6-7.8-9.9-10 / 7*

O Lord, come and save us.

It is he who keeps faith for ever,
who is just to those who are oppressed.
It is he who gives bread to the
hungry,
the Lord, who sets prisoners free. ℞.

It is the Lord who loves the just
but thwarts the path of the wicked.
The Lord will reign for ever,
Zion's God, from age to age. ℞.

The Lord who gives sight to the blind,
who raises up those who are bowed
down,
the Lord, who protects the stranger,
and upholds the widow and orphan. ℞.

READING II   *James 5, 7-10 / 7*

GOSPEL   *Matthew 11, 2-11 / 7*

773 THIRD SUNDAY OF ADVENT / B

READING I *Isaiah 61, 1-2.10-11 / 8*

RESPONSORIAL PSALM *Luke 1, 46-48.49-50.53-54 / 8*

My soul re - joic - es, my soul re - joic - es in my God.

My soul glorifies the Lord,
my spirit rejoices in God, my savior.
He looks on his servant in her
  nothingness;
henceforth all ages will call me
  blessed. ℟.

The Almighty works marvels for me.
Holy his name!
His mercy is from age to age,
on those who fear him. ℟.

He fills the starving with good things,
sends the rich away empty.
He protects Israel his servant,
remembering his mercy. ℟.

READING II *1 Thessalonians 5, 16-24 / 8*

GOSPEL *John 1, 6-8.19-28 / 8*

774 THIRD SUNDAY OF ADVENT / C

READING I *Zephaniah 3, 14-18 / 9*

RESPONSORIAL PSALM *Isaiah 12, 2-3.4.5-6 / 9*

Cry out with joy and glad - ness: for a-
mong you is the great and Ho-ly One of Is - ra - el.

Truly, God is my salvation,
I trust, I shall not fear.
For the Lord is my strength, my song,
he became my savior.
With joy you will draw water
from the wells of salvation. ℟.

Give thanks to the Lord, give praise to
  his name!
Make his mighty deeds known to the
  peoples! ℟.

Declare the greatness of his name,
sing a psalm to the Lord!
For he has done glorious deeds,
make them known to all the earth!
People of Zion, sing and shout for joy
for great in your midst is the Holy One
  of Israel. ℞.

READING II   *Philippians 4, 4-7 / 9*

GOSPEL   *Luke 3, 10-18 / 9*

FOURTH SUNDAY OF ADVENT / A   775

READING I   *Isaiah 7, 10-14 / 10*

RESPONSORIAL PSALM   *Psalm (23)24, 1-2.3-4.5-6 / 10*

RP

Let the Lord en-ter; he is king of glo-ry.

The Lord's is the earth and its fullness,
the world and all its peoples.
It is he who set it on the seas;
on the waters he made it firm. ℞.

Who shall climb the mountain of the
  Lord?
Who shall stand in his holy place?
The man with clean hands and pure heart,
who desires not worthless things. ℞.

He shall receive blessings from the
  Lord
and reward from the God who saves
  him.
Such are the men who seek him,
seek the face of the God of Jacob. ℞.

READING II   *Romans 1, 1-7 / 10*

GOSPEL   *Matthew 1, 18-24 / 10*

776 FOURTH SUNDAY OF ADVENT / B

READING I   *2 Samuel 7, 1-5.8-11.16 / 11*

RESPONSORIAL PSALM   *Psalm (88)89, 2-3.4-5.27.29 / 11*

For ev - er I will sing the good-ness of the Lord.

I will sing for ever of your love, O
Lord;
through all ages my mouth will
proclaim your truth.
Of this I am sure, that your love lasts
for ever,
that your truth is firmly established as
the heavens. ℞.

"With my chosen one I have made a
covenant;
I have sworn to David my servant:
I will establish your dynasty for ever
and set up your throne through all
ages." ℞.

He will say to me: "You are my father,
my God, the rock who saves me."
I will keep my love for him always;
with him my covenant shall last. ℞.

READING II   *Romans 16, 25-27 / 11*

GOSPEL   *Luke 1, 26-38 / 11*

777 FOURTH SUNDAY OF ADVENT / C

READING I   *Micah 5, 1-4 / 12*

RESPONSORIAL PSALM   *Psalm (79)80, 2-3.15-16.18-19 / 12*

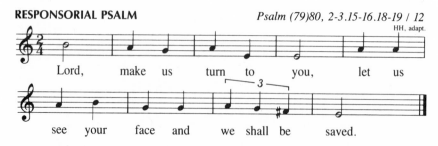

Lord, make us turn to you, let us
see your face and we shall be saved.

O shepherd of Israel, hear us,
shine forth from your cherubim throne.
O Lord, rouse up your might,
O Lord, come to our help. ℞.

God of hosts, turn again, we implore,
look down from heaven and see.
Visit this vine and protect it,
the vine your right hand has
planted. ℞.

May your hand be on the man you have
  chosen,
the man you have given your strength.
And we shall never forsake you again;
give us life that we may call upon your
  name. ℞.

READING II   *Hebrews 10, 5-10 / 12*

GOSPEL   *Luke 1, 39-45 / 12*

DECEMBER 25: CHRISTMAS–VIGIL   778

READING I   *Isaiah 62, 1-5 / 13*

RESPONSORIAL PSALM   *Psalm (88)89, 4-5.16-17.27.29 / 13*

For ev - er I will sing the good-ness of the Lord.

"With my chosen one I have made a
  covenant;
I have sworn to David my servant:
I will establish your dynasty for ever
and set up your throne through all
  ages." ℞.

Happy the people who acclaim such a
  king,
who walk, O Lord, in the light of your
  face,

who find their joy every day in your
  name,
who make your justice the source of
  their bliss. ℞.

He will say to me: "You are my father,
my God, the rock who saves me."
I will keep my love for him always;
with him my covenant shall last. ℞.

READING II   *Acts 13, 16-17.22-25 / 13*

GOSPEL   *Matthew 1, 1-25 or 1, 18-25 / 13*

779 DECEMBER 25: CHRISTMAS—MASS AT MIDNIGHT

READING I   *Isaiah 9, 1-6 / 14*

RESPONSORIAL PSALM   *Psalm (95)96, 1-2.2-3.11-12.13 / 14*
RP

To - day   is   born our Sav - ior,   Christ the Lord.

O sing a new song to the Lord,
sing to the Lord all the earth.
O sing to the Lord, bless his name. ℟.

Let the heavens rejoice and earth be
glad,
let the sea and all within it thunder
praise,
let the land and all it bears rejoice,
all the trees of the wood shout for
joy. ℟.

Proclaim his help day by day,
tell among the nations his glory
and his wonders among all the
peoples. ℟.

At the presence of the Lord for he
comes,
he comes to rule the earth.
With justice he will rule the world,
he will judge the peoples with his
truth. ℟.

READING II   *Titus 2, 11-14 / 14*

GOSPEL   *Luke 2, 1-14 / 14*

780 DECEMBER 25: CHRISTMAS—MASS AT DAWN

READING I   *Isaiah 62, 11-12 / 15*

RESPONSORIAL PSALM   *Psalm (96)97, 1.6.11-12 / 15*
JRC

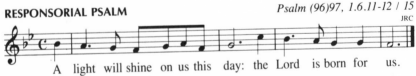

A light will shine on us this day: the Lord is born for us.

The Lord is king, let earth rejoice,
let all the coastlands be glad.
The skies proclaim his justice;
all peoples see his glory. ℟.

Light shines forth for the just
and joy for the upright of heart.
Rejoice, you just, in the Lord;
give glory to his holy name. ℟.

READING II   *Titus 3, 4-7 / 15*

GOSPEL   *Luke 2, 15-20*

DECEMBER 25: CHRISTMAS—MASS DURING THE DAY   781

READING I   *Isaiah 52, 7-10 / 16*

RESPONSORIAL PSALM   *Psalm (97)98, 1.2-3.3-4.5-6 / 16*

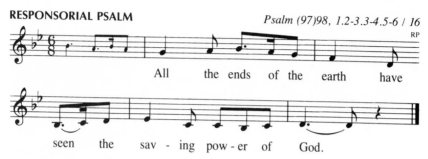

All the ends of the earth have seen the sav - ing pow - er of God.

Sing a new song to the Lord
for he has worked wonders.
His right hand and his holy arm
have brought salvation. ℞.

The Lord has made known his
    salvation;
has shown his justice to the nations.
He has remembered his truth and love
for the house of Israel. ℞.

All the ends of the earth have seen
the salvation of our God.
Shout to the Lord all the earth,
ring out your joy. ℞.

Sing psalms to the Lord with the harp
with the sound of music.
With trumpets and the sound of the
    horn
acclaim the King, the Lord. ℞.

READING II   *Hebrews 1, 1-6 / 16*

GOSPEL   *John, 1-18 or 1, 1-5.9-14 / 16*

782 SUNDAY IN THE OCTAVE OF CHRISTMAS—HOLY FAMILY

READING I *Sirach 3, 2-6.12-14 / 17*

RESPONSORIAL PSALM *Psalm (127)128, 1-2.3.4-5 / 17*

O hap-py are those who fear the Lord and walk in his ways.

O blessed are those who fear the Lord
and walk in his ways!
By the labor of your hands you shall
 eat.
You will be happy and prosper. ℟.

Your wife like a fruitful vine
in the heart of your house;
your children like shoots of the olive,
around your table. ℟.

Indeed thus shall be blessed
the man who fears the Lord.
May the Lord bless you from Zion
all the days of your life!
May you see your children's children
in a happy Jerusalem! ℟.

READING II *Colossians 3, 12-21 / 17*

GOSPEL/A *Matthew 2, 13-15.19-23 / 17*

GOSPEL/B *Luke 2, 22-40 or 2, 22.39-40 / 17*

GOSPEL/C *Luke 2, 41-52 / 17*

783 JANUARY 1: SOLEMNITY OF MARY, MOTHER OF GOD

READING I *Numbers 6, 22-27 / 18*

RESPONSORIAL PSALM *Psalm (66)67, 2-3.5.6.8 / 18*

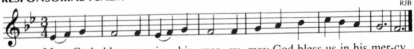

May God bless us in his mer-cy, may God bless us in his mer-cy.

O God, be gracious and bless us
and let your face shed its light upon us.
So will your ways be known upon earth
and all nations learn your saving
 help. ℟.

Let the nations be glad and exult
for you rule the world with justice.
With fairness you rule the peoples,
you guide the nations on earth. ℟.

Let the peoples praise you, O God;
let all the peoples praise you.
May God still give us his blessing
till the ends of the earth revere him. ℟.

READING II   *Galatians 4,4-7 / 18*

GOSPEL   *Luke 2, 16-21 / 18*

EPIPHANY   784

READING I   *Isaiah 60, 1-6 / 20*

RESPONSORIAL PSALM   *Psalm (71)72, 1-2.7-8.10-11.12-13 / 20*

Lord, ev'-ry na-tion on earth will a-dore you.

O God, give your judgment to the king,
to a king's son your justice,
that he may judge your people in justice
and your poor in right judgment. ℟.

In his days justice shall flourish
and peace till the moon fails.
He shall rule from sea to sea,
from the Great River to earth's
  bounds. ℟.

The kings of Tarshish and the seacoasts
shall pay him tribute.
The kings of Sheba and Seba
shall bring him gifts.
Before him all kings shall fall prostrate,
all nations shall serve him. ℟.

For he shall save the poor when they
  cry
and the needy who are helpless.
He will have pity on the weak
and save the lives of the poor. ℟.

READING II   *Ephesians 3, 2-3.5-6 / 20*

GOSPEL   *Matthew 2, 1-12 / 20*

785 BAPTISM OF THE LORD

READING I *Isaiah 42, 1-4.6-7 / 21*

RESPONSORIAL PSALM *Psalm (28)29, 1-2.3-4.3.9-10 / 21*

The Lord will bless his peo-ple with peace.

O give the Lord you sons of God,
give the Lord glory and power;
give the Lord the glory of his name.
Adore the Lord in his holy court. ℟.

The Lord's voice resounding on the
   waters,
the Lord on the immensity of waters;
the voice of the Lord, full of power,
the voice of the Lord, full of
   splendor. ℟.

The God of glory thunders.
In his temple they all cry: "Glory!"
The Lord sat enthroned over the flood;
the Lord sits as king for ever. ℟.

READING II *Acts 10, 34-38 / 21*

GOSPEL/A *Matthew 3, 13-17 / 21*

GOSPEL/B *Mark 1, 7-11 / 21*

GOSPEL/C *Luke 3, 15-16.21-22 / 22*

Lent/Easter

On a Wednesday in February or early March the church enters into prayer and fasting and almsgiving, attending with great seriousness to its calling. Forty days later on a Thursday evening, that season of Lent ends. From Holy Thursday night until Easter Sunday afternoon, the church keeps the Paschal Triduum, the "Easter Three Days." Good Friday and Holy Saturday find Christians fasting, keeping vigil, remembering the passion, death and resurrection of the Lord until, at the great Vigil liturgy, the church celebrates this paschal mystery in baptism, confirmation and eucharist. Then, for the fifty days of Eastertime the church again sings the alleluia and rejoices to bring God's peace to the world.

The origins of Lent are bound up with the final stages in the initiation of those seeking to be baptized. After months or years of learning gradually the Christian way of life, the catechumens were called to spend the last weeks before baptism in fasting and prayer. The whole church stayed by the catechumens in these days. The lenten season was also kept intensely by those doing penance for their sins. Today both catechumens and penitents keep Lent with the whole church. Lent's scriptures, prayers and rites give clarity and strength to the life-long struggle against evil. That struggle is waged with many forms of prayer and fasting and practices of charity.

The origins of the fifty days of Eastertime are even more ancient. This is the springtime rejoicing of people who know their dependence on fields and flocks. It is the rejoicing of Israel remembering the exodus from slavery to freedom. It became the rejoicing of the church in the resurrection of Jesus and the presence of that risen life in the newly baptized. The Eastertime lectionary is filled with a lively peace and the quiet exuberance of those who believe that evil is not finally triumphant. When the fifty days conclude at Pentecost the church knows again how disturbing, how restless, how strong is the Spirit given by Christ.

787 FIRST SUNDAY OF LENT/A

READING I *Genesis 2, 7-9; 3, 1-7 / 22*

RESPONSORIAL PSALM *Psalm (50)51, 3-4.5-6.12-13.14.17 / 22*

PC

Be mer - ci - ful, O Lord, for we have sinned.

Have mercy on me, God, in your
kindness.
In your compassion blot out my
offense.
O wash me more and more from my
guilt
and cleanse me from my sin. ℞.

My offenses truly I know them;
my sin is always before me.
Against you, you alone, have I sinned;
what is evil in your sight I have
done. ℞.

A pure heart create for me, O God,
put a steadfast spirit within me.
Do not cast me away from your
presence,
nor deprive me of your holy
spirit. ℞.

Give me again the joy of your help;
with a spirit of fervor sustain me.
O Lord, open my lips
and my mouth shall declare your
praise. ℞.

READING II *Romans 5, 12-19 or 5, 12.17-19 / 22*

GOSPEL *Matthew 4, 1-11 / 22*

RITE OF ELECTION

*At the beginning of Lent, is the responsibility of the bishop to call those who
are judged ready to prepare for the sacraments of initiation at Easter. The
bishop is to consult first with the pastors, catechists and others. The rite may
take place at the cathedral. If the rite takes place in the parish church, the
bishop may designate the pastor to act in his place.*

*This rite is also called the "Enrollment of Names." Each candidate now
gives his/her name, or writes it down. When all have been enrolled, the
bishop says: "You have been chosen to be initiated into the sacred mysteries
at the Easter Vigil." He then speaks to them and to their sponsors about their
lenten preparation for baptism.*

*The faithful join in prayers of intercession for the elect, as the catechu-
mens are now called. If the eucharist is to be celebrated, the elect are first
dismissed.*

FIRST SUNDAY OF LENT/B

READING I

Genesis 9, 8-15 / 23

RESPONSORIAL PSALM

Psalm (24)25, 4-5.6-7.8-9 / 23

JRC

Your ways, O Lord, are love and truth, to those who keep your cov - e - nant.

Lord, make me know your ways.
Lord, teach me your paths.
Make me walk in your truth, and teach me,
for you are God my savior. ℞.

Remember your mercy, Lord,
and the love you have shown from of old.
In your love remember me,
because of your goodness, O Lord. ℞.

The Lord is good and upright.
He shows the path to those who stray,
he guides the humble in the right path,
he teaches his way to the poor. ℞.

READING II

1 Peter 3, 18-22 / 23

GOSPEL

Mark 1, 12-15 / 23

RITE OF ELECTION
See no. 787

789 **FIRST SUNDAY OF LENT/C**

READING I *Deuteronomy 26, 4-10 / 24*

RESPONSORIAL PSALM *Psalm (90)91, 1-2.10-11.12-13.14-15 / 24*

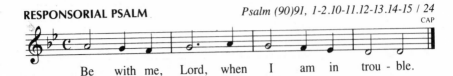

Be with me, Lord, when I am in trou - ble.

He who dwells in the shelter of the
  Most High
and abides in the shade of the Almighty
says to the Lord: "My refuge,
my stronghold, my God in whom I
  trust!" ℟.

Upon you no evil shall fall,
no plague approach where you dwell.
For you has he commanded his angels
to keep you in all your ways. ℟.

They shall bear you upon their hands
lest you strike your foot against a stone.
On the lion and the viper you will tread
and trample the young lion and the
  dragon. ℟.

Since he clings to me in love,
  I will free him,
protect him for he knows my name.
When he calls I shall answer: "I am
  with you."
I will save him in distress and give him
  glory.

READING II *Romans 10, 8-13 / 24*

GOSPEL *Luke 4, 1-13 / 24*

RITE OF ELECTION
See no. 787

790 **SECOND SUNDAY OF LENT/A**

READING I *Genesis 12, 1-4 / 25*

RESPONSORIAL PSALM *Psalm (32)33, 4-5.18-19.20.22 / 25*

Lord, let your mer - cy be on us,

as we place our trust in you.

For the word of the Lord is faithful
and all his works to be trusted.
The Lord loves justice and right
and fills the earth with his love. ℞.

The Lord looks on those who revere
    him,
on those who hope in his love,
to rescue their souls from death,
to keep them alive in famine. ℞.

Our soul is waiting for the Lord.
The Lord is our help and our shield.
May your love be upon us, O Lord,
as we place all our hope in you. ℞.

READING II

2 Timothy 1, 8-10 / 25

GOSPEL

Matthew 17, 1-9 / 25

SECOND SUNDAY OF LENT / B

791

READING I

Genesis 22, 1-2.9.10-13.15-18 / 26

RESPONSORIAL PSALM

Psalm (115)116, 10.15.16-17.18-19 / 26

I will walk in the pres-ence of the Lord, in the land of the liv-ing.

I trusted, even when I said:
"I am sorely afflicted,"
O precious in the eyes of the Lord
is the death of his faithful. ℞.

Your servant, Lord, your servant am I;
you have loosened my bonds.
A thanksgiving sacrifice I make;
I will call on the Lord's name. ℞.

My vows to the Lord I will fulfill
before all his people,
in the courts of the house of the Lord,
in your midst, O Jerusalem. ℞.

READING II

Romans 8, 31-34 / 26

GOSPEL

Mark 9, 2-10 / 26

792 SECOND SUNDAY OF LENT/C

READING I   *Genesis 15, 5-12.17-18 / 27*

RESPONSORIAL PSALM   *Psalm (26)27, 1.7-8.8-9.13-14 / 27*

The Lord is my light and my sal-va-tion.

The Lord is my light and my help;
whom shall I fear?
The Lord is the stronghold of my life;
before whom shall I shrink? ℟.

O Lord, hear my voice when I call;
have mercy and answer.
Of you my heart has spoken:
"Seek his face." ℟.

It is your face, O Lord, that I seek;
hide not your face.

Dismiss not your servant in anger;
you have been my help.
Do not abandon or forsake me,
O God my help! ℟.

I am sure I shall see the Lord's
goodness
in the land of the living.
Hope in him, hold firm and take
heart.
Hope in the Lord! ℟.

READING II   *Philippians 3, 17-4,1 or 3, 20-4,1 / 27*

GOSPEL   *Luke 9, 28-36 / 27*

793 THIRD SUNDAY OF LENT/A

READING I   *Exodus 17, 3-7 / 28*

RESPONSORIAL PSALM   *Psalm (94)95, 1-2.6-7.8-9 / 28*

If to-day you hear his voice, O hard-en not your hearts.

Come, ring out our joy to the Lord;
hail the rock who saves us.
Let us come before him, giving thanks,
with songs let us hail the Lord. ℟.

Come in; let us bow and bend low;
let us kneel before the God who made
us
for he is our God and we
the people who belong to his pasture,
the flock that is led by his hand. ℟.

O that today you would listen to his
voice!
"Harden not your hearts as at Meribah,
as on that day at Massah in the desert
when your fathers put me to the test;
when they tried me, though they saw
my work." ℟.

READING II   *Romans 5, 1-2.5-8 / 28*

GOSPEL   *John 4, 5-42 or 4, 5-15.19-26.39.40-42 / 28*

FIRST SCRUTINY

During Lent, the elect (those catechumens who have been called to prepare for baptism at Easter) are called to come before the community for exorcisms and prayers. This takes place after the liturgy of the word on the Third, Fourth and Fifth Sundays of Lent. These rites are intended to purify the hearts and minds of the elect, to strengthen them against temptation, to help them progress in the love of God.

The presider asks the assembly to pray in silence for the elect, then to join in intercessions for them. The presider lays hands on each of the elect and prays that the elect be delivered from the power of evil and become witnesses to the gospel. A song or psalm may be sung, then the elect are dismissed as usual and the faithful continue with the liturgy of the eucharist.

THIRD SUNDAY OF LENT/B   794

READING I   *Exodus 20, 1-17 or 20, 1-3.7-8.12-17 / 29*

RESPONSORIAL PSALM   *Psalm (18)19, 8.9.10.11 / 29*

Lord, you have the words of ev-er-last-ing life.

The law of the Lord is perfect,
it revives the soul.
The rule of the Lord is to be trusted,
it gives wisdom to the simple. ℟.

The precepts of the Lord are right,
they gladden the heart.
The command of the Lord is clear,
it gives light to the eyes. ℟.

The fear of the Lord is holy,
abiding for ever.
The decrees of the Lord are truth
and all of them just. ℟.

They are more to be desired than gold,
than the purest of gold
and sweeter are they than honey,
than honey from the comb. ℟.

READING II   *1 Corinthians 1, 22-25 / 29*

GOSPEL   *John 2, 13-25 / 29*

FIRST SCRUTINY
See no.793

795 **THIRD SUNDAY OF LENT/C**

READING I *Exodus 3, 1-8.13-15 / 30*

RESPONSORIAL PSALM *Psalm (102)103, 1-2.3-4.6-7.8.11 / 30*

The Lord is kind and mer - ci - ful.

My soul, give thanks to the Lord,
all my being, bless his holy name.
My soul, give thanks to the Lord
and never forget all his blessings. ℞.

It is he who forgives all your guilt,
who heals every one of your ills,
who redeems your life from the grave,
who crowns you with love and
    compassion. ℞.

The Lord does deeds of justice,
gives judgment for all who are
    oppressed.
He made known his ways to Moses
and his deeds to Israel's sons. ℞.

The Lord is compassion and love,
slow to anger and rich in mercy.
For as the heavens are high above the
    earth
so strong is his love for those who fear
    him. ℞.

READING II *1 Corinthians 10, 1-6.10-12 / 30*

GOSPEL *Luke 13, 1-9 / 30*

FIRST SCRUTINY
See no. 793

796 **FOURTH SUNDAY OF LENT/A**

READING I *1 Samuel 16, 1.6-7.10-13 / 31*

RESPONSORIAL PSALM *Psalm (22)23, 1-3.3-4.5.6 / 31*

The Lord is my shep-herd; there is noth-ing I shall want.

The Lord is my shepherd;
there is nothing I shall want.
Fresh and green are the pastures
where he gives me repose.
Near restful waters he leads me,
to revive my drooping spirit. ℞.

He guides me along the right path;
he is true to his name.
If I should walk in the valley of
    darkness
no evil would I fear.
You are there with your crook and
your staff; with these you give me
    comfort. ℞.

You have prepared a banquet for me
in the sight of my foes.
My head you have anointed with oil;
my cup is overflowing. ℞.

Surely goodness and kindness shall
   follow me
all the days of my life.
In the Lord's own house shall I dwell
for ever and ever. ℞.

READING II

Ephesians 5, 8-14 / 31

GOSPEL

John 9, 1-41 or 9, 1.6-9.13-17.34-38 / 31

SECOND SCRUTINY

During Lent, the elect (those catechumens who have been called to prepare for baptism at Easter) are called to come before the community for exorcisms and prayers. This takes place after the liturgy of the word on the Third, Fourth and Fifth Sundays of Lent. These rites are intended to purify the hearts and minds of the elect, to strengthen them against temptation, to help them progress in the love of God.

The presider asks the assembly to pray in silence for the elect, then to join in intercessions for them. The presider lays hands on each of the elect and prays that the elect be delivered from the power of evil and become witnesses to the gospel. A song or psalm may be sung, then the elect are dismissed as usual and the faithful continue with the liturgy of the eucharist.

797 FOURTH SUNDAY OF LENT/B

READING I   *2 Chronicles 36, 14-17.19-23 / 32*

RESPONSORIAL PSALM   *Psalm (136)137, 1-2.3.4-5.6 / 32*

Let my tongue be si - lenced, if I ev - er for - get you!

By the rivers of Babylon
there we sat and wept,
remembering Zion;
on the poplars that grew there
we hung up our harps. ℟.

For it was there that they asked us,
our captors, for songs,
our oppressors, for joy.
"Sing to us," they said,
"one of Zion's songs." ℟.

O how could we sing
the song of the Lord
on alien soil?
If I forget you, Jerusalem,
let my right hand wither! ℟.

O let my tongue
cleave to my mouth
if I remember you not,
if I prize not Jerusalem
above all my joys! ℟.

READING II   *Ephesians 2, 4-10 / 32*

GOSPEL   *John 3, 14-21 / 32*

SECOND SCRUTINY
See no. 796

798 FOURTH SUNDAY OF LENT/C

READING I   *Joshua 5, 9.10-12 / 33*

RESPONSORIAL PSALM   *Psalm (33)34, 2-3.4-5.6-7 / 33*

Taste and see the good - ness of the Lord.

I will bless the Lord at all times,
his praise always on my lips;
in the Lord my soul shall make its
    boast.
The humble shall hear and be glad. ℟.

Glorify the Lord with me.
Together let us praise his name.
I sought the Lord and he answered me;
from all my terrors he set me free. ℟.

Look towards him and be radiant;
let your faces not be abashed.
This poor man called; the Lord
    heard him
and rescued him from all his
    distress. ℟.

READING II   *2 Corinthians 5, 17-21 / 33*

GOSPEL   *Luke 15,1-3.11-32 / 33*

SECOND SCRUTINY
See no. 796

FIFTH SUNDAY OF LENT/A   799

READING I   *Ezekiel 37, 12-14 / 34*

RESPONSORIAL PSALM   *Psalm (129)130, 1-2.3-4.5-6.7-8. / 34*

With the Lord there is mer-cy, and full-ness of re-demp-tion.

Out of the depths I cry to you, O Lord,
Lord, hear my voice!
O let your ears be attentive
to the voice of my pleading. ℞.

My soul is waiting for the Lord,
I count on his word.
My soul is longing for the Lord
more than watchman for daybreak.
(Let the watchman count on daybreak
and Israel on the Lord.) ℞.

If you, O Lord, should mark our guilt,
Lord, who would survive?
But with you is found forgiveness:
for this we revere you. ℞.

Because with the Lord there is mercy
and fullness of redemption,
Israel indeed he will redeem
for all its iniquity. ℞.

READING II   *Romans 8, 8-11 / 34*

GOSPEL   *John 11, 1-45 or 11,3-7.17.20-27.33-45 / 34*

THIRD SCRUTINY

During Lent, the elect (those catechumens who have been called to prepare for baptism at Easter) are called to come before the community for exorcisms and prayers. This takes place after the liturgy of the word on the Third, Fourth and Fifth Sundays of Lent. These rites are intended to purify the hearts and minds of the elect, to strengthen them against temptation, to help them progress in the love of God.

The presider asks the assembly to pray in silence for the elect, then to join in intercessions for them. The presider lays hands on each of the elect and prays that the elect be delivered from the power of evil and become witnesses to the gospel. A song or psalm may be sung, then the elect are dismissed as usual and the faithful continue with the liturgy of the eucharist.

800 FIFTH SUNDAY OF LENT/B

READING I *Jeremiah 31, 31-34 / 35*

RESPONSORIAL PSALM *Psalm (50)51, 3-4.12-13.14-15 / 35*

Cre - ate a clean heart, a clean heart in me, O God.

Have mercy on me, God, in your
  kindness.
In your compassion blot out my
  offense.
O wash me more and more from my
  guilt
and cleanse me from my sin. ℟.

A pure heart create for me, O God,
put a steadfast spirit within me.

Do not cast me away from your
  presence,
nor deprive me of your holy spirit. ℟.

Give me again the joy of your help;
with a spirit of fervor sustain me,
that I may teach transgressors your
  ways
and sinners may return to you. ℟.

READING II *Hebrews 5, 7-9 / 35*

GOSPEL *John 12, 20-33 / 35*

THIRD SCRUTINY
See no. 799

801 FIFTH SUNDAY OF LENT/C

READING I *Isaiah 43, 16-21 / 36*

RESPONSORIAL PSALM *Psalm (125)126, 1-2.2-3.4-5.6 / 36*

The Lord has done great things for us;

we are filled with joy, we are filled with joy.

When the Lord delivered Zion from
  bondage,
it seemed like a dream.
Then was our mouth filled with
  laughter,
on our lips there were songs. ℟.

The heathens themselves said: "What
  marvels
the Lord worked for them!"
What marvels the Lord worked for us!
Indeed we were glad. ℟.

Deliver us, O Lord, from our bondage
as streams in dry land.
Those who are sowing in tears
will sing when they reap. ℟.

They go out, they go out, full of tears,
carrying seed for the sowing;
they come back, they come back, full
of song,
carrying their sheaves. ℟.

READING II

Philippians 3, 8-14 / 36

GOSPEL

John 8, 1-11 / 36

THIRD SCRUTINY
See no. 799

PASSION SUNDAY (PALM SUNDAY)

802

Passion or Palm Sunday is the last Sunday in Lent. Its closeness to the end of
Lent has given this liturgy two distinct features: the procession with palms and
the gospel reading of the Lord's passion. The blessing and carrying of palms celebrates Jesus' entrance into Jerusalem to accomplish his paschal mystery. The reading of the passion comes as a conclusion to all the gospel readings of the lenten
Sundays: these scriptures yearly prepare catechumens and the faithful to approach the celebration of Christ's death and resurrection. That celebration takes
place most especially in the sacraments of initiation at the Easter Vigil.

COMMEMORATION OF THE LORD'S ENTRANCE INTO JERUSALEM

*This rite may be very simple or may involve the entire assembly in a procession
with the blessing of palms and the gospel reading of Jesus' entrance into
Jerusalem. Depending on the local church, then, some of the following hymns,
psalms and readings will be used.*

OPENING ANTIPHON

803

The following or another appropriate acclamation may be sung.

Mode VII
Adapt. Richard Proulx, 1986

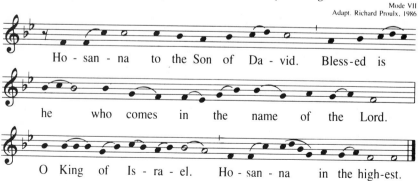

Ho - san - na to the Son of Da - vid. Bless-ed is
he who comes in the name of the Lord.
O King of Is - ra - el. Ho - san - na in the high-est.

BLESSING OF BRANCHES

804

*All hold branches as these are blessed. The branches may be of palm or from a
tree that is native to the area. The green or flowering branches signify the victory
of life.*

GOSPEL/A	*Matthew 21, 1-11 / 37*
GOSPEL/B	*Mark 11, 1-10 / 37*
GOSPEL/B	*John 12, 12-16 / 37*
GOSPEL/C	*Luke 19, 28-40 / 37*

805   PROCESSION

All join in the procession or at least in the song. Such a movement of people expresses the experience of Lent: the church has been called to move on, to go ever further toward the paschal mystery of death and resurrection.

Theodulph of Orleans, c.760-821
Tr. by John M. Neale, 1818-1866, alt.

Gloria, laus et honor, Mode I
Realization in proportional rhythm by Schola Antiqua, 1983
Acc. by Richard Proulx, 1983

All glo - ry, laud, and hon - or to you, Re - deem - er, King! to whom the lips of chil - dren made sweet ho - san - nas ring.

1. You are the King of Is - ra - el, and
2. The com - pa - ny of an - gels are
3. The peo - ple of the He - brews with
4. To you be - fore your pas - sion they
5. Their prais - es you ac - cept - ed, ac-

Da - vid's roy - al Son, now in the Lord's Name
prais - ing you on high; and mor - tals joined with
palms be - fore you went: our praise and prayers and
sang their hymns of praise: to you now high ex-
cept the prayers we bring, great source of love and

D.C.

com - ing, our King and Bless - ed One.
all things cre - a - ted, make re - ply.
an - thems be - fore you we pre - sent.
al - ted, our mel - o - dy we raise.
good - ness, our Sav - ior and our King.

The commemoration of the Lord's entrance into Jerusalem, whether this is done in a simple or solemn manner, concludes with the opening prayer of the Mass.

LITURGY OF THE WORD

806

READING I   *Isaiah 50, 4-7 / 38*

RESPONSORIAL PSALM   *Psalm (21)22, 8-9.17-18.19-20.23-24 / 38*

My God, my God, why have you a - ban-doned me?

All who see me deride me.
They curl their lips, they toss their
   heads.
"He trusted in the Lord, let him save
   him;
let him release him if this is his
   friend." ℞.

Many dogs have surrounded me,
a band of the wicked beset me.
They tear holes in my hands and my
   feet.
I can count every one of my bones. ℞.

They divide my clothing among them.
They cast lots for my robe.
O Lord, do not leave me alone,
my strength, make haste to help
   me! ℞.

I will tell of your name to my brethren
and praise you where they are
   assembled.
"You who fear the Lord give him
   praise;
all sons of Jacob, give him glory." ℞.

READING II   *Philippians 2, 6-11 / 38*

807   GOSPEL/A   *Matthew 26, 14-27, 66 or 27, 11-54 / 38*

The symbols of the following passion narrative represent:

N *narrator;*

+ *Christ;*

S *speakers other than Christ;*

P *groups of speakers.*

N The passion of our Lord Jesus Christ according to Matthew.

For short form read only the part in brackets.

N One of the Twelve whose name was Judas Iscariot went off to the chief priests and said,

S "What are you willing to give me if I hand Jesus over to you?"

N They paid him thirty pieces of silver, and from that time on he kept looking for an opportunity to hand him over. On the first day of the feast of Unleavened Bread, the disciples came up to Jesus and said,

P "Where do you wish us to prepare the Passover supper for you?"

+ "Go to this man in the city and tell him, 'The Teacher says, My appointed time draws near. I am to celebrate the Passover with my disciples in your house.' "

N The disciples then did as Jesus had ordered, and prepared the Passover supper. When it grew dark he reclined at table with the Twelve. In the course of the meal he said,

+ "I give you my word one of you is about to betray me."

N Distressed at this, they began to say to him one after another,

S "Surely it is not I, Lord?"

+ "The man who has dipped his hand into the dish with me is the one who will hand me over. The Son of Man is departing, as Scripture says of him, but woe to that man by whom the Son of Man is betrayed. Better for him if he had never been born."

N Then Judas, his betrayer, spoke:

S "Surely it is not I, Rabbi?"

+ "It is you who have said it."

N During the meal Jesus took bread, blessed it, broke it, and gave it to his disciples.

+ "Take this and eat it, this is my body."

N Then he took a cup, gave thanks, and gave it to them.

+ "All of you must drink from it, for this is my blood, the blood of the covenant, to be poured out in behalf of many for the forgiveness of sins. I tell you, I will not drink this fruit of the vine from now until the day when I drink it new with you in my Father's reign."

N Then, after singing songs of praise, they walked out to the Mount of Olives. Jesus then said to them,

+ "Tonight your faith in me will be shaken, for Scripture has it:
'I will strike the shepherd
and the sheep of the flock will be dispersed.'
But after I am raised up, I will go to Galilee ahead of you."

N Peter responded,

S "Though all may have their faith in you shaken, mine will never be shaken!"

+ "I give you my word, before the cock crows tonight you will deny me three times."

S "Even though I have to die with you, I will never disown you."

N And all the other disciples said the same. Then Jesus went with them to a place called Gethsemani.

+ "Stay here while I go over there and pray."

N He took along Peter and Zebedee's two sons. and began to experience sorrow and distress. Then he said to them,

+ "My heart is nearly broken with sorrow. Remain here and stay awake with me."

N He advanced a little and fell prostrate in prayer.

+ "My Father, if it is possible, let this cup pass me by. Still, let it be as you would have it, not as I.

N When he returned to his disciples, he found them asleep. He said to Peter,

+ "So you could not stay awake with me for even an hour? Be on guard, and pray that you may not undergo trial. The spirit is willing but nature is weak."

N Withdrawing a second time, he began to pray:

+ "My Father, if this cannot pass me by without my drinking it, your will be done!"

Once more, on his return, he found them asleep; they could not keep their eyes open. He left them again, withdrew somewhat, and began to pray a third time, saying the same words as before. Finally he returned to his disciples and said to them:

+ "Sleep on now. Enjoy your rest! The hour is on us when the Son of Man is to be handed over to the power of evil men. Get up! Let us be on our way! See, my betrayer is here."

N While he was still speaking, Judas, one of the Twelve, arrived accompanied by a great crowd with swords and clubs. They had been sent by the chief priests and elders of the people. His betrayer had arranged to give them a signal, saying,

S "The man I shall embrace is the one; take hold of him."

N He immediately went over to Jesus, embraced him, and said to him,

S "Peace, Rabbi."

+ "Friend, do what you are here for!"

N At that moment they stepped forward to lay hands on Jesus, and arrested him. Suddenly one of those who accompanied Jesus put his hand to his sword, drew it, and slashed at the high priest's servant, cutting off his ear. Jesus said to him:

+ "Put back your sword where it belongs. Those who use the sword are sooner or later destroyed by it. Do you not suppose I can call on my Father to provide at a moment's notice more than twelve legions of angels? But then how would the Scriptures be fulfilled which say it must happen this way?"

N At that very time Jesus said to the crowd:

+ "Am I a brigand, that you have come armed with swords and clubs to arrest me? From day to day I sat teaching in the temple precincts, yet you never arrested me. Nonetheless, all this has happened in fulfillment of the writings of the prophets."

N Then all the disciples deserted him and fled. Those who had apprehended Jesus led him off to Caiaphas, the high priest, where the scribes and elders were convened. Peter kept following him at a distance as far as the high priest's residence. Going inside, he sat down with the guards to see the outcome. The chief priests, with the whole Sanhedrin, were busy trying to obtain false testimony against Jesus so that they might put him to death. They discovered none, despite the many false witnesses who took the stand. Finally two came forward who stated:

P "This man has declared, 'I can destroy God's sanctuary and rebuild it in three days.' "

N The high priest rose to his feet and addressed him:

S "Have you no answer to the testimony leveled against you?"

N But Jesus remained silent. The high priest then said to him:

S "I order you to tell us under oath before the living God whether you are the Messiah, the Son of God."

+ "It is you who say it. But I tell you this: Soon you will see the Son of Man seated at the right hand of the Power and coming on the clouds of heaven."

N At this the high priest tore his robes:

S "He has blasphemed! What further need have we of witnesses? Remember, you heard the blasphemy. What is your verdict?"

P "He deserves death!"

N Then they began to spit in his face and hit him. Others slapped him, saying:

P "Play the prophet for us, Messiah! Who struck you?"

N Peter was sitting in the courtyard when one of the serving girls came over to him and said,

S "You too were with Jesus the Galilean."

N He denied it in front of everyone:

S "I don't know what you are talking about!"

N When he went out to the gate another girl saw him and said to those nearby,

S "This man was with Jesus the Nazorean."

N Again he denied it with an oath:

S "I don't know the man!"

N A little while later some bystanders came over to Peter and said,

P "You are certainly one of them! Even your accent gives you away!"

N At that he began cursing and swore,

S "I don't even know the man!"

N Just then a rooster began to crow and Peter remembered the prediction Jesus had made: "Before the rooster crows you will three times disown me." He went out and began to weep bitterly.

At daybreak all the chief priests and the elders of the people took formal action against Jesus to put him to death. They bound him and led him away to be handed over to the procurator Pilate. Then Judas, who had handed him over, seeing that Jesus had been condemned, began to regret his action deeply. He took the thirty pieces of silver back to the chief priests and elders and said,

S "I did wrong to deliver up an innocent man!"

P "What is that to us? It is your affair!"

N So Judas flung the money into the temple and left. He went off and hanged himself. The chief priests picked up the silver, observing,

P "It is not right to deposit this in the temple treasury since it is blood money."

N After consultation, they used it to buy the potter's field as a cemetery for foreigners. That is why that field, even today, is called Blood Field. On that occasion, what was said through Jeremiah the prophet was fulfilled: "They took the thirty pieces of silver, the value of a man with a price on his head, a price set by the Israelites, and they paid it out for the potter's field just as the Lord had commanded me." [Jesus was arraigned before the procurator, (Pontius Pilate,) who questioned him:

S "Are you the king of the Jews?"

+ "As you say."

N Yet when he was accused by the chief priests and elders, he had made no reply. Then Pilate said to him,

S "Surely you hear how many charges they bring against you?"

N He did not answer him on a single count, much to the procurator's surprise. Now on the occasion of a festival the procurator was accustomed to release one prisoner, whom the crowd would designate. They had at the time a notorious prisoner named Barabbas. Since they were already assembled, Pilate said to them,

S "Which one do you wish me to release for you, Barabbas or Jesus the so-called Messiah?"

N He knew, of course, that it was out of jealousy that they had handed him over. While he was still presiding on the bench, his wife sent him a message:

S "Do not interfere in the case of that holy man. I had a dream about him today which has greatly upset me."

N Meanwhile, the chief priests and elders convinced the crowds that they should ask for Barabbas and have Jesus put to death. So when the procurator asked them,

S "Which one do you wish me to release for you?"

P "Barabbas,"

N Pilate said to them,

S "Then what am I to do with Jesus, the so-called Messiah?"

P "Crucify him!"

S "Why? What crime has he committed?"

N But they only shouted the louder,

P "Crucify him!"

N Pilate finally realized that he was making no impression and that a riot was breaking out instead. He called for water and washed his hands in front of the crowd, declaring as he did so,

S "I am innocent of the blood of this just man. The responsibility is yours."

N The whole people said in reply,

P "Let his blood be on us and on our children."

N At that, he released Barabbas to them. Jesus, however, he first had scourged; then he handed him over to be crucified. The procurator's soldiers took Jesus inside the praetorium and collected the whole cohort around him. They stripped off his clothes and wrapped him in a scarlet military cloak. Weaving a crown out of thorns they fixed it on his head, and stuck a reed in his right hand. Then they began to mock him by dropping to their knees before him, saying,

P "All hail, king of the Jews!"

N They also spat at him. Afterward they took hold of the reed and kept striking him on the head. Finally, when they had finished making a fool of him, they stripped him of the cloak, dressed him in his own clothes, and led him off to crucifixion. On their way out they met a Cyrenian named Simon. This man they pressed into service to carry the cross. Upon arriving at a site called Golgotha (a name which means Skull Place), they gave him a drink of wine flavored with gall, which he tasted but refused to drink. When they had crucified him, they divided his clothes among them by casting lots; then they sat down there and kept watch over him. Above his head they put the charge against him in writing: "This is Jesus, King of the Jews." Two insurgents were crucified along with him, one at his right and one at his left. People going by kept insulting him, tossing their heads and saying:

P "So you are the one who was going to destroy the temple and rebuild it in three days! Save yourself, why don't you? Come down off that cross if you are God's Son!"

N The chief priests, the scribes, and the elders also joined in the jeering:

P "He saved others but he cannot save himself! So he is the king of Israel! Let's see him come down from that cross, and then we will believe in him. He relied on God; let God rescue him now if he wants to. After all, he claimed, 'I am God's Son.' "

N The insurgents who had been crucified with him kept taunting him in the same way. From noon onward, there was darkness over whole land until midafternoon. Then toward midafternoon Jesus cried out in a loud tone,

+ "Eli, Eli, lema sabachthani?"

N That is,

+ "My God, my God, why have you forsaken me?"

N This made some of the bystanders who heard it remark,

P "He is invoking Elijah!"

N Immediately one of them ran off and got a sponge. He soaked it in cheap wine, and sticking it on a reed, tried to make him drink. Meanwhile the rest said,

P "Leave him alone. Let's see whether Elijah comes to his rescue."

N Once again Jesus cried out in a loud voice, and then gave up his spirit. Suddenly the curtain of the sanctuary was torn in two from top to bottom. The earth quaked, boulders split, tombs opened. Many bodies of saints who had fallen asleep were raised. After Jesus' resurrection they came forth from their tombs and entered the holy city and appeared to many. The centurion and his men who were keeping watch over Jesus were terror-stricken at seeing the earthquake and all that was happening, and said,

P "Clearly this was the Son of God!"]

N Many women were present looking on from a distance. They had followed Jesus from Galilee to attend to his needs. Among them were Mary Magdalene, and Mary the mother of James and Joseph, and the mother of Zebedee's sons. When evening fell, a wealthy man from Arimathea arrived, Joseph by name. He was another of Jesus' disciples, and had gone to request the body of Jesus. Thereupon Pilate issued an order for its release. Taking the body, Joseph wrapped it in fresh linen and laid it in his own new tomb which had been hewn from a formation of rock. Then he rolled a huge stone across the entrance of the tomb and went away. But Mary Magdalene and the other Mary remained sitting there, facing the tomb. The next day, the one following the Day of Preparation, the chief priests and the Pharisees called at Pilate's residence.

P "Sir, we have recalled that that impostor while he was still alive made the claim, 'After three days I will rise.' You should issue an order having the tomb kept under surveillance until the third day. Otherwise his disciples may go and steal him and tell the people, 'He has been raised from the dead!' This final imposture would be worse than the first."

S "You have a guard. Go and secure the tomb as best you can."

N So they went and kept it under surveillance of the guard, after fixing a seal to the stone.

GOSPEL/B

Mark 14, 1-15, 47 or 15, 1-39 / 38   808

The symbols of the following passion narrative represent:

N *narrator;*

+ *Christ;*

S speakers other than Christ;

P groups of speakers.

N The passion of our Lord Jesus Christ according to Mark.

For short form read only the part in brackets.

N The feasts of the Passover and Unleavened Bread were to be observed in two days' time, and therefore the chief priests and scribes began to look for a way to arrest Jesus by some trick and kill him. Yet they pointed out,

P "Not during the festival, or the people may riot."

N When Jesus was in Bethany reclining at table in the house of Simon the leper, a woman entered carrying an alabaster jar of perfume made from expensive aromatic nard. Breaking the jar, she began to pour the perfume on his head. Some were saying to themselves indignantly:

P "What is the point of this extravagant waste of perfume? It could have been sold for over three hundred silver pieces and the money given to the poor."

N They were infuriated at her. But Jesus said:

+ "Let her alone. Why do you criticize her? She has done me a kindness. The poor you will always have with you and you can be generous to them whenever you wish, but you will not always have me. She has done what she could. By perfuming my body she is anticipating its preparation for burial. I assure you, wherever the good news is proclaimed throughout the world, what she has done will be told in her memory."

N Then Judas Iscariot, one of the Twelve, went off to the chief priests to hand Jesus over to them. Hearing what he had to say, they were jubilant and promised to give him money. He for his part kept looking for an opportune way to hand him over. On the first day of Unleavened Bread, when it was customary to sacrifice the paschal lamb, his disciples said to him,

P "Where do you wish us to go to prepare the Passover supper for you?"

N He sent two of his disciples with these instructions:

+ "Go into the city and you will come upon a man carrying a water jar. Follow him. Whatever house he enters, say to the owner, 'The Teacher asks, Where is my guest room where I may eat the Passover with my disciples?' Then he will show you an upstairs room, spacious, furnished, and all in order. That is the place you are to get ready for us."

N The disciples went off. When they reached the city they found it just as he had told them, and they prepared the Passover supper. As it grew dark he arrived with the Twelve. They reclined at table, and in the course of the meal Jesus said,

+ "I give you my word, one of you is about to betray me, yes, one of you who is eating with me."

N They began to say to him sorrowfully, one by one,

S "Surely not I!"

+ "It is one of the Twelve—a man who dips into the dish with me. The Son of Man is going the way the Scripture tells of him. Still, accursed be that man by whom the Son of Man is betrayed. It were better for him had he never been born."

N During the meal he took bread, blessed and broke it, and gave it to them.

+ "Take this, this is my body."

N He likewise took a cup, gave thanks and passed it to them, and they all drank from it.

+ "This is my blood, the blood of the covenant, to be poured out on behalf of many. I solemnly assure you, I will never again drink of the fruit of the vine until the day when I drink it in the reign of God."

N After singing songs of praise, they walked out to the Mount of Olives. Jesus then said to them:

+ "Your faith in me shall be shaken, for Scripture has it,

'I will strike the shepherd
and the sheep will be dispersed.'

But after I am raised up, I will go to Galilee ahead of you."

N Peter said to him,

S "Even though all are shaken in faith, it will not be that way with me."

+ "I give you my assurance, this very night before the cock crows twice, you will deny me three times."

N But Peter kept reasserting vehemently,

S "Even if I have to die with you, I will not deny you."

N They all said the same. They went then to a place named Gethsemani.

+ "Sit down here while I pray."

N At the same time he took along with him Peter, James, and John. Then he began to be filled with fear and distress. He said to them,

+ "My heart is filled with sorrow to the point of death. Remain here and stay awake."

N He advanced a little and fell to the ground, praying that if it were possible this hour might pass him by. He kept saying,

+ "Abba (O Father), you have the power to do all things. Take this cup away from me. But let it be as you would have it, not as I."

N When he returned he found them asleep. He said to Peter,

+ "Asleep, Simon? You could not stay awake for even an hour? Be on guard and pray that you may not be put to the test. The spirit is willing but nature is weak."

N Going back again he began to pray in the same words. Once again he found them asleep on his return. They could not keep their eyes open, nor did they know what to say to him. He returned a third time and said to them,

+ "Still sleeping? Still taking your ease? It will have to do. The hour is on us. You will see that the Son of Man is to be handed over to the clutches of evil men. Rouse yourselves and come along. See! My betrayer is near."

N Even while he was still speaking, Judas, one of the Twelve, made his appearance accompanied by a crowd with swords and clubs; these people had been sent by the chief priests, the scribes, and the elders. The betrayer had arranged a signal for them, saying,

S "The man I shall embrace is the one; arrest him and lead him away, taking every precaution."

N He then went directly over to him and said, embracing him,

S "Rabbi!"

N At this, they laid hands on him and arrested him. One of the bystanders drew his sword and struck the high priest's slave, cutting off his ear. Addressing himself to them, Jesus said,

+ "You have come out to arrest me armed with swords and clubs as if against a brigand. I was within your reach daily, teaching in the temple precincts, yet you never arrested me. But now, so that the Scriptures may be fulfilled..."

N With that, all deserted him and fled. There was a young man following him who was covered by nothing but a linen cloth. As they seized him he left the cloth behind and ran off naked. Then they led Jesus off to the high priest, and all the chief priests, the el-

ders, and the scribes came together. Peter followed him at a distance right into the high priest's courtyard, where he found a seat with the temple guard and began to warm himself at the fire. The chief priests with the whole Sanhedrin were busy soliciting testimony against Jesus that would lead to his death, but they could not find any. Many spoke against him falsely under oath but their testimony did not agree. Some, for instance, on taking the stand, testified falsely by alleging,

P "We heard him declare, 'I will destroy this temple made by human hands.' and 'In three days I will construct another not made by human hands.'

N Even so, their testimony did not agree. The high priest rose to his feet before the court and began to interrogate Jesus:

S "Have you no answer to what these men testify against you?"

N But Jesus remained silent; he made no reply. Once again the high priest interrogated him:

S "Are you the Messiah, the Son of the Blessed One?"

+ "I am; and you will see the Son of Man seated at the right hand of the Power and coming with the clouds of heaven."

N At that the high priest tore his robes and said:

S "What further need do we have of witnesses? You have heard the blasphemy. What is your verdict?"

N They all concurred in the verdict "guilty," with its sentence of death. Some of them began to spit on him. They blindfolded him and hit him while the officers manhandled him, saying,

P "Play the prophet!"

N While Peter was down in the courtyard, one of the servant girls of the high priest came along. When she noticed Peter warming himself, she looked more closely at him and said,

S "You too were with Jesus of Nazareth."

N But he denied it:

S "I don't know what you are talking about! What are you getting at?"

N Then he went out into the gateway. At that moment a cock crowed. The servant girl, keeping an eye on him, started again to tell the bystanders,

S "This man is one of them."

N Once again he denied it. A little later

the bystanders said to Peter once more,

P "You are certainly one of them! You're a Galilean, are you not?"

N He began to curse, and to swear,

S "I do not even know the man you are talking about!"

N Just then a second cockcrow was heard and Peter recalled the prediction Jesus had made to him, "Before the cock crows twice you will disown me three times." He broke down and began to cry. [As soon as it was daybreak the chief priests, with the elders and scribes (that is, the whole Sanhedrin), reached a decision. They bound Jesus, led him away, and handed him over to Pilate. Pilate interrogated him:

S "Are you the king of the Jews?"

+ "You are the one who is saying it."

N The chief priests, meanwhile, brought many accusations against him. Pilate interrogated him again:

S "Surely you have some answer? See how many accusations they are leveling against you."

N But greatly to Pilate's surprise, Jesus made no further response. Now on the occasion of a festival he would release for them one prisoner–any man they asked for. There was a prisoner named Barabbas jailed along with rebels who had committed murder in the uprising. When the crowd came up to press their demand that he honor the custom, Pilate rejoined,

S "Do you want me to release the king of the Jews for you?"

N He was aware, of course, that it was out of jealousy that the chief priests had handed him over. Meanwhile, the chief priests incited the crowd to have him release Barabbas instead. Pilate again asked them,

S "What am I to do with the man you call the king of the Jews?"

P "Crucify him!"

N Pilate protested,

S "Why? What crime has he committed?

N They only shouted the louder,

P "Crucify him!"

N So Pilate, who wished to satisfy the crowd, released Barabbas to them, and after he had had Jesus scourged, he handed him over to be crucified. The soldiers now led Jesus away into the hall known as the praetorium; at the same time they assembled the whole cohort. They dressed him in royal pur-

ple, then wove a crown of thorns and put it on him, and began to salute him,

P "All hail!" King of the Jews!"

N Continually striking Jesus on the head with a reed and spitting at him, they genuflected before him and pretended to pay him homage. When they had finished mocking him, they stripped him of the purple, dressed him in his own clothes, and led him out to crucify him. A man named Simon of Cyrene, the father of Alexander and Rufus, was coming in from the fields, and they pressed him into service to carry the cross. When they brought Jesus to the site of Golgotha (which means "Skull Place"), they tried to give him wine drugged with myrrh, but he would not take it. Then they crucified him and divided up his garments by rolling dice for them to see what each should take. It was about nine in the morning when they crucified him. The inscription proclaiming his offense read, "The King of the Jews." With him they crucified two insurgents, one at his right and one at his left. People going by kept insulting him, tossing their heads and saying,

P "Ha, ha! So you were going to destroy the temple and rebuild it in three days! Save yourself now by coming down from the cross!"

N The chief priests and the scribes also joined in and jeered:

P "He saved others but he cannot save himself! Let the 'Messiah,' the 'king of Israel,' come down from that cross here and now, so that we can see it and believe in him!"

N The men who had been crucified with him likewise kept taunting him. When noon came, darkness fell on the whole countryside and lasted until midafternoon. At that time Jesus cried in a loud voice,

+ "Eloi, Eloi, lama sabachthani?"

N Which means,

+ "My God, my God, why have you forsaken me?"

N A few of the bystanders who heard it remarked,

P "Listen! He is calling on Elijah!"

N Someone ran off and, soaking a sponge in sour wine, stuck it on a reed to try to make him drink. The man said,

S "Now let's see whether Elijah comes to take him down."

N Then Jesus, uttering a loud cry,

breathed his last. At that moment the curtain in the sanctuary was torn in two from top to bottom. The centurion who stood guard over him, on seeing the manner of his death, declared,

S "Clearly this man was the Son of God!"]

N There were also women looking on from a distance. Among them were Mary Magdalene, Mary the mother of James the younger of Joses, and Salome. These women had followed Jesus when he was in Galilee and attended to his needs. There were also many others who had come up with him to Jerusalem. As it grew dark (it was Preparation Day, that is the eve of the sabbath), Joseph of Arimathea arrived—a distinguished member of the Sanhedrin. He was another who looked forward to the reign of God. He was bold enough to seek an audience with Pilate, and urgently requested the body of Jesus. Pilate was surprised that Jesus should have died so soon. He summoned the centurion and inquired whether Jesus was already dead. Learning from him that he was dead, Pilate released the corpse to Joseph. Then, having bought a linen shroud, Joseph took him down, wrapped him in the linen, and laid him in a tomb which had been cut out of rock. Finally he rolled a stone across the entrance of the tomb. Meanwhile, Mary Magdalene and Mary the mother of Joses observed where he had been laid.

GOSPEL/C
Luke 22, 14-23, 56 or 23, 1-49 / 38   **809**

The symbols of the following passion narrative represent:

N narrator;

+ Christ;

S speakers other than Christ;

P groups of speakers.

N The Passion of our Lord Jesus Christ according to Luke.

For short form read only the part in brackets.

N When the hour arrived, Jesus took his place at table, and the apostles with him. He said to them:

+ "I have greatly desired to eat this Passover with you before I suffer. I tell you, I will not eat again until it is fulfilled in the kingdom of God."

N Then taking a cup he offered a blessing in thanks and said:

+ "Take this and divide it among you; I tell you, from now on I will not drink of the fruit of the vine until the coming of the reign of God."

N Then taking bread and giving thanks, he broke it and gave it to them, saying:

+ "This is my body to be given for you. Do this as a remembrance of me."

N He did the same with the cup after eating, saying as he did so:

+ "This cup is the new covenant in my blood, which will be shed for you." "And yet the hand of my betrayer is with me at this table. The Son of Man is following out his appointed course, but woe to that man by whom he is betrayed."

N Then they began to dispute among themselves as to which of them would do such a deed.

A dispute arose among them about who would be regarded as the greatest.

+ "Earthly kings lord it over their people. Those who exercise authority over them are called their benefactors. Yet it cannot be that way with you. Let the greater among you be as the junior, the leader as the servant. Who, in fact, is the greater—he who reclines at table or he who serves the meal? Is it not the one who reclines at table? Yet I am in your midst as the one who serves you. You are the ones who have stood loyally by me in my temptations. I for my part assign to you the dominion my Father has assigned to me. In my kingdom, you will eat and drink at my table, and you will sit on thrones judging the twelve tribes of Israel.

"Simon, Simon! Remember that Satan has asked for you to sift you all like wheat. But I have prayed for you that your faith may never fail. You in turn must strengthen your brothers."

S "Lord, at your side I am prepared to face imprisonment and death itself."

+ "I tell you, Peter, the rooster will not crow today until you have three times denied that you know me."

N He asked them,

+ "When I sent you on mission without purse or traveling bag or sandals, were you in need of anything?"

P "Not a thing,"

+ "Now, however, the man who has a purse must carry it; the same with the traveling bag. And the man without a sword must sell his coat and buy one. It is written in Scripture,
'He was counted among the
    wicked,'
and this, I tell you, must come to be fulfilled in me. All that has to do with me approaches its climax."

P "Lord, here are two swords!"

+ "Enough."

N Then he went out and made his way, as was his custom, to the Mount of Olives; his disciples accompanied him. On reaching the place he said to them,

+ "Pray that you may not be put to the test."

N He withdrew from them about a stone's throw, then went down on his knees and prayed in these words:

+ "Father, if it is your will, take this cup from me; yet not my will but yours be done."

N An angel then appeared to him from heaven to strengthen him. In his anguish he prayed with all the greater intensity, and his sweat became like drops of blood falling to the ground. Then he rose from prayer and came to his disciples, only to find them asleep, exhausted with grief.

+ "Why are you sleeping? Wake up, and pray that you may not be subjected to the trial."

N While he was still speaking a crowd came, led by the man named Judas, one of the Twelve. He approached Jesus to embrace him. Jesus said to him,

+ "Judas, would you betray the Son of Man with a kiss?"

N When the companions of Jesus saw what was going to happen, they said,

P "Lord, shall we use the sword?"

N One of them went so far as to strike the high priest's servant and cut off his right ear. Jesus said in answer to their question,

+ "Enough!"

N Then he touched the ear and healed the man.
But to those who had come out against him–the chief priests, the chiefs of the temple guard, and the ancients–Jesus said,

+ "Am I a criminal that you come out after me armed with swords and clubs? When I was with you day after day in the temple you never raised a hand against me. But this is your hour–the triumph of darkness!"

N They led him away under arrest and brought him to the house of the high priest, while Peter followed at a distance. Later they lighted a fire in the middle of the courtyard and were sitting beside it, and Peter sat among them. A servant girl saw him sitting in the light of the fire. She gazed at him intently, then said,

S "This man was with him."

N He denied the fact, saying,

S "Woman, I do not know him."

N A little while later someone else saw him and said,

S "You are one of them too."

S "No, sir, not I!"

N About an hour after that another spoke more insistently:

S "This man was certainly with him, for he is a Galilean."

S "My friend, I do not know what you are talking about."

N At the very moment he was saying this, a rooster crowed. The Lord turned around and looked at Peter, and Peter remembered the word that the Lord had spoken to him, "Before the rooster crows today you will deny me three times." He went out and wept bitterly. Meanwhile the men guarding Jesus amused themselves at his expense. They blindfolded him first, slapped him, and then taunted him:

P "Play the prophet; which one struck you?"

N And they directed many other insulting words at him. At daybreak the council, which was made up of the elders of the people, the chief priests, and the scribes, assembled again. Once they had brought him before their council, they said,

P "Tell us, are you the Messiah?"

+ "If I tell you, you will not believe me, and if I question you, you will not answer. This much only will I say: 'From now on, the Son of Man will have his seat at the right hand of the Power of God.' "

P "So you are the Son of God?"

+ "It is you who say I am."

P "What need have we of witnesses? We have heard it from his own mouth."

N [Then the entire assembly rose up and led him (Jesus) before Pilate. They started his prosecution by saying,

P "We found this man subverting our nation, opposing the payment of taxes to Caesar, and calling himself the Messiah, a king."

N Pilate asked him,

S "Are you the king of the Jews?"

+ "That is your term."

N Pilate reported to the chief priests and the crowds,

S "I do not find a case against this man."

N But they insisted,

P "He stirs up the people by his teaching throughout the whole of Judea, from Galilee, where he began, to this very place."

N On hearing this Pilate asked if the man was a Galilean; and when he learned that he was under Herod's jurisdiction, he sent him to Herod, who also happened to be in Jerusalem at the time. Herod was extremely pleased to see Jesus. From the reports about him he had wanted for a long time to see him, and he was hoping to see him work some miracle. He questioned Jesus at considerable length, but Jesus made no answer. The chief priests and scribes were at hand to accuse him vehemently. Herod and his guards then treated him with contempt and insult, after which they put a magnificent robe on him and sent him back to Pilate. Herod and Pilate, who had previously been set against each other, became friends from that day. Pilate then called together the chief priests, the ruling class, and the people, and said to them:

S "You have brought this man before me as one who subverts the people. I have examined him in your presence and have no charge against him arising from your allegations. Neither has

Herod, who therefore has sent him back to us; obviously this man has done nothing to deserve death. Therefore I mean to release him, once I have taught him a lesson."

N The whole crowd cried out,

P "Away with this man; release Barabbas for us!"

N This Barabbas had been thrown in prison for causing an uprising in the city, and for murder. Pilate addressed them again, for he wanted Jesus to be the one he released. But they shouted back,

P "Crucify him, crucify him!"

N He said to them for the third time,

S "What wrong is this man guilty of? I have not discovered anything about him deserving the death penalty. I will therefore chastise him and release him."

N But they demanded with loud cries that he be crucified, and their shouts increased in violence. Pilate then decreed that what they demanded should be done. He released the one they asked for, who had been thrown in prison for insurrection and murder, and delivered Jesus up to their wishes. As they led him away, they laid hold of one Simon the Cyrenean who was coming in from the fields. They put a crossbeam on Simon's shoulder for him to carry along behind Jesus. A great crowd of people followed him, including women who beat their breasts and lamented over him. Jesus turned to them and said:

+ "Daughters of Jerusalem, do not weep for me. Weep for yourselves and for your children. The days are coming when they will say, 'Happy are the sterile, the wombs that never bore and the breasts that never nursed,' Then they will begin saying to the mountains, 'Fall on us,' and to the hills, 'Cover us.' If they do these things in the green wood, what will happen in the dry?"

N Two others who were criminals were led along with him to be crucified. When they came to Skull Place, as it was called, they crucified him there and the criminals as well, one on his right and the other on his left. Jesus said,

+ ["Father, forgive them; they do not know what they are doing."]

N They divided his garments, rolling dice for them. The people stood there watching, and the leaders kept jeering at him, saying,

P "He saved others; let him save himself if he is the Messiah of God, the chosen one."

N The soldiers also made fun of him, coming forward to offer him their sour wine and saying,

S "If you are the king of the Jews, save yourself."

N There was an inscription over his head: "THIS IS THE KING OF THE JEWS."
One of the criminals hanging in crucifixion blasphemed him,

S "Aren't you the Messiah? Then save yourself and us.

N But the other rebuked him:

S "Have you no fear of God, seeing you are under the same sentence? We deserve it, after all. We are only paying the price for what we've done, but this man has done nothing wrong. Jesus, remember me when you enter upon your reign."

+ "I assure you: this day you will be with me in paradise."

N It was now around midday, and darkness came over the whole land until midafternoon with an eclipse of the sun. The curtain in the sanctuary was torn in two. Jesus uttered a loud cry and said,

+ "Father, into your hands I commend my spirit."

N After he said this, he expired. The centurion, upon seeing what had happened, gave glory to God by saying,

S "Surely this was an innocent man."

N After the crowd assembled for this spectacle witnessed what had happened, they returned beating their breasts. All his friends and the women who had accompanied him from Galilee were standing at a distance watching everything.] There was a man named Joseph, an upright and holy member of the Sanhedrin, who had not been associated with their plan or their action. He was from Arimathea, a Jewish town, and he looked expectantly for the reign of God. This man approached Pilate with a request for Jesus' body. He took it down, wrapped it in fine linen, and laid it in a tomb hewn out of the rock, in which no one had yet been buried. That was the day of Preparation, and the sabbath was about to begin. The women who had come with him from Galilee followed along behind. They saw the tomb and how his body was buried. Then they went back home to prepare spices and perfumes. They observed the sabbath as a day of rest, in accordance with the law.

Easter Triduum

"The Easter Triduum of the passion and resurrection of Christ is...the culmination   810
of the entire liturgical year. What Sunday is to the week, the solemnity of Easter is
to the liturgical year." (General Norms for the Liturgical Year, #18)

Lent ends quietly on Thursday afternoon. The church enters the Triduum ("three
days"). On Thursday night the church begins a time of prayer and fasting, a time
of keeping watch, that lasts into the great Vigil between Saturday and Sunday. The
church emphasizes that the fasting of Good Friday and, if possible, of Holy Saturday
are integral to the keeping of these days and the preparation for the sacraments of
initiation celebrated at the Vigil. On Thursday night and on Friday afternoon or
evening the church gathers to pray and to remember the many facets of the single
mystery.

811 HOLY THURSDAY: EVENING MASS OF THE LORD'S SUPPER

On Thursday night Lent has ended and the church, at this Mass of the Lord's Supper, enters into the Easter Triduum. From the very first moment the all-embracing experience of these three days is proclaimed: "We should glory in the cross of our Lord Jesus Christ. For he is our salvation, our life, and our resurrection. Through him we are saved and made free." This is the whole of the great Triduum. On Thursday night, the liturgy draws us toward this through the scriptures, through the mandatum or washing of the feet which is the direct expression of our service to one another and the world, through the eucharistic banquet itself.

LITURGY OF THE WORD

READING I *Exodus 12, 1-8, 11-14 / 40*

RESPONSORIAL PSALM *Psalm (115)116B, 12-13.15-16.17-18 / 40*

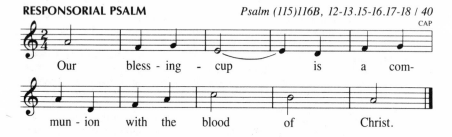

Our bless - ing - cup is a com- mun - ion with the blood of Christ.

How can I repay the Lord
for his goodness to me?
The cup of salvation I will raise;
I will call on the Lord's name. ℟.

A thanksgiving sacrifice I make:
I will call on the Lord's name.
My vows to the Lord I will fulfill
before all his people. ℟.

O precious in the eyes of the Lord
is the death of his faithful.
Your servant, Lord, your servant am I;
you have loosened my bonds. ℟.

READING II *1 Corinthians 11, 23-26 / 40*

GOSPEL *John 13, 1-15 / 40*

WASHING OF FEET

The homily is followed by the washing of feet, the mandatum (from the Latin word for "command": "A new commandment I give to you..."). This is a simple gesture of humble service: the presider and others wash the feet of various members of the assembly. Such a gesture, with the song which accompanies it, speaks directly of the way of life Christians seek.

I give you a new commandment
Taizé Community, 1979
Jacques Berthier, b.1923

Man - da - tum no - vum do   vo - bis,

di - cit Do - mi - nus,   di - cit Do - mi - nus.

Other appropriate songs are: Ubi Caritas, no. 598 or 604, and Jesus Took a Towel, no. 432.

The Mass continues with the general intercessions.

813 TRANSFER OF THE HOLY EUCHARIST

When the communion rite is concluded, the eucharistic bread that remains is solemnly carried from the altar. The following hymn accompanies the procession.

Thomas Aquinas, 1227-1274
Tr. by James Quinn, SJ, b.1919

Mode III
Acc. by Gerard Farrell, OSB, b.1919

1. Hail our Sav - ior's glo - rious Bod - y, Which his
2. To the Vir - gin, for our heal - ing, His own
3. On that pas - chal eve - ning see him With the
4. By his word the Word al - might - y Makes of
1. *Pan - ge lín - gua glo - ri - ó - si, Cor - po-*
2. *No - bis da - tus, no - bis na - tus Ex in-*
3. *In su - pré - mae no - cte coe - nae, Re - cum-*
4. *Ver - bum ca - ro, pa - nem ve - rum Ver - bo*

Vir - gin Moth - er bore; Hail the Blood which,
Son the Fa - ther sends; From the Fa - ther's
cho - sen twelve re - cline, To the old law
bread his flesh in - deed; Wine be - comes his
ris my - sté - ri - um San - gui - nís - que
tá - cta Vír - gi - ne, Et in mún - do
bens cum frá - tri - bus, Ob - ser - vá - ta
car - nem éf - fi - cit: Fit - que san - guis

shed for sin - ners, Did a bro - ken world re - store;
love pro - ceed - ing Sow - er, seed and word de - scends;
still o - be - dient In its feast of love di - vine;
ver - y life-blood; Faith God's liv - ing Word must heed!
pre - ti - ó - si, Quem in mún - di pré - ti - um
con - ver - sá - tus, Spar - so vér - bi sé - mi - ne,
le - ge ple - ne Ci - bis in le - gá - li - bus,
Chri - sti me - rum, Et si sen - sus dé - fi - cit,

Hail the sac - ra - ment most ho - ly,
Won - drous life of Word in - car - nate
Love di - vine, the new law giv - ing,
Faith a - lone may safe - ly guide us
Fru - ctus ven - tris ge - ne - ró - si
Su - i mo - ras in - co - lá - tus
Ci - bum tur - bae du - o - dé - nae
Ad fir - mán - dum cor sin - cé - rum

Flesh	and	Blood	of	Christ	a - dore!		
With	his	great - est		won -	der ends.		
Gives	him - self	as		Bread	and Wine.		
Where	the	sens - es	can -	not lead!	A - men.
Rex	*ef - fú - dit*		*gén -*	*ti - um.*		
Mi - ro	*clau - sit*		*ór -*	*di - ne.*		
Se	*dat*	*su - is*	*má -*	*ni - bus.*		
So - la	*fi - des*	*súf -*	*fi - cit.*	*A - men.*

5. Come, adore this wondrous presence;
    Bow to Christ, the source of grace!
Here is kept the ancient promise
    Of God's earthly dwelling place!
Sight is blind before God's glory,
    Faith alone may see his face!

6. Glory be to God the Father,
    Praise to his coequal Son,
Adoration to the Spirit,
    Bond of love, in Godhead one!
Blest be God by all creation
    Joyously while ages run! Amen.

5. *Tantum ergo Sacraméntum*
    Venerémur cérnui:
Et antíquum documéntum
    Novo cedat rítui;
Praestet fides suppleméntum
    Sénsuum deféctui.

6. *Genitóri, Genitóque*
    Laus et jubilátio,
Salus, honor, virtus quoque
    Sit et benedíctio:
Procedénti ab utróque
    Compar sit laudátio. Amen.

The liturgy has no concluding rite, no dismissal. Rather, the church continues to watch and pray throughout the Triduum.

814 GOOD FRIDAY

In Good Friday's liturgy of the word and veneration of the cross there is great solemnity: a pondering of the "mystery of our faith," the passion, death and resurrection of our Lord Jesus Christ. Fasting and praying during these days, the catechumens and the baptized assemble on Good Friday in the afternoon or evening for a time of prayer together. This begins a time of silence.

LITURGY OF THE WORD

READING I   *Isaiah 52, 13-53.12 / 41*

RESPONSORIAL PSALM   *Psalm (30)31, 2.6.12-13.15-16.17.25 / 41*

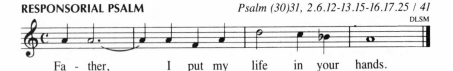

Fa - ther,   I   put my   life   in   your   hands.

In you, O Lord, I take refuge.
Let me never be put to shame.
In your justice, set me free,
Into your hands I commend my spirit.
It is you who will redeem me,
    Lord. ℟.

But as for me, I trust in you, Lord;
I say: "You are my God.
My life is in your hands, deliver me
from the hands of those who hate
    me. ℟.

In the face of all my foes
I am a reproach,
an object of scorn to my neighbors
and of fear to my friends. ℟.

Let your face shine on your servant.
Save me in your love."
Be strong, let your heart take courage,
all who hope in the Lord. ℟.

Those who see me in the street
run far away from me.
I am like a dead man, forgotten,
like a thing thrown away. ℟.

READING II   *Hebrews 4, 14-16; 5, 7-9 / 41*

GOSPEL   *John 18, 1-19, 42 / 41*

The symbols of the following passion narrative represent:

N narrator;

+ Christ;

S speakers other than Christ;

P groups of speakers.

N The Passion of our Lord Jesus Christ according to John.

For short form read only the part in brackets.

N Jesus went out with his disciples across the Kidron valley. There was a garden there, and he and his disciples entered it. The place was known to Judas as well (the one who was to hand him over) because Jesus had often met there with his disciples. Judas took the cohort as well as police supplied by the chief priests and the Pharisees, and came there with lanterns, torches and weapons. Jesus, aware of all that would happen to him, stepped forward and said to them,

+ "Who is it you want?"

P "Jesus the Nazorean."

+ "I am he."

N (Now Judas, the one who was to hand him over, was right there with them.) As Jesus said to them, "I am he, " they retreated slightly and fell to the ground. Jesus put the question to them again,

+ "Who is it you want?"

P "Jesus the Nazorean."

+ "I have told you, I am he. If I am the one you want, let these men go."

N (This was to fulfill what he had said, "I have not lost one of those you gave me.") Then Simon Peter, who had a sword, drew it and struck the slave of the high priest, severing his right ear. (The slave's name was Malchus.) At that Jesus said to Peter,

+ "Put your sword back in its sheath. Am I not to drink the cup the Father has given me?"

N Then the soldiers of the cohort, their tribune, and the Jewish police arrested Jesus and bound him. They led him first to Annas, the father-in-law of Caiaphas who was high priest that year. (It was Caiaphas who had proposed to the Jews the advantage of having one man die for the people.) Simon Peter, in company with another disciple, kept following Jesus closely. This disciple, who was known to the high priest, stayed with Jesus as far as the high priest's courtyard, while Peter was left standing at the gate. The disciple known to the high priest came out and spoke to the woman at the gate, and then brought Peter in. This servant girl who kept the gate said to Peter,

S "Aren't you one of this man's followers?"

S "Not I."

N Now the night was cold, and the servants and the guards who were standing around had made a charcoal fire to warm themselves by. Peter joined them and stood there warming himself.

N The high priest questioned Jesus, first about his disciples, then about his teaching. Jesus answered by saying:

+ "I have spoken publicly to any who would listen.
I always taught in a synagogue or in the temple area where all the Jews come together.
There was nothing secret about anything I said.
Why do you question me? Question those who heard me when I spoke. It should be obvious they will know what I said."

N At this reply, one of the guards who was standing nearby gave Jesus a sharp blow on the face.

S "Is that any way to answer the high priest?"

+ "If I said anything wrong produce the evidence, but if I spoke the truth why hit me?"

N Annas next sent him, bound, to the high priest Caiaphas. All through this, Simon Peter had been standing there warming himself. They said to him,

P "Are you not a disciple of his?"

S "I am not!"

P "But did I not see you with him in the garden?"

N One of the high priest's slaves insisted—as it happened, a relative of the man whose ear Peter had severed. Peter denied it again. At that moment a cock began to crow.
At daybreak they brought Jesus from Caiaphas to the praetorium. They did not enter the praetorium themselves, for they had to avoid ritual impurity if they were to eat the Passover supper. Pilate came out to them.

S "What accusation do you bring against this man?"

P "If he were not a criminal, we would certainly not have handed him over to you."

S "Why do you not take him and pass judgment on him according to your law?"

P "We may not put anyone to death."

N (This was to fulfill what Jesus had said, indicating the sort of death he would die.) Pilate went back into the praetorium and summoned Jesus.

S "Are you the King of the Jews?"

+ "Are you saying this on your own, or have others been telling you about me?"

S "I am no Jew! It is your own people and the chief priests who have handed you over to me. What have you done?"

+ "My kingdom does not belong to this world.
If my kingdom were of this world, my subjects would be fighting to save me from being handed over to the Jews.
As it is, my kingdom is not here."

S "So, then, you are a king?"

+ "It is you who say I am a king.
The reason I was born,
the reason why I came into the world,
is to testify to the truth.
Anyone committed to the truth hears my voice."

S "Truth! What does that mean?"

N After this remark, Pilate went out again to the Jews and told them:

S "Speaking for myself, I find no case against this man. Recall your custom whereby I release to you someone at Passover time. Do you want me to release to you the king of the Jews?"

P "We want Barabbas, not this one!"

N (Barabbas was an insurrectionist.) Pilate's next move was to take Jesus and have him scourged. The soldiers then wove a crown of thorns and fixed it on his head, throwing around his shoulders a cloak of royal purple. Repeatedly they came up to him and said,

P "All hail, King of the Jews!"

N slapping his face as they did so. Pilate went out a second time and said to the crowd:

S "Observe what I do. I am going to bring him out to you to make you realize that I find no case against him."

N When Jesus came out wearing the crown of thorns and the purple cloak, Pilate said to them,

S "Look at the man!"

N As soon as the chief priests and the temple police saw him they shouted,

P "Crucify him! Crucify him!"

S "Take him and crucify him yourselves; I find no case against him."

P "We have our law, and according to that law he must die because he made himself God's Son."

N When Pilate heard this kind of talk, he was more afraid than ever. Going back into the praetorium, he said to Jesus,

S "Where do you come from?"

N Jesus would not give him any answer.

S "Do you refuse to speak to me? Do you not know that I have the power to release you and the power to crucify you?"

+ "You would have no power over me whatever
unless it were given to you from above.
That is why he who handed me over to you
is guilty of the greater sin."

N After this, Pilate was eager to release him, but the Jews shouted,

P "If you free this man, you are no 'Friend of Caesar.' Anyone who makes himself a king becomes Caesar's rival."

N Pilate heard what they were saying, then brought Jesus outside and took a seat on a judge's bench at the place called the Stone Pavement–Gabbatha in Hebrew. (It was the Preparation Day for Passover, and the hour was about noon.) He said to the Jews,

S "Look at your king!"

P "Away with him! Away with him! Crucify him!"

S "What! Shall I crucify your king?"

P "We have no king but Caesar."

N In the end, Pilate handed Jesus over to be crucified. Jesus was led away, and carrying the cross by himself, went out to what is called the Place of the Skull (in Hebrew, Golgotha). There they crucified him, and two others with him: one on either side, Jesus in the middle. Pilate had an inscription placed on the cross which read,

JESUS THE NAZOREAN
THE KING OF THE JEWS

This inscription, in Hebrew, Latin and Greek, was read by many of the Jews, since the place where Jesus was crucified was near the city. The chief priests of the Jews tried to tell Pilate,

P "You should not have written, 'The King of the Jews.' Write instead, 'This man claimed to be the king of the Jews.' "

S "What I have written, I have written."

N After the soldiers had crucified Jesus they took his garments and divided them four ways, one for each soldier. There was also his tunic, but this tunic was woven in one piece from top to bottom and had no seam. They said to each other,

P "We shouldn't tear it. Let's throw dice to see who gets it."

N (The purpose of this was to have the Scripture fulfilled:

"They divided my garments among them;

for my clothing they cast lots.")

And this was what the soldiers did.

Near the cross of Jesus there stood his mother, his mother's sister, Mary the wife of Clopas, and Mary Magdalene. Seeing his mother there with the disciple whom he loved, Jesus said to his mother,

+ "Woman, this is your son."

N In turn he said to the disciple,

+ "There is your mother."

N From that hour onward, the disciple took her into his care. After that, Jesus, realizing that everything was now finished, to bring the Scripture to fulfillment said,

+ "I am thirsty."

N There was a jar there, full of common wine. They stuck a sponge soaked in this wine on some hyssop and raised it to his lips. When Jesus took the wine, he said,

+ "Now it is finished."

N Then he bowed his head, and delivered over his spirit.

Since it was the Preparation Day, the Jews did not want to have the bodies left on the cross during the sabbath, for that sabbath was a solemn feast day. They asked Pilate that the legs be broken and the bodies be taken away. Accordingly, the soldiers came and broke the legs of the men crucified with Jesus, first of one, then of the other. When they came to Jesus and saw that he was already dead, they did not break his legs. One of the soldiers ran a lance into his side, and immediately blood and water flowed out. (This testimony has been given by an eyewitness, and his testimony is true. He tells what he knows is true, so that you may believe.) These events took place for the fulfillment of Scripture:

"Break none of his bones."

There is still another Scripture passage which says:

"They shall look on him whom they have pierced."

Afterward, Joseph of Arimathea, a disciple of Jesus (although a secret one for fear of the Jews), asked Pilate's permission to remove Jesus' body. Pilate granted it, so they came and took the body away. Nicodemus (the man who had first come to Jesus at night) likewise came, bringing a mixture of myrrh and aloes which weighed about a hundred pounds. They took Jesus' body, and in accordance with Jewish burial custom bound it up in wrappings of cloth with perfumed oils. In the place where he had been crucified there was a garden, and in the garden a new tomb in which no one had ever been laid. Because of the Jewish Preparation Day they laid Jesus there, for the tomb was close at hand.

GENERAL INTERCESSIONS

As at Sunday liturgy, the word service concludes with prayers of intercession. Today these prayers take a more solemn form as the church lifts up to God its own needs and those of the world.

VENERATION OF THE CROSS

815

An ancient liturgical text reads: "See here the true and most revered Tree. Hasten to kiss it and to cry out with faith: You are our help, most revered Cross." For many centuries the church has solemnly venerated the relic or image of the cross on Good Friday. It is not present as a picture of suffering only but as a symbol of Christ's passover, where "dying he destroyed our death and rising restored our life." It is the glorious, the life-giving cross that the faithful venerate with song, prayer, kneeling and a kiss.

As the cross is shown to the assembly, the following is sung.

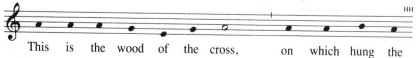

This is the wood of the cross, on which hung the

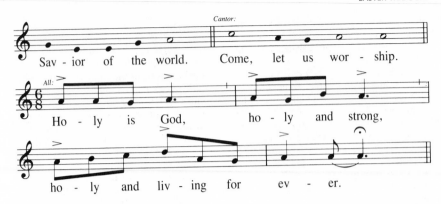

Sav - ior of the world. Come, let us wor - ship.

Ho - ly is God, ho - ly and strong,

ho - ly and liv - ing for ev - er.

As the assembly comes forward to venerate the cross, the following or other chants and hymns may be sung.

We adore you, Lord
Taizé Community, 1979
Jacques Berthier, b.1923

A - do - ra-mus te, A - do - ra-mus te, Do-mi - ne. (hum)

816   HOLY COMMUNION

This liturgy concludes with a simple communion rite. All recite the Lord's Prayer and receive holy communion. There is no concluding rite or dismissal for the church continues to be at prayer throughout the Triduum.

817   HOLY SATURDAY

The church continues to fast and pray and to make ready for this night's great Vigil. Saturday is a day of great quiet and reflection. Catechumens, sponsors and some of the faithful may assemble during the day for prayer, the recitation of the Creed, and for the rite of Ephpheta (opening of ears and mouth).

818   EASTER VIGIL

The long preparation of the catechumens, the lenten disciplines and fast of the faithful, the vigiling and fasting and prayer that have gone on since Thursday night—all culminate in the great liturgy of this night. On this night the church assembles to spend much time listening to scriptures, praying psalms, acclaiming the death and resurrection of the Lord. Only then are the catechumens called forward and prayed over, challenged to renounce evil and affirm their faith in God, led to the font and baptized in the blessed water. The newly baptized are then anointed with chrism and the entire assembly joins in intercession and finally in the eucharist.

INTRODUCTORY RITE

BLESSING OF THE FIRE AND LIGHTING OF THE PASCHAL CANDLE

The night vigil begins with the kindling of new fire and the lighting of the assembly's paschal candle.

PROCESSION

The ministers and assembly go in procession to the place where the scriptures will be read. The following is sung during the procession.

Deacon or Priest: Christ our light. All: Thanks be to God.

EASTER PROCLAMATION: THE EXSULTET

In this ancient text the church gives thanks and praise to God for all that is recalled this night: Adam's fall, the deliverance from Egypt, the passover of Christ, the wedding of earth and heaven, our reconciliation.

LITURGY OF THE WORD

At the Vigil, the liturgy of the word is an extended time of readings, silence and the chanting of psalms. On this night when the faithful know the death and resurrection of the Lord in baptism and eucharist, the church needs first to hear these scriptures which are the foundation of our life together: the creation story, Abraham and Isaac, the dividing of the sea, the poetry of Isaiah and Baruch and Ezekiel, the proclamation of Paul to the Romans and the gospel account of Jesus' resurrection.

READING I   *Genesis 1, 1 - 2, 2 or 1, 1.26-31 / 42*   819

RESPONSORIAL PSALM   *Psalm (103)104, 1-2.5-6.10.12.13-14.24.35 / 42*

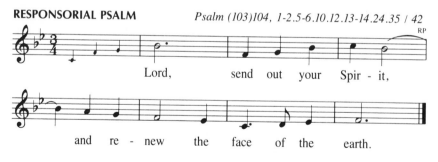

Lord, send out your Spir-it, and re-new the face of the earth.

Bless the Lord, my soul!
Lord God, how great you are,
clothed in majesty and glory,
wrapped in light as in a robe! ℟.

You founded the earth on its base,
to stand firm from age to age.
You wrapped it with the ocean like a
cloak:

the waters stood higher than the
mountains. ℟.

You make springs gush forth in the
valleys;
they flow in between the hills.
On their banks dwell the birds of
heaven;
from the branches they sing their
song. ℟.

From your dwelling you water the hills;
earth drinks its fill of your gift.
You make the grass grow for the cattle
and the plants to serve man's needs,
that he may bring forth bread from the
earth. ℞.

How many are your works, O Lord!
In wisdom you have made them all.
The earth is full of your riches.
Bless the Lord, my soul. ℞.

Or:

RESPONSORIAL PSALM *Psalm (32)33, 4-5.6-7.12-13.20-22 / 42*

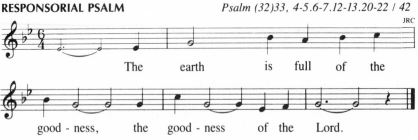

For the word of the Lord is faithful
and all his works are to be trusted.
The Lord loves justice and right
and fills the earth with his love. ℞.

They are happy, whose God is the Lord,
the people he has chosen as his own.
From the heavens the Lord looks forth,
he sees all the children of men. ℞.

By his word the heavens were made,
by the breath of his mouth all the stars.
He collects the waves of the ocean;
he stores up the depths of the sea. ℞.

Our soul is waiting for the Lord.
The Lord is our help and our shield.
May your love be upon us, O Lord,
as we place all our hope in you. ℞.

820 READING II *Genesis 22, 1-18 or 22, 1-2.9.10-13.15-18 / 42*

RESPONSORIAL PSALM *Psalm (15)16, 5.8.9-10.11 / 42*

O Lord, it is you who are my portion
and cup;
it is you yourself who are my prize.
I keep the Lord ever in my sight;
since he is at my right hand, I shall
stand firm. ℞.

And so my heart rejoices, my soul is
glad;
even my body shall rest in safety.
For you will not leave my soul among
the dead,
nor let your beloved know decay. ℞.

You will show me the path of life,
the fullness of joy in your presence,
at your right hand happiness for
ever. ℞.

READING III

Exodus 14, 15 - 15, 1 / 42   821

RESPONSORIAL PSALM   Exodus 15, 1-2.3-4.5-6.17-18 / 42

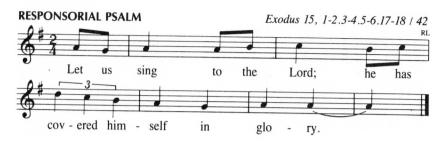

Let us sing to the Lord; he has cov-ered him-self in glo-ry.

I will sing to the Lord; glorious his triumph!
Horse and rider he has thrown into the sea!
The Lord is my strength, my song, my salvation.
This is my God and I extol him, my father's God and I give him praise. ℟.

The Lord is a warrior! The Lord is his name.
The chariots of Pharaoh he hurled into the sea, the flower of his army is drowned in the sea. ℟.

The deeps hide them; they sank like a stone.
Your right hand, Lord glorious in its power,
shattered the enemy. ℟.

The people you have redeemed pass
You will lead them and plant them on your mountain,
the place, O Lord, where you have
made your home, the sanctuary, Lord which your hands have made.
The Lord will reign for ever and ever! ℟.

READING IV

Isaiah 54, 5-14 / 42   822

RESPONSORIAL PSALM   Psalm (29)30, 2.4.5-6.11-12.13 / 42

I will praise you, Lord, for you have res-cued me.

I will praise you, Lord, you have rescued me
and have not let my enemies rejoice over me.
O Lord, you have raised my soul from the dead,
restored me to life from those who sink into the grave. ℟.

Sing psalms to the Lord, you who love him,
give thanks to his holy name.
His anger lasts a moment; his favor all through life.
At night there are tears, but joy comes with dawn. ℟.

The Lord listened and had pity.
The Lord came to my help.
For me you have changed my mourning into dancing.
O Lord my God, I will thank you for ever. ℟.

823 **READING V** *Isaiah 55,1-11 / 45*

RESPONSORIAL PSALM *Isaiah 12, 2-3.4.5-6 / 42*

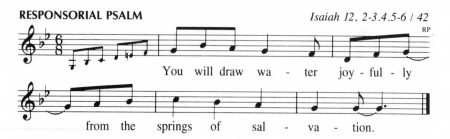

You will draw wa - ter joy - ful - ly
from the springs of sal - va - tion.

Truly, God is my salvation, I trust, I
shall not fear.
For the Lord is my strength, my song,
he became my savior.
With joy you will draw water from the
wells of salvation. ℞.

Give thanks to the Lord, give praise to
his name!
Make his mighty deeds known to the
peoples!
Declare the greatness of his name. ℞.

Sing a psalm to the Lord!
For he has done glorious deeds,
make them known to all the earth!
People of Zion, sing and shout for joy,
for great in your midst is the Holy One
of Israel. ℞.

824 **READING VI** *Baruch 3, 9-15.32-4, 4 / 42*

RESPONSORIAL PSALM *Psalm (18)19, 8.9.10.11 / 42*

Lord, you have the words of
ev - er - last - ing life.

The law of the Lord is perfect,
it revives the soul.
The rule of the Lord is to be trusted,
it gives wisdom to the simple. ℞.

The precepts of the Lord are right,
They gladden the heart.
The command of the Lord is clear,
it gives light to the eyes. ℞.

The fear of the Lord is holy,
abiding for ever.
The decrees of the Lord are truth
and all of them just. ℞.

They are more to be desired than gold,
than the purest of gold,
and sweeter are they than honey,
than honey from the comb.

READING VII

RESPONSORIAL PSALM

Psalm (41)42, 3.5; (42)43, 3.4 / 42

Like a deer that longs for run - ning streams, so my soul longs for you, my God.

My soul is thirsting for God,
the God of my life;
when can I enter and see
the face of God? ℟.

How I would lead the rejoicing crowd
into the house of God,
amid cries of gladness and thanksgiving,
the throng wild with joy. ℟.

O send forth your light and your truth;
let these be my guide.
Let them bring me to your holy
mountain,
to the place where you dwell. ℟.

And I will come to the altar of God,
the God of my joy.
My redeemer, I will thank you on the
harp,
O God, my God. ℟.

Or:

RESPONSORIAL PSALM

Psalm (50)51, 12-13.14-15.18-19 / 42

Cre - ate a clean heart, a clean heart in me, O God.

A pure heart create for me, O God,
put a steadfast spirit within me.
Do not cast me away from your
presence,
nor deprive me of your holy
spirit. ℟.

Give me again the joy of your help;
with a spirit of fervor sustain me,

that I may teach transgressors your
ways
and sinners may return to you. ℟.

For in sacrifice you take no delight,
burnt offering from me you would
refuse;
my sacrifice, a contrite spirit;
a humbled, contrite heart you will
not spurn. ℟.

GLORIA

PRAYER

826   **EPISTLE**   *Romans 6, 3-11 / 42*

RESPONSORIAL PSALM   *Psalm (117)118, 1-2.16.17.22-23 / 42*

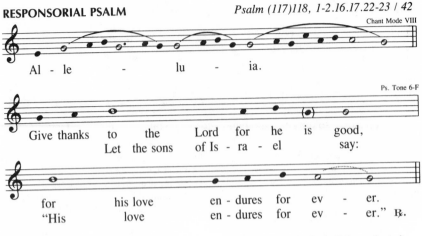

Al - le - lu - ia.

Give thanks   to   the   Lord   for   he   is   good,
Let   the sons   of Is - ra - el   say:

for   his love   en - dures   for   ev - er.
"His   love   en - dures   for   ev - er." ℟.

The Lord's right hand has triumphed;
his right hand raised me.
The Lord's right hand has triumphed;
I shall not die, I shall live and recount
 his deeds. ℟.

The stone which the builders rejected
has become the cornerstone.
This is the work of the Lord,
a marvel in our eyes. ℟.

GOSPEL/A   *Matthew 28, 1-10 / 42*

GOSPEL/B   *Mark 16, 1-8 / 42*

GOSPEL/C   *Luke 24, 1-12 / 42*

827   **LITURGY OF BAPTISM**

*After the homily the catechumens are called forward. The assembly chants the
litany of the saints, invoking the holy women and men of all centuries. Patron saints
of the church and of the catechumens and the faithful may be included in the litany.*

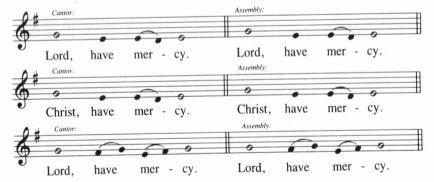

Cantor: Assembly:
Lord,   have   mer - cy.   Lord,   have   mer - cy.

Cantor: Assembly:
Christ,   have   mer - cy.   Christ,   have   mer - cy.

Cantor: Assembly:
Lord,   have   mer - cy.   Lord,   have   mer - cy.

Cantor: Assembly:

					pray	for	us
Holy Mary,	Mother	of	God		pray	for	us
Saint			Mich - ael		pray	for	us
Holy angels	of		God		pray	for	us
Saint John	the		Bap - tist		pray	for	us
Saint			Jo - seph		pray	for	us
Saint Peter	and	Saint	Paul		pray	for	us
Saint			An - drew		pray	for	us
Saint			John		pray	for	us
Saint Mary			Mag - dalene		pray	for	us
Saint			Ste - phen		pray	for	us
Saint Ig	-	-	na - tius		pray	for	us
Saint			Law - rence		pray	for	us
Saint Perpetua	and	Saint Fe -lic	- ity		pray	for	us
Saint			Ag - nes		pray	for	us
Saint			Gre - gory		pray	for	us
Saint Au	-	-	gus - tine		pray	for	us
Saint Atha	-	-	na - sius		pray	for	us
Saint			Ba - sil		pray	for	us
Saint			Mar - tin		pray	for	us
Saint			Ben - edict		pray	for	us
Saint Francis	and	Saint Dom	- inic		pray	for	us
Saint Francis			Xa - vier		pray	for	us
Saint John	Vi	-	an - ney		pray	for	us
Saint			Cath - erine		pray	for	us
Saint Te	-	-	re - sa		pray	for	us
All holy	men	and	wo - men		pray	for	us

Lord,	be mer - ci - ful,	Lord,	save your peo - ple.
From	all e - vil,	Lord,	save your peo - ple.
From	ev -'ry sin,	Lord,	save your peo - ple.
From	ev - er - last - ing death,	Lord,	save your peo - ple.

By your com - ing as man,	Lord,	save your peo - ple.
By your death and ris-ing to new life,	Lord,	save you peo - ple.
By your gift of the Ho - ly Spir - it,	Lord,	save your peo - ple.

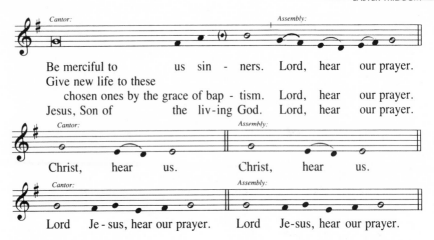

Cantor: *Assembly:*

Be merciful to us sin - ners.   Lord, hear our prayer.
Give new life to these
   chosen ones by the grace of bap - tism.   Lord, hear our prayer.
   Jesus, Son of the liv-ing God.   Lord, hear our prayer.

Christ, hear us.   Christ, hear us.

Lord Je - sus, hear our prayer.   Lord Je-sus, hear our prayer.

828   BLESSING OF WATER

The presider gives thanks and praise to God over the waters of baptism. This acclamation is sung by all.

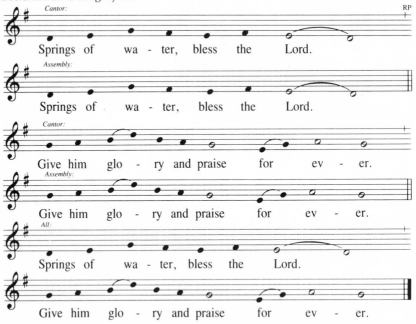

Cantor: RP

Springs of wa - ter, bless the Lord.

Assembly:

Springs of wa - ter, bless the Lord.

Cantor:

Give him glo - ry and praise for ev - er.

Assembly:

Give him glo - ry and praise for ev - er.

All:

Springs of wa - ter, bless the Lord.

Give him glo - ry and praise for ev - er.

829   RENUNCIATION OF SIN AND PROFESSION OF FAITH

Each candidate for baptism is asked to reject sin and the ways of evil and to testify to faith in Father, Son and Holy Spirit. All join to affirm this faith.

THE BAPTISMS

830

One by one the candidates are led into the waters, or they bend over the font, and water is poured over them as the presider says: "N., I baptize you in the name of the Father, and of the Son, and of the Holy Spirit." After each baptism, the assembly sings an acclamation.

You have put on Christ, in him you have been bap-tized.

Al - le - lu - ia, al - le - lu - ia.

Each of the newly baptized is then clothed in a baptismal garment.

RECEPTION INTO FULL COMMUNION

831

Those who have been previously baptized are now called forward to profess their faith and to be received into the full communion of the Roman Catholic Church.

CONFIRMATION

832

Infants who have been baptized are anointed with chrism. Children and adults are usually confirmed: the presider prays and lays hands on them, then anoints each of the newly baptized with chrism saying: "N., be sealed with the Gift of the Holy Spirit."

RENEWAL OF BAPTISMAL PROMISES

833

All of the faithful repeat and affirm the rejection of sin made at baptism and profess faith in the Father, Son and Holy Spirit. The assembly is sprinkled with the baptismal water. The newly baptized then take their places in the assembly and, for the first time, join in the prayer of the faithful, the prayers of intercession.

LITURGY OF THE EUCHARIST

834

The gifts and table are prepared and the eucharist is celebrated in the usual way.

CONCLUDING RITE

835

The dismissal is sung with "alleluia", and all respond.

Go in the peace of Christ, al - le - lu - ia, al - le - lu - ia.
Thanks be to God, al - le - lu - ia, al - le - lu - ia.

836 EASTER SUNDAY

READING I *Acts 10, 34.37-43 / 43*

RESPONSORIAL PSALM *Psalm (117)118, 1-2.16-17.22-23 / 43*

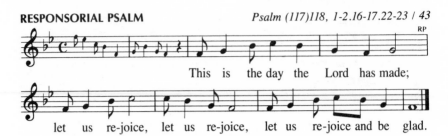

RP

This is the day the Lord has made;

let us re-joice, let us re-joice, let us re-joice and be glad.

Give thanks to the Lord for he is good,
for his love endures for ever.
Let the sons of Israel say:
"His love endures for ever." ℞.

The Lord's right hand has triumphed;
his right hand raised me.
The Lord's right hand has triumphed;
I shall not die, I shall live
and recount his deeds. ℞.

The stone which the builders rejected
has become the cornerstone.
This is the work of the Lord,
a marvel in our eyes. ℞.

READING II *Colossians 3, 1-4 / 43*

Or:

READING II *1 Corinthians 5, 6-8 / 43*

837 SEQUENCE

Ascr. to Wipo of Burgundy, d. 1048
Tr. by Peter J. Scagnelli, b. 1949

Mode 1
Acc. by Richard Proulx, b. 1937

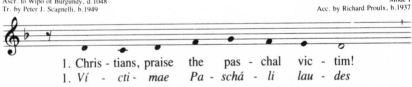

1. Chris - tians, praise the pas - chal vic - tim!
1. Ví - cti - mae Pa - schá - li lau - des

Of - fer thank - ful sac - ri - fice!
im - mó - lent Chri - sti - á - ni.

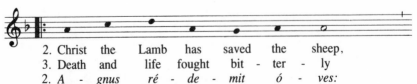

2. Christ the Lamb has saved the sheep,
3. Death and life fought bit - ter - ly
2. A - gnus ré - de - mit ó - ves:
3. Mors et vi - ta du - él - lo

(music)

Christ the just one paid the price,
For this won - drous vic - to - ry;
Chri - stus ín - no - cens Pá - tri
con - fli - xé - re mi - rán - do:

Re - con - cil - ing sin - ners to the Fa - ther.
The Lord of life who died reigns glo - ri - fied!
re - con - ci - li - á - vit pec - ca - tó - res.
dux vi - tae mór - tu - us re - gnat vi - vus.

4. O Mar - y, come and say what you
6. Bright an - gels tes - ti - fied, Shroud and
4. *Dic no - bis Ma - rí - a, quid vi-*
6. *An - gé - li - cos te - stes, su - dá-*

saw at break of day. 5. "The emp - ty tomb
grave clothes side by side! 7. "Yes, Christ my hope
dí - sti in vi - a? 5. Se - púl - crum Chri-
ri - um, et ve - stes. 7. Sur - ré - xit Chri-

of my liv - ing Lord! I saw Christ Je-
rose glo - ri - ous - ly. He goes be - fore
sti vi - vén - tis, et gló - ri - am
stus spes me - a: prae - cé - det su-

sus ris - en and a - dored!
you in - to Ga - li - lee."
vi - di re - sur - gén - tis.
os in Ga - li - láe - am.

8. Share the good news, sing joy - ful-
8. *Scí - mus Chrí - stum sur - re - xís-*

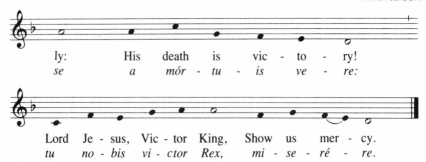

ly: His   death is   vic - to - ry!
se   a   mór - tu - is ve - re:

Lord Je - sus, Vic - tor King, Show us mer - cy.
tu   no - bis vi - ctor Rex, mi - se - ré - re.

GOSPEL   *John 20, 1-9 / 43*

---

838 SECOND SUNDAY OF EASTER

READING I/A   *Acts 2, 42-47 / 44*

READING I/B   *Acts 4, 32-35 / 45*

READING I/C   *Acts 5, 12-16 / 46*

RESPONSORIAL PSALM   *Psalm (117)118, 2-4.13-15.22-24 / 44,45,46*

Give   thanks to the Lord for   he   is

good,   his   love is ev - er - last - ing.

Let the sons of Israel say:
"His love endures for ever."
Let the sons of Aaron say:
"His love endures for ever."
Let those who fear the Lord say:
"His love endures for ever." ℟.

I was thrust down, thrust down and
   falling
but the Lord was my helper.
The Lord is my strength and my song;

he was my savior.
There are shouts of joy and victory
in the tents of the just. ℟.

The stone which the builders rejected
has become the cornerstone.
This is the work of the Lord,
a marvel in our eyes.
This day was made by the Lord;
we rejoice and are glad. ℟.

READING II/A   *1 Peter 1, 3-9 / 44*

READING II/B   *1 John 5, 1-6 / 45*

READING II/C   *Revelation 1, 9-11.12-13.17-19 / 46*

GOSPEL   *John 20, 19-31 / 44,45,46*

THIRD SUNDAY OF EASTER/A 839

READING I *Acts 2, 14.22-28 / 47*

RESPONSORIAL PSALM *Psalm (15)16, 1-2.5.7-8.9-10.11 / 47*

Lord, you will show us the path of life.

Preserve me, God, I take refuge in you.
I say to the Lord: "You are my God.
My happiness lies in you alone."
O Lord, it is you who are my portion
   and cup,
it is you yourself who are my prize. ℞.

I will bless the Lord who gives me
   counsel,
who even at night directs my heart.
I keep the Lord ever in my sight;
since he is at my right hand, I shall
   stand firm. ℞.

And so my heart rejoices, my soul is
   glad;
even my body shall rest in safety.
For you will not leave my soul among
   the dead,
nor let your beloved know decay. ℞.

You will show me the path of life,
the fullness of joy in your presence,
at your right hand happiness for
ever. ℞.

READING II *1 Peter 1, 17-21 / 47*

GOSPEL *Luke 24, 13-35 / 47*

THIRD SUNDAY OF EASTER/B 840

READING I *Acts 3, 13-15.17-19 / 48*

RESPONSORIAL PSALM *Psalm 4, 2.4.7-8.9 / 48*

Lord, let your face shine on us.

When I call, answer me, O God of
   justice;
from anguish you released me, have
   mercy and hear me! ℞.

It is the Lord who grants favors to those
   whom he loves;
the Lord hears me whenever I call
   him. ℞.

Lift up the light of your face on us, O
   Lord.
You have put into my heart a greater
   joy
than they have from abundance of corn
   and new wine. ℞.

I will lie down in peace and sleep
   comes at once
for you alone, Lord, make me dwell in
   safety. ℞.

READING II *1 John 2, 1-5 / 48*

GOSPEL *Luke 24, 35-48 / 48*

841 THIRD SUNDAY OF EASTER/C

READING I *Acts 5, 27-32.40-41 / 49*

RESPONSORIAL PSALM *Psalm (29)30, 2.4.5-6.11-12.13 / 49*

I will praise you, Lord, for you have res-cued me.

I will praise you, Lord, you have
  rescued me
and have not let my enemies rejoice
  over me.
O Lord, you have raised my soul from
  the dead,
restored me to life from those who sink
  into the grave. ℟.

Sing psalms to the Lord, you who love
  him,
give thanks to his holy name.
His anger lasts a moment; his favor all
  through life.
At night there are tears, but joy comes
  with dawn. ℟.

The Lord listened and had pity.
The Lord came to my help.
For me you have changed my mourning
  into dancing.
O Lord my God, I will thank you for
  ever. ℟.

READING II *Revelations 5, 11-14 / 49*

GOSPEL *John 21, 1-19 or 21, 1-14 / 49*

842 FOURTH SUNDAY OF EASTER/A

READING I *Acts 2, 14.36-41 / 50*

RESPONSORIAL PSALM *Psalm (22)23, 1-3.3-4.5.6 / 50*

The Lord is my shep - herd;
there is noth - ing I shall want.

The Lord is my shepherd;
there is nothing I shall want.
Fresh and green are the pastures
where he gives me repose.
Near restful water he leads me,
to revive my drooping spirit. ℟.

He guides me along the right path;
he is true to his name.
If I should walk in the valley of
    darkness
no evil would I fear.
You are there with your crook and your
    staff;
with these you give me comfort. ℟.

You have prepared a banquet for me
in the sight of my foes.
My head you have anointed with oil;
my cup is overflowing. ℟.

Surely goodness and kindness shall
    follow me
all the days of my life.
In the Lord's own house shall I dwell
for ever and ever. ℟.

READING II   *1 Peter 2, 20-25 / 50*

GOSPEL   *John 10,1-10 / 50*

FOURTH SUNDAY OF EASTER/B   843

READING I   *Acts 4, 8-12 / 51*

RESPONSORIAL PSALM   *Psalm (117)118, 1.8-9.21-23.26.21.29 / 51*

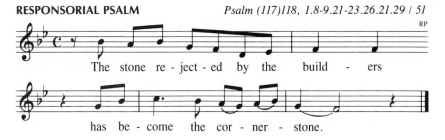

The stone rejected by the builders has become the cornerstone.

Give thanks to the Lord for he is good,
for his love endures for ever.
It is better to take refuge in the Lord
than to trust in men;
It is better to take refuge in the Lord
than to trust in the princes. ℟.

I will thank you for you have answered
and you are my savior.
The stone which the builders rejected
has become the cornerstone.
This is the work of the Lord,
a marvel in our eyes. ℟.

Blessed in the name of the Lord is he
who comes.
We bless you from the house of the
    Lord;
I will thank you for you have answered
and you are my savior.
Give thanks to the Lord for he is good;
for his love endures for ever. ℟.

READING II   *1 John 3, 1-2 / 51*

GOSPEL   *John 10, 11-18 / 51*

844 **FOURTH SUNDAY OF EASTER/C**

READING I *Acts 13, 14.43-52 / 52*

RESPONSORIAL PSALM *Psalm (99)100, 1-2.3.5 / 52*

We are his peo-ple: the sheep of his flock.

Cry out with joy to the Lord, all the
   earth.
Serve the Lord with gladness.
Come before him, singing for joy. ℞.

Know that he, the Lord, is God.
He made us, we belong to him,
we are his people, the sheep of his
   flock. ℞.

Indeed, how good is the Lord,
eternal his merciful love.
He is faithful from age to age. ℞.

READING II *Revelation 7, 9.14-17 / 52*

GOSPEL *John 10, 27-30 / 52*

845 **FIFTH SUNDAY OF EASTER/A**

READING I *Acts 6, 1-7 / 53*

RESPONSORIAL PSALM *Psalm (32)33, 1-2.4-5.18-19 / 53*

Lord, let your mer - cy be on us,

as we place our trust in you.

Ring out your joy to the Lord, O you
   just;
for praise is fitting for loyal hearts.
Give thanks to the Lord upon the harp,
with a ten-stringed lute sing him
   songs. ℞.

For the word of the Lord is faithful
and all his works to be trusted.
The Lord loves justice and right
and fills the earth with his love. ℞.

The Lord looks on those who revere
   him,
on those who hope in his love,
to rescue their souls from death,
to keep them alive in famine. ℞.

READING II   *1 Peter 2, 4-9 / 53*

GOSPEL   *John 14, 1-12 / 53*

FIFTH SUNDAY OF EASTER/B   846

READING I   *Acts 9, 26-31 / 54*

RESPONSORIAL PSALM   *Psalm (21)22, 26-27.28.30.31-32 / 54*

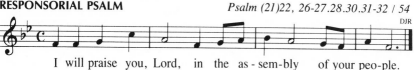

I will praise you, Lord, in the as - sem - bly of your peo-ple.

My vows I will pay before those who
fear him.
The poor shall eat and shall have their
fill.
They shall praise the Lord, those who
seek him.
May their hearts live for ever and
ever! ℟.

All the earth shall remember and return
to the Lord,
all families of the nations worship
before him.
They shall worship him, all the mighty
of the earth;
before him shall bow all who go down
to the dust. ℟.

And my soul shall live for him, my
children serve him.
They shall tell of the Lord to
generations yet to come,
declare his faithfulness to peoples yet
unborn:
"These things the Lord has done." ℟.

READING II   *1 John 3, 18-24 / 54*

GOSPEL   *John 15, 1-8 / 54*

847 FIFTH SUNDAY OF EASTER/C

READING I   *Acts 14, 21-27 / 55*

RESPONSORIAL PSALM   *Psalm (144)145, 8.9.10-11.12-13 / 55*

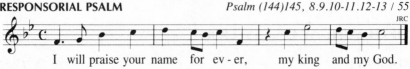

I will praise your name for ev-er, my king and my God.

The Lord is kind and full of
   compassion,
slow to anger, abounding in love.
How good is the Lord to all,
compassionate to all his creatures. ℞.

To make known to men your mighty
   deeds
and the glorious splendor of your
   reign.
Yours is an everlasting kingdom;
your rule lasts from age to age. ℞.

All your creatures shall thank you, O
   Lord,
and your friends shall repeat their
   blessing.
They shall speak of the glory of your
   reign
and declare your might, O God. ℞.

READING II   *Revelation 21, 1-5 / 55*

GOSPEL   *John 13, 31-33.34-35 / 55*

848 SIXTH SUNDAY OF EASTER/A

READING   *Acts 8, 5-8. 14-17 / 56*

RESPONSORIAL PSALM   *Psalm (65)66, 1-3.4-5.6-7.16.20 / 56*

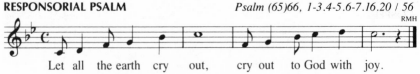

Let all the earth cry out, cry out to God with joy.

Cry out with joy to God all the earth,
O sing to the glory of his name.
O render him glorious praise.
Say to God: "How tremendous your
   deeds! ℞.

He turned the sea into dry land,
they passed through the river dry-shod.
Let our joy then be in him;
he rules for ever by his might. ℞.

Before you all the earth shall bow,
shall sing to you, sing to your name!"
Come and see the works of God,
tremendous his deeds among men. ℞.

Come and hear, all who fear God.
I will tell what he did for my soul;
Blessed be God who did not reject my
   prayer
nor withold his love from me. ℞.

READING II   *1 Peter 3, 15-18 / 56*

GOSPEL   *John 14, 15-21 / 56*

SIXTH SUNDAY OF EASTER/B   849

READING I   *Acts 10, 25-26. 34-35. 44-48 / 57*

RESPONSORIAL PSALM   *Psalm (97)98, 1.2-3.3-4 / 57*

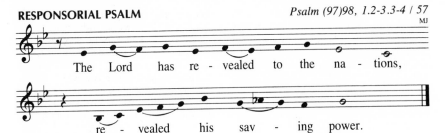

The Lord has re - vealed to the na - tions,
re - vealed his sav - ing power.

Sing a new song to the Lord
for he has worked wonders.
His right hand and his holy arm
have brought salvation. ℞.

The Lord has made known his salvation;
has shown his justice to the nations.
He has remembered his truth and love
for the house of Israel. ℞.

All the ends of the earth have seen
the salvation of our God.
Shout to the Lord, all the earth,
ring out your joy. ℞.

READING II   *1 John 4, 7-10 / 57*

GOSPEL   *John 15, 9-17 / 57*

850 SIXTH SUNDAY OF EASTER/C

READING I 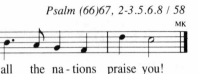 *Acts 15, 1-2. 22-29 / 58*

RESPONSORIAL PSALM *Psalm (66)67, 2-3.5.6.8 / 58*

MK

O God, O God, let all the na-tions praise you!

O God, be gracious and bless us
and let your face shed its light upon us.
So will your ways be known upon
  earth
and all nations learn your saving
  help. ℟.

Let the nations be glad and exult
for you rule the world with justice.
With fairness you rule the peoples,
you guide the nations on earth.

Let the peoples praise you, O God;
let all the peoples praise you.
May God still give us his blessing
till the ends of the earth revere him. ℟.

READING II *Revelation 21, 10-14. 22-23 / 58*

GOSPEL *John 14, 23-29 / 58*

851 ASCENSION

READING I *Acts 1, 1-11 / 59*

RESPONSORIAL PSALM *Psalm (46)47, 2-3.6-7.8-9 / 59*

RP

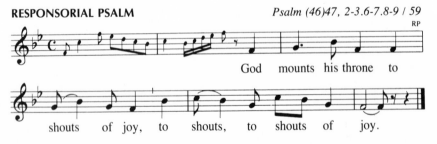

God mounts his throne to

shouts of joy, to shouts, to shouts of joy.

All peoples, clap your hands,
cry to God with shouts of joy!
For the Lord, the Most High, we must
  fear,
great king over all the earth. ℟.

God goes up with shouts of joy;
the Lord goes up with trumpet blast.
Sing praise for God, sing praise,
sing praise to our king, sing praise. ℟.

God is king of all the earth,
Sing praise with all your skill.
God is king over the nations;
God reigns on his holy throne. ℟.

READING II   *Ephesians 1, 17-23 / 59*

GOSPEL/A   *Matthew 28, 16-20 / 59*

GOSPEL/B   *Mark 16, 15-20 / 59*

GOSPEL/C   *Luke 24, 46-53 / 59*

SEVENTH SUNDAY OF EASTER/A   852

READING I   *Acts 1, 12-14 / 60*

RESPONSORIAL PSALM   *Psalm (26)27, 1.4.7-8 / 60*

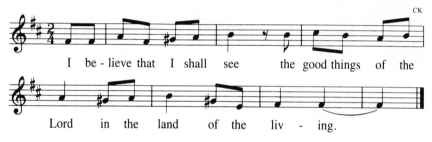

I be - lieve that I shall see the good things of the
Lord in the land of the liv - ing.

The Lord is my light and my help;
whom shall I fear?
The Lord is the stronghold of my life;
before whom shall I shrink? ℟.

There is one thing I ask of the Lord,
for this I long,
to live in the house of the Lord,
all the days of my life,
to savor the sweetness of the Lord,
to behold his temple. ℟.

O Lord, hear my voice when I call;
have mercy and answer.
Of you my heart has spoken:
"Seek his face."
It is your face, O Lord, that I seek. ℟.

READING II   *1 Peter 4, 13-16 / 60*

GOSPEL   *John 17,1-11 / 60*

853 SEVENTH SUNDAY OF EASTER/B

READING I *Acts 1, 15-17. 20-26 / 61*

RESPONSORIAL PSALM *Psalm (102)103, 1-2.11-12.19-20 / 61*

My soul, give thanks to the Lord,
all my being, bless his holy name.
My soul, give thanks to the Lord
and never forget all his blessings. ℞.

The Lord has set his sway in heaven
and his kingdom is ruling over all.
Give thanks to the Lord, all his angels,
mighty in power, fulfilling his word. ℞.

For as the heavens are high above the
    earth
so strong is his love for those who fear
    him.
As far as the east is from the west
so far does he remove our sins. ℞.

READING II *1 John 4,11-16 / 61*

GOSPEL *John 17, 11-19 / 61*

854 SEVENTH SUNDAY OF EASTER/C

READING I *Acts 7, 55-60 / 62*

RESPONSORIAL PSALM *Psalm (96)97, 1-2.6-7.9 / 62*

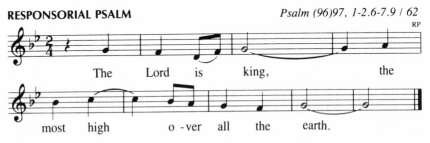

The Lord is king, let earth rejoice,
let all the coastlands be glad.
His throne, justice and right. ℞.

For you indeed are the Lord
most high above all the earth,
exalted far above all spirits. ℞.

The skies proclaim his justice;
all peoples see his glory.
All you spirits, worship him. ℞.

READING II *Revelation 22, 12-14.16-17.20 / 62*

GOSPEL *John 17, 20-26 / 62*

PENTECOST/VIGIL 855

READING I *Genesis 11, 1-9 / 63*

Or:

READING I *Exodus 19, 3-8.16-20 / 63*

Or:

READING I *Ezekiel 37, 1-14 / 63*

Or:

READING I *Joel 3, 1-5 / 63*

RESPONSORIAL PSALM *Psalm (103)104, 1-2.24.35.27-28.29.30 / 63*

Bless the Lord, my soul!
Lord God, how great you are,
clothed in majesty and glory,
wrapped in light as in a robe! ℟.

How many are your works, O Lord!
In wisdom you have made them all.
The earth is full of your riches.
Bless the Lord, my soul. ℟.

All of these look to you
to give them their food in due season.
You give it, they gather it up;
you open your hand, they have their
fill. ℟.

You take back your spirit, they die,
returning to the dust from which they
came.
You send forth your spirit, they are
created;
and you renew the face of the earth. ℟.

READING II *Romans 8, 22-27 / 63*

GOSPEL *John 7, 37-39 / 63*

856 PENTECOST SUNDAY

READING I   *Acts 2, 1-11 / 64*

RESPONSORIAL PSALM   *Psalm (103)104, 1.24.29-30.31.34 / 64*

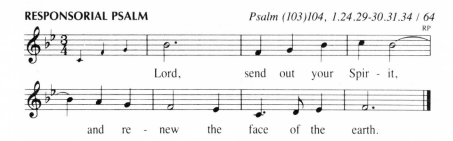

Lord, send out your Spir - it,
and re - new the face of the earth.

Bless the Lord, my soul!
Lord God, how great you are.
How many are your works, O Lord!
The earth is full of your riches. ℟.

You take back your spirit, they die,
returning to the dust from which they
    came.
You send forth your spirit, they are
    created;
and you renew the face of the earth. ℟.

May the glory of the Lord last for ever!
May the Lord rejoice in his works!
May my thoughts be pleasing to him.
I find my joy in the Lord. ℟.

READING II   *1 Corinthians 12, 3-7. 12-13 / 64*

857 SEQUENCE

13th C.
Tr. by Peter J. Scagnelli, b.1949

Mode I
Acc. by Adriaan Engels, b.1906

1. Ho - ly Spir - it, Lord Di - vine, Come, from heights of
2. Come, O Fa - ther of the poor, Come, whose treas - ured

heav'n and shine, Come with bless - ed ra - diance bright!
gifts en - dure, Come, our heart's un - fail - ing light!

3. Of con - so - lers, wis - est, best, And our soul's most
4. In our la - bor rest most sweet, Pleas - ant cool - ness

wel - come guest, Sweet re - fresh - ment, sweet re - pose.
in the heat, Con - so - la - tion in our woes.

5. Light most bless - ed, shine with grace In our heart's most
6. Left with - out your pres - ence here, Life it - self would

se - cret place, Fill your faith - ful through and through.
dis - ap - pear, Noth - ing thrives a - part from you!

7. Cleanse our soil - ed hearts of sin, Ar - id souls re-
8. Bend the stub - born heart and will, Melt the fro - zen,

fresh with - in, Wound - ed lives to health re - store.
warm the chill, Guide the way - ward home once more!

9. On the faith - ful who are true And pro - fess their
10. Give us vir - tue's sure re - ward, Give us your sal-

faith in you, In your sev'n - fold gift de - scend!
va - tion, Lord, Give us joys that nev - er end!

GOSPEL   *John 20, 19-23 / 64*

Ordinary Time

858   When the church assembles, there is always time to read from the scriptures. This is the book the church carries: the Law and the prophets, the books of wisdom and psalms, the letters and writings of Paul and of the other apostles, the gospels themselves. In various places and times the readings from scripture have been arranged so that the various Sundays have their assigned texts. This book of assigned scriptures is the lectionary. In the present Roman lectionary the scriptures are marked for reading through a cycle of three years.

Most of each year is called "Ordinary Time" or "Sundays of the Year." These are the weeks between the Christmas season and Lent, and the long period between Pentecost (the conclusion of the Easter season) and Advent (usually the first Sunday in December). On the Sundays of Ordinary Time, the lectionary has us read in order through the letters of the New Testament and the gospels. In the first year of the cycle, the gospel of Matthew is read from beginning to end; in the second year, Mark; in the third, Luke. Likewise, each Sunday finds the church picking up the reading of one of the letters of the New Testament roughly where the previous week's reading concluded. At present, the first reading at Sunday Mass in Ordinary Time is chosen from the Hebrew Scriptures; these texts show the richness and the continuity of faith.

Sunday by Sunday, year after year, the church reads through its book in the weeks of Ordinary Time. Each Christian, each local church, each generation listens and so finds its own life in God's word.

The Church assembles around the scriptures and around the Lord's table on Sunday. This day is called by Christians the Lord's Day. Whether the church is in Ordinary Time or in the seasons of Advent/Christmas or Lent/Easter, the Lord's Day is kept holy; it is the original feast day. The rhythm of the weekdays and the Sunday is the basic rhythm of life in Christian churches. The practices with which a church keeps the Lord's Day vary, but always and everywhere Christians assemble on this day so that the church may listen to God's word. Through the days of the week, the Sunday's scriptures are to be for reflection and nourishment as they are repeated and pondered in the households of the assembly.

SUNDAY AFTER PENTECOST–TRINITY SUNDAY/A   859

READING I   *Exodus 34, 4-6. 8-9 / 165*

RESPONSORIAL PSALM   *Daniel 3, 52.53.54.55.56 / 165*

> You are blest, Lord   God   of   our   fa   -   thers.
> Blest   be   your   glo - ri - ous   ho - ly name.
> You are blest in the tem - ple of your glo   -   ry.
> You are blest on the throne   of your king - dom.
> You are blest who   gaze   in   -   to   the depths.
> You are blest who   sit a - bove the   che - ru - bim.
> You are blest in the firm - a - ment of   hea - ven.

> To   you   glo - ry and   praise for   ev - er - more.

READING II   *2 Corinthians 13, 11-13 / 165*

GOSPEL   *John 3, 16-18 / 165*

SUNDAY AFTER PENTECOST–TRINITY SUNDAY/B   860

READING I   *Deuteronomy 4, 32-34.39-40 / 166*

RESPONSORIAL PSALM   *Psalm (32)33, 4-5.6.9.18-19.20.22 / 166*

> Hap-py the peo-ple the Lord has cho-sen to be his own.

For the word of the Lord is faithful
and all his works to be trusted.
The Lord loves justice and right
and fills the earth with his love. ℟.

The Lord looks on those who revere
  him,
on those who hope in his love,
to rescue their souls from death,
to keep them alive in famine. ℟.

By his word the heavens were made,
by the breath of his mouth all the stars.
He spoke; and it came to be.
He commanded; it sprang into
  being. ℟.

Our soul is waiting for the Lord.
The Lord is our help and our shield.
May your love be upon us, O Lord,
as we place all our hope in you. ℟.

READING II   *Romans 8, 14-17 / 166*

GOSPEL   *Matthew 28, 16-20 / 166*

---

861 **SUNDAY AFTER PENTECOST–TRINITY SUNDAY/C**

READING I   *Proverbs 8, 22-31 / 167*

RESPONSORIAL PSALM   *Psalm 8, 4-5.6-7.8-9 / 167*

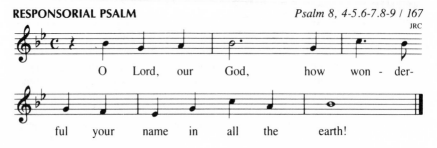

O Lord, our God, how won - der-ful your name in all the earth!

When I see the heavens, the work of
  your hands,
the moon and the stars which you
  arranged,
what is man that you should keep him
  in mind,
mortal man that you care for him? ℞.

Yet you have made him little less than a
  god;
with glory and honor you crowned him,
gave him power over the works of your
  hand,
put all things under his feet. ℞.

All of them, sheep and cattle,
yes, even the savage beasts,
birds of the air, and fish
that make their way through the
  waters. ℞.

READING II   *Romans 5, 1-5 / 167*

GOSPEL   *John 16, 12-15 / 167*

---

862 **BODY AND BLOOD OF CHRIST/A**

READING I   *Deuteronomy 8, 2-3.14-16 / 168*

RESPONSORIAL PSALM   *Psalm 147, 12-13.14-15.19-20 / 168*

Praise the Lord, Je - ru - sa - lem.

O praise the Lord, Jerusalem!
Zion, praise your God!
He has strengthened the bars of your
  gates,
he has blessed the children within
  you. ℞.

He established peace on your borders,
he feeds you with finest wheat.
He sends out his word to the earth
and swiftly runs his command. ℞.

He makes his word known to Jacob,
to Israel his laws and decrees.
He has not dealt thus with other
  nations;
he has not taught them his decrees. ℞.

READING II   *1 Corinthians 10, 16-17 / 168*

GOSPEL   *John 6, 51-58 / 168*

BODY AND BLOOD OF CHRIST/B   863

READING I   *Exodus 24, 3-8 / 169*

RESPONSORIAL PSALM   *Psalm (115)116, 12-13.15-16.17-18 / 169*

I will take the cup of sal - va - tion, and call on the name of the Lord.

How can I repay the Lord
for his goodness to me?
The cup of salvation I will raise;
I will call on the Lord's name. ℞.

O precious in the eyes of the Lord
is the death of his faithful.
Your servant, Lord, your servant am I;
you have loosened my bonds. ℞.

A thanksgiving sacrifice I make;
I will call on the Lord's name.
My vows to the Lord I will fulfill
before all his people. ℞.

READING II   *Hebrews 9, 11-15 / 169*

GOSPEL   *Mark 14, 12-16.22-26 / 169*

864 BODY AND BLOOD OF CHRIST/C

READING I   *Genesis 14, 18-20 / 170*

RESPONSORIAL PSALM   *Psalm (109)110, 1.2.3.4 / 170*

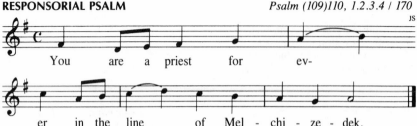

You are a priest for ev-er in the line of Mel - chi - ze - dek.

The Lord's revelation to my Master:
"Sit on my right;
your foes I will put beneath your
   feet." ℟.

The Lord will wield from Zion
your scepter of power;
rule in the midst of all your foes. ℟.

A prince from the day of your birth
on the holy mountains;
from the womb before the dawn I begot
   you. ℟.

The Lord has sworn an oath he will not
   change.
"You are a priest for ever,
a priest like Melchizedek of old." ℟.

READING II   *1 Corinthians 11, 23-26 / 170*

GOSPEL   *Luke 9, 11-17 / 170*

865 SACRED HEART/A

READING I   *Deuteronomy 7, 6-11 / 171*

RESPONSORIAL PSALM   *Psalm (102)103, 1-2.3-4.6-7.8.10 / 171*

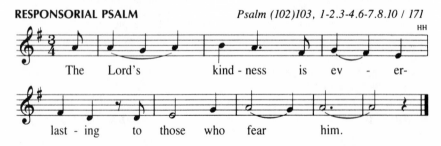

The Lord's kind - ness is ev - er-last - ing to those who fear him.

My soul, give thanks to the Lord,
all my being, bless his holy name.
My soul, give thanks to the Lord
and never forget all his blessings. ℟.

It is he who forgives all your guilt,
who heals every one of your ills,
who redeems your life from the grave,
who crowns you with love and
   compassion. ℟.

The Lord does deeds of justice,
gives judgment for all who are
  oppressed.
He made known his ways to Moses
and his deeds to Israel's sons. ℞.

The Lord is compassion and love,
slow to anger and rich in mercy.
He does not treat us according to our
  sins
nor repay us according to our faults. ℞.

READING II   *1 John 4, 7-16 / 171*

GOSPEL   *Matthew 11, 25-30 / 171*

SACRED HEART/B   866

READING I   *Hosea 11, 1.3-4.8-9 / 172*

RESPONSORIAL PSALM   *Isaiah 12, 2-3.4.5-6 / 172*

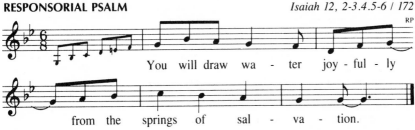

Truly, God is my salvation,
I trust, I shall not fear.
For the Lord is my strength, my song,
he became my savior.
With joy you will draw water
from the wells of salvation. ℞.

For he has done glorious deeds,
make them known to all the earth!
People of Zion,
sing and shout for joy
for great in your midst
is the Holy One of Israel. ℞.

Give thanks to the Lord,
give praise to his name!
Make his mighty deeds
known to the peoples!
Declare the greatness of his name.
Sing a psalm to the Lord! ℞.

READING II   *Ephesians 3, 8-12. 14-19 / 172*

GOSPEL   *John 19, 31-37 / 172*

867 SACRED HEART/C

READING I   *Ezekiel 34, 11-16 / 173*

RESPONSORIAL PSALM   *Psalm (22)23, 1-3.3-4.5.6 / 173*

The Lord is my shepherd;
there is nothing I shall want.
Fresh and green are the pastures
where he gives me repose.
Near restful waters he leads me,
To revive my drooping spirit. ℞.

He guides me along the right path;
he is true to his name.
If I should walk in the valley of
    darkness
no evil would I fear.
You are there with your crook and your
    staff;
with these you give me comfort. ℞.

You have prepared a banquet for me
in the sight of my foes.
My head you have anointed with oil;
my cup is overflowing. ℞.

Surely goodness and kindness shall
    follow me
all the days of my life.
In the Lord's own house shall I dwell
for ever and ever. ℞.

READING II   *Romans 5, 5-11 / 173*

GOSPEL   *Luke 15, 3-7 / 173*

868 SECOND SUNDAY IN ORDINARY TIME/A

READING I   *Isaiah 49, 3.5-6 / 65*

RESPONSORIAL PSALM   *Psalm (39)40, 2.4.7-8.8-9.10 / 65*

Here am I, Lord; I come to do your will.

I waited, I waited for the Lord
and he stooped down to me;
he heard my cry.
He put a new song into my mouth,
praise of our God. ℞.

You do not ask for sacrifice and
    offerings,
but an open ear.
You do not ask for holocaust and
    victim.
Instead, here am I. ℞.

In the scroll of the book it stands
written
that I should do your will.
My God, I delight in your law
in the depth of my heart. ℞.

Your justice I have proclaimed
in the great assembly.
My lips I have not sealed;
you know it, O Lord. ℞.

READING II   *1 Corinthians 1, 1-3 / 65*

GOSPEL   *John 1, 29-34 / 65*

SECOND SUNDAY IN ORDINARY TIME/B   869

READING I   *1 Samuel 3, 3-10.19 / 66*

RESPONSORIAL PSALM   *Psalm (39)40, 2.4.7-8.8-9.10 / 66*

Here am I, Lord; I come to do your will.

I waited, I waited for the Lord
and he stooped down to me;
he heard my cry.
He put a new song into my mouth,
praise of our God. ℞.

You do not ask for sacrifice and
offerings,
but an open ear.
You do not ask for holocaust and
victim.
Instead, here am I. ℞.

In the scroll of the book it stands
written
that I should do your will.
My God, I delight in your law
in the depth of my heart. ℞.

Your justice I have proclaimed
in the great assembly.
My lips I have not sealed;
you know it, O Lord. ℞.

READING II   *1 Corinthians 6, 13-15. 17-20 / 66*

GOSPEL   *John 1, 35-42 / 66*

870   SECOND SUNDAY IN ORDINARY TIME/C

READING I   *Isaiah 62, 1-5 / 67*

RESPONSORIAL PSALM   *Psalm (95)96, 1-2.2-3.7-8.9-10 / 67*

Proclaim his marvelous deeds to all the nations.

O sing a new song to the Lord,
sing to the Lord all the earth.
O sing to the Lord, bless his name. ℟.

Proclaim his help day by day,
tell among the nations his glory
and his wonders among all the
   peoples. ℟.

Give the Lord, you families of peoples,
give the Lord glory and power;
give the Lord the glory of his name. ℟.

Worship the Lord in his temple.
O earth, tremble before him.
Proclaim to the nations: "God is king."
He will judge the peoples in
   fairness. ℟.

READING II   *1 Corinthians 12, 4-11 / 67*

GOSPEL   *John 2, 1-12 / 67*

871   THIRD SUNDAY IN ORDINARY TIME/A

READING I   *Isaiah 8, 23-9,3 / 68*

RESPONSORIAL PSALM   *Psalm (26)27, 1.4.13-14 / 68*

The Lord is my light and my salvation.

The Lord is my light and my help;
whom shall I fear?
The Lord is the stronghold of my life;
before whom shall I shrink? ℟.

There is one thing I ask of the Lord,
for this I long,
to live in the house of the Lord,
all the days of my life,

to savor the sweetness of the Lord,
to behold his temple. ℟.

I am sure I shall see the Lord's
   goodness
in the land of the living.
Hope in him, hold firm and take heart.
Hope in the Lord! ℟.

READING II   *1 Corinthians 1, 10-13.17 / 68*

GOSPEL   *Matthew 4, 12-23 or 4, 12-17 / 68*

THIRD SUNDAY IN ORDINARY TIME/B 872

READING I *Jonah 3, 1-5.10 / 69*

RESPONSORIAL PSALM *Psalm (24)25, 4-5.6-7.8-9 / 69*

Teach me your ways, O Lord, teach me your ways.

Lord, make me know your ways.
Lord, teach me your paths.
Make me walk in your truth, and teach
   me,
for you are God my savior. ℟.

The Lord is good and upright.
He shows the path to those who stray,
he guides the humble in the right path,
he teaches his way to the poor. ℟.

Remember your mercy, Lord,
and the love you have shown from of
   old.
In your love remember me,
because of your goodness, O Lord. ℟.

READING II *1 Corinthians 7, 29-31 / 69*

GOSPEL *Mark 1, 14-20 / 69*

THIRD SUNDAY IN ORDINARY TIME/C 873

READING I *Nehemiah 8, 2-4.5-6.8-10 / 70*

RESPONSORIAL PSALM *Psalm (18)19, 8.9.10.15 / 70*

Your words, Lord, are spir - it and life.

The law of the Lord is perfect,
it revives the soul.
The rule of the Lord is to be trusted,
it gives wisdom to the simple. ℟.

The fear of the Lord is holy,
abiding forever.
The decrees of the Lord are truth
and all of them just. ℟.

The precepts of the Lord are right,
they gladden the heart.
The command of the Lord is clear,
it gives light to the eyes. ℟.

May the spoken words of my mouth,
the thoughts of my heart,
win favor in your sight, O Lord,
my rescuer, my rock! ℟.

READING II *1 Corinthians 12, 12-30 or 12, 12-14.27 / 70*

GOSPEL *Luke 1, 1-4; 4, 14-21 / 70*

874 FOURTH SUNDAY IN ORDINARY TIME / A

READING I   *Zephaniah 2, 3; 3, 12-13 / 71*

RESPONSORIAL PSALM   *Psalm (145)146, 6-7.8-9.9-10 / 71*

Hap - py   the   poor   in   spir - it;
the   king - dom of   heav - en   is   theirs!

It is he who keeps faith for ever,
who is just to those who are oppressed.
It is he who gives bread to the hungry,
the Lord, who sets prisoners free. ℞.

The Lord who gives sight to the blind,
who raises up those who are bowed
    down.
It is the Lord who loves the just;
the Lord, who protects the stranger. ℞.

The Lord upholds the widow and
    orphan,
but thwarts the path of the wicked.
The Lord will reign for ever,
Zion's God, from age to age.
    Alleluia. ℞.

READING II   *1 Corinthians 1, 26-31 / 71*

GOSPEL   *Matthew 5, 1-12 / 71*

875 FOURTH SUNDAY IN ORDINARY TIME / B

READING I   *Deuteronomy 18, 15-20 / 72*

RESPONSORIAL PSALM   *Psalm (94)95, 1-2.6-7.7-9 / 72*

If to - day you hear his   voice, O   hard - en not your hearts.

Come, ring out our joy to the Lord;
hail the rock who saves us.
Let us come before him, giving thanks,
with songs let us hail the Lord. ℞.

Come in; let us bow and bend low;
let us kneel before the God who made
    us
for he is our God and we
the people who belong to his pasture,
the flock that is led by his hand. ℞.

O that today you would listen to his
    voice!
"Harden not your hearts as at Meribah,
as on that day at Massah in the desert
when your fathers put me to the test;
when they tried me, though they saw
    my work." ℞.

READING II   *1 Corinthians 7, 32-35 / 72*

GOSPEL   *Mark 1, 21-28 / 72*

FOURTH SUNDAY IN ORDINARY TIME / C   876

READING I   *Jeremiah 1, 4-5.17-19 / 73*

RESPONSORIAL PSALM   *Psalm (70)71, 1-2.3-4.5-6.15-17 / 73*

I will sing of your sal - va - tion.

In you, O Lord, I take refuge;
let me never be put to shame.
In your justice rescue me, free me;
pay heed to me and save me. ℟.

Be a rock where I can take refuge,
a mighty stronghold to save me;
for you are my rock, my stronghold.
Free me from the hand of the
   wicked. ℟.

It is you, O Lord, who are my hope,
my trust, O Lord, since my youth.
On you I have leaned from my birth,
from my mother's womb you have been
   my help. ℟.

My lips will tell of your justice
and day by day of your help.
O God, you have taught me from my
   youth
and I proclaim your wonders still. ℟.

READING II   *1 Corinthians 12, 31-13, 13 or 13, 4-13 / 73*

GOSPEL   *Luke 4, 21-30 / 73*

877 FIFTH SUNDAY IN ORDINARY TIME / A

READING I *Isaiah 58, 7-10 / 74*

RESPONSORIAL PSALM *Psalm (111)112, 4-5.6-7.8-9 / 74*

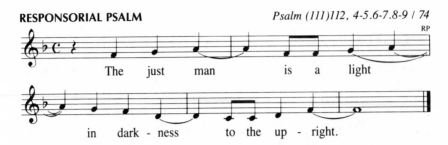

The just man is a light in dark-ness to the up-right.

He is a light in the darkness for the
  upright;
he is generous, merciful and just.
The good man takes pity and lends,
he conducts his affairs with
  honor. ℟.

The just man will never waver;
he will be remembered for ever.

He has no fear of evil news;
with a firm heart he trusts in the
  Lord. ℟.

With a steadfast heart he will not fear;
Open-handed, he gives to the poor;
his justice stands firm for ever.
His head will be raised in glory. ℟.

READING II *1 Corinthians 2, 1-5 / 74*

GOSPEL *Matthew 5, 13-16 / 74*

878 FIFTH SUNDAY IN ORDINARY TIME / B

READING I *Job 7, 1-4.6-7 / 75*

RESPONSORIAL PSALM *Psalm (146)147, 1-2.3-4.5-6 / 75*

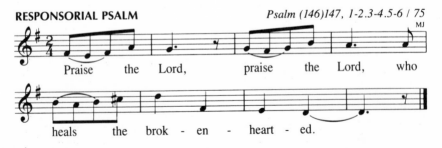

Praise the Lord, praise the Lord, who heals the brok-en-heart-ed.

Praise the Lord for he is good;
sing to our God for he is loving:
to him our praise is due.
The Lord builds up Jerusalem
and brings back Israel's exiles. ℟.

He heals the broken-hearted,
he binds up all their wounds.
He fixes the number of the stars;
he calls each one by its name. ℟.

Our Lord is great and almighty;
his wisdom can never be measured.
The Lord raises the lowly;
he humbles the wicked to the dust. ℟.

READING II   *1 Corinthians 9, 16-19.22-23 / 75*

GOSPEL   *Mark 1, 29-39 / 75*

FIFTH SUNDAY IN ORDINARY TIME / C   879

READING I   *Isaiah 6, 1-2.3-8 / 76*

RESPONSORIAL PSALM   *Psalm (137) 138, 1-2.2-3.4-5.7-8 / 76*

In the sight of the an-gels I will sing your prais-es, Lord.

I thank you, Lord, with all my heart,
you have heard the words of my mouth.
In the presence of the angels I will
  bless you.
I will adore before your holy
  temple. ℟.

I thank you for your faithfulness and
  love
which excel all we ever knew of you.
On the day I called, you answered;
you increased the strength of my
  soul. ℟.

All earth's kings shall thank you
when they hear the words of your
  mouth.
They shall sing of the Lord's ways:
"How great is the glory of the
  Lord!" ℟.

You stretch out your hand and save me,
your hand will do all things for me.
Your love, O Lord, is eternal,
discard not the work of your hands. ℟.

READING II   *1 Corinthians 15, 1-11 or 15, 3-8.11 / 76*

GOSPEL   *Luke 5, 1-11 / 76*

880   SIXTH SUNDAY IN ORDINARY TIME / A

READING I   *Sirach 15, 15-20 / 77*

RESPONSORIAL PSALM   *Psalm (118)119, 1-2.4-5.17-18.33-34 / 77*

Hap - py are they who fol-low the law of the Lord!

They are happy whose life is blameless,
who follow God's law!
They are happy who do his will,
seeking him with all their hearts. ℟.

You have laid down your precepts
to be obeyed with care.
May my footsteps be firm
to obey your statutes. ℟.

Bless your servant and I shall live
and obey your word.
Open my eyes that I may see
the wonders of your law. ℟.

Teach me the demands of your statutes
and I will keep them to the end.
Train me to observe your law,
to keep it with my heart. ℟.

READING II   *1 Corinthians 2, 6-10 / 77*

GOSPEL   *Matthew 5, 17-37 or 5, 20-22.27-28.33-34.37 / 77*

881   SIXTH SUNDAY IN ORDINARY TIME / B

READING I   *Leviticus 13, 1-2.44-46 / 78*

RESPONSORIAL PSALM   *Psalm (31)32, 1-2.5.11 / 78*

I turn to you, O Lord, in time of trou - ble,

and you fill me with the joy of sal - va - tion.

Happy the man whose offense is
forgiven,
whose sin is remitted.
O happy the man to whom the Lord
imputes no guilt,
in whose spirit is no guile. ℟.

But now I have acknowledged my sins;
my guilt I did not hide.

I said: "I will confess my offense to the
Lord."
And you, Lord, have forgiven the guilt
of my sin. ℟.

Rejoice, rejoice in the Lord,
exult, you just!
O come, ring out your joy,
all you upright of heart. ℟.

READING II   *1 Corinthians 10, 31-11, 1 / 78*

GOSPEL   *Mark 1, 40-45 / 78*

SIXTH SUNDAY IN ORDINARY TIME / C   882

READING I   *Jeremiah 17, 5-8 / 79*

RESPONSORIAL PSALM   *Psalm 1, 1-2.3.4.6 / 79*

RJT

Hap-py are they who hope, who hope in the Lord.

Happy indeed is the man
who follows not the counsel of the
    wicked,
nor lingers in the way of sinners
nor sits in the company of scorners,
but whose delight is the law of the
    Lord
and who ponders his law day and
    night. ℟.

He is like a tree that is planted
beside the flowing waters,
that yields its fruit in due season
and whose leaves shall never fade;
and all that he does shall prosper. ℟.

Not so are the wicked, not so!
For they like winnowed chaff
shall be driven away by the wind.
For the Lord guards the way of the just
but the way of the wicked leads to
    doom. ℟.

READING II   *1 Corinthians 15, 12.16-20 / 79*

GOSPEL   *Luke 6, 17.20-26 / 79*

883   SEVENTH SUNDAY IN ORDINARY TIME / A

READING I   *Leviticus 19, 1-2.17-18 / 80*

RESPONSORIAL PSALM   *Psalm (102)103, 1-2.3-4.8.10.12.12-13 / 80*

The Lord is kind and mer-ci-ful.

My soul, give thanks to the Lord,
all my being, bless his holy name.
My soul, give thanks to the Lord
and never forget all his blessings. ℟.

It is he who forgives all your guilt,
who heals every one of your ills,
who redeems your life from the grave,
who crowns you with love and
    compassion. ℟.

The Lord is compassion and love,
slow to anger and rich in mercy.
He does not treat us according to our
    sins
nor repay us according to our faults. ℟.

As far as the east is from the west
so far does he remove our sins.
As a father has compassion on his sons,
the Lord has pity on those who fear
    him. ℟.

READING II   *1 Corinthians 3, 16-23 / 80*

GOSPEL   *Matthew 5, 38-48 / 80*

884   SEVENTH SUNDAY IN ORDINARY TIME / B

READING I   *Isaiah 43, 18-19.21-22.24-25 / 81*

RESPONSORIAL PSALM   *Psalm (40)41, 2-3.4-5.13-14 / 81*

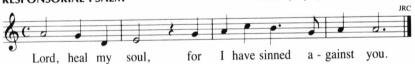

Lord, heal my soul, for I have sinned a-gainst you.

Happy the man who considers the poor
    and the weak.
The Lord will save him in the day of evil,
will guard him, give him life, make
    him happy in the land
and will not give him up to the will of
    his foes. ℟.

The Lord will help him on his bed
    of pain,
he will bring him back from sickness to
    health.

As for me, I said: "Lord, have mercy
    on me,
heal my soul for I have sinned against
    you." ℟.

If you uphold me I shall be unharmed
and set in your presence for evermore.
Blessed be the Lord, the God of Israel
from age to age. Amen. Amen. ℟.

READING II   *2 Corinthians 1, 18-22 / 81*

GOSPEL   *Mark 2, 1-12 / 81*

SEVENTH SUNDAY IN ORDINARY TIME/C   885

READING I   *1 Samuel 26, 2.7-9.12-13.22-23 / 82*

RESPONSORIAL PSALM   *Psalm (102)103, 1-2.3-4.8.10.12-13 / 82*

The Lord is kind and mer - ci - ful.

My soul, give thanks to the Lord,
all my being, bless his holy name.
My soul, give thanks to the Lord
and never forget all his blessings. ℞.

It is he who forgives all your guilt,
who heals every one of your ills,
who redeems your life from the grave,
who crowns you with love and
    compassion. ℞.

The Lord is compassion and love,
slow to anger and rich in mercy.
He does not treat us according to our
    sins
nor repay us according to our
    faults. ℞.

As far as the east is from the west
so far does he remove our sins.
As a father has compassion on his
    sons,
the Lord has pity on those who fear
    him. ℞.

READING II   *1 Corinthians 15, 45-49 / 82*

GOSPEL   *Luke 6, 27-38 / 82*

886 EIGHTH SUNDAY IN ORDINARY TIME / A

READING I   *Isaiah 49, 14-15 / 83*

RESPONSORIAL PSALM   *Psalm (61)62, 2-3.6-7.8-9 / 83*

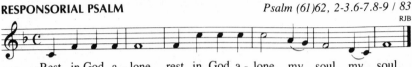

Rest in God a-lone, rest in God a-lone, my soul, my soul.

In God alone is my soul at rest;
my help comes from him.
He alone is my rock, my stronghold,
my fortress; I stand firm. ℟.

In God alone be at rest, my soul,
for my hope comes from him.
He alone is my rock, my stronghold,

my fortress; I stand firm. ℟.

In God is my safety and glory,
the rock of my strength.
Take refuge in God, all you people.
Trust him at all times.
Pour out your hearts before him. ℟.

READING II   *1 Corinthians 4, 1-5 / 83*

GOSPEL   *Matthew 6, 24-34 / 83*

887 EIGHTH SUNDAY IN ORDINARY TIME/B

READING I   *Hosea 2, 16-17.21-22 / 84*

RESPONSORIAL PSALM   *Psalm (102)103, 1-2.3-4.8.10.12-13 / 84*

The Lord is kind and mer-ci-ful.

My soul, give thanks to the Lord,
all my being, bless his holy name.
My soul, give thanks to the Lord
and never forget all his blessings. ℟.

It is he who forgives all your guilt,
who heals every one of your ills,
who redeems your life from the grave,
who crowns you with love and
  compassion. ℟.

The Lord is compassion and love,
slow to anger and rich in mercy.
He does not treat us according to our
  sins
nor repay us according to our faults. ℟.

As far as the east is from the west
so far does he remove our sins.
As a father has compassion on his
  sons,
the Lord has pity on those who fear
  him. ℟.

READING II   *2 Corinthians 3, 1-6 / 84*

GOSPEL   *Mark 2, 18-22 / 84*

EIGHTH SUNDAY IN ORDINARY TIME / C   888

READING I   *Sirach 27, 4-7 / 85*

RESPONSORIAL PSALM   *Psalm (91)92, 2-3.13-14.15-16 / 85*

Lord, it is good to give thanks to you.

It is good to give thanks to the Lord,
to make music to your name, O Most
    High,
to proclaim your love in the morning
and your truth in the watches of the
    night. ℟.

The just will flourish like the palm tree
and grow like a Lebanon cedar.

Planted in the house of the Lord
they will flourish in the courts of our
    God. ℟.

Still bearing fruit when they are old,
still full of sap, still green,
to proclaim that the Lord is just.
In him, my rock, there is no wrong. ℟.

READING II   *1 Corinthians 15, 54-58 / 85*

GOSPEL   *Luke 6, 39-45 / 85*

NINTH SUNDAY IN ORDINARY TIME / A   889

READING I   *Deuteronomy 11, 18.26-28 / 86*

RESPONSORIAL PSALM   *Psalm (30)31, 2-3.3-4.17.25 / 86*

Lord, Lord, be my rock of safe-ty.

In you, O Lord, I take refuge.
Let me never be put to shame.
In your justice, set me free,
hear me and speedily rescue me. ℟.

Be a rock of refuge for me,
a mighty stronghold to save me,
for you are my rock, my stronghold.
For your name's sake, lead me and
    guide me. ℟.

Let your face shine on your servant.
Save me in your love.
Be strong, let your heart take courage,
all who hope in the Lord. ℟.

READING II   *Romans 3, 21-25.28 / 86*

GOSPEL   *Matthew 7, 21-27 / 86*

890   NINTH SUNDAY IN ORDINARY TIME / B

READING I   *Deuteronomy 5, 12-15 / 87*

RESPONSORIAL PSALM   *Psalm (80)81, 3-4.5-6.6-8.10-11 / 87*

RC

Sing with joy   to   God!   Sing   to God our   help!

Raise a song and sound the timbrel,
the sweet-sounding harp and the lute;
blow the trumpet at the new moon,
when the moon is full, on our feast. ℟.

For this is Israel's law,
a command of the God of Jacob.
He imposed it as a rule on Joseph,
when he went out against the land of
    Egypt. ℟.

A voice I did not know said to me:
"I freed your shoulder from the burden;
your hands were freed from the load.
You called in distress and I saved
    you. ℟.

Let there be no foreign god among you,
no worship of an alien god.
I am the Lord your God,
who brought you from the land of
    Egypt." ℟.

READING II   *2 Corinthians 4, 6-11 / 87*

GOSPEL   *Mark 2, 23-3, 6 or 2, 23-28 / 87*

891   NINTH SUNDAY IN ORDINARY TIME / C

READING I   *1 Kings 8, 41-43 / 88*

RESPONSORIAL PSALM   *Psalm(116)117, 1.2 / 88*

CAP

Go   out   to   all   the   world,   and   tell the Good News.

O praise the Lord, all you nations,
acclaim him all you peoples! ℟.

Strong is his love for us;
he is faithful for ever. ℟.

READING II   *Galatians 1, 1-2. 6-10 / 88*

GOSPEL   *Luke 7, 1-10 / 88*

892   TENTH SUNDAY IN ORDINARY TIME / A

READING I   *Hosea 6, 3-6 / 89*

RESPONSORIAL PSALM   *Psalm (49)50, 1.8.12-13.14-15 / 89*

To the up-right I will show the sav-ing pow'r of God.

The God of gods, the Lord,
has spoken and summoned the earth,
from the rising of the sun to its setting.
"I find no fault with your sacrifices,
your offerings are always before
    me. ℟.

Were I hungry, I would not tell you,
for I own the world and all it holds.

Do you think I eat the flesh of bulls,
or drink the blood of goats? ℟.

Pay your sacrifice of thanksgiving to
    God
and render him your votive offerings.
Call on me in the day of distress.
I will free you and you shall honor
    me." ℟.

READING II   *Romans 4, 18-25 / 89*

GOSPEL   *Matthew 9, 9-13 / 89*

TENTH SUNDAY IN ORDINARY TIME / B   893

READING I   *Genesis 3, 9-15 / 90*

RESPONSORIAL PSALM   *Psalm (129)130, 1-2.3-4.5-6.7-8 / 90*

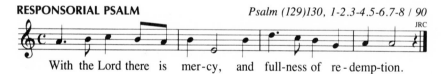

With the Lord there is mer-cy, and full-ness of re-demp-tion.

Out of the depths I cry to you, O Lord,
Lord, hear my voice!
O let your ears be attentive
to the voice of my pleading. ℟.

If you, O Lord, should mark our guilt,
Lord, who would survive?
But with you is found forgiveness:
for this we revere you. ℟.

My soul is waiting for the Lord,
I count on his word.
My soul is longing for the Lord
more than watchman for daybreak.
(Let the watchman count on daybreak
and Israel on the Lord.) ℟.

Because with the Lord there is mercy
and fullness of redemption,
Israel indeed he will redeem
from all its iniquity. ℟.

READING II   *2 Corinthians 4, 13-5, 1 / 90*

GOSPEL   *Mark 3, 20-35 / 90*

894 TENTH SUNDAY IN ORDINARY TIME / C

READING I *1 Kings 17, 17-24 / 91*

RESPONSORIAL PSALM *Psalm (29)30,2.4.5-6.11.12.13 / 91*

I will praise you, Lord, for you have res-cued me.

I will praise you, Lord, you have rescued me
and have not let my enemies rejoice over me.
O Lord, you have raised my soul from the dead,
restored me to life from those who sink into the grave. ℟.

Sing psalms to the Lord, you who love him,
give thanks to his holy name.

His anger lasts a moment; his favor all through life.
At night there are tears, but joy comes with dawn. ℟.

The Lord listened and had pity.
The Lord came to my help.
For me you have changed my mourning into dancing,
O Lord my God, I will thank you for ever. ℟.

READING II *Galatians 1, 11-19 / 91*

GOSPEL *Luke 7, 11-17 / 91*

895 ELEVENTH SUNDAY IN ORDINARY TIME / A

READING I *Exodus 19, 2-6 / 92*

RESPONSORIAL PSALM *Psalm (99)100, 1-2.3.5 / 92*

We are his peo-ple: the sheep of his flock.

Cry out with joy to the Lord, all the earth.
Serve the Lord with gladness.
Come before him singing for joy. ℟.

Know that he, the Lord, is God.
He made us, we belong to him,

we are his people, the sheep of his flock. ℟.

Indeed, how good is the Lord,
eternal his merciful love.
He is faithful from age to age. ℟.

READING II *Romans 5, 6-11 / 92*

GOSPEL *Matthew 9, 36-10, 8 / 92*

ELEVENTH SUNDAY IN ORDINARY TIME / B   896

READING I   *Ezekiel 17, 22-24 / 93*

RESPONSORIAL PSALM   *Psalm (91)92, 2-3.13-14.15-16 / 93*

Lord, it is good to give thanks to you.

It is good to give thanks to the Lord,
to make music to your name, O Most
   High,
to proclaim your love in the morning
and your truth in the watches of the
   night. ℞.

The just will flourish like the palm tree
and grow like a Lebanon cedar.

Planted in the house of the Lord
they will flourish in the courts of our
   God. ℞.

Still bearing fruit when they are old,
still full of sap, still green,
to proclaim that the Lord is just.
In him, my rock, there is no wrong. ℞.

READING II   *2 Corinthians 5, 6-10 / 93*

GOSPEL   *Mark 4, 26-34 / 93*

ELEVENTH SUNDAY IN ORDINARY TIME / C   897

READING I   *2 Samuel 12, 7-10.13 / 94*

RESPONSORIAL PSALM   *Psalm (31)32, 1-2.5.7.11 / 94*

Lord, for - give the wrong I have done.

Happy the man whose offense is
forgiven, whose sin is remitted.
O happy the man to whom the
   Lord imputes no guilt,
in whose spirit is no guile. ℞.

But now I have acknowledged my sins;
my guilt I did not hide.
I said: "I will confess my offense to the
   Lord."
And you, Lord, have forgiven the guilt
   of my sin. ℞.

You are my hiding place, O Lord;
you save me from distress.
(You surround me with cries of
   deliverance.) ℞.

Rejoice, rejoice in the Lord,
exult, you just!
O come, ring out your joy,
all you upright of heart. ℞.

READING II   *Galatians 2, 16.19-21 / 94*

GOSPEL   *Luke 7, 36-8, 3 or 7, 36-50 / 94*

898 TWELFTH SUNDAY IN ORDINARY TIME / A

READING I *Jeremiah 20, 10-13 / 95*

RESPONSORIAL PSALM *Psalm (68)69, 8-10.14.17.33-35 / 95*

CAP

Lord, in your great love, an-swer me.

It is for you that I suffer taunts,
that shame covers my face,
that I have become a stranger to my
  brothers,
an alien to my own mother's sons.
I burn with zeal for your house
and taunts against you fall on me. ℟.

The poor when they see it will be glad
and God-seeking hearts will revive;
for the Lord listens to the needy
and does not spurn his servants in their
  chains.
Let the heavens and the earth give him
  praise,
the sea and all its living creatures. ℟.

This is my prayer to you,
my prayer for your favor.
In your great love, answer me, O God,
with your help that never fails;
Lord, answer, for your love is kind;
in your compassion, turn towards
  me. ℟.

READING II *Romans 5, 12-15 / 95*

GOSPEL *Matthew 10, 26-33 / 95*

899 TWELFTH SUNDAY IN ORDINARY TIME / B

READING I *Job 38, 1.8-11 / 96*

RESPONSORIAL PSALM *Psalm (106)107, 23-24.25-26.28-29.30-31 / 96*

JRC

Give thanks to the Lord, his love is ev-er-last-ing.

Some sailed to the sea in ships
to trade on the mighty waters.
These men have seen the Lord's deeds,
the wonders he does in the deep. ℟.

For he spoke; he summoned the gale,
tossing the waves of the sea
up to heaven and back into the deep;
their soul melted away in their
  distress. ℟.

Then they cried to the Lord in their
  need
and he rescued them from their distress.
He stilled the storm to a whisper;
all the waves of the sea were
  hushed. ℟.

They rejoiced because of the calm
and he led them to the haven they
  desired.
Let them thank the Lord for his love,
the wonders he does for men. ℟.

READING II   *2 Corinthians 5, 14-17 / 96*

GOSPEL   *Mark 4, 35-41 / 96*

TWELFTH SUNDAY IN ORDINARY TIME / C   900

READING I   *Zechariah 12, 10-11 / /97*

RESPONSORIAL PSALM   *Psalm (62)63, 2.3-4.5-6.8-9 / 97*

My soul is thirst-ing for you, O Lord, thirst-ing for you my God.

O God, you are my God, for you I
  long;
for you my soul is thirsting.
My body pines for you
like a dry, weary land without
  water. ℟.

So I gaze on you in the sanctuary
to see your strength and your glory.
For your love is better than life,
my lips will speak your praise. ℟.

So I will bless you all my life,
in your name I will lift up my hands.
My soul shall be filled as with a
  banquet,
my mouth shall praise you with joy. ℟.

For you have been my help;
in the shadow of your wings I rejoice.
My soul clings to you;
your right hand holds me fast. ℟.

READING II   *Galatians 3, 26-29 / 97*

GOSPEL   *Luke 9, 18-24 / 97*

901 THIRTEENTH SUNDAY IN ORDINARY TIME / A

READING I *2 Kings 4, 8-11.14-16 / 98*

RESPONSORIAL PSALM *Psalm (88)89, 2-3.16-17.18-19 / 98*
JRC

For ev - er I will sing the good-ness of the Lord.

I will sing for ever of your love, O
Lord;
through all ages my mouth will proclaim
your truth.
Of this I am sure, that your love lasts
for ever,
that your truth is firmly established as
the heavens. ℟.

Happy the people who acclaim such a
king,
who walk, O Lord, in the light of your
face,
who find their joy every day in your
name,
who make your justice the source of
their bliss. ℟.

For you, O Lord, are the glory of their
strength;
by your favor it is that our might is
exalted;
for our ruler is in the keeping of the
Lord;
our king in the keeping of the Holy One
of Israel. ℟.

READING II *Romans 6, 3-4.8-11 / 98*

GOSPEL *Matthew 10, 37-42 / 98*

902 THIRTEENTH SUNDAY IN ORDINARY TIME / B

READING I *Wisdom 1, 13-15; 2, 23-24 / 99*

RESPONSORIAL PSALM *Psalm (29)30, 2.4.5-6.11.12.13 / 99*
JRC

I will praise you, Lord, for you have res-cued me.

I will praise you, Lord, you have
rescued me
and have not let my enemies rejoice
over me.
O Lord, you have raised my soul from
the dead,
restored me to life from those who sink
into the grave. ℟.

Sing psalms to the Lord, you who love
him,
give thanks to his holy name.
His anger lasts a moment; his favor all
through life.
At night there are tears, but joy comes
with dawn. ℟.

The Lord listened and had pity.
The Lord came to my help.
For me you have changed my mourning into dancing.
O Lord my God, I will thank you for ever. ℟.

READING II   *2 Corinthians 8, 7.9.13-15 / 99*

GOSPEL   *Mark 5, 21-43 or 5, 21-24.35-43 / 99*

THIRTEENTH SUNDAY IN ORDINARY TIME / C   903

READING I   *1 Kings 19, 16.19-21 / 100*

RESPONSORIAL PSALM   *Psalm (15)16, 1-2.5.7-8.9-10.11 / 100*

You are my in-her-i-tance, you, O Lord.

Preserve me, God, I take refuge in you.
I say to the Lord: "You are my God."
O Lord, it is you who are my portion
    and cup,
it is you yourself who are my prize. ℟.

I will bless the Lord who gives me
    counsel,
who even at night directs my heart.
I keep ther Lord ever in my sight;
since he is at my right hand, I shall
    stand firm. ℟.

And so my heart rejoices, my soul is
    glad;
even my body shall rest in safety.
For you will not leave my soul among
    the dead,
nor let your beloved know decay. ℟.

You will show me the path of life,
the fullness of joy in your presence,
at your right hand happiness for
    ever. ℟.

READING II   *Galatians 5, 1.13-18 / 100*

GOSPEL   *Luke 9, 51-62 / 100*

904 FOURTEENTH SUNDAY IN ORDINARY TIME / A

READING I   *Zechariah 9, 9-10 / 101*

RESPONSORIAL PSALM   *Psalm (144)145, 1-2.8-9.10-11.13-14 / 101*

I will praise your name for ev - er, my king and my God.

I will give you glory, O God my King,
I will bless your name for ever.
I will bless you day after day
and praise your name for ever. ℟.

The Lord is kind and full of compassion,
slow to anger, abounding in love.
How good is the Lord to all,
compassionate to all his
  creatures. ℟.

All your creatures shall thank you, O
  Lord,
and your friends shall repeat their
  blessing.
They shall speak of the glory of your
  reign
and declare your might, O God. ℟.

The Lord is faithful in all his words
and loving in all his deeds.
The Lord supports all who fall
and raises all who are bowed
  down. ℟.

READING II   *Romans 8, 9.11-13 / 101*

GOSPEL   *Matthew 11, 25-30 / 101*

905 FOURTEENTH SUNDAY IN ORDINARY TIME / B

READING I   *Ezekiel 2, 2-5 / 102*

RESPONSORIAL PSALM   *Psalm (122)123, 1-2.3-4 / 102*

Our eyes are fixed on the Lord, plead-ing for his mer-cy.

To you have I lifted up my eyes,
you who dwell in the heavens;
my eyes, like the eyes of slaves
on the hand of their lords. ℟.

Like the eyes of a servant
on the hand of her mistress,
so our eyes are on the Lord our God
till he show us his mercy. ℟.

Have mercy on us, Lord, have mercy.
We are filled with contempt.
Indeed all too full is our soul
with the scorn of the rich,
(with the proud man's disdain). ℟.

READING II   *2 Corinthians 12, 7-10 / 102*

GOSPEL   *Mark 6, 1-6 / 102*

FOURTEENTH SUNDAY IN ORDINARY TIME / C   906

READING I   *Isaiah 66, 10-14 / 103*

RESPONSORIAL PSALM   *Psalm (65)66, 1-3.4-5.6-7.16.20 / 103*

Let all the earth cry out, cry out to God with joy.

Cry out with joy to God all the earth,
O sing to the glory of his name.
O render him glorious praise.
Say to God: "How tremendous your
   deeds! ℞.

Before you all the earth shall bow,
shall sing to you, sing to your name!"
Come and see the works of God,
tremendous his deeds among
   men. ℞.

He turned the sea into dry land,
they passed through the river dry-shod.
Let joy then be in him;
he rules for ever by his might. ℞.

Come and hear, all who fear God.
I will tell what he did for my soul;
Blessed be God who did not reject my
   prayer
nor withhold his love from me. ℞.

READING II   *Galatians 6, 14-18 / 103*

GOSPEL   *Luke 10, 1-12.17-20 or 10, 1-9 / 103*

907 FIFTEENTH SUNDAY IN ORDINARY TIME / A

READING I   *Isaiah 55, 10-11 / 104*

RESPONSORIAL PSALM   *Psalm (64)65, 10.11.12-13.14 / 104*

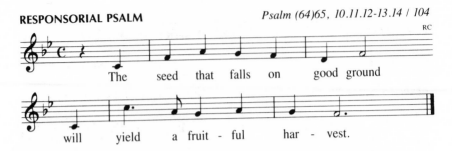

The seed that falls on good ground will yield a fruitful harvest.

You care for the earth, give it water;
you fill it with riches.
Your river in heaven brims over
to provide its grain. ℟.

And thus you provide for the earth;
you drench its furrows;
you level it, soften it with showers;
you bless its growth. ℟.

You crown the year with your goodness.
Abundance flows in your steps;
in the pastures of the wilderness it
flows. ℟.

The hills are girded with joy,
the meadows covered with flocks,
the valleys are decked with wheat.
They shout for joy, yes, they sing. ℟.

READING II   *Romans 8, 18-23 / 104*

GOSPEL   *Matthew 13, 1-23 or 13, 1-9 / 104*

908 FIFTEENTH SUNDAY IN ORDINARY TIME / B

READING I   *Amos 7, 12-15 / 105*

RESPONSORIAL PSALM   *Psalm (84)85, 9-10.11-12.13-14 / 105*

Lord, let us see your kindness, and grant us your salvation.

I will hear what the Lord God has to
say,
a voice that speaks of peace.
His help is near for those who fear him
and his glory will dwell in our land. ℟.

Mercy and faithfulness have met;
justice and peace have embraced.

Faithfulness shall spring from the earth
and justice look down from heaven. ℟.

The Lord will make us prosper
and our earth shall yield its fruit.
Justice shall march before him
and peace shall follow his steps. ℟.

READING II   *Ephesians 1, 3-14 or 1, 3-10 / 105*

GOSPEL   *Mark 6, 7-13 / 105*

FIFTEENTH SUNDAY IN ORDINARY TIME / C   909

READING I   *Deuteronomy 30, 10-14 / 106*

RESPONSORIAL PSALM   *Psalm (68)69, 14.17.30-31.33-34.36.37 / 106*

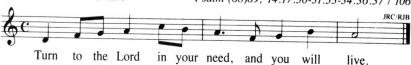

Turn to the Lord in your need, and you will live.

This is my prayer to you,
my prayer for your favor.
In your great love, answer me, O God,
with your help that never fails.
Lord, answer, for your love is kind;
in your compassion, turn towards
    me. ℞.

The poor when they see it will be glad
and God-seeking hearts will revive;
for the Lord listens to the needy
and does not spurn his servants in their
    chains. ℞.

As for me in my poverty and pain,
let your help, O God, lift me up.
I will praise God's name with a song;
I will glorify him with
    thanksgiving. ℞.

For God will bring help to Zion
and rebuild the cities of Judah.
The sons of his servants shall inherit
    it;
those who love his name shall dwell
    there. ℞.

READING II   *Colossians 1, 15-20 / 106*

GOSPEL   *Luke 10, 25-37 / 106*

910   SIXTEENTH SUNDAY IN ORDINARY TIME / A

READING I   *Wisdom 12, 13.16-19 / 107*

RESPONSORIAL PSALM   *Psalm (85)86, 5-6.9-10.15-17 / 107*

Lord, you are good and for-giv-ing.

O Lord, you are good and forgiving,
full of love to all who call.
Give heed, O Lord, to my prayer
and attend to the sound of my
   voice. ℞.

But you, God of mercy and compassion,
slow to anger, O Lord,
abounding in love and truth,
turn and take pity on me.
O give your strength to your
   servant. ℞.

All the nations shall come to adore you
and glorify your name, O Lord,
for you are great and do marvelous
   deeds,
you who alone are God. ℞.

READING II   *Romans 8, 26-27 / 107*

GOSPEL   *Matthew 13, 24-43 or 13, 24-30 / 107*

911   SIXTEENTH SUNDAY IN ORDINARY TIME / B

READING I   *Jeremiah 23, 1-6 / 108*

RESPONSORIAL PSALM   *Psalm (22)23, 1-3.3-4.5.6 / 108*

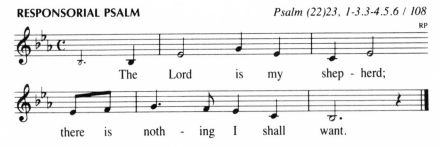

The Lord is my shep-herd; there is noth-ing I shall want.

The Lord is my shepherd;
there is nothing I shall want.
Fresh and green are the pastures
where he gives me repose.
Near restful waters he leads me,
to revive my drooping spirit. ℞.

He guides me along the right path;
he is true to his name.
If I should walk in the valley of
   darkness
no evil would I fear.
You are there with your crook and your
   staff;
with these you give me comfort. ℞.

You have prepared a banquet for me
in the sight of my foes.
My head you have anointed with oil;
my cup is overflowing. ℞.

Surely goodness and kindness shall
follow me
all the days of my life.
In the Lord's own house shall I dwell
for ever and ever. ℞.

READING II   *Ephesians 2, 13-18 / 108*

GOSPEL   *Mark 6, 30-34 / 108*

SIXTEENTH SUNDAY IN ORDINARY TIME / C   912

READING I   *Genesis 18, 1-10 / 109*

RESPONSORIAL PSALM   *Psalm (14)15, 2-3.3-4.5 / 109*

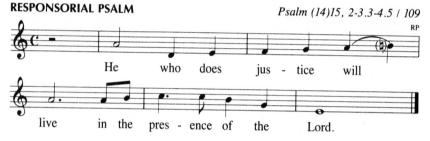

He who does jus-tice will live in the pres-ence of the Lord.

He who walks without fault,
he who acts with justice
and speaks the truth from his heart,
he who does not slander with his
tongue. ℞.

Who takes no interest on a loan
and accepts no bribes against the
innocent.
Such a man will stand firm for
ever. ℞.

He who does no wrong to his
brother,
who casts no slur on his neighbor,
who holds the godless in disdain,
but honors those who fear the Lord; ℞.

READING II   *Colossians 1, 24-28 / 109*

GOSPEL   *Luke 10, 38-42 / 109*

913 SEVENTEENTH SUNDAY IN ORDINARY TIME / A

READING I   *1 Kings 3, 5.7-12 / 110*

RESPONSORIAL PSALM   *Psalm (118)119, 57.72.76-77.127-128.129-130 / 110*

Lord,   I   love   your com - mands.

My part, I have resolved, O Lord,
is to obey your word.
The law from your mouth means more
    to me
than silver and gold. ℞.

Let your love be ready to console me
by your promise to your servant.
Let your love come and I shall live
for your law is my delight. ℞.

That is why I love your commands
more than finest gold,
why I rule my life by your precepts,
and hate false ways. ℞.

Your will is wonderful indeed;
therefore I obey it.
The unfolding of your word gives light
and teaches the simple. ℞.

READING II   *Romans 8, 28-30 / 110*

GOSPEL   *Matthew 13, 44-52 or 13, 44-46 / 110*

914 SEVENTEENTH SUNDAY IN ORDINARY TIME / B

READING I   *2 Kings 4, 42-44 / 111*

RESPONSORIAL PSALM   *Psalm (144)145, 10-11.15-16.17-18 / 111*

The   hand   of   the Lord   feeds   us;

he   an - swers   all   our   needs.

All your creatures shall thank you, O
    Lord,
and your friends shall repeat their
    blessing.
They shall speak of the glory of your
    reign
and declare your might, O God. ℞.

The eyes of all creatures look to you
and you give them their food in due
    time.
You open wide your hand,
grant the desires of all who live. ℞.

The Lord is just in all his ways
and loving in all his deeds.
He is close to all who call him,
who call on him from their hearts. ℞.

READING II *Ephesians 4, 1-6 / 111*

GOSPEL *John 6, 1-15 / 111*

SEVENTEENTH SUNDAY IN ORDINARY TIME / C 915

READING I *Genesis 18, 20-32 / 112*

RESPONSORIAL PSALM *Psalm (137)138, 1-2.2-3.6-7.7-8 / 112*

Lord, on the day I called for help, you answered me.

I thank you, Lord, with all my heart,
you have heard the words of my mouth.
In the presence of the angels I will
  bless you.
I will adore before your holy
  temple. ℟.

I thank you for your faithfulness and
  love
which excel all we ever knew of you.
On the day I called, you answered;
you increased the strength of my
  soul. ℟.

The Lord is high yet he looks on the
  lowly
and the haughty he knows from afar.
Though I walk in the midst of affliction
you give me life and frustrate my
  foes. ℟.

You stretch out your hand and save me,
your hand will do all things for me.
Your love, O Lord, is eternal,
discard not the work of your hands. ℟.

READING II *Colossians 2, 12-14 / 112*

GOSPEL *Luke 11, 1-13 / 112*

916 EIGHTEENTH SUNDAY IN ORDINARY TIME / A

READING I   *Isaiah 55, 1-3 / 113*

RESPONSORIAL PSALM   *Psalm (144)145, 8-9.15-16.17-18 / 113*

The hand of the Lord feeds us;·
he an-swers all our needs.

The Lord is kind and full of compassion,
slow to anger, abounding in love.
How good is the Lord to all,
compassionate to all his creatures. ℟.

The eyes of all creatures look to you
and you give them their food in due
  time.
You open wide your hand,
grant the desires of all who live. ℟.

The Lord is just in all his ways
and loving in all his deeds.
He is close to all who call him,
who call on him from their hearts. ℟.

READING II   *Romans 8, 35.37-39 / 113*

GOSPEL   *Matthew 14, 13-21 / 113*

917 EIGHTEENTH SUNDAY IN ORDINARY TIME / B

READING I   *Exodus 16, 2-4.12-15 / 114*

RESPONSORIAL PSALM   *Psalm (77)78, 3-4.23-24.25.54 / 114*

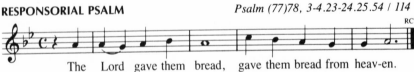

The Lord gave them bread, gave them bread from heav-en.

The things we have heard and
  understood,
the things our fathers have told us
these we will not hide from their
  children
but will tell them to the next generation:
the glories of the Lord and his might
and the marvelous deeds he has
  done. ℟.

Yet he commanded the clouds above
and opened the gates of heaven.
He rained down manna for their food,
and gave them bread from heaven. ℟.

Mere men ate the bread of angels.
He sent them abundance of food.
So he brought them to his holy land,
to the mountain which his right hand
  had won. ℟.

READING II   *Ephesians 4, 17.20-24 / 114*

GOSPEL   *John 6, 24-35 / 114*

EIGHTEENTH SUNDAY IN ORDINARY TIME / C   918

READING I   *Ecclesiastes 1, 2; 2, 21-23 / 115*

RESPONSORIAL PSALM   *Psalm (94)95, 1-2.6-7.8-9 / 115*

If to-day you hear his voice, O hard-en not your hearts.

Come, ring out our joy to the Lord;
hail the rock who saves us.
Let us come before him, giving thanks,
with songs let us hail the Lord. ℞.

Come in; let us bow and bend low;
let us kneel before the God who made
   us
for he is our God and we
the people who belong to his pasture,
the flock that is led by his hand. ℞.

O that today you would listen to his
   voice!
"Harden not your hearts as at Meribah,
as on that day at Massah in the desert
when your fathers put me to the test;
when they tried me, though they saw
   my work." ℞.

READING II   *Colossians 3, 1-5.9-11 / 115*

GOSPEL   *Luke 12, 13-21 / 115*

919 NINETEENTH SUNDAY IN ORDINARY TIME / A

READING I   *1 Kings 19, 9.11-13 / 116*

RESPONSORIAL PSALM   *Psalm (84)85, 9.10.11-12.13-14 / 116*

Lord, let us see your kind-ness, and grant us your sal - va-tion.

I will hear what the Lord God has to
  say,
a voice that speaks of peace.
His help is near for those who fear him
and his glory will dwell in our land. ℟.

Mercy and faithfulness have met;
justice and peace have embraced.

Faithfulness shall spring from the earth
and justice look down from heaven. ℟.

The Lord will make us prosper
and our earth shall yield its fruit.
Justice shall march before him
and peace shall follow his steps. ℟.

READING II   *Romans 9, 1-5 / 116*

GOSPEL   *Matthew 14, 22-33 / 116*

---

920 NINETEENTH SUNDAY IN ORDINARY TIME / B

READING I   *1 Kings 19, 4-8 / 117*

RESPONSORIAL PSALM   *Psalm (33)34, 2-3.4-5.6-7.8-9 / 117*

Taste and   see   the   good - ness of   the   Lord.

I will bless the Lord at all times,
his praise always on my lips;
in the Lord my soul shall make its
  boast.
The humble shall hear and be glad. ℟.

Glorify the Lord with me.
Together let us praise him name.
I sought the Lord and he answered me;
from all my terrors he set me free. ℟.

Look towards him and be radiant;

let your faces not be abashed.
This poor man called; the Lord heard
  him
and rescued him from all his
  distress. ℟.

The angel of the Lord is encamped
around those who revere him, to rescue
  them.
Taste and see that the Lord is good.
He is happy who seeks refuge in
  him. ℟.

READING II   *Ephesians 4, 30-5, 2 / 117*

GOSPEL   *John 6, 41-51 / 117*

NINETEENTH SUNDAY IN ORDINARY TIME / C

READING I   *Wisdom 18, 6-9 / 118*

RESPONSORIAL PSALM   *Psalm (32)33, 1.12.18-19.20-22 / 118*

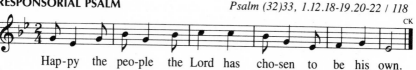

Hap-py the peo-ple the Lord has cho-sen to be his own.

Ring out your joy to the Lord, O you
   just;
for praise is fitting for loyal hearts.
They are happy, whose God is the Lord,
the people he has chosen as his
   own. ℟.

The Lord looks on those who revere
him,

on those who hope in his love,
to rescue their souls from death,
to keep them alive in famine. ℟.

Our soul is waiting for the Lord.
The Lord is our help and our shield.
May your love be upon us, O Lord,
as we place all our hope in you. ℟.

READING II   *Hebrews 11, 1-2.8-19 or 11, 1-2.8-12 / 118*

GOSPEL   *Luke 12, 32-48 or 12, 35-40 / 118*

TWENTIETH SUNDAY IN ORDINARY TIME / A

READING I   *Isaiah 56, 1.6-7 / 119*

RESPONSORIAL PSALM   *Psalm (66)67, 2-3.5.6.8 / 119*

O God, O God, let all the na-tions praise you!

O God, be gracious and bless us
and let your face shed its light upon us.
So will your ways be known upon earth
and all nations learn your saving
   help. ℟.

Let the nations be glad and exult
for you rule the world with justice.
With fairness you rule the peoples,
you guide the nations on earth. ℟.

Let the peoples praise you, O God;
let all the peoples praise you.
May God still give us his blessing
till the ends of the earth revere him. ℟.

READING II   *Romans 11, 13-15.29-32 / 119*

GOSPEL   *Matthew 15, 21-28 / 119*

923 TWENTIETH SUNDAY IN ORDINARY TIME / B

READING I   *Proverbs 9, 1-6 / 120*

RESPONSORIAL PSALM   *Psalm (33)34, 2-3.10-11.12-13.14-15 / 120*

I will bless the Lord at all times,
his praise always on my lips;
in the Lord my soul shall make its
  boast.
The humble shall hear and be glad. ℟.

Come, children, and hear me
that I may teach you the fear of the
  Lord.
Who is he who longs for life
and many days, to enjoy his
  prosperity? ℟.

Revere the Lord, you his saints.
They lack nothing, those who revere
  him.
Strong lions suffer want and go hungry
but those who seek the Lord lack no
  blessing. ℟.

Then keep your tongue from evil
and your lips from speaking deceit.
Turn aside from evil and do good;
seek and strive after peace. ℟.

READING II   *Ephesians 5, 15-20 / 120*

GOSPEL   *John 6, 51-58 / 120*

924 TWENTIETH SUNDAY IN ORDINARY TIME / C

READING I   *Jeremiah 38, 4-6.8-10 / 121*

RESPONSORIAL PSALM   *Psalm (39)40, 2.3.4.18 / 121*

I waited, I waited for the Lord
and he stooped down to me. ℟.

He put a new song into my mouth,
praise of our God.
Many shall see and fear
and shall trust in the Lord. ℟.

He heard my cry.
He drew me from the deadly pit,
from the miry clay.
He set my feet upon a rock
and made my footsteps firm. ℟.

As for me, wretched and poor,
the Lord thinks of me.
You are my rescuer, my help,
O God, do not delay. ℟.

READING II   *Hebrews 12, 1-4 / 121*

GOSPEL *Luke 12, 49-53 / 121*

TWENTY-FIRST SUNDAY IN ORDINARY TIME / A   925

READING I *Isaiah 22, 15.19-23 / 122*

RESPONSORIAL PSALM *Psalm (137)138, 1-2.2-3.6.8 / 122*

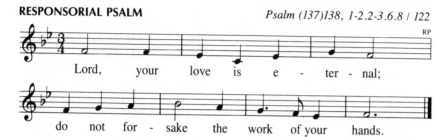

Lord, your love is e - ter - nal; do not for - sake the work of your hands.

I thank you, Lord, with all my heart,
you have heard the words of my mouth.
In the presence of the angels I will
   bless you.
I will adore before your holy
   temple. ℞.

I thank you for your faithfulness and
   love
which excel all we ever knew of you.
On the day I called, you answered;
you increased the strength of my
   soul. ℞.

The Lord is high yet he looks on the
   lowly
and the haughty he knows from afar.
Your love, O Lord, is eternal,
discard not the work of your hands. ℞.

READING II *Romans 11, 33-36 / 122*

GOSPEL *Matthew 16, 13-20 / 122*

926   TWENTY-FIRST SUNDAY IN ORDINARY TIME / B

READING I   *Joshua 24, 1-2.15-17.18 / 123*

RESPONSORIAL PSALM   *Psalm (33)34, 2-3.16-17.18-19.20-21.22-23 / 123*

RP

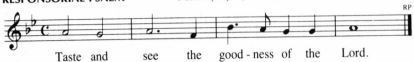

Taste and see the good-ness of the Lord.

I will bless the Lord at all times,
his praise always on my lips;
in the Lord my soul shall make its
    boast.
The humble shall hear and be glad. ℟.

The Lord turns his face against the
    wicked
to destroy their remembrance from the
    earth.
The Lord turns his eyes to the just
and his ears to their appeal. ℟.

They call and the Lord hears
and rescues them in all their distress.
The Lord is close to the broken-hearted;
those whose spirit is crushed he will
    save. ℟.

Many are the trials of the just man but
from them all the Lord will rescue him.
He will keep guard over all his bones,
not one of his bones shall be
    broken. ℟.

Evil brings death to the wicked;
those who hate the good are doomed.
The Lord ransoms the souls of his
    servants.
Those who hide in him shall not be
    condemned. ℟.

READING II   *Ephesians 5, 21-32 / 123*

GOSPEL   *John 6, 60-69 / 123*

927   TWENTY-FIRST SUNDAY IN ORDINARY TIME / C

READING I   *Isaiah 66, 18-21 / 124*

RESPONSORIAL PSALM   *Psalm (116)117, 1.2 / 124*

CAP

Go out to all the world and tell the Good News.

O praise the Lord, all you nations,
acclaim him all you peoples! ℟.

Strong is his love for us;
he is faithful for ever. ℟.

READING II   *Hebrews 12, 5-7.11-13 / 124*

GOSPEL   *Luke 13, 22-30 / 124*

TWENTY-SECOND SUNDAY IN ORDINARY TIME / A   928

READING I   *Jeremiah 20, 7-9 / 125*

RESPONSORIAL PSALM   *Psalm (62)63, 2.3-4.5-6.8-9 / 125*

My soul is thirst-ing for you, O Lord, thirst-ing for you my God.

O God, you are my God, for you I long;
for you my soul is thirsting.
My body pines for you
like a dry, weary land without water. ℟.

So I gaze on you in the sanctuary
to see your strength and your glory.
For your love is better than life,
my lips will speak your praise. ℟.

So, I will bless you all my life,
in your name I will lift up my hands.
My soul shall be filled as with a
  banquet,
my mouth shall praise you with joy. ℟.

For you have been my help;
in the shadow of your wings I rejoice.
My soul clings to you;
your right hand holds me fast. ℟.

READING II   *Romans 12, 1-2 / 125*

GOSPEL   *Matthew 16, 21-27 / 125*

929 TWENTY-SECOND SUNDAY IN ORDINARY TIME / B

READING I   *Deuteronomy 4, 1-2.6-8 / 126*

RESPONSORIAL PSALM   *Psalm (14)15, 2-3.3-4.4-5 / 126*

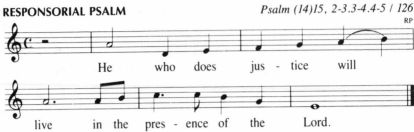

He who walks without fault,
he who acts with justice
and speaks the truth from his heart,
he who does not slander with his
    tongue, ℞.

He who does no wrong to his
    brother,
who casts no slur on his neighbor,
who holds the godless in disdain,
but honors those who fear the Lord. ℞.

He who keeps his pledge, come what
    may,
who takes no interest on a loan
and accepts no bribes against the
    innocent.
Such a man will stand firm for ever. ℞.

READING II   *James 1, 17-18.21-22.27 / 126*

GOSPEL   *Mark 7, 1-8.14-15.21-23 / 126*

930 TWENTY-SECOND SUNDAY IN ORDINARY TIME / C

READING I   *Sirach 3, 17-18.20.28-29 / 127*

RESPONSORIAL PSALM   *Psalm (67)68, 4-5.6-7.10-11 / 127*

But the just shall rejoice at the presence
    of God,
they shall exult and dance for joy.
O sing to the Lord, make music to his
    name.
Rejoice in the Lord, exult at his
    presence. ℞.

Father of the orphan, defender
    of the widow,
such is God in his holy place.
God gives the lowly a home
    to live in;
he leads the prisoners forth
    into freedom. ℞.

You poured down, O God, a generous rain;
when your people were starved you gave them new life.

It was there that your people found a home,
prepared in your goodness, O God, for the poor. ℟.

READING II   *Hebrews 12, 18-19.22-24 / 127*

GOSPEL   *Luke 14, 1.7-14 / 127*

TWENTY-THIRD SUNDAY IN ORDINARY TIME / A   931

READING I   *Ezekiel 33, 7-9 / 128*

RESPONSORIAL PSALM   *Psalm (94)95, 1-2.6-7.8-9 / 128*

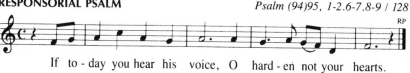

If to-day you hear his voice, O hard-en not your hearts.

Come, ring out our joy to the Lord;
hail the rock who saves us.
Let us come before him, giving thanks,
with songs let us hail the Lord. ℟.

Come in let us bow and bend low;
let us kneel before the God who made us
for he is our God and we the
people who belong to his pasture,
the flock that is led by his hand. ℟.

O that today you would listen to his voice!
"Harden not your hearts as at Meribah,
as on that day at Massah in the desert
when your fathers put me to the test;
when they tried me, though they saw my work." ℟.

READING II   *Romans 13, 8-10 / 128*

GOSPEL   *Matthew 18, 15-20 / 128*

932 TWENTY-THIRD SUNDAY IN ORDINARY TIME / B

READING I   *Isaiah 35, 4-7 / 129*

RESPONSORIAL PSALM   *Psalm (145)146, 7.8-9.9-10 / 129*

Praise the Lord, my soul! Praise the Lord!

It is he who keeps faith for ever,
who is just to those who are oppressed.
It is he who gives bread to the
    hungry,
the Lord, who sets prisoners free. ℞.

The Lord who gives sight to the blind,
who raises up those who are bowed
    down,
the Lord, who protects the stranger
and upholds the widow and orphan. ℞.

It is the Lord who loves the just
but thwarts the path of the wicked.
The Lord will reign for ever,
Zion's God, from age to age. ℞.

READING II   *James 2, 1-5 / 129*

GOSPEL   *Mark 7, 31-37 / 129*

933 TWENTY-THIRD SUNDAY IN ORDINARY TIME / C

READING I   *Wisdom 9, 13-18 / 130*

RESPONSORIAL PSALM   *Psalm (89)90, 3-4.5-6.12-13.14, 17 / 130*

In ev-'ry age, O Lord, you have been our re - fuge.

You turn men back into dust
and say: "Go back, sons of men."
To your eyes a thousand years
are like yesterday, come and gone,
no more than a watch in the night. ℞.

You sweep men away like a dream,
like grass which springs up in the
    morning.
In the morning it springs up and
    flowers;
by evening it withers and fades. ℞.

Make us know the shortness of our life
that we may gain wisdom of heart.
Lord, relent! Is your anger for ever?
Show pity to your servants. ℞.

In the morning, fill us with your love;
we shall exult and rejoice all our days.
Let the favor of the Lord be upon us:
give success to the work of our hands
(give success to the work of our
    hands). ℞.

READING II   *Philemon 9-10.12-17 / 130*

GOSPEL   *Luke 14, 25-33 / 130*

TWENTY-FOURTH SUNDAY IN ORDINARY TIME / A   934

READING I   *Sirach 27, 30-28, 7 / 131*

RESPONSORIAL PSALM   *Psalm (102)103, 1-2.3-4.9-10.11-12 / 131*

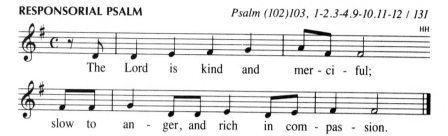

The Lord is kind and mer - ci - ful;
slow to an - ger, and rich in com - pas - sion.

My soul, give thanks to the Lord,
all my being, bless his holy name.
My soul, give thanks to the Lord
and never forget all his blessings. ℟.

It is he who forgives all your guilt,
who heals every one of your ills,
who redeems your life from the grave,
who crowns you with love and
   compassion. ℟.

His wrath will come to an end;
he will not be angry for ever.
He does not treat us according to our
   sins
nor repay us according to our
   faults. ℟.

For as the heavens are high above the
   earth
so strong is his love for those who fear
   him.
As far as the east is from the west,
so far does he remove our sins. ℟.

READING II   *Romans 14, 7-9 / 131*

GOSPEL   *Matthew 18, 21-35 / 131*

935 TWENTY-FOURTH SUNDAY IN ORDINARY TIME / B

READING I   *Isaiah 50, 4-9 / 132*

RESPONSORIAL PSALM   *Psalm (114)115, 1-2.3-4.5-6.8-9 / 132*

I will walk in the pres-ence of the Lord, in the land of the liv-ing.

I love the Lord for he has heard
the cry of my appeal;
for he turned his ear to me
in the day when I called him. ℞.

They surrounded me, the snares of
 death,
with the anguish of the tomb;
they caught me, sorrow and distress.
I called on the Lord's name.
O Lord, my God, deliver me! ℞.

How gracious is the Lord, and just;
our God has compassion.
The Lord protects the simple hearts;
I was helpless so he saved me. ℞.

He has kept my soul from death,
(my eyes from tears)
and my feet from stumbling.
I will walk in the presence of the Lord
in the land of the living. ℞.

READING II   *James 2, 14-18 / 132*

GOSPEL   *Mark 8, 27-35 / 132*

---

936 TWENTY-FOURTH SUNDAY IN ORDINARY TIME / C

READING I   *Exodus 32, 7-11.13-14 / 133*

RESPONSORIAL PSALM   *Psalm (50)51, 3-4.12-13.17.19 / 133*

I will rise and go to my fa - ther.

Have mercy on me, God, in your
 kindness.
In your compassion blot out my
 offense.
O wash me more and more from my
 guilt
and cleanse me from my sin. ℞.

A pure heart create for me, O God,
put a steadfast spirit within me.

Do not cast me away from your
 presence,
nor deprive me of your holy spirit. ℞.

O Lord, open my lips
and my mouth shall declare your praise.
My sacrifice, a contrite spirit,
a humbled, contrite heart you will not
 spurn. ℞.

READING II   *1 Timothy 1, 12-17 / 133*

GOSPEL *Luke 15, 1-32 or 15, 1-10 / 133*

TWENTY-FIFTH SUNDAY IN ORDINARY TIME / A   937

READING I *Isaiah 55, 6-9 / 134*

RESPONSORIAL PSALM *Psalm (144)145, 2-3.8-9.17-18 / 134*

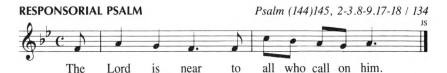

The Lord is near to all who call on him.

I will bless you day after day
and praise your name for ever.
The Lord is great, highly to be
   praised,
his greatness cannot be measured. ℟.

The Lord is kind and full of compassion,
slow to anger, abounding in love.

How good is the Lord to all,
compassionate to all his creatures. ℟.

The Lord is just in all his ways
and loving in all his deeds.
He is close to all who call him,
who call on him from their hearts. ℟.

READING II *Philippians 1, 20-24.27 / 134*

GOSPEL *Matthew 20, 1-16 / 134*

TWENTY-FIFTH SUNDAY IN ORDINARY TIME / B   938

READING I *Wisdom 2, 12.17-20 / 135*

RESPONSORIAL PSALM *Psalm (53)54, 3-4.5.6-8 / 135*

The Lord up-holds my life.

O God, save me by your name;
by your power, uphold my cause.
O God, hear my prayer;
listen to the words of my mouth. ℟.

For proud men have risen against me,
ruthless men seek my life.

They have no regard for God. ℟.

But I have God for my help.
The Lord upholds my life.
I will sacrifice to you with willing
   heart
and praise your name for it is good. ℟.

READING II *James 3, 16-4, 3 / 135*

GOSPEL *Mark 9, 30-37 / 135*

939 TWENTY-FIFTH SUNDAY IN ORDINARY TIME / C

READING I *Amos 8, 4-7 / 136*

RESPONSORIAL PSALM *Psalm (112)113, 1-2.4-6.7-8 / 136*

Praise the Lord who lifts up the poor.

Praise, O servants of the Lord,
praise the name of the Lord!
May the name of the Lord be blessed
both now and for evermore! ℞.

High above all nations is the Lord,
above the heavens his glory.
Who is like the Lord, our God,
who has risen on high to his throne

yet stoops from the heights to look
down,
to look down upon heaven and
earth? ℞.

From the dust he lifts up the lowly,
from the dungheap he raises the poor
to set him in the company of princes,
yes, with the princes of his people. ℞.

READING II *1 Timothy 2, 1-8 / 136*

GOSPEL *Luke 16, 1-13 or 16, 10-13 / 136*

940 TWENTY-SIXTH SUNDAY IN ORDINARY TIME / A

READING I *Ezekiel 18, 25-28 / 137*

RESPONSORIAL PSALM *Psalm (24)25, 4-5.6-7.8-9 / 137*

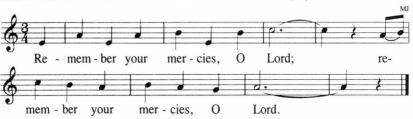

Re - mem - ber your mer - cies, O Lord; re-

mem - ber your mer - cies, O Lord.

Lord, make me know your ways.
Lord, teach me your paths.
Make me walk in your truth, and
teach me,
for you are God my savior. ℞.

Remember your mercy, Lord,
and the love you have shown from of
old.

Do not remember the sins of my youth.
In your love remember me,
because of your goodness, O Lord. ℞.

The Lord is good and upright.
He shows the path to those who stray,
he guides the humble in the right path,
he teaches his way to the poor. ℞.

READING II *Philippians 2, 1-11 or 2, 1-5 / 137*

GOSPEL *Matthew 21, 28-32 / 137*

TWENTY-SIXTH SUNDAY IN ORDINARY TIME / B 941

READING I *Numbers 11, 25-29 / 138*

RESPONSORIAL PSALM *Psalm (18)19, 8.10.12-13.14 / 138*

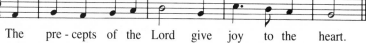

The pre - cepts of the Lord give joy to the heart.

The law of the Lord is perfect,
it revives the soul.
The rule of the Lord is to be trusted,
it gives wisdom to the simple. ℞.

So in them your servant finds
  instruction;
great reward is in their keeping.
But who can detect all his errors?
From hidden faults acquit me. ℞.

The fear of the Lord is holy,
abiding for ever.
The decrees of the Lord are truth
and all of them just. ℞.

From presumption restrain your servant
and let it not rule me.
Then shall I be blameless,
clean from grave sin. ℞.

READING II *James 5, 1-6 / 138*

GOSPEL *Mark 9, 38-43.45.47-48 / 138*

TWENTY-SIXTH SUNDAY IN ORDINARY TIME / C 942

READING I *Amos 6, 1.4-7 / 139*

RESPONSORIAL PSALM *Psalm (145)146, 7.8-9.9-10 / 139*

Praise the Lord, my soul! Praise the Lord!

It is he who keeps faith for ever,
who is just to those who are oppressed.
It is he who gives bread to the
  hungry,
the Lord, who sets prisoners free. ℞.

down,
the Lord, who protects the stranger
and upholds the widow and orphan. ℞.

The Lord who gives sight to the blind,
who raises up those who are bowed

It is the Lord who loves the just
but thwarts the path of the wicked.
The Lord will reign for ever,
Zion's God, from age to age. ℞.

READING II *1 Timothy 6, 11-16 / 139*

GOSPEL *Luke 16, 19-31 / 139*

943 TWENTY-SEVENTH SUNDAY IN ORDINARY TIME / A

READING I *Isaiah 5, 1-7 / 140*

RESPONSORIAL PSALM *Psalm (79)80, 9.12.13-14.15-16.19-20 / 140*

The vine-yard of the Lord is the house of Is - ra - el.

You brought a vine out of Egypt;
to plant it you drove out the nations.
It stretched out its branches to the sea,
to the Great River it stretched out its
shoots. ℞.

Then why have you broken down its
walls?
It is plucked by all who pass by.
It is ravaged by the boar of the forest,
devoured by the beasts of the field. ℞.

God of hosts, turn again, we implore,
look down from heaven and see.
Visit this vine and protect it,
the vine your right hand has
planted. ℞.

And we shall never forsake you again;
give us life that we may call upon your
name.
God of hosts, bring us back;
let your face shine on us and we shall
be saved. ℞.

READING II *Philippians 4, 6-9 / 140*

GOSPEL *Matthew 21, 33-43 / 140*

944 TWENTY-SEVENTH SUNDAY IN ORDINARY TIME / B

READING I *Genesis 2, 18-24 / 141*

RESPONSORIAL PSALM *Psalm (127)128, 1-2.3.4-5.6 / 141*

May the Lord bless and pro-tect us all the days of our life.

O blessed are those who fear the Lord
and walk in his ways!
By the labor of your hands you shall
eat.
You will be happy and prosper. ℞.

Your wife like a fruitful vine
in the heart of your house;
your children like shoots of the olive
around your table. ℞.

Indeed thus shall be blessed
the man who fears the Lord.
May the Lord bless you from Zion
all the days of your life! ℞.

May you see your children's children
in a happy Jerusalem!
On Israel, peace! ℞.

READING II *Hebrews 2, 9-11 / 141*

GOSPEL   *Mark 10, 2-16 or 10, 2-12 / 141*

TWENTY-SEVENTH SUNDAY IN ORDINARY TIME / C   945

READING I   *Habakkuk 1, 2-3; 2, 2-4 / 142*

RESPONSORIAL PSALM   *Psalm (94)95, 1-2.6-7.8-9 / 142*

If to-day you hear his voice, O hard-en not your hearts.

Come, ring out your joy to the Lord;
hail the rock who saves us.
Let us come before him giving thanks,
with songs let us hail the Lord. ℟.

Come in, let us bow and bend low;
let us kneel before the God who made
 us
for he is our God, and we
the people who belong to his pasture,
the flock that is led by his hand. ℟.

O that today you would listen to his
 voice!
"Harden not your hearts as at Meribah,
as on that day at Massah in the desert
when your forbears put me to the test;
when they tried me, though they saw
 my work." ℟.

READING II   *2 Timothy 1, 6-8.13-14 / 142*

GOSPEL   *Luke 17, 5-10 / 142*

946 TWENTY-EIGHTH SUNDAY IN ORDINARY TIME / A

READING I *Isaiah 25, 6-10 / 143*

RESPONSORIAL PSALM *Psalm (22)23, 1-3.3-4.5.6 / 143*

RJB

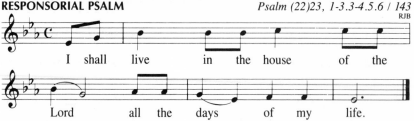

I shall live in the house of the Lord all the days of my life.

The Lord is my shepherd;
there is nothing I shall want.
Fresh and green are the pastures
where he gives me repose.
Near restful waters he leads me,
to revive my drooping spirit. ℞.

He guides me along the right path;
he is true to his name.
If I should walk in the valley of
darkness
no evil would I fear.
You are there with your crook and your
staff;
with these you give me comfort. ℞.

You have prepared a banquet for me
in the sight of my foes.
My head you have anointed with oil;
my cup is overflowing. ℞.

Surely goodness and kindness shall
follow me
all the days of my life.
In the Lord's own house shall I dwell
for ever and ever. ℞.

READING II *Philippians 4, 12-14.19-20 / 143*

GOSPEL *Matthew 22, 1-14 or 22, 1-10 / 143*

947 TWENTY-EIGHTH SUNDAY IN ORDINARY TIME / B

READING I *Wisdom 7, 7-11 / 144*

RESPONSORIAL PSALM *Psalm (89)90, 12-13.14-15.16-17 / 144*

RJB

Fill us with your love, O Lord, and we will sing for joy!

Make us know the shortness of our life
that we may gain wisdom of heart.
Lord, relent! Is your anger for ever?
Show pity to your servants. ℞.

In the morning, fill us with your love;
we shall exult and rejoice all our days.
Give us joy to balance our affliction
for the years when we knew
misfortune. ℞.

Show forth your work to your servants;
let your glory shine on their children.
Let the favor of the Lord be upon us:
give success to the work of our hands
(give success to the work of our
    hands). ℞.

READING II   *Hebrews 4, 12-13 / 144*

GOSPEL   *Mark 10, 17-30 or 10, 17-27 / 144*

TWENTY-EIGHTH SUNDAY IN ORDINARY TIME / C   948

READING I   *2 Kings 5, 14-17 / 145*

RESPONSORIAL PSALM   *Psalm (97)98, 1.2-3.3-4 / 145*

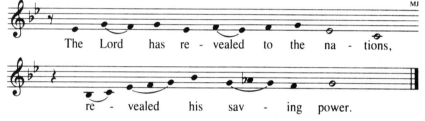

The Lord has re - vealed to the na - tions,
re - vealed his sav - ing power.

Sing a new song to the Lord
for he has worked wonders.
His right hand and his holy arm
have brought salvation. ℞.

All the ends of the earth have seen
the salvation of our God.
Shout to the Lord, all the earth,
ring out your joy, ℞.

The Lord has made known his
    salvation;
has shown his justice to the nations.
He has remembered his truth and love
for the house of Israel. ℞.

READING II   *2 Timothy 2, 8-13 / 145*

GOSPEL   *Luke 17, 11-19 / 145*

949 TWENTY-NINTH SUNDAY IN ORDINARY TIME / A

READING I   *Isaiah 45, 1.4-6 / 146*

RESPONSORIAL PSALM   *Psalm (95)96, 1.3.4-5.7-8.9-10 / 146*

Give the Lord glo - ry, glo - ry and hon - or.

O sing a new song to the Lord,
sing to the Lord all the earth.
Tell among the nations his glory
and his wonders among all the
   peoples. ℟.

The Lord is great and worthy of praise,
to be feared above all gods;
the gods of the heathens are naught.
It was the Lord who made the
   heavens. ℟.

Give the Lord, you families of peoples,
give the Lord glory and power;
give the Lord the glory of his name.
Bring an offering and enter his
   courts. ℟.

Worship the Lord in his temple.
O earth, tremble before him.
Proclaim to the nations: "God is king."
He will judge the peoples in
   fairness. ℟.

READING II   *1 Thessalonians 1, 1-5 / 146*

GOSPEL   *Matthew 22, 15-21 / 146*

950 TWENTY-NINTH SUNDAY IN ORDINARY TIME / B

READING I   *Isaiah 53, 10-11 / 147*

RESPONSORIAL PSALM   *Psalm (32)33, 4-5.18-19.20.22 / 147*

Lord, let your mer - cy be on us,

as we place our trust in you.

For the word of the Lord is faithful
and all his works to be trusted.
The Lord loves justice and right
and fills the earth with his love. ℟.

The Lord looks on those who revere
   him,
on those who hope in his love,
to rescue their souls from death,
to keep them alive in famine. ℟.

Our soul is waiting for the Lord.
The Lord is our help and our shield.
May your love be upon us, O Lord,
as we place all our hope in you. ℟.

READING II   *Hebrews 4, 14-16 / 147*

GOSPEL   *Mark 10, 35-45 or 10, 42-45 / 147*

TWENTY-NINTH SUNDAY IN ORDINARY TIME / C   951

READING I   *Exodus 17, 8-13 / 148*

RESPONSORIAL PSALM   *Psalm (120)121, 1-2.3-4.5-6.7-8 / 148*

Our help is from the Lord who made heav - en and earth.

I lift up my eyes to the mountains;
from where shall come my help?
My help shall come from the Lord
who made heaven and earth. ℞.

May he never allow you to stumble!
Let him sleep not, your guard.
No, he sleeps not nor slumbers,
Israel's guard. ℞.

The Lord is your guard and your shade;
at your right side he stands.
By day the sun shall not smite you
nor the moon in the night. ℞.

The Lord will guard you from evil,
he will guard your soul.
The Lord will guard your going and
    coming
both now and for ever. ℞.

READING II   *2 Timothy 3, 14-4, 2 / 148*

GOSPEL   *Luke 18, 1-8 / 148*

952 THIRTIETH SUNDAY IN ORDINARY TIME / A

READING I *Exodus 22, 20-26 / 149*

RESPONSORIAL PSALM *Psalm (17)18, 2-3.3-4.47.51 / 149*

I love you, I love you, Lord, my strength.

I love you, Lord, my strength,
my rock, my fortress, my savior. ℞.

My God is the rock where I take refuge;
my shield, my mighty help, my
  stronghold.
The Lord is worthy of all praise,
when I call I am saved from my
  foes. ℞.

Long life to the Lord, my rock!
Praised be the God who saves me.
He has given great victories to his
  king
and shown his love for his
  anointed. ℞.

READING II *1 Thessalonians 1, 5-10 / 149*

GOSPEL *Matthew 22, 34-40 / 149*

953 THIRTIETH SUNDAY IN ORDINARY TIME / B

READING I *Jeremiah 31, 7-9 / 150*

RESPONSORIAL PSALM *Psalm (125)126, 1-2.2-3.4-5.6 / 150*

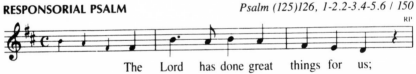

The Lord has done great things for us;

we are filled with joy, we are filled with joy.

When the Lord delivered Zion from
  bondage,
it seemed like a dream.
Then was our mouth filled with
  laughter,
on our lips there were songs. ℞.

The heathens themselves said: "What
  marvels
the Lord worked for them!"
What marvels the Lord worked for us!
Indeed we were glad. ℞.

Deliver us, O Lord, from our bondage
as streams in dry land.
Those who are sowing in tears
will sing when they reap. ℞.

They go out, they go out, full of tears,
carrying seed for the sowing;
they come back, they come back, full
of song,
carrying their sheaves. ℞.

READING II   *Hebrews 5, 1-6 / 150*

GOSPEL   *Mark 10, 46-52 / 150*

THIRTIETH SUNDAY IN ORDINARY TIME / C   954

READING I   *Sirach 35, 12-14.16-18 / 151*

RESPONSORIAL PSALM   *Psalm (33)34, 2-3.17-18.19.23 / 151*

The Lord hears the cry of the poor.

I will bless the Lord at all times,
his praise always on my lips;
in the Lord my soul shall make its boast.
The humble shall hear and be glad. ℞.

The Lord turns his eyes to the just
and his ears to their appeal.
They call and the Lord hears
and rescues them in all their
distress. ℞.

The Lord is close to the broken-hearted;
those whose spirit is crushed he will
save.
The Lord ransoms the souls of his
servants.
Those who hide in him shall not be
condemned. ℞.

READING II   *2 Timothy 4, 6-8, 16-18 / 151*

GOSPEL   *Luke 18, 9-14 / 151*

955 THIRTY-FIRST SUNDAY IN ORDINARY TIME / A

READING I *Malachi 1, 14-2, 2.8-10 / 152*

RESPONSORIAL PSALM *Psalm (130)131, 1.2.3 / 152*

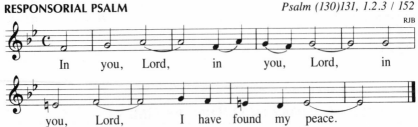

In you, Lord, in you, Lord, in you, Lord, I have found my peace.

O Lord, my heart is not proud
nor haughty my eyes.
I have not gone after things too great
nor marvels beyond me. ℟.

Truly I have set my soul
in silence and peace.

A weaned child on its mother's breast,
even so is my soul. ℟.

O Israel, hope in the Lord
both now and for ever. ℟.

READING II *1 Thessalonians 2, 7-9.13 / 152*

GOSPEL *Matthew 23, 1-12 / 152*

956 THIRTY-FIRST SUNDAY IN ORDINARY TIME / B

READING I *Deuteronomy 6, 2-6 / 153*

RESPONSORIAL PSALM *Psalm (17)18, 2-3.3-4.47.51 / 153*

I love you, I love you, Lord, my strength.

I love you, Lord, my strength,
my rock, my fortress, my savior. ℟.

My God is the rock where I take
refuge;
my shield, my mighty help, my
stronghold.
The Lord is worthy of all praise;
when I call I am saved from my
foes. ℟.

Long life to the Lord, my rock!
Praised be the God who saves me.
He has given great victories to his
king
and shown his love for his
anointed. ℟.

READING II *Hebrews 7, 23-28 / 153*

GOSPEL   *Mark 12, 28-34 / 153*

THIRTY-FIRST SUNDAY IN ORDINARY TIME / C   957

READING I   *Wisdom 11, 22-12, 1 / 154*

RESPONSORIAL PSALM   *Psalm (144)145, 1-2.8-9.10-11.13.14 / 154*

I will praise your name for ev - er, my king and my God.

I will give you glory, O God my King,
I will bless your name for ever.
I will bless you day after day
and praise your name for ever. ℟.

All your creatures shall thank you, O
    Lord,
and your friends shall repeat their
    blessing.
They shall speak of the glory of your
    reign
and declare your might, O God. ℟.

The Lord is kind and full of compassion,
slow to anger, abounding in love.
How good is the Lord to all,
compassionate to all his creatures. ℟.

The Lord is faithful in all his words
and loving in all his deeds.
The Lord supports all those who fall
and raises all who are bowed
    down. ℟.

READING II   *2 Thessalonians 1, 11-2,2 / 154*

GOSPEL   *Luke 19, 1-10 / 154*

958 THIRTY-SECOND SUNDAY IN ORDINARY TIME / A

READING I *Wisdom 6, 12-16 / 155*

RESPONSORIAL PSALM *Psalm (62)63, 2.3-4.5-6.7-8 / 155*

My soul is thirst-ing for you, O Lord, thirst-ing for you my God.

O God, you are my God, for you I
   long;
for you my soul is thirsting.
My body pines for you
like a dry, weary land without
   water. ℟.

So I gaze on you in the sanctuary
to see your strength and your glory.
For your love is better than life,
my lips will speak your praise. ℟.

So I will bless you all my life,
in your name I will lift up my hands.
My soul shall be filled as with a
   banquet,
my mouth shall praise you with
   joy. ℟.

On my bed I remember you.
On you I muse through the night
for you have been my help;
in the shadow of your wings I
   rejoice. ℟.

READING II *1 Thessalonians 4, 13-18 or 4, 13-14 / 155*

GOSPEL *Matthew 25, 1-13 / 155*

959 THIRTY-SECOND SUNDAY IN ORDINARY TIME / B

READING I *1 Kings 17, 10-16 / 156*

RESPONSORIAL PSALM *Psalm (145)146, 7.8-9.9-10 / 156*

Praise the Lord, my soul! Praise the Lord!

It is he who keeps faith for ever,
who is just to those who are oppressed.
It is he who gives bread to the
   hungry,
the Lord, who sets prisoners free. ℟.

The Lord who gives sight to the blind,
who raises up those who are bowed

   down,
the Lord, who protects the stranger
and upholds the widow and orphan. ℟.

It is the Lord who loves the just
but thwarts the path of the wicked.
The Lord will reign for ever,
Zion's God, from age to age. ℟.

READING II   *Hebrews 9, 24-28 / 156*

GOSPEL   *Mark 12, 38-44 or 12, 41-44 / 156*

THIRTY-SECOND SUNDAY IN ORDINARY TIME / C   960

READING I   *2 Maccabees 7, 1-2. 9-14 / 157*

RESPONSORIAL PSALM   *Psalm (16)17, 1.5-6.8.15 / 157*

Lord, when your glo-ry ap-pears, my joy will be full.

Lord, hear a cause that is just,
pay heed to my cry.
Turn your ear to my prayer,
no deceit is on my lips. ℟.

Guard me as the apple of your eye.
Hide me in the shadow of your wings.
As for me, in my justice I shall see
   your face
and be filled, when I awake, with the
   sight of your glory. ℟.

I kept my feet firmly in your paths;
there was no faltering in my steps.
I am here and I call, you will hear me,
   O God.
Turn your ear to me; hear my words. ℟.

READING II   *2 Thessalonians 2, 16-3, 5 / 157*

GOSPEL   *Luke 20, 27-38 or 20, 27.34-38 / 157*

961 THIRTY-THIRD SUNDAY IN ORDINARY TIME / A

READING I *Proverbs 31, 10-13.19-20.30-31 / 158*

RESPONSORIAL PSALM *Psalm (127)128, 1-2.3.4-5 / 158*

O hap-py are those who fear the Lord and walk in his ways.

O blessed are those who fear the
 Lord
and walk in his ways!
By the labor of your hands you shall
 eat.
You will be happy and prosper. ℞.

Your wife like a fruitful vine
in the heart of your house;
your children like shoots of the olive,
around your table. ℞.

Indeed thus shall be blessed
the man who fears the Lord.
May the Lord bless you from Zion
all the days of your life!
May you see your children's children
in a happy Jerusalem! ℞.

READING II *1 Thessalonians 5, 1-6 / 158*

GOSPEL *Matthew 25, 14-30 or 25, 14-15.19-20 / 158*

962 THIRTY-THIRD SUNDAY IN ORDINARY TIME / B

READING I *Daniel 12, 1-3 / 159*

RESPONSORIAL PSALM *Psalm (15)16, 5.8.9-10.11 / 159*

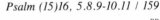

Keep me safe, O God; you are my hope.

O Lord, it is you who are my portion
 and cup,
it is you yourself who are my prize.
I keep you, Lord, ever in my sight;
since you are at my right hand, I shall
 stand firm. ℞.

And so my heart rejoices, my soul is
 glad;

even my body shall rest in safety.
For you will not leave my soul among
 the dead,
nor let your beloved know decay. ℞.

You will show me the path of life,
the fullness of joy in your presence,
at your right hand happiness for
 ever. ℞.

READING II *Hebrews 10, 11-14.18 / 159*

GOSPEL *Mark 13, 24-32 / 159*

THIRTY-THIRD SUNDAY IN ORDINARY TIME / C   963

READING I   *Malachi 3, 19-20 / 160*

RESPONSORIAL PSALM   *Psalm (97)98, 5-6.7-8.9 / 160*

The Lord comes to rule the earth, to rule with jus - tice.

Sing psalms to the Lord with the harp
with the sound of music.
With trumpets and the sound of the
   horn
acclaim the King, the Lord. ℟.

Let the sea and all within it, thunder;
the world, and all its peoples.

Let the rivers clap their hands
and the hills ring out their joy. ℟.

At the presence of the Lord, for he
   comes,
he comes to rule the earth.
He will rule the world with justice
and the peoples with fairness. ℟.

READING II   *2 Thessalonians 3, 7-12 / 160*

GOSPEL   *Luke 21, 5-19 / 160*

LAST SUNDAY IN ORDINARY TIME—CHRIST THE KING / A   964

READING I   *Ezekiel 34, 11-12.15-17 / 161*

RESPONSORIAL PSALM   *Psalm (22)23, 1-2.2-3.5-6 / 161*

The Lord is my shep - herd;

there is noth - ing I shall want.

The Lord is my shepherd;
there is nothing I shall want.
Fresh and green are the pastures
where he gives me repose. ℟.

Near restful waters he leads me,
to revive my drooping spirit.
He guides me along the right path;
he is true to his name. ℟.

You have prepared a banquet for me
in the sight of my foes.
My head you have anointed with oil;
my cup is overflowing. ℟.

Surely goodness and kindness shall
   follow me
all the days of my life.
In the Lord's own house shall I dwell
for ever and ever. ℟.

READING II   *1 Corinthians 15, 20-26.28 / 161*

GOSPEL   *Matthew 25, 31-46 / 161*

965 LAST SUNDAY IN ORDINARY TIME–CHRIST THE KING / B

READING I   *Daniel 7, 13-14 / 162*

RESPONSORIAL PSALM   *Psalm (92)93, 1.1-2.5 / 162*

RJB

The Lord is king; he is robed in maj - es - ty.

The Lord is king, with majesty
  enrobed;
the Lord has robed himself with might,
he has girded himself with power. ℟.

The world you made firm, not to be
  moved;
your throne has stood firm from of old.
From all eternity, O Lord, you are. ℟.

Truly your decrees are to be trusted.
Holiness is fitting to your house,
O Lord, until the end of time. ℟.

READING II   *Revelation 1, 5-8 / 162*

GOSPEL   *John 18, 33-37 / 162*

966 LAST SUNDAY IN ORINARY TIME–CHRIST THE KING / C

READING I   *2 Samuel 5, 1-3 / 163*

RESPONSORIAL PSALM   *Psalm (121)122, 1-2.3-4.4-5 / 163*

RJB

I re-joiced when I heard them say: let us go to the house of the Lord.

I rejoiced when I heard them say:
"Let us go to God's house."
And now our feet are standing
within your gates, O Jerusalem. ℟.

Jerusalem is built as a city
strongly compact.
It is there that the tribes go up,
the tribes of the Lord. ℟.

For Israel's law it is,
there to praise the Lord's name.
There were set the thrones of
  judgment
of the house of David. ℟.

READING II   *Colossians 1, 12-20 / 163*

GOSPEL   *Luke 23, 35-43 / 163*

Seasons:
Weekday Psalm Responses

FIRST WEEK OF ADVENT

Monday / *176*
I rejoiced when I heard them say:
let us go to the house of the Lord.

Tuesday / *177*
Justice shall flourish in his time,
and fullness of peace for ever.

Wednesday / *178*
I shall live in the house of the Lord
all the days of my life.

Thursday / *179*
Blessed is he who comes in the
name of the Lord.

Or: Alleluia.

Friday / *180*
The Lord is my light and my
salvation.

Or: Alleluia.

Saturday / *181*
Happy are all who long for the
coming of the Lord.

Or: Alleluia.

SECOND WEEK OF ADVENT

Monday / *182*
Our God will come to save us!

Tuesday / *183*
The Lord our God comes in
strength.

Wednesday / *184*
O bless the Lord, my soul.

Thursday / *185*
The Lord is kind and merciful;
slow to anger, and rich in
compassion.

Friday / *186*
Those who follow you, Lord, will
have the light of life.

Saturday / *187*
Lord, make us turn to you,
let us see your face and we shall be
saved.

969 THIRD WEEK OF ADVENT

Monday / *188*
Teach me your ways, O Lord.

Tuesday / *189*
The Lord hears the cry of the poor.

Wednesday / *190*
Let the clouds rain down the Just
    One,
and the earth bring forth a savior.

Thursday / *191*
I will praise you, Lord,
for you have rescued me.

Friday / *192*
O God, let all the nations praise
    you!

970 LAST DAYS OF ADVENT

December 17 / *194*
Justice shall flourish in his time,
and fullness of peace for ever.

December 18 / *195*
Justice shall flourish in his time,
and fullness of peace for ever.

December 19 / *196*
Fill me with your praise
and I will sing your glory!

December 20 / *197*
Let the Lord enter;
he is king of glory

December 21 / *198*
Cry out with joy in the Lord, you
    holy ones;
sing a new song to him.

December 22 / *199*
My heart rejoices in the Lord, my
    Savior.

December 23 / *200*
Lift up your heads and see;
your redemption is near at hand.

December 24 / *201*
Mass in the Morning
For ever I will sing the goodness of
    the Lord.

971 SEASON OF CHRISTMAS

December 29 / *203*
Let heaven and earth exult in joy!

December 30 / *204*
Let heaven and earth exult in joy!

December 31 / *205*
Let heaven and earth exult in joy!

January 2 / *206*
All the ends of the earth have seen
    the saving power of God.

January 3 / *207*
All the ends of the earth have seen
    the saving power of God.

January 4 / *208*
All the ends of the earth have seen
    the savings power of God.

January 5 / *208*
Let all the earth cry out to God
    with joy.

January 6 / *209*
Praise the Lord, Jerusalem.
Or: Alleluia.

January 7 / *211*
The Lord takes delight in his
    people.
Or: Alleluia.

AFTER EPIPHANY

Monday / *213*
I will give you all the nations for
    your heritage.

Tuesday / *214*
Lord, every nation on earth will
    adore you.

Wednesday / *215*
Lord, every nation on earth will
    adore you.

Thursday / *216*
Lord, every nation on earth will
    adore you.

Friday / *217*
Praise the Lord, Jerusalem.
Or: Alleluia.

Saturday / *218*
The Lord takes delight in his
    people.
Or: Alleluia.

ASH WEDNESDAY

READING I   *Joel 2, 12-18* / *220*

RESPONSORIAL PSALM   *Psalm (50)51, 3-4.5-6.12-13.14.17* / *220*

Be mer - ci - ful, O Lord, for we have sinned.

Have mercy on me, God, in your
    kindness.
In your compassion blot out my
    offense.
O wash me more amd more from my
    guilt
and cleanse me from my sin. ℞.

My offenses truly I know them;
my sin is always before me.
Against you, you alone, have I sinned;
what is evil in your sight I have
    done. ℞.

A pure heart create for me, O God,
put a steadfast spirit within me.
Do not cast me away from your
    presence,
nor deprive me of your holy spirit. ℞.

Give me again the joy of your help;
with a spirit of fervor sustain me,
O Lord, open my lips
and my mouth shall declare your
    praise. ℞.

READING II   *2 Corinthians 5, 20-6, 2* / *220*

GOSPEL   *Matthew 6, 1-6.16-18* / *220*

AFTER ASH WEDNESDAY

Thursday / *221*
Happy are they who hope in the
    Lord.

Friday / *222*
A broken, humbled heart, O God,
    you will not scorn.

Saturday / *223*
Teach me your way, O Lord, that I
    may be faithful in your sight.

975 FIRST WEEK OF LENT

Monday / 225
Your words, Lord, are spirit and
life.

Tuesday / 226
From all their afflictions
God will deliver the just.

Wednesday / 227
A broken, humbled heart,
O God, you will not scorn.

Thursday / 228
Lord, on the day I called for help,
you answered me.

Friday / 229
If you, O Lord, laid bare our guilt
who could endure it?

Saturday / 230
Happy are they who follow the law
of the Lord.

976 SECOND WEEK OF LENT

Monday / 231
Lord, do not deal with us as our
sins deserve.

Tuesday / 232
To the upright
I will show the saving power of God.

Wednesday / 233
Save me, O Lord, in your steadfast
love.

Thursday / 234
Happy are they who hope in the
Lord.

Friday / 235
Remember the marvels the Lord has
done.

Saturday / 236
The Lord is kind and merciful.

977 THIRD WEEK OF LENT

Optional Mass / 237
If today you hear his voice,
harden not your hearts.

Monday / 238
My soul is thirsting for the living
God:
when shall I see him face to face?

Tuesday / 239
Remember your mercies, O Lord.

Wednesday / 240
Praise the Lord, Jerusalem.

Thursday / 241
If today you hear his voice,
harden not your hearts.

Friday / 242
I am the Lord, your God:
hear my voice.

Saturday / 243
It is steadfast love, not sacrifice,
that God desires.

978 FOURTH WEEK OF LENT

Optional Mass / 244
The Lord is my light and my
salvation.

Monday / 245
I will praise you, Lord, for you
have rescued me.

Tuesday / 246
The mighty Lord is with us;
The God of Jacob is our refuge

Wednesday / 247
The Lord is kind and merciful.

Thursday / *248*
Lord, remember us,
for the love you bear your people.

Friday / *249*
The Lord is near to broken hearts.

Saturday / *250*
Lord, my God, I take shelter in
you.

FIFTH WEEK OF LENT

979

Optional Mass / *251*
Lord, when your glory appears,
my joy will be full.

Monday / *252*
Though I walk in the valley of
darkness,
I fear no evil, for you are with me.

Tuesday / *253*
O Lord, hear my prayer,
and let my cry come to you.

Wednesday / *254*
Glory and praise for ever!

Thursday / *255*
The Lord remembers his covenant
for ever.

Friday / *256*
In my distress I called upon the
Lord,
and he heard my voice.

Saturday / *257*
The Lord will guard us,
like a shepherd guarding his flock.

HOLY WEEK

980

Monday / *258*
The Lord is my light and my
salvation.

Tuesday / *259*
I will sing of your salvation.

Wednesday / *260*
Lord, in your great love, answer
me.

OCTAVE OF EASTER

981

Monday / *261*
Keep me safe, O God;
you are my hope.
Or: Alleluia.

Tuesday / / *262*
The earth is full of the goodness of
the Lord.
Or: Alleluia.

Wednesday / *263*
The earth is full of the goodness of
the Lord.
Or: Alleluia.

Thursday / *264*
O Lord, our God,
how wonderful your name in all the
earth!
Or: Alleluia.

Friday / *265*
The stone rejected by the builders
has become the cornerstone.
Or: Alleluia.

Saturday / *266*
I praise you, Lord,
for you have answered me.
Or: Alleluia.

982 SECOND WEEK OF EASTER

Monday / 267
Happy are all who put their trust in
the Lord.
Or: Alleluia.

Tuesday / 268
The Lord is king;.
he is robed in majesty.
Or: Alleluia.

Wednesday / 269
The Lord hears the cry of the poor.
Or: Alleluia.

Thursday / 270
The Lord hears the cry of the poor.
Or: Alleluia.

Friday / 271
One thing I seek: to dwell in the
house of the Lord.
Or: Alleluia.

Saturday / 272
Lord, let your mercy be on us,
as we place our trust in you.
Or: Alleluia.

983 THIRD WEEK OF EASTER

Monday / 273
Happy are those of blameless life.
Or: Alleluia.

Tuesday / 274
Into your hands, O Lord,
I entrust my spirit.
Or: Alleluia.

Wednesday / 275
Let all the earth cry out to God
with joy.
Or: Alleluia.

Thursday / 276
Let all the earth cry out to God
with joy.
Or: Alleluia.

Friday / 277
Go out to all the world,
and tell the Good News.
Or: Alleluia.

Saturday / 278
What return can I make to the Lord
for all that he gives to me?
Or: Alleluia.

984 FOURTH WEEK OF EASTER

Monday / 279
My soul is thirsting for the living
God.
Or: Alleluia.

Tuesday / 280
All you nations, praise the Lord.
Or: Alleluia.

Wednesday / 281
O God, let all the nations praise
you!
Or: Alleluia.

Thursday / 282
For ever I will sing the goodness of
the Lord.
Or: Alleluia.

Friday / 283
You are my Son;
this day have I begotten you.
Or: Alleluia.

Saturday / 284
All the ends of the earth have seen
the saving power of God.
Or: Alleluia.

FIFTH WEEK OF EASTER

Monday / 285
Not to us, O Lord,
but to your name give the glory.
Or: Alleluia.

Tuesday / 286
Your friends tell the glory of your
kingship, Lord.
Or: Alleluia.

Wednesday / 287
I rejoiced when I heard them say:
let us go to the house of the Lord.
Or: Alleluia.

Thursday / 288
Proclaim his marvelous deeds
to all the nations.
Or: Alleluia.

Friday / 289
I will praise you among the nations,
O Lord.
Or: Alleluia.

Saturday / 290
Let all the earth cry out to God
with joy.
Or: Alleluia.

SIXTH WEEK OF EASTER

Monday / 291
The Lord takes delight in his people.
Or: Alleluia.

Tuesday / 292
Your right hand has saved me, O
Lord.
Or: Alleluia.

Wednesday / 293
Heaven and earth are filled with
your glory.
Or: Alleluia.

Thursday / 294
The Lord has revealed to the nations
his saving power.
Or: Alleluia.

Friday / 295
God is king of all the earth.
Or: Alleluia.

Saturday / 296
God is king of all the earth.
Or: Alleluia.

SEVENTH WEEK OF EASTER

Monday / 297
Sing to God, O kingdoms of the
earth.
Or: Alleluia.

Tuesday / 298
Sing to God, O kingdoms of the
earth.
Or: Alleluia.

Wednesday / 299
Sing to God, O kingdoms of the
earth.
Or: Alleluia.

Thursday / 300
Keep me safe, O God;
you are my hope.
Or: Alleluia.

Friday / 301
The Lord has set his throne in
heaven.
Or: Alleluia.

Saturday / 302
The just will gaze on your face, O
Lord.
Or: Alleluia.

Ordinary Time: Psalm Responses

988 **FIRST WEEK IN ORDINARY TIME**

Monday / *305*
I   Let all his angels worship him.
II To you, Lord, I will offer a
    sacrifice of praise.
    Or: Alleluia.

Tuesday / *306*
I   You gave your Son authority
    over all creation.
II My heart rejoices in the Lord,
    my Savior.

Wednesday / *307*
I   The Lord remembers his
    covenant for ever.
    Or: Alleluia.
II Here am I, Lord; I come to do
    your will.

Thursday / *308*
I   If today you hear his voice,
    harden not your hearts.
II Save us, Lord, in your mercy.

Friday / *309*
I   Do not forget the works of the
    Lord!
II For ever I will sing the
    goodness of the Lord.

Saturday / *310*
I   Your words, Lord, are spirit
    and life.
II Lord, your strength gives joy to
    the king.

989 **SECOND WEEK IN ORDINARY TIME**

Monday / *311*
I   You are a priest for ever, in the
    line of Melchizedek.

II To the upright I will show the
    saving power of God.

Tuesday / *312*
I   The Lord will remember his
    covenant for ever.
    Or: Alleluia.
II I have found David, my
    servant.

Wednesday / *313*
I You are a priest for ever,
in the line of Melchizedek.

II Blessed be the Lord, my Rock!

Thursday / *314*
I Here am I, Lord;
I come to do your will.

II In God I trust;
I shall not fear.

Friday / *315*
I Kindness and truth shall meet.
II Have mercy on me, God, have
mercy.

Saturday / *316*
I God mounts his throne to
shouts of joy;
a blare of trumpets for the Lord.

II Let us see your face, Lord,
and we shall be saved.

THIRD WEEK IN ORDINARY TIME   990

Monday / *317*
I Sing to the Lord a new song,
for he has done marvelous
deeds.

II My faithfulness and love shall
be with him.

Tuesday / *318*
I Here am I, Lord;
I come to do your will.

II Who is this king of glory?
It is the Lord!

Wednesday / *319*
I You are a priest for ever,
in the line of Melchizedek.

II For ever I will keep my love for
him.

Thursday / *320*
I Lord, this is the people that
longs to see your face.

II God will give him the throne of
David, his father.

Friday / *321*
I The salvation of the just comes
from the Lord.

II Be merciful, O Lord, for we
have sinned.

Saturday / *322*
I Blessed be the Lord God of
Israel,
for he has visited his people.

II Create a clean heart in me, O
God.

FOURTH WEEK IN ORDINARY TIME   991

Monday / *323*
I Let your hearts take comfort,
all who hope in the Lord.

II Lord, rise up and save me.

Tuesday / *324*
I They will praise you, Lord,
who long for you.

II Listen, Lord, and answer me.

Wednesday / *325*
I The Lord's kindness is
everlasting to those who
fear him.

II Lord, forgive the wrong I
have done.

Thursday / *326*
I God, in your temple, we ponder
your love.

II Lord, you are exalted over all.

Friday / *327*
I The Lord is my light and my
salvation.

II Blessed be God my salvation!

Saturday / *328*
I The Lord is my shepherd;
there is nothing I shall want.

II Lord, teach me your decrees.

992 FIFTH WEEK IN ORDINARY TIME

Monday / *329*

I   May the Lord be glad in his works.

II   Lord, go up to the place of your rest!

Tuesday / *330*

I   O Lord, our God,
how wonderful your name in all the earth!

II   How lovely is your dwelling-place,
Lord, mighty God!

Wednesday / *331*

I   Oh, bless the Lord, my soul!

II   The mouth of the just man murmurs wisdom.

Thursday / *332*

I   Happy are those who fear the Lord.

II   Lord, remember us,
for the love you bear your people.

Friday / *333*

I   Happy are those whose sins are forgiven.

II   I am the Lord, your God:
hear my voice.

Saturday / *334*

I   In every age, O Lord, you have been our refuge.

II   Lord, remember us,
for the love you bear your people.

993 SIXTH WEEK IN ORDINARY TIME

Monday / *335*

I   Offer to God a sacrifice of praise.

II   Be kind to me, Lord, and I shall live.

Tuesday / *336*

I   The Lord will bless his people with peace.

II   Happy the man you teach, O O Lord.

Wednesday / *337*

I   To you, Lord, I will offer a sacrifice of praise.

Or: Alleluia.

II   He who does justice shall live on the Lord's holy mountain.

Thursday / *338*

I   From heaven the Lord looks down on the earth.

II   The Lord hears the cry of the poor.

Friday / *339*

I   Happy the people the Lord has chosen to be his own.

II   Happy are those who do what the Lord commands.

Saturday / *340*

I   I will praise your name for ever, Lord.

II   You will protect us, Lord.

SEVENTH WEEK IN ORDINARY TIME 994

Monday / *341*

I   The Lord is king; he is robed in majesty.

II The precepts of the Lord give joy to the heart.

Tuesday / *342*

I   Commit your life to the Lord, and he will help you.

II Throw your cares on the Lord, and he will support you.

Wednesday / *343*

I   O Lord, great peace have they who love the law.

II Happy the poor in spirit; the kingdom of heaven is theirs!

Thursday / *344*

I   Happy are they who hope in the Lord.

II Happy the poor in spirit; the kingdom of heaven is theirs!

Friday / *345*

I   Guide me, Lord, in the way of your commands.

II The Lord is kind and merciful.

Saturday / *346*

I   The Lord's kindness is everlasting to those who fear him.

II Let my prayer come like incense before you.

EIGHTH WEEK IN ORDINARY TIME 995

Monday / *347*

I   Let the just exult and rejoice in the Lord.

II The Lord will remember his covenant for ever.

    Or: Alleluia.

Tuesday / *348*

I   To the upright I will show the saving power of God.

II The Lord has made known his salvation.

Wednesday / *349*

I   Show us, O Lord, the light of your kindness.

II Praise the Lord, Jerusalem.

    Or: Alleluia.

Thursday / *350*

I   By the word of the Lord the heavens were made.

II Come with joy into the presence of the Lord.

Friday / *351*

I   The Lord takes delight in his people.

II The Lord comes to judge the earth.

Saturday / *352*

I   The precepts of the Lord give joy to the heart.

II My soul is thirsting for you, O Lord my God.

NINTH WEEK IN ORDINARY TIME 996

Monday / *353*

I   Happy the man who fears the Lord.

    Or: Alleluia.

II In you, my God, I place my trust.

Tuesday / *354*

I   The heart of the just man is secure, trusting in the Lord.

    Or: Alleluia.

II In every age, O Lord, you have been our refuge.

Wednesday / *355*
I   To you, O Lord, I lift my
     soul.

II To you, O Lord, I lift up my
     eyes.

Thursday / *356*
I   Happy are those who fear the
     Lord.

II Teach me your ways, O Lord.

Friday / *357*
I   Praise the Lord, my soul!
     Or: Alleluia.

II O Lord, great peace have they
     who love your law.

Saturday / *358*
I   Blessed be God, who lives for
     ever.

II I will sing of your salvation.

997 TENTH WEEK IN ORDINARY TIME

Monday / *359*
I   Taste and see the goodness of
     the Lord.

II Our help is from the Lord
     who made heaven and earth.

Tuesday / *360*
I   Lord, let your face shine on
     me.

II Lord, let your face shine on us.

Wednesday / *361*
I   Holy is the Lord our God.

II Keep me safe, O God;
     you are my hope.

Thursday / *362*
I   The glory of the Lord will
     dwell in our land.

II It is right to praise you in Zion,
     O God.

Friday / *363*
I   To you, Lord, I will offer a
     sacrifice of praise.
     Or: Alleluia.

II I long to see your face, O Lord.

Saturday / *364*
I   The Lord is kind and merciful.

II You are my inheritance, O
     Lord.

998 ELEVENTH WEEK IN ORDINARY TIME

Monday / *365*
I   The Lord has made known his
     salvation.

II Lord, listen to my groaning.

Tuesday / *366*
I   Praise the Lord, my soul!
     Or: Alleluia.

II Be merciful, O Lord, for we
     have sinned.

Wednesday / *367*
I   Happy the man who fears the
     Lord.
     Or: Alleluia.

II Let your hearts take comfort,
     all who hope in the Lord.

Thursday / *368*
I   Your works, O Lord, are justice
     and truth.
     Or: Alleluia.

II Let good men rejoice in the
     Lord.

Friday / *369*

I   From all their afflictions God will deliver the just.

II   The Lord has chosen Zion for his dwelling.

Saturday / *370*

    Taste and see the goodness of the Lord.

II   For ever I will keep my love for him.

TWELFTH WEEK IN ORDINARY TIME   999

Monday / *371*

I   Happy the people the Lord has chosen to be his own.

II   Help us with your right hand, O Lord, and answer us.

Tuesday / *372*

I   He who does justice will live in the presence of the Lord.

II   God upholds his city for ever.

Wednesday / *373*

I   The Lord remembers his covenant for ever.

    Or: Alleluia.

II   Teach me the way of your decrees, O Lord.

Thursday / *374*

I   Give thanks to the Lord for he is good.

    Or: Alleluia.

II   For the glory of your name, O Lord, deliver us.

Friday / *375*

I   See how the Lord blesses those who fear him.

II   Let my tongue be silenced, if I ever forget you!

Saturday / *376*

I   The Lord has remembered his mercy.

II   Lord, forget not the life of your poor ones.

THIRTEENTH WEEK IN ORDINARY TIME   1000

Monday / *377*

I   The Lord is kind and merciful.

II   Remember this, you who never think of God.

Tuesday / *378*

I   O Lord, your kindness is before my eyes.

II   Lead me in your justice, Lord.

Wednesday / *379*

I   The Lord hears the cry of the poor.

II   To the upright I will show the saving power of God.

Thursday / *380*

I   I will walk in the presence of the Lord,
in the land of the living.

    Or: Alleluia.

II   The judgments of the Lord are true,
and all of them just.

Friday / *381*

I   Give thanks to the Lord for he is good.

Or: Alleluia.

II   Man does not live on bread alone,
but on every word that comes from the mouth of God.

Saturday / *382*

I   Praise the Lord for he is good!

Or: Alleluia.

II   The Lord speaks of peace to his people.

1001   **FOURTEENTH WEEK IN ORDINARY TIME**

Monday / *383*

I   In you, my God, I place my trust.

II   The Lord is kind and merciful.

Tuesday / *384*

I   In my justice, I shall see your face, O Lord.

II   The house of Israel trusts in the Lord.

Or: Alleluia.

Wednesday / *385*

I   Lord, let your mercy be on us, as we place our trust in you.

II   Seek always the face of the Lord.

Or: Alleluia.

Thursday / *386*

I   Remember the marvels the Lord has done.

Or: Alleluia.

II   Let us see your face, Lord, and we shall be saved.

Friday / *387*

I   The salvation of the just comes from the Lord.

II   My mouth will declare your praise.

Saturday / *388*

I   Turn to the Lord in your need and you will live.

II   The Lord is king;
he is robed in majesty.

1002   **FIFTEENTH WEEK IN ORDINARY TIME**

Monday / *389*

I   Our help is in the name of the Lord.

II   To the upright I will show the saving power of God.

Tuesday / *390*

I   Turn to the Lord in your need, and you will live.

II   God upholds his city for ever.

Wednesday / *391*

I   The Lord is kind and merciful.

II   The Lord will not abandon his people.

Thursday / *392*

I   The Lord remembers his covenant for ever.

Or: Alleluia.

II   From heaven the Lord looks down on the earth.

Friday / *393*

I I will take the cup of salvation, and call on the name of the Lord.

Or: Alleluia.

II You saved my life, O Lord; I shall not die.

Saturday / *394*

I His love is everlasting.

Or: Alleluia.

II Do not forget the poor, O Lord!

SIXTEENTH WEEK IN ORDINARY TIME   1003

Monday / *395*

I Let us sing to the Lord; he has covered himself in glory.

II To the upright I will show the saving power of God.

Tuesday / *396*

I Let us sing to the Lord; he has covered himself in glory.

II Lord, let us see your kindness.

Wednesday / *397*

I The Lord gave them bread from heaven.

II I will sing of your salvation.

Thursday / *398*

I Glory and praise for ever!

II You are the source of life, O Lord.

Friday / *399*

I Lord, you have the words of everlasting life.

II The Lord will guard us, like a shepherd guarding his flock.

Saturday / *400*

I Offer to God a sacrifice of praise.

II How lovely is your dwelling-place, Lord, mighty God!

SEVENTEENTH SUNDAY IN ORDINARY TIME   1004

Monday / *401*

I Give thanks to the Lord for he is good.

Or: Alleluia.

II You have forgotten God who gave you birth.

Tuesday / *402*

I The Lord is kind and merciful.

II For the glory of your name, O Lord, deliver us.

Wednesday / *403*

I Holy is the Lord our God.

II God is my refuge on the day of distress.

Thursday / *404*

I How lovely is your dwelling-place, Lord, mighty God!

II Blest are they whose help is the God of Jacob.

Or: Alleluia.

Friday / *405*

I Sing with joy to God our help.

II Lord, in your great love, answer me.

Saturday / *406*

I O God, let all the nations praise you!

II Lord, in your great love, answer me.

1005 EIGHTEENTH WEEK IN ORDINARY TIME

Monday / *407*

I   Sing with joy to God our help.

II   Teach me your laws, O Lord.

Tuesday / *408*

I   Be merciful, O Lord, for we
     have sinned.

II   The Lord will build up Zion
     again,
     and appear in all his glory.

Wednesday / *409*

I   Lord, remember us,
     for the love you bear your
     people.

     Or: Alleluia.

II   The Lord will guard us,
     like a shepherd guarding his
     flock.

Thursday / *410*

I   If today you hear his voice,
     harden not your hearts.

II   Create a clean heart in me, O
     God.

Friday / *411*

I   I remember the deeds of the
     Lord.

II   It is I who deal death and give
     life.

Saturday / *412*

I   I love you, Lord, my strength.

II   You will never abandon those
     who seek you, Lord.

1006 NINETEENTH WEEK IN ORDINARY TIME

Monday / *413*

I   Praise the Lord, Jerusalem.

     Or: Alleluia.

II   Heaven and earth are filled with
     your glory.

     Or: Alleluia.

Tuesday / *414*

I   The portion of the Lord is his
     people.

II   How sweet to my taste is your
     promise!

Wednesday / *415*

I   Blessed be God who filled my
     soul with life!

II   The glory of the Lord is higher
     than the skies.

     Or: Alleluia.

Thursday / *416*

I   Alleluia.

II   Do not forget the works of the
     Lord!

Friday / *417*

I   His love is everlasting.

     Or: Alleluia.

II   You have turned from your
     anger to comfort me.

Saturday / *418*

I   You are my inheritance, O
     Lord.

II   Create a clean heart in me, O
     God.

TWENTIETH WEEK IN ORDINARY TIME

Monday / 419

I   Lord, remember us,
    for the love you bear your
        people.

II You have forgotten God who
    gave you birth.

Tuesday / 420

I   The Lord speaks of peace to his
        people.

II It is I who deal death and give
    life.

Wednesday / 421

I   Lord, your strength gives joy to
        the king.

II The Lord is my shepherd;
    there is nothing I shall want.

Thursday / 422

I   Here am I, Lord;
    I come to do your will.

II I will pour clean water on you
    and wash away all your sins.

Friday / 423

I   Praise the Lord, my soul!
    Or: Alleluia.

II Give thanks to the Lord,
    his love is everlasting.
    Or: Alleluia.

Saturday / 424

I   See how the Lord blesses those
        who fear him.

II The glory of the Lord will
    dwell in our land.

TWENTY-FIRST WEEK IN ORDINARY TIME

Monday / 425

I   The Lord takes delight in his
        people.
    Or: Alleluia.

II Proclaim his marvelous deeds to
    all the nations.

Tuesday / 426

I   You have searched me
    and you know me, Lord.

II The Lord comes to judge the
    earth.

Wednesday / 427

I   You have searched me
    and you know me, Lord.

II Happy are those who fear the
    Lord.

Thursday / 428

I   Fill us with your love, O Lord,
    and we will sing for joy!

II I will praise your name for
        ever, Lord.

Friday / 429

I   Let good men rejoice in the
        Lord.

II The earth is full of the
        goodness of the Lord.

Saturday / 430

I   The Lord comes to rule the
        earth with justice.

II Happy the people the Lord has
        chosen to be his own.

1009 TWENTY-SECOND WEEK IN ORDINARY TIME

Monday / 431
I The Lord comes to judge the earth.

II Lord, I love your commands.

Tuesday / 432
I I believe that I shall see the good things of the Lord in the land of the living.

II The Lord is just in all his ways.

Wednesday / 433
I I trust in the kindness of God for ever.

II Happy the people the Lord has chosen to be his own.

Thursday / 434
I The Lord has made known his salvation.

II To the Lord belongs the earth and all that fills it.

Friday / 435
I Come with joy into the presence of the Lord.

II The salvation of the just comes from the Lord.

Saturday / 436
I God himself is my help.

II The Lord is near to all who call him.

1010 TWENTY-THIRD WEEK IN ORDINARY TIME

Monday / 437
I In God is my safety and my glory.

II Lead me in your justice, Lord.

Tuesday / 438
I The Lord is compassionate to all his creatures.

II The Lord takes delight in his people.

  Or: Alleluia.

Wednesday / 439
I The Lord is compassionate to all his creatures.

II Listen to me, daughter; see and bend your ear.

Thursday / 440
I Let everything that breathes praise the Lord!

  Or: Alleluia.

II Guide me, Lord, along the everlasting way.

Friday / 441
I You are my inheritance, O Lord.

II How lovely is your dwelling-place, Lord, mighty God!

Saturday / 442
I Blessed be the name of the Lord for ever.

  Or: Alleluia.

II To you, Lord, I will offer a sacrifice of praise.

TWENTY-FOURTH WEEK IN ORDINARY TIME

Monday / *443*

I   Blest be the Lord for he has
    heard my prayer.

II Proclaim the death of the Lord
    until he comes again.

Tuesday / *444*

I   I will walk with blameless
    heart.

II We are his people:
    the sheep of his flock.

Wednesday / *445*

I   How great are the works of the
    Lord!

    Or: Alleluia.

II Happy the people the Lord has
    chosen to be his own.

Thursday / *446*

I   How great are the works of the
    Lord!

    Or: Alleluia.

II Give thanks to the Lord, for he
    is good.

    Or: Alleluia.

Friday / *447*

I   Happy the poor in spirit;
    the kingdom of heaven is theirs!

II Lord, when your glory appears,
    my joy will be full.

Saturday / *448*

I   Come with joy into the
    presence of the Lord.

II I will walk in the presence of
    God,
    with the light of the living.

TWENTY-FIFTH WEEK IN ORDINARY TIME

Monday / *449*

I   The Lord has done marvels for
    us.

II He who does justice shall live
    on the Lord's holy
    mountain.

Tuesday / *450*

I   I rejoiced when I heard them
    say:
    let us go to the house of the
    Lord.

II Guide me, Lord, in the way of
    your commands.

Wednesday / *451*

I   Blessed be God, who lives for
    ever.

II Your word, O Lord, is a lamp
    for my feet.

Thursday / *452*

I   The Lord takes delight in his
    people.

II In every age, O Lord, you have
    been our refuge.

Friday / *453*

I   Hope in God; I will praise him,
    my savior and my God.

II Blessed be the Lord, my Rock!

Saturday / *454*

I   The Lord will guard us,
    like a shepherd guarding his
    flock.

II In every age, O Lord, you have
    been our refuge.

1013   TWENTY-SIXTH WEEK IN ORDINARY TIME

Monday / 455
I   The Lord will build up Zion again,
     and appear in all his glory.

II   Lord, bend your ear and hear my prayer.

Tuesday / 456
I   God is with us.

II   Let my prayer come before you, Lord.

Wednesday / 457
I   Let my tongue be silenced, if I ever forget you!

II   Let my prayer come before you, Lord.

Thursday / 458
I   The precepts of the Lord give joy to the heart.

II   I believe that I shall see the good things of the Lord in the land of the living.

Friday / 459
I   For the glory of your name, O Lord, deliver us.

II   Guide me, Lord, along the everlasting way.

Saturday / 460
I   The Lord listens to the poor.

II   Lord, let your face shine on me.

1014   TWENTY-SEVENTH WEEK IN ORDINARY TIME

Monday / 461
I   You will rescue my life from the pit, O Lord.

II   The Lord will remember his covenant for ever.
     Or: Alleluia.

Tuesday / 462
I   If you, O Lord, laid bare our guilt,
     who could endure it?

II   Guide me, Lord, along the everlasting way.

Wednesday / 463
I   Lord, you are tender and full of love.

II   Go out to all the world, and tell the Good News.
     Or: Alleluia.

Thursday / 464
I   Happy are they who hope in the Lord.

II   Blessed be the Lord God of Israel,
     for he has visited his people.

Friday / 465
I   The Lord will judge the world with justice.

II   The Lord will remember his covenant for ever.
     Or: Alleluia.

Saturday / 466
I   Let good men rejoice in the Lord.

II   The Lord remembers his covenant for ever.
     Or: Alleluia.

TWENTY-EIGHTH WEEK IN ORDINARY TIME

Monday / 467

I   The Lord has made known his
    salvation.

II Blessed be the name of the
    Lord for ever.

    Or: Alleluia.

Tuesday / 468

I   The heavens proclaim the glory
    of God.

II Let your loving kindness come
    to me, O Lord.

Wednesday / 469

I   Lord, you give back to every
    man,
    according to his works.

II Those who follow you, Lord,
    will have the light of life.

Thursday / 470

I   With the Lord there is mercy,
    and fullness of redemption.

II The Lord has made known his
    salvation.

Friday / 471

I   I turn to you, Lord, in time of
    trouble,
    and you fill me with the joy of
    salvation.

II Happy the people the Lord has
    chosen to be his own.

Saturday / 472

I   The Lord remembers his
    covenant for ever.

    Or: Alleluia.

II You gave your Son authority
    over all your creation.

TWENTY-NINTH WEEK IN ORDINARY TIME

Monday / 473

I   Blessed be the Lord God of
    Israel,
    for he has visited his people.

II The Lord made us, we belong
    to him.

Tuesday / 474

I   Here am I, Lord;
    I come to do your will.

II The Lord speaks of peace to his
    people.

Wednesday / 475

I   Our help is in the name of the
    Lord.

II You will draw water joyfully
    from the springs of
    salvation.

Thursday / 476

I   Happy are they who hope in the
    Lord.

II The earth is full of the
    goodness of the Lord.

Friday / 477

I   Teach me your laws, O Lord.

II Lord, this is the people that
    longs to see your face.

Saturday / 478

I   Lord, this is the people that
    longs to see your face.

II I rejoiced when I heard them
    say:
    let us go to the house of the
    Lord.

1017 THIRTIETH WEEK IN ORDINARY TIME

Monday / 479

I   Our God is the God of
     salvation.

II Behave like God as his very
     dear children.

Tuesday / 480

I   The Lord has done marvels for
     us.

II Happy are those who fear the
     Lord.

Wednesday / 481

I   All my hope, O Lord,
     is in your loving kindness.

II The Lord is faithful in all his
     words.

Thursday / 482

I   Save me, O Lord,
     in your kindness.

II Blessed be the Lord, my Rock!

Friday / 483

I   Praise the Lord, Jerusalem.

II How great are the works of the
     Lord!

    Or: Alleluia.

Saturday / 484

I   The Lord will not abandon his
     people.

II My soul is thirsting for the
     living God.

1018 THIRTY-FIRST WEEK IN ORDINARY TIME

Monday / 485

I   Lord, in your great love,
     answer me.

II In you, Lord, I have found my
     peace.

Tuesday / 486

I   In you, Lord, I have found my
     peace.

II I will praise you, Lord, in the
     assembly of your people.

Wednesday / 487

I   Happy the man who is merciful
     and lends to those in need.

    Or: Alleluia.

II The Lord is my light and my
     salvation.

Thursday / 488

I   I believe that I shall see the
     good things of the Lord in
     the land of the living.

II Let hearts rejoice who search
     for the Lord.

    Or: Alleluia.

Friday / 489

I   The Lord has revealed to the
     nations his saving power.

II I rejoiced when I heard
     them say:
     Let us go to the house
     of the Lord.

Saturday / 490

I   I will praise your name for
     ever, Lord.

II Happy the man who fears the
     Lord.

    Or: Alleluia.

THIRTY-SECOND WEEK IN ORDINARY TIME

Monday / *491*

I   Guide me, Lord, along the ever-lasting way.

II   Lord, this is the people that longs to see your face.

Tuesday / *492*

I   I will bless the Lord at all times.

II   The salvation of the just comes from the Lord.

Wednesday / *493*

I   Rise up, O God, bring judgment to the earth.

II   The Lord is my shepherd; there is nothing I shall want.

Thursday / *494*

I   Your word is for ever, O Lord.

II   Blest are they whose help is the God of Jacob.

Or: Alleluia.

Friday / *495*

I   The heavens proclaim the glory of God.

II   Happy are they who follow the law of the Lord!

Saturday / *496*

I   Remember the marvels the Lord has done.

Or: Alleluia.

II   Happy the man who fears the Lord.

Or: Alleluia.

THIRTY-THIRD WEEK IN ORDINARY TIME

Monday / *497*

I   Give me life, O Lord, and I will do your commands.

II   Those who are victorious I will feed from the tree of life.

Tuesday / *498*

I   The Lord upholds me.

II   Him who is victorious I will sit beside me on my throne.

Wednesday / *499*

I   Lord, when your glory appears, my joy will be full.

II   Holy, holy, holy Lord, mighty God!

Or: Alleluia.

Thursday / *500*

I   To the upright I will show the saving power of God.

II   The Lamb has made us a kingdom of priests to serve our God.

Or: Alleluia.

Friday / *501*

I   We praise your glorious name, O mighty God.

II   How sweet to my taste is your promise!

Saturday / *502*

I   I will rejoice in your salvation, O Lord.

II   Blessed be the Lord, my Rock!

1021 THIRTY-FOURTH WEEK IN ORDINARY TIME

Monday / 503

I   Glory and praise for ever!

II   Lord, this is the people that
       longs to see your face.

Tuesday / 504

I   Give glory and eternal praise to
       him.

II   The Lord comes to judge the
       earth.

Wednesday / 505

I   Give glory and eternal praise to
       him.

II   Great and wonderful are all
       your works,
       Lord, mighty God!

Thursday / 506

I   Give glory and eternal praise to
       him.

II   Blessed are they who are called
       to the wedding feast of the
       Lamb.

Friday / 507

I   Give glory and eternal praise to
       him.

II   Here God lives among his
       people.

Saturday / 508

I   Give glory and eternal praise to
       him.

II   Maranatha! Come, Lord Jesus!

Saints:
Weekday Psalm Responses

January 2 / *510*
**BASIL THE GREAT
AND GREGORY NAZIANZEN**
cf. 1065 or 1066

January 4
ELIZABETH ANN SETON
cf. 1068

January 5
JOHN NEUMANN
Proclaim his marvelous deeds
to all the nations.

January 6
ANDRE BESSETTE
cf. 1068

January 7 / *511*
RAYMOND OF PENYAFORT
cf.1065

January 13 / *512*
HILARY
cf. 1065 or 1066

January 17 / *513*
ANTHONY
cf. 1068

January 20 / *514*
FABIAN
cf. 1064 or 1065

SEBASTIAN / *515*
cf. 1064

January 21 / *516*
AGNES
cf. 1064 or 1067

Jaunary 22 / *517*
VINCENT
cf. 1064

January 24 / *518*
FRANCIS DE SALES
cf. 1065 or 1066

January 25 / *519*
CONVERSION OF PAUL
Go out to all the world,
and tell the Good News.

Or: Alleluia.

January 26 / *520*
TIMOTHY AND TITUS
cf. 1065

January 28 / *522*
THOMAS AQUINAS
cf. 1065 or 1066

January 27 / *521*
ANGELA MERICI
cf. 1067 or 1068

January 31 / *523*
JOHN BOSCO
cf. 1065 or 1068

1023 FEBRUARY 2: PRESENTATION OF THE LORD

Forty days after the celebration of Christmas, this feast tells of how Mary and Joseph brought the child to the Temple. There the aged Simeon took the baby in his arms and proclaimed that Jesus would be "a light to the Gentiles, the glory of Israel." These words have been sung for centuries on February 2 as Christians have blessed and carried lighted candles in procession.

BLESSING OF CANDLES AND PROCESSION

As the candles are lighted, this antiphon (with optional verses) may be sung:

Antiphon

Chant Mode VIII
Setting by Richard Proulx, 1985

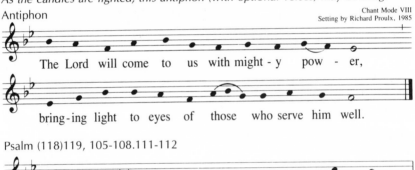

The Lord will come to us with might-y pow-er, bring-ing light to eyes of those who serve him well.

Psalm (118)119, 105-108.111-112

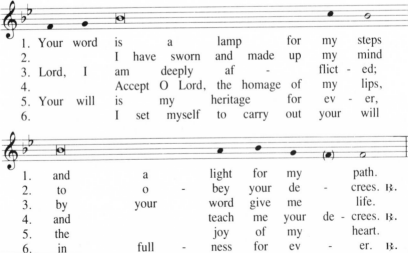

1. Your word	is	a	lamp	for	my	steps
2.	I have	sworn	and made	up	my	mind
3. Lord, I	am	deeply	af -		flict -	ed;
4.	Accept	O Lord,	the homage	of	my	lips,
5. Your will	is	my	heritage	for	ev -	er,
6.	I set	myself	to carry	out	your	will

1. and	a	light	for	my	path.
2. to	o -	bey	your	de -	crees. ℟.
3. by	your	word	give	me	life.
4. and		teach	me	your	de - crees. ℟.
5. the		joy	of	my	heart.
6. in	full -	ness	for	ev -	er. ℟.

When the candles have been blessed, the presider invites all: "Let us go forth in *peace to meet the Lord." During the procession, the following may be sung:*

Antiphon

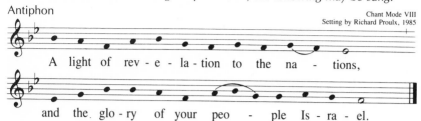

Chant Mode VIII
Setting by Richard Proulx, 1985

A light of rev - e - la - tion to the na - tions,

and the glo - ry of your peo - ple Is - ra - el.

Canticle, Luke 2:29-32

1. Lord, now you have set your ser - vant free

to go in peace as you have prom - ised. ℟.

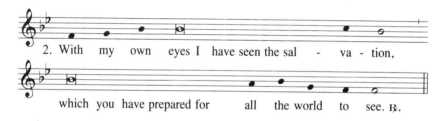

2. With my own eyes I have seen the sal - va - tion,

which you have prepared for all the world to see. ℟.

READING I

Malachi 3, 1-4 / 524

RESPONSORIAL PSALM

Psalm (23)24, 7.8.9.10 / 524

RP

Who is this king of glo - ry? It is the Lord.

O gates, lift high your heads;
grow higher, ancient doors.
Let him enter, the king of glory! ℟.

Who is the king of glory?
The Lord, the mighty, the valiant,
the Lord, the valiant in war. ℟.

O gates, lift high your heads;
grow higher, ancient doors.
Let him enter, the king of glory! ℟.

Who is he, the king of glory?
He, the Lord of armies,
he is the king of glory. ℟.

READING II

Hebrews 2, 14-18 / 524

GOSPEL

Luke 2, 22-40 or 22-32 / 524

1025

February 3 / *525*
BLASE
cf. 1064 or 1065

ANSGAR / *526*
cf. 1065

February 5 / *527*
AGATHA
cf. 1064 or 1067

February 6 / *528*
PAUL MIKI AND COMPANIONS
cf. 1064

February 8 / *529*
JEROME EMILIANI
cf. 1068

February 10 / *530*
SCHOLASTICA
cf. 1067 or 1068

February 11 / *531*
OUR LADY OF LOURDES
cf. 1063

February 14 / *532*
CYRIL AND METHODIUS
cf. 1065 or 1068

February 17 / *533*
**SEVEN FOUNDERS OF THE
ORDER OF SERVITES**
cf. 1068

February 21 / *534*
PETER DAMIAN
cf. 1065 or 1066 or 1068

February 22 / *535*
CHAIR OF PETER
The Lord is my shepherd;
there is nothing I shall want.

February 23 / *536*
POLYCARP
cf. 1064 or 1065

1026 # MARCH

March 4 / *537*
CASIMIR
cf. 1068

March 7 / *538*
PERPETUA AND FELICITY
cf. 1064

March 8 / *539*
JOHN OF GOD
cf. 1068

March 9 / *540*
FRANCES OF ROME
cf. 1068

March 17 / *541*
PATRICK
cf. 1065

March 18 / *542*
CYRIL OF JERUSALEM
cf. 1065 or 1066

1027 # MARCH 19: JOSEPH, HUSBAND OF MARY

READING I   *2 Samuel 7, 4-5.12-14.16* / *543*

RESPONSORIAL PSALM   *Psalm (88)89, 2-3.4-5.27.29* / *543*

RC

The Son of Da-vid will live for ev - er.

I will sing for ever of your love, O
  Lord;
through all ages my mouth will
  proclaim your truth.
Of this I am sure, that your love lasts
  for ever,
that your truth is firmly established
  as the heavens. ℞.

'With my chosen one I have made a
  covenant;
I have sworn to David my servant:
I will establish your dynasty for ever
and set up your throne through all
  ages.' ℞.

He will say to me: "You are my father,
my God, the rock who saves me."
I will keep my love for him always;
with him my covenant shall last. ℞.

READING II   *Romans 4, 13.16-18.22 / 543*

GOSPEL   *Matthew 1, 16.18-21.24 / 543*

Or:

GOSPEL   *Luke 2, 41-51 / 543*

March 23 / *544*   1028
TURIBUS DE MOGROVEJO
cf. 1065

MARCH 25: ANNUNCIATION OF OUR LORD   1029

READING I   *Isaiah 7, 10-14 / 545*

RESPONSORIAL PSALM   *Psalm (39)40, 7-8.8-9.10.11 / 545*

Here am I, Lord; I come to do your will.

You do not ask for sacrifice and
  offerings,
but an open ear.
You do not ask for holocaust and
  victim.
Instead, here am I. ℞.

In the scroll of the book it stands
  written
that I should do your will.
My God, I delight in your law
in the depth of my heart. ℞.

Your justice I have proclaimed
in the great assembly.
My lips I have not sealed;
you know it, O Lord. ℞.

I have not hidden your justice in my
  heart
but declared your faithful help.
I have not hidden your love and your
  truth
from the great assembly. ℞.

READING II   *Hebrews 10, 4-10 / 545*

GOSPEL   *Luke 1, 26-38 / 545*

1030   APRIL

April 2 / 546
FRANCIS OF PAOLA
cf. 1068

April 4 / 547
ISIDORE
cf. 1065 or 1066

April 5 / 548
VINCENT FERRER
cf. 1065

April 7 / 549
JOHN BAPTIST DE LA SALLE
cf. 1065 or 1068

April 11 / 550
STANISLAUS
cf. 1064 or 1065

April 13 / 551
MARTIN I
cf. 1064 or 1065

April 21 / 552
ANSELM
cf. 1065 or 1066

April 23 / 553
GEORGE
cf. 1064

April 24 / 554
FIDELIS OF SIGMARINGEN
cf. 1064 or 1065

April 25 / 555
MARK
For ever I will sing the
      goodness of the Lord.
Or: Alleluia.

April 28 / 556
PETER CHANEL
cf. 1064 or 1065

April 29 / 557
CATHERINE OF SIENA
cf. 1067

April 30 / 558
PIUS V
cf. 1065

1031   MAY

May 1 / 559
JOSEPH THE WORKER
Lord, give success to the work of
      our hands.
Or: Alleluia.

May 2 / 560
ATHANASIUS
cf. 1065 or 1066

May 3 / 561
PHILIP AND JAMES
Their message goes out through
      all the earth.
Or: Alleluia.

May 12 / 562
NEREUS AND ACHILLEUS
cf. 1064

PANCRAS / 563
cf. 1064

May 14 / 564
MATTHIAS
The Lord will give him a seat with
      the leaders of his people.
Or: Alleluia.

May 15
ISIDORE
cf. 1068

May 18 / *565*
JOHN I
cf. 1064 or 1065

May 20 / *566*
BERNARDINE OF SIENA
cf. 1065

May 25 / *567*
VENERABLE BEDE
cf. 1065 or 1066

GREGORY VII / *568*
cf. 1065

MARY MAGDALENE
DE PAZZI / *569*
cf. 1067 or 1068

May 26 / *570*
PHILIP NERI
cf. 1065 or 1068

May 27 / *571*
AUGUSTINE OF CANTERBURY
cf. 1065

May 31 / *572*
VISITATION
Among you is the great and Holy
   One of Israel.

Saturday following the Second
Sunday after Pentecost / *573*
IMMACULATE HEART OF MARY
cf. 1063

JUNE

June 1 / *574*
JUSTIN
cf. 1064

June 2 / *575*
MARCELLINUS AND PETER
cf. 1064

June 3 / *576*
CHARLES LWANGA AND
COMPANIONS
cf. 1064

June 5 / *577*
BONIFACE
cf. 1064 or 1065

June 6 / *578*
NORBERT
cf. 1065 or 1068

June 9 / *579*
EPHREM
cf. 1066

June 11 / *580*
BARNABAS
The Lord has revealed to the
   nations his saving power.

June 13 / *581*
ANTHONY OF PADUA
cf. 1065 or 1066 or 1068

June 19 / *582*
ROMUALD
cf. 1068

June 21 / *583*
ALOYSIUS GONZAGA
cf. 1068

June 22 / *584*
PAULINUS OF NOLA
cf. 1065

JOHN FISHER / *585*
AND THOMAS MORE
cf. 1064

1033 JUNE 24: BIRTH OF JOHN THE BAPTIST / VIGIL

READING I *Jeremiah 1, 4-10 / 586*

RESPONSORIAL PSALM *Psalm (70)71, 1-2.3-4.5-6.15.17 / 586*
RC

Since my moth-er's womb, you have been my strength.

In you, O Lord, I take refuge;
let me never be put to shame.
In your justice rescue me, free me;
pay heed to me and save me. ℟.

Be a rock where I can take refuge,
a mighty stronghold to save me;
for you are my rock, my stronghold.
Free me from the hand of the
wicked. ℟.

It is you, O Lord, who are my hope,
my trust, O Lord, since my youth.
On you I have leaned from my birth,
from my mother's womb you have
been my help. ℟.

My lips will tell of your justice
and day by day of your help.
O God, you have taught me from my
youth
and I proclaim your wonders still. ℟.

READING II *1 Peter 1, 8-12 / 586*

GOSPEL *Luke 1, 5-17 / 586*

1034 JUNE 24: BIRTH OF JOHN THE BAPTIST/DURING THE DAY

READING I *Isaiah 49, 1-6 / 587*

RESPONSORIAL PSALM *Psalm (138)139, 1-3.13-14.14-15 / 587*
RC

I praise you, O Lord, for

I am won - der-ful - ly made.

O Lord, you search me and you know
me,
you know my resting and my rising,
you discern my purpose from afar.
You mark when I walk or lie down,
all my ways lie open to you. ℟.

For it was you who created my being,
knit me together in my mother's womb.

I thank you for the wonder of my
being,
for the wonders of all your creation. ℟.

Already you knew my soul,
my body held no secret from you
when I was being fashioned in secret
and moulded in the depths of the
earth. ℟.

READING II   *Acts 13, 22-26 / 587*

GOSPEL   *Luke 1, 57-66.80 / 587*

June 27 / *588*   **June 28** / *589*   1035
CYRIL OF ALEXANDRIA   **IRENAEUS**
cf. 1065 or 1066   *cf. 1064 or 1066*

JUNE 29: PETER AND PAUL/VIGIL   1036

READING I   *Acts 3, 1-10 / 590*

RESPONSORIAL PSALM   *Psalm (18)19, 2-3.4-5 / 590*

Their mes - sage goes out through all the earth.

The heavens proclaim the glory of God
and the firmament shows forth the work
    of his hands.
Day unto day takes up the story
and night unto night makes known the
    message. ℞.

No speech, no word, no voice is heard
yet their span extends through all the
    earth,
their words to the utmost bounds of the
    world. ℞.

READING II   *Galatians 1, 11-20 / 590*

GOSPEL   *John 21, 15-19 / 590*

1037   ## JUNE 29: PETER AND PAUL/MASS DURING THE DAY

READING I   *Acts 12, 1-11 / 591*

RESPONSORIAL PSALM   *Psalm (33)34, 2-3.4-5.6-7.8-9 / 591*

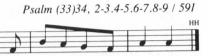

The an-gel of the Lord will res-cue those who fear him.

I will bless the Lord at all times,
his praise always on my lips;
in the Lord my soul shall make its
  boast.
The humble shall hear and be glad. ℞.

Glorify the Lord with me.
Together let us praise his name.
I sought the Lord and he answered me;
from all my terrors he set me free. ℞.

Look towards him and be radiant;
let your faces not be abashed.
This poor man called; the Lord heard
  him
and rescued him from all his
  distress. ℞.

The angel of the Lord is encamped
around those who revere him, to rescue
  them.
Taste and see that the Lord is good.
He is happy who seeks refuge in
  him. ℞.

READING II   *2 Timothy 4, 6-8.17-18 / 591*

GOSPEL   *Matthew 16, 13-19 / 591*

1038   **June 30** / *592*
FIRST MARTYRS OF THE CHURCH OF ROME
cf. 1064

1039   ## JULY

July 3 / *593*
THOMAS
Go out to all the world,
and tell the Good News.

July 4 / *594*
ELIZABETH OF PORTUGAL
cf. 1068

JULY 4: INDEPENDENCE DAY

RESPONSORIAL PSALM *Psalm (84)85, 9-10.11-12.13-14*

The Lord speaks of peace to his peo - ple.

I will hear what the Lord God has to
say,
a voice that speaks of peace,
peace for his people and his friends
and those who turn to him in their
hearts.
His help is near for those who fear him
and his glory will dwell in our land. ℟.

Mercy and faithfulness have met;
justice and peace have embraced.
Faithfulness shall spring from the earth
and justice look down from heaven. ℟.

The Lord will make us prosper
and our earth shall yield its fruit.
Justice shall march before him
and peace shall follow his steps. ℟.

July 5 / *595*
ANTHONY ZACCARIA
cf. 1065 or 1068

July 6 / *596*
MARIA GORETTI
cf. 1064 or 1067

July 11 / *597*
BENEDICT
cf. 1068

July 13 / *598*
HENRY
cf. 1068

July 14 / *599*
KATERI TEKAKWITHA /
cf. 1067

CAMILLUS DE LELLIS
cf. 1068

July 15 / *600*
BONAVENTURE
cf. 1065 or 1066

July 16 / *601*
OUR LADY OF MOUNT CARMEL
cf. 1063

July 21 / *602*
LAWRENCE OF BRINDISI
cf. 1065 or 1066

July 22 / *603*
MARY MAGDALENE
My soul is thirsting for you, O
Lord, my God.

July 23 / *604*
BRIDGET
cf. 1068

July 25 / *605*
JAMES
Those who sow in tears, shall reap
with shouts of joy.

July 26 / *606*
JOACHIM AND ANN
God will give him the throne of
    David, his father.

July 29 / *607*
MARTHA
cf. 1068

July 30 / *608*
PETER CHRYSOLOGUS
cf. 1065 or 1066

July 31 / *609*
IGNATIUS OF LOYOLA
cf. 1065 or 1068

1042   # AUGUST

August 1 / *610*
ALPHONSUS LIGUORI
cf. 1065 or 1066

August 2 / *611*
EUSEBIUS OF VERCELLI
cf. 1065

August 4 / *612*
JOHN VIANNEY
cf. 1065

August 5 / *613*
**DEDICATION OF SAINT MARY
MAJOR**
cf. 1062

1043   # AUGUST 6: TRANSFIGURATION

READING I   *Daniel 7, 9-10.13-14 / 615*

RESPONSORIAL PSALM   *Psalm (96)97, 1-2.5-6.9 / 615*

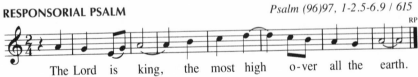

The Lord is king, the most high o-ver all the earth.

The Lord is king, let earth rejoice,
let all the coastlands be glad.
Cloud and darkness are his raiment;
his throne, justice and right. ℞.

The mountains melt like wax
before the Lord of all the earth.
The skies proclaim his justice;
all peoples see his glory. ℞.

For you indeed are the Lord
most high above all the earth,
exalted far above all spirits. ℞.

READING II   *2 Peter 1, 16-19 / 615*

GOSPEL/A   *Matthew 17, 1-9 / 615*

GOSPEL/B   *Mark 9, 2-10 / 615*

GOSPEL/C   *Luke 9, 28-36 / 615*

August 7 / *618*
SIXTUS II
cf. 1064

CAJETAN
cf. 1065 or 1068

August 11 / *619*
CLARE
cf. 1068

1044

August 8 / *617*
DOMINIC
cf. 1065 or 1068

August 13 / *620*
PONTIAN AND HIPPOLYTUS
cf. 1064 or 1065

August 10
LAWRENCE
Happy the man who is merciful
and lends to those in need.

August 14 /
MAXIMILIAN MARY KOLBE
Precious in the eyes of the Lord
is the death of his faithful ones.

AUGUST 15: ASSUMPTION/VIGIL

1045

READING I   *1 Chronicles 15, 3-4.15.16; 16, 1-2* / *621*

RESPONSORIAL PSALM   *Psalm (131)132, 6-7.9-10.13-14* / *621*

Lord, go up to the place of your rest,
you and the ark of your ho - li - ness.

At Ephrata we heard of the ark;
we found it in the plains of Yearim.
"Let us go to the place of his dwelling;
let us go to kneel at his footstool." ℞.

For the Lord has chosen Zion;
he has desired it for his dwelling:
"This is my resting-place for ever,
here have I chosen to live." ℞.

Your priests shall be clothed with
    holiness;
your faithful shall ring out their joy.
For the sake of David your servant
do not reject your anointed. ℞.

READING II   *1 Corinthians 15, 54-57* / *621*

GOSPEL   *Luke 11, 27-28* / *621*

AUGUST 15: ASSUMPTION/MASS DURING THE DAY

READING I *Revelation 11, 19; 12, 1-6.10 / 622*

RESPONSORIAL PSALM *Psalm (44)45, 10.11.12.16 / 622*

The queen stands at your right hand, ar-rayed in gold.

Listen, O daughter, give ear to my words:
forget your own people and your father's house. ℟.

So will the king desire your beauty;
he is your lord, pay homage to him. ℟.

They are escorted amid gladness and joy;
they pass within the palace of the king. ℟.

READING II *1 Corinthians 15, 20-26 / 622*

GOSPEL *Luke 1, 39-56 / 622*

FIRST MONDAY IN SEPTEMBER: LABOR DAY

1048

RESPONSORIAL PSALM   *Psalm (89)90, 2.3-4.12-13.14.16*

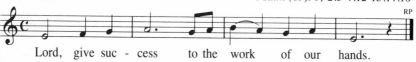

Lord, give suc - cess to the work of our hands.

Before the mountains were born
or the earth or the world brought forth,
you are God, without beginning or
    end. ℟.

You turn men back into dust
and say: "Go back, sons of men."
To your eyes a thousand years
are like yesterday, come and gone,
no more than a watch in the night. ℟.

Make us know the shortness of our life
that we may gain wisdom of heart.
Lord, relent! Is your anger for ever?
Show pity to your servants. ℟.

In the morning, fill us with your love;
we shall exult and rejoice all our days.
Show forth your work to your servants;
let your glory shine on their
    children. ℟.

SEPTEMBER

1049

September 3 / *635*
GREGORY THE GREAT
cf. 1065 or 1066

September 8 / *636*
BIRTH OF MARY
With delight I rejoice in the Lord.

September 9
PETER CLAVER
cf. 1065

September 13 / *637*
JOHN CHRYSOSTOM
cf. 1065 or 1066

1050   **SEPTEMBER 14: TRIUMPH OF THE CROSS**

READING I   *Numbers 21, 4-9 / 638*

RESPONSORIAL PSALM   *Psalm (77)78, 1-2.34-35.36-37.38 / 638*

Do not for - get the works of the Lord.

Give heed, my people, to my teaching;
turn your ear to the words of my
  mouth.
I will open my mouth in a parable
and reveal hidden lessons of the
  past. ℞.

When he slew them then they would
  seek him,
return and seek him in earnest.
They would remember that God was
  their rock,
God the Most High their redeemer. ℞.

But the words they spoke were mere
  flattery;
they lied to him with their lips.
For their hearts were not truly with him;
they were not faithful to his
  covenant. ℞.

Yet he who is full of compassion
forgave their sin and spared them.
So often he held back his anger
when he might have stirred up his
  rage. ℞.

READING II   *Philippians 2, 6-11 / 638*

GOSPEL   *John 3, 13-17 / 638*

September 15 / *639*
OUR LADY OF SORROWS
Save me, O Lord, in your steadfast
   love.

September 16 / *640*
CORNELIUS AND CYPRIAN
cf. 1064 or 1065

September 17 / *641*
ROBERT BELLARMINE
cf. 1065 or 1066

September 19 / *642*
JANUARIUS
cf. 1064 or 1065

September 20 /
ANDREW KIM TAEGŎN,
PAUL CHŎNG HASANG,
AND COMPANIONS
Those who sow in tears shall sing
for joy when they reap.

September 21 / *643*
MATTHEW
Their message goes out through all
   the earth.

September 26 / *644*
COSMAS AND DAMIAN
cf. 1064

September 27 / *645*
VINCENT DE PAUL
cf. 1065 or 1068

September 28 / *646*
WENCESLAUS
cf. 1064

September 29 / *647*
MICHAEL, GABRIEL, AND RAPHAEL
In the sight of the angels
I will sing your praise, Lord.

September 30 / *648*
JEROME
cf. 1065 or 1066

OCTOBER

October 1 / *649*
THERESA OF THE CHILD JESUS
cf. 1067 or 1068

October 2 / *650*
GUARDIAN ANGELS
He has put his angels in charge of
   you,
to guard you in all your ways.

October 4 / *651*
FRANCIS OF ASSISI
cf. 1068

October 6 / *652*
BRUNO
cf. 1065 or 1068

MARIE ROSE DUROCHER
cf. 1067

October 7 / *653*
OUR LADY OF THE ROSARY
cf. 1063

October 9 / *654*
DENIS AND COMPANIONS
cf. 1064

JOHN LEONARDI / *655*
cf. 1065 or 1068

October 14 / *656*
CALLISTUS I
cf. 1064 or 1065

October 15 / *657*
TERESA OF JESUS
1067 or 1068

October 16 / *658*
HEDWIG
cf. 1068

MARGARET MARY ALACOQUE / *659*
cf.1067 or 1068

October 17 / *660*
IGNATIUS OF ANTIOCH
cf. 1064 or 1065

October 18 / *661*
LUKE
Your friends tell the glory of your
   kingship, Lord.

October 19 / *662*
ISAAC JOGUES AND COMPANIONS
cf. 1064 or 1065

PAUL OF THE CROSS / *663*
cf. 1065 or 1068

October 23 / *664*
JOHN OF CAPISTRANO
cf. 1065

October 24 / *665*
ANTHONY CLARET
cf. 1065

October 28 / *666*
SIMON AND JUDE
Their message goes out through all
   the earth.

1053   NOVEMBER 1: ALL SAINTS

READING I   *Revelation 7, 2-4.9-14 / 667*

RESPONSORIAL PSALM   *Psalm (23)24, 1-2.3-4.5-6 / 667*

Lord, this is the peo-ple that longs to see your face.

The Lord's is the earth and its fullness,
the world and all its peoples.
It is he who set it on the seas;
on the waters he made it firm. ℟.

Who shall climb the mountain of the
   Lord?
Who shall stand in his holy place?
The man with clean hands and pure
   heart,
who desires not worthless things. ℟.

He shall receive blessings from the Lord
and reward from the God who saves
   him.
Such are the men who seek him,
seek the face of the God of Jacob. ℟.

READING II   *1 John 3, 1-3 / 667*

GOSPEL   *Matthew 5, 1-12 / 667*

November 2 / *668*   **November 4** / *670*   1054
ALL SOULS   **CHARLES BORROMEO**
cf. 163 or 193 to 202   *cf. 1065*

November 3 / *669*
MARTIN DE PORRES
cf. 1068

NOVEMBER 9: DEDICATION OF SAINT JOHN LATERAN   1055

RESPONSORIAL PSALM   *1 Chronicles 29, 10.11.11-12 / 703*
cf. 1062 or the following:

We praise your glo-ri-ous name, O might-y God.

Blessed are you, O Lord,
the God of Israel our father,
for ever, for ages unending. ℟.

Yours, Lord, are greatness and power,
and splendor, triumph and glory.
All is yours, in heaven and on
  earth. ℟.

Yours, O Lord, is the kingdom,
you are supreme over all.
Both honor and riches come from
  you. ℟.

You are the ruler of all,
from your hand come strength and
  power,
from your hand come greatness and
  might. ℟.

November 10 / *672*
LEO THE GREAT
cf. 1065 or 1066

November 11 / *673*
MARTIN OF TOURS
cf. 1068

November 12 / *674*
JOSAPHAT
cf. 1064 or 1065

November 13
FRANCES XAVIER CABRINI
cf. 1067

November 15 / *675*
ALBERT THE GREAT
cf. 1065 or 1066

November 16 / *676*
MARGARET OF SCOTLAND
cf. 1068

GERTRUDE / *677*
cf. 1067 or 1068

November 17 / *678*
ELIZABETH OF HUNGARY
cf. 1068

November 18 / *679*
DEDICATION OF THE CHURCHES OF PETER AND PAUL
The Lord has revealed to the
  nations his saving power.

November 21 / *680*
PRESENTATION OF MARY
cf. 1063

November 22 / *681*
CECILIA
cf. 1064 or 1067

November 23 / *682*
CLEMENT I
cf. 1064 or 1065

COLUMBAN / *683*
cf. 1065 or 1068

November 30 / *684*
ANDREW
Their message goes out through all
  the earth.

THANKSGIVING DAY

RESPONSORIAL PSALM　　　　　　　　　*Psalm (66)67, 2-3.5.7-8*

The earth has yield - ed its fruits;
God, our God has blessed us.

O God, be gracious and bless us
and let your face shed its light upon us.
So will your ways be known upon earth
and all nations learn your saving
　help. ℞.

Let the nations be glad and exult
for you rule the world with justice.
With fairness you rule the peoples,
you guide the nations on earth. ℞.

The earth has yielded its fruit
for God, our God, has blessed us.
May God still give us his blessing
till the ends of the earth revere him. ℞.

Or:

RESPONSORIAL PSALM　　　　　*Psalm (137)138, 1-2.2-3.4-5*　**1058**

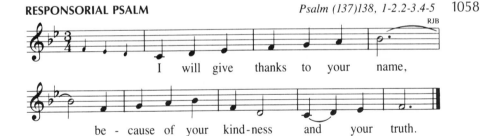

I will give thanks to your name,
be - cause of your kind-ness and your truth.

I thank you, Lord, with all my heart,
you have heard the words of my mouth.
In the presence of the angels I will
　bless you.
I will adore before your holy
　temple. ℞.

I thank you for your faithfulness and
　love
which excel all we ever knew of you.
On the day I called, you answered;
you increased the strength of my
　soul. ℞.

All earth's kings shall thank you
when they hear the words of your
　mouth.
They shall sing of the Lord's ways:
"How great is the glory of the
　Lord!" ℞.

1059 DECEMBER

December 3 / *685*
FRANCIS XAVIER
cf. 1065

December 4 / *686*
JOHN DAMASCENE
cf. 1065 or 1066

December 6 / *687*
NICHOLAS
cf. 1065

December 7 / *688*
AMBROSE
cf. 1065 or 1066

1060 DECEMBER 8: IMMACULATE CONCEPTION

READING I   *Genesis 3, 9-15.20 / 689*

RESPONSORIAL PSALM   *Psalm (97)98, 1.2-3.3-4 / 689*

JRC

Sing to the Lord a new song, for he has done mar-vel-ous deeds.

Sing a new song to the Lord
for he has worked wonders.
His right hand and his holy arm
have brought salvation. ℟.

The Lord has made known his
  salvation;
has shown his justice to the nations.
He has remembered his truth and love
for the house of Israel. ℟.

All the ends of the earth have seen
the salvation of our God.
Shout to the Lord, all the earth,
ring out your joy. ℟.

READING II   *Ephesians 1, 3-6.11-12 / 689*

GOSPEL   *Luke 1, 26-38 / 689*

December 11 / *690*
DAMASUS I
cf. 1065

December 12 / *691*
OUR LADY OF GUADALUPE
cf. 1063

JANE FRANCES DE CHANTAL
cf. 1068

December 13 / *692*
LUCY
cf. 1064 or 1067

December 14 / *693*
JOHN OF THE CROSS
cf. 1065 or 1066

December 21 / *694*
PETER CANISIUS
cf. 1065 or 1066

December 23 / *695*
JOHN OF KANTY
cf. 1065

December 26 / *696*
STEPHEN
Into your hands, O Lord,
I entrust my spirit.

December 27 / *697*
JOHN
Let good men rejoice in the Lord.

December 28 / *698*
HOLY INNOCENTS
Our soul has escaped like a bird
 from the hunter's net.

December 29 / *699*
THOMAS BECKET
cf. 1064 or 1065

December 31 / *700*
SYLVESTER I
cf. 1065

Commons: Psalm Responses

1062 **DEDICATION OF A CHURCH** / *703*

1 We praise your glorious name,
   O mighty God.

2 How lovely is your dwelling-
   place, Lord, mighty God!

   Or: Here God lives among
   his people.

3 Let us come before the Lord
   and praise him.

4 I rejoiced when I heard them
   say:
   let us go to the house of the
   Lord.

   Or: Let us go rejoicing to the
   house of the Lord.

1063 **COMMON OF THE BLESSED VIRGIN MARY** / *709*

1 My heart rejoices in the Lord,
   my Savior.

2 You are the highest honor of
   our race.

3 Listen to me, daughter;
   see and bend your ear.

4 Blessed be the name of the
   Lord for ever.

   Or: Alleluia.

5 The Almighty has done great
   things for me and holy is
   his name.

   Or: O Blessed Virgin Mary,
   you carried the Son of the
   eternal Father.

1064 **COMMON OF MARTYRS** / *715*

1 Into your hands, O Lord,
   I entrust my spirit.

2 The Lord set me free from all
   my fears.

3 Our soul has escaped like a bird
   from the hunter's net.

4 Those who sow in tears, shall
   reap with shouts of joy.

COMMON OF PASTORS / *721* 1065

1 You are my inheritance, O
Lord.

2 The Lord is my shepherd;
there is nothing I shall want.

3 For ever I will sing the
goodness of the Lord.

4 Proclaim his marvelous deeds to
all the nations.

5 You are a priest for ever,
in the line of Melchizedek.

6 Go out to all the world,
and tell the Good News.

Or: Alleluia.

COMMON OF DOCTORS OF THE CHURCH / *727* 1066

1 The judgments of the Lord are
true,
and all of them just.

Or: Your words, Lord, are
spirit and life.

2 The mouth of the just man
murmurs wisdom.

3 Lord, teach me your decrees.

COMMON OF VIRGINS / *733* 1067

1 Listen to me, daughter;
see and bend your ear.

Or: The bridegroom is here;
let us go out to meet Christ
the Lord.

2 Alleluia.

COMMON OF SAINTS / *739* 1068

1 Happy are they who hope in the
Lord.

Or: The just man will flourish
like a palm tree
in the garden of the Lord.

2 He who does justice shall live
on the Lord's holy
mountain.

3 You are my inheritance, O
Lord.

4 I will bless the Lord at all
times.

Or: Taste and see the goodness
of the Lord.

5 Oh, bless the Lord, my soul.

6 Happy the man who fears
the Lord
Or: Alleluia.

7 Happy are those who fear
the Lord.

8 In you, Lord, I have
found my peace.

Seasonal Psalms

The lectionary provides that a seasonal psalm may be used in place of the appointed responsorial psalm for the day. The following is a representative selection of these seasonal psalms.

ADVENT SEASON

1069 **RESPONSORIAL PSALM**   *Psalm (24)25, 4-5.8-9.10.14 / 175*

To you, O Lord, I lift my soul.

Lord, make me know your ways.
Lord, teach me your paths.
Make me walk in your truth, and
   teach me,
for you are God my savior.
In you I hope all day long. ℟.

The Lord is good and upright.
He shows the path to those who stray,
he guides the humble in the right path,
he teaches his way to the poor. ℟.

His ways are faithfulness and love
for those who keep his covenant and
   will.
The Lord's friendship is for those who
   revere him;
to them he reveals his covenant. ℟.

CHRISTMAS
Use the psalm for Christmas Mass During the Day, no. 781

LENT

RESPONSORIAL PSALM   *Psalm (50)51, 3-4.5-6.12-13.14.17 / 175*   1070

Be mer - ci-ful, O Lord, for we have sinned.

Have mercy on me, God, in your
   kindness.
In your compassion blot out my
   offense.
O wash me more and more from my
   guilt and cleanse me from my sin. ℟.

My offenses truly I know them;
my sin is always before me.
Against you, you alone, have I sinned;
what is evil in your sight I have
   done. ℟.

A pure heart create for me, O God,
put a steadfast spirit within me.
Do not cast me away from your
   presence,
nor deprive me of your holy spirit. ℟.

Give me again the joy of your help;
with a spirit of fervor sustain me.
O Lord, open my lips
and my mouth shall declare your
   praise. ℟.

EASTER

RESPONSORIAL PSALM   *Psalm (117)118, 1-2.16-17.22-23 / 175*   1071

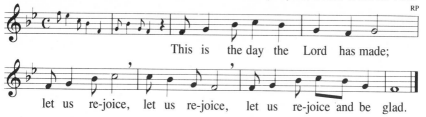

This is the day the Lord has made;

let us re-joice, let us re-joice, let us re-joice and be glad.

Give thanks to the Lord for he is good,
for his love endures for ever.
Let the sons of Israel say:
'His love endures for ever.' ℟.

The Lord's right hand has triumphed;
his right hand raised me.
The Lord's right hand has triumphed;
I shall not die, I shall live
and recount his deeds. ℟.

The stone which the builders rejected
has become the cornerstone.
This is the work of the Lord,
a marvel in our eyes. ℟.

ORDINARY TIME

1072 RESPONSORIAL PSALM   *Psalm (18)19, 8.9.10.11 / 175*

DRH

The Lord is kind and mer-ci-ful.

The law of the Lord is perfect,
it revives the soul.
The rule of the Lord is to be trusted,
it gives wisdom to the simple. ℞.

The precepts of the Lord are right,
they gladden the heart.
The command of the Lord is clear,
it gives light to the eyes. ℞.

The fear of the Lord is holy,
abiding for ever.
The decrees of the Lord are
truth
and all of them just. ℞.

They are more to be desired
than gold,
than the purest of gold
and sweeter are they than
honey,
than honey from the comb. ℞.

1073 RESPONSORIAL PSALM   *Psalm (62)63,2.3-4.5-6.8-9 / 175*

RP

My soul is thirst-ing for you, O Lord, thirst-ing for you my God.

O God, you are my God, for you I
long;
for you my soul is thirsting.
My body pines for you
like a dry, weary land without
water. ℞.

So I gaze on you in the sanctuary
to see your strength and your glory.
For your love is better than life,
my lips will speak your praise. ℞.

So I will bless you all my life,
in your name I will lift up my hands.
My soul shall be filled as with a
banquet,
my mouth shall praise you with joy. ℞.

For you have been my help;
in the shadow of your wings I rejoice.
My soul clings to you;
your right hand holds me fast. ℞.

1074 RESPONSORIAL PSALM   *Psalm (99)100,1-2.3.5 / 175*

MK

We are his peo-ple: the sheep of his flock.

Cry out with joy to the Lord, all the
earth.
Serve the Lord with gladness.
Come before him, singing for joy. ℞.

Know that he, the Lord, is God.
He made us, we belong to him,
we are his people, the sheep of his
flock. ℞.

Indeed, how good is the Lord,
eternal his merciful love.
He is faithful from age to age. ℞.

RESPONSORIAL PSALM   *Psalm (144)145,1-2.8-9.10-11.13-14 / 175*   1075

JRC

I will praise your name for ev - er,
my king and my God.

I will give you glory, O God my King,
I will bless your name for ever.
I will bless you day after day
and praise your name for ever. ℟.

The Lord is kind and full of compassion
slow to anger, abounding in love.
How good is the Lord to all,
compassionate to all his creatures. ℟.

All your creatures shall thank you, O
    Lord,
and your friends shall repeat their
    blessing.
They shall speak of the glory of your
    reign
and declare your might, O God. ℟.

The Lord is faithful in all his words
and loving in all his deeds.
The Lord supports all who fall
and raises all who are bowed down. ℟.

Seasonal Responses

The following psalm responses are drawn from five previously published psalm collections in wide use throughout the church. They are: "Songs of Israel" Vols. I and II (Peloquin), "Seasonal Responsorial Psalms" (Roff), "Psalms for the Church Year" (Isele), and "Psalms for the Church Year" (Haugen/Haas).

ADVENT SEASON

Psalm (84)85
CAP

1080

Lord, let us see your kind - ness,

and grant us your sal - va - tion.

Psalm (84)85
MH

1081

Lord, let us see your kind - ness;

Lord, let us see your kind - ness.

CHRISTMAS SEASON

Psalm (97)98
JR

1082

All the ends of the earth have

seen the sav - ing pow'r of God.

Psalm (97)98
CAP

1083

All the ends of the earth have seen the sav - ing

pow - er of God. All the ends of the

earth have seen the sav - ing pow - er of God.

Psalm (97)98
DCI

1084

the ends of the earth have

seen the sav - ing pow'r of God.

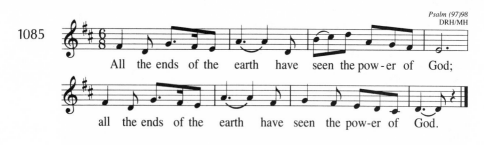

Psalm (97)98
DRH/MH

1085

All the ends of the earth have seen the pow-er of God;

all the ends of the earth have seen the pow-er of God.

EPIPHANY

Psalm (71)72
JR

1086

Lord, ev-'ry na - tion on earth will a - dore you.

Psalm (71)72
CAP

1087

Lord, ev-'ry na - tion on earth will a - dore you;

Lord, ev-'ry na - tion on earth will a - dore you.

Psalm (71)72
DCI

1088

Lord ev - 'ry na - tion on earth will a - dore you.

Psalm (71)72
MH

1089

Lord ev - 'ry na - tion on earth will a - dore you,

and all peo - ple shall walk by your light.

LENTEN SEASON

Psalm (50)51
JR

1090

Be mer - ci - ful, O Lord, for we have sinned.

Psalm (50)51
CAP

1091

Be mer - ci - ful, O Lord, for we have sinned.

Psalm (50)51
DCI

1092

Be mer - ci - ful, O Lord, for we have sinned.

Psalm (50)51
MH

1093

Be mer - ci - ful, O Lord, for we have sinned; be

mer - ci - ful, O Lord, for we have sinned.

Psalm (90)91
CAP

1094

Be with me, Lord, when I am in trou - ble.

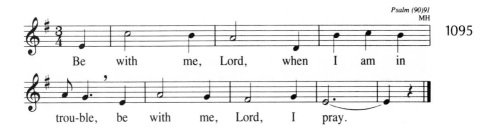

Psalm (90)91
MH

1095

Be with me, Lord, when I am in

trou-ble, be with me, Lord, I pray.

Psalm (129)130
CAP

1096

With the Lord there is mer - cy,

and full - ness of re - demp - tion.

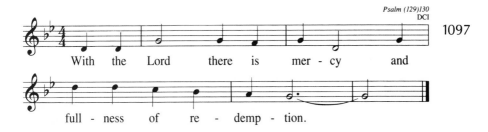

Psalm (129)130
DCI

1097

With the Lord there is mer - cy and

full - ness of re - demp - tion.

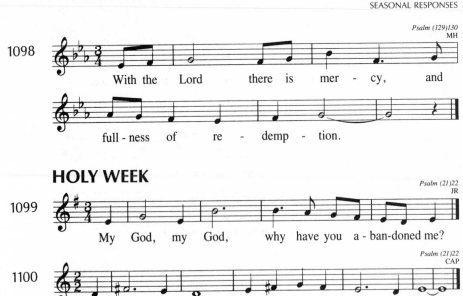

Psalm (129)130
MH

1098 With the Lord there is mer - cy, and full - ness of re - demp - tion.

HOLY WEEK

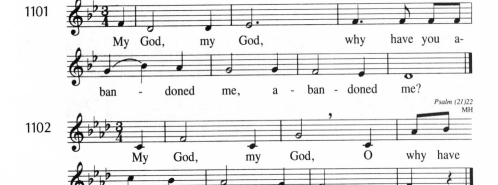

Psalm (21)22
JR

1099 My God, my God, why have you a - ban-doned me?

Psalm (21)22
CAP

1100 My God, my God, why have you a - ban - doned me?

Psalm (21)22
DCI

1101 My God, my God, why have you a-ban - doned me, a - ban - doned me?

Psalm (21)22
MH

1102 My God, my God, O why have you a - ban - doned me?

EASTER VIGIL

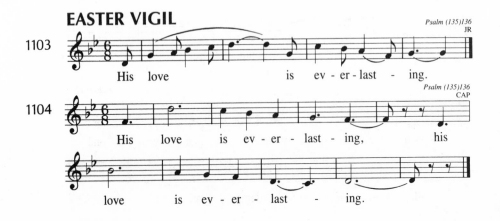

Psalm (135)136
JR

1103 His love is ev - er - last - ing.

Psalm (135)136
CAP

1104 His love is ev - er - last - ing, his love is ev - er - last - ing.

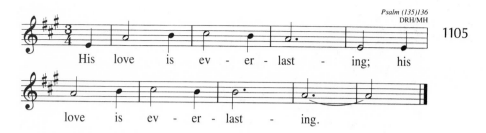

Psalm (135)136
DRH/MH

1105

His love is ev - er - last - ing; his

love is ev - er - last - ing.

EASTER SEASON

Psalm (117)118
CAP

1106

This is the day the Lord has made,

let us re - joice and be glad.

Psalm (117)118
DCI

1107

This is the day the Lord has made;

let us re - joice, re - joice and be glad.

Psalm (117)118
MH

1108

This is the day the Lord has made, let us re-
Al - le - lu - ia, al - le - lu - ia! Al - lu-

joice and be glad; this is the day the
lu - ia! Al - le - lu - ia, al-

Lord has made, let us re - joice and be glad!
le - lu - ia! Al - le - lu - ia!

Psalm (65)66
JR

1109

Let all the earth cry out to God with joy. Al-le-lu - ia.

1110 *Psalm (65)66*
CAP

Let all the earth cry out, let all the earth cry out to God with joy.

1111 *Psalm (65)66*
DCI

Let all the earth cry out to God with joy!

1112 *Psalm (65)66*
MH

Let all the earth cry out with joy to the Lord;
let all the earth cry out with joy to the Lord!

ASCENSION

1113 *Psalm (46)47*
JR

God mounts his throne to shouts of joy.

1114 *Psalm (46)47*
CAP

God mounts his throne to shouts of joy;
God mounts his throne to shouts of joy.

1115 *Psalm (46)47*
DCI

God mounts his throne to shouts of
joy, to shout, shout, shouts, of joy.

Psalm (46)47
MH

1116

God mounts his throne to shouts of joy, O

sing your prais - es to the Lord!

PENTECOST

Psalm (103)104
JR

1117

Lord, send out your Spir - it, and re-

new the face of the earth, and re-

new the face of the earth.

Psalm (103)104
CAP

1118

Lord, send out your Spir-it and re - new the face of the earth.

Lord, send out your Spir - it and re - new the face of the

earth, and re - new the face of the earth.

Psalm (103)104
DCI

1119

Lord, send out your Spir - it and re - new the face of the earth.

Psalm (103)104
DRH

1120

Lord, send out your Spir - it, and re-

new the face of the earth; Lord, send out your

Spir - it,   and   re - new   the face   of   the   earth.

ORDINARY TIME

Psalm (18)19
CAP

1121   Lord, you have the words of ev - er - last - ing   life.

Psalm (18)19
DCI

1122   Lord, you have the words of ev - er - last - ing   life.

Psalm (18)19
DRH

1123   Lord, you have the   words   of   ev - er - last - ing   life.

Psalm (26)27
JR

1124   The   Lord   is   my   light   and   my sal - va - tion.

Psalm (26)27
CAP

1125   The   Lord   is   my   light   and   my   sal-

va - tion.

Psalm (26)27
DRH

1126   The   Lord   is   my   light   and   my sal - va - tion,   of

whom should I be   a - fraid,   of   whom should I   be   a - fraid?

Psalm (33)34
JR

1127   I   will bless   the   Lord,   I   will bless the   Lord   at   all   times.

1128 — *Psalm (33)34* CAP

Taste and see the good - ness of the Lord.

1129 — *Psalm (33)34* DCI

O taste and see the good-ness of the Lord. O
taste and see the good-ness of the Lord.

1130 — *Psalm (33)34* MH

Taste and see the good-ness of the Lord, the
good - ness of the Lord.

1131 — *Psalm (62)63* CAP

My soul is thirst-ing for you, O Lord, my God.

1132 — *Psalm (62)63* MH

O God, I seek you, my soul thirsts for
you, your love is fin - er than life.

1133 — *Psalm (94)95* CAP

If to - day you hear his voice,
hard - en not your hearts.

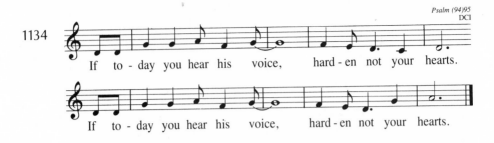

Psalm (94)95
DCI

1134

If to-day you hear his voice, hard-en not your hearts.

If to-day you hear his voice, hard-en not your hearts.

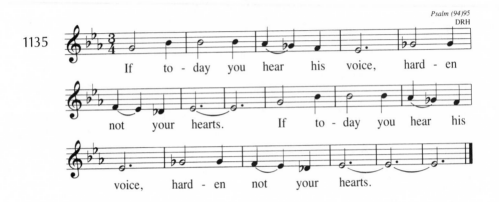

Psalm (94)95
DRH

1135

If to - day you hear his voice, hard - en

not your hearts. If to - day you hear his

voice, hard - en not your hearts.

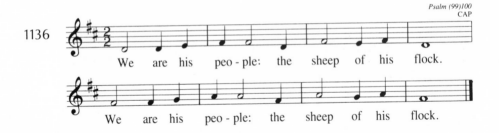

Psalm (99)100
CAP

1136

We are his peo - ple: the sheep of his flock.

We are his peo - ple: the sheep of his flock.

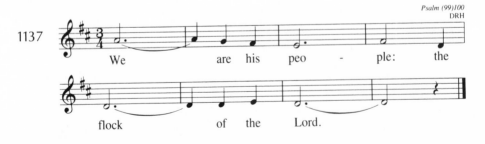

Psalm (99)100
DRH

1137

We are his peo - ple: the

flock of the Lord.

Psalm (102)103
JR

1138

The Lord is kind and mer - ci - ful.

Psalm (102)103
CAP
1139

The Lord is kind and mer - ci - ful. The Lord is
kind and mer - ci - ful.

Psalm (102)103
DCI
1140

The Lord is kind and mer - ci - ful. The
Lord is kind and mer - ci - ful.

Psalm (102)103
MH
1141

The Lord is kind and mer - ci - ful,
the Lord is kind and mer-ci - ful.

Psalm (144)145
CAP
1142

I will praise your name for ev - er, my king and my God.

Psalm (144)145
DRH
1143

I will praise your name, my king and my God.
I will praise your name, my king and my God.

LAST WEEKS IN ORDINARY TIME

Psalm (121)122
JR
1144

Let us go re - joic - ing to the house of the Lord.

Psalm (121)122
CAP

1145

Let us go re - joic - ing to the house of the Lord. Let us go re - joic - ing to the house of the Lord.

Psalm (121)122
DCI

1146

Let us go re - joic - ing to the house of the Lord.

Psalm (121)122
MH

1147

Come, let us go re - joic - ing to the house of the Lord; Come, let us go re - joic - ing to the house of the Lord.

MISCELLANEOUS

Psalm (22)23
DCI

1148

I shall live in the house of the Lord all the days of my life.

Psalm (22)23
DCI

1149

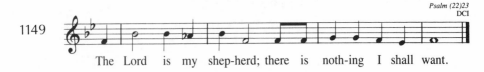

The Lord is my shep-herd; there is noth-ing I shall want.

Psalm (30)31
MH

1150

Fa - ther, I put my life in your hands.

Psalm (115)116
MH

1151

Our bless - ing cup is a com - mun - ion with the

blood of the Lord.

Prayers of the Individual and Household

1152 This book contains the texts and music which are used when the church assembles for the liturgy. With these pages members of the assembly may join fully in the Sunday eucharist, the liturgy of the hours, the celebration of the sacraments. All of these liturgies are, in fact, the work of the assembly, the work of Christians who gather to do those deeds—in word, in song, in gesture—which are the foundation and the strength of our lives. Over the years, the book itself becomes less and less necessary for we gradually learn many things by heart, making these words and tunes fully our own.

The texts in this section are not those of the assembly but those of the individual or household. They are included here because the daily prayer of Christians, prayers alone or in small groups, are part of our tradition, part of what we need for the daily expression of our faith. Many of the texts which follow have been the strength and sustenance of those who have walked the way of Jesus. Some of these prayers we already know by heart. Others will be learned with repetition. That is the intention, for most of these prayers are not meant to be read. They are words to be in the heart and on the lips at various times: by morning, by night, at table. Others are for special circumstances: when someone is ill, at the time of death, at times of thanksgiving.

Some of the prayers found in the liturgy itself are included or suggested here. When these become the regular prayer of an individual, the liturgy itself is the source of the Christian's spirit and life. This happens also when the scriptures read in the Sunday assembly are read and pondered again through the week. It happens when the verses of the psalm sung on Sunday become part of morning and evening prayer all week long. Such habits mean that we begin to come to the Sunday liturgy not as spectators but as celebrants, as the ones responsible for the liturgy.

The task of these prayers is to be with us day by day, over the years, to shape our lives. The prayers known by heart are a daily remembering and affirming of what became of us by baptism. Such prayers, coming day after day, in season and out, whatever the mood and circumstances, have us pray as the church. The individual becomes the voice of creation's praise, becomes the lament of the oppressed and suffering, becomes the whole world's giving of thanks.

MORNING PRAYERS

THE SIGN OF THE CROSS 1153
This prayer is not the words but the sign itself. The cross is made on the whole upper part of the body, or simply on the forehead, or the lips, or the heart. By this gesture the Christian renews that baptism which plunged us into the death of the Lord so that we live now in Christ. The common words of the sign of the cross recall our baptism.

In the name of the Father,
and of the Son,
and of the Holy Spirit.

Or, when signing the lips:

Lord, open my lips and my mouth will proclaim your praise.

GLORY TO GOD 1154
The strongest note of morning prayer is the praise of God who has kept us through the night and given us this new day. There are two common forms of the Gloria.

Glory to the Father, and to the Son, and to the Holy Spirit:
as it was in the beginning, is now, and will be forever. Amen.

Or:

Glory to God in the highest,
and peace to his people on earth.

Lord God, heavenly King,
almighty God and Father,
we worship you, we give you thanks,
we praise you for your glory.

Lord Jesus Christ, only Son of the Father,
Lord God, Lamb of God,
you take away the sin of the world:
have mercy on us;
you are seated at the right hand of the Father:
receive our prayer.

For you alone are the Holy One,
you alone are the Lord,
you alone are the Most High,
Jesus Christ,
with the Holy Spirit,
in the glory of God the Father. Amen.

1155   **THE LORD'S PRAYER**
This prayer is used by many to mark not only the morning but several times of the day. The first translation is the one to which most Catholics are accustomed, the second is a translation used more and more by Christians of many churches.

Our Father, who art in heaven,
hallowed be thy name.
Thy kingdom come.
Thy will be done on earth
   as it is in heaven.
Give us this day our daily bread,
and forgive us our trespasses
as we forgive those who trespass against us;
and lead us not into temptation
but deliver us from evil. Amen.

Or:

1156   Our Father in heaven,
   hallowed be your Name,
   your kingdom come,
   your will be done,
      on earth as in heaven.
Give us today our daily bread.
Forgive us our sins
   as we forgive those who sin against us.
Save us from the time of trial
   and deliver us from evil.
For the kingdom, the power
   and the glory are yours,
   now and for ever. Amen.

1157   **ANCIENT PRAYERS FOR MORNING**
The first of these is the beginning of the "Hear, O Israel" prayer; this is the cornerstone of Jewish prayer and would have been the daily prayer of Jesus, his family and his disciples. The blessings which follow accompany some of the actions of early morning. The final text is from Psalm 95, long used at morning prayer.

Hear, O Israel: the Lord is our God, the Lord is One!
Blessed is his glorious kingdom for ever and ever!

Blessed are you, Lord our God, ruler of the universe,
opening the eyes of the blind.

Blessed are you, Lord our God, ruler of the universe,
clothing the naked.

Blessed are you, Lord our God, ruler of the universe,
setting captives free.

Blessed are you, Lord our God, ruler of the universe,
guiding our footsteps.

Blessed are you, Lord our God, ruler of the universe,
taking the sleep from my eyes and the slumber from my eyelids.

Come, let us sing to the Lord; 1158
    and shout with joy to the Rock who saves us.
Let us approach him with praise and thanksgiving
    and sing joyful songs to the Lord.

Come, then, let us bow down and worship,
    bending the knee before the Lord, our maker.
For he is our God and we are his people,
    the flock he shepherds.

MORNING PSALMS 1159
In addition to Psalm 95, above, the psalms of morning are the psalms of praise, especially Psalms 148, 149 and 150 (nos. 79, 80 and 81). Other morning prayers are Psalm 51 (no. 41) and Psalm 63 (no.42).

MORNING HYMNS 1160
Morning hymns will be found at nos. 4, and 671 through 675.

THE BENEDICTUS 1161
The Benedictus or Song of Zachary from Luke 1:68-79 is a morning prayer for the day when God's compassion like "the dawn from on high shall break upon us, to shine on those who dwell in darkness and the shadow of death, and to guide our feet into the way of peace." It is found at no. 89, with a metrical setting at no. 6.

MORNING PRAYER OF SAINT PATRICK 1162
The Lorica or "Breastplate" is an ancient Celtic prayer attributed to Saint Patrick. A metrical setting is found at no. 671.

I arise today
through the strength of heaven,
light of the sun,
radiance of the moon,
splendor of fire,
speed of lightning,
swiftness of the wind,
depth of the sea,
stability of the earth,
firmness of the rock.

I arise today
through God's strength to pilot me,
God's might to uphold me,
God's wisdom to guide me,
God's eye to look before me,
God's ear to hear me,
God's word to speak for me,
God's hand to guard me,
God's way to lie before me,
God's shield to protect me,
God's hosts to save me
from the snares of the devil,

from everyone who desires me ill,
afar and near,
alone or in a multitude.
Christ with me, Christ before me, Christ behind me,
Christ in me, Christ beneath me, Christ above me,
Christ on my right, Christ on my left,
Christ when I lie down, Christ when I sit down, Christ when I arise,
Christ in the heart of everyone who thinks of me,
Christ in mouth of everyone who speaks of me,
Christ in the eye that sees me,
Christ in the ear that hears me.

DAYTIME PRAYERS

1163 **THE JESUS PRAYER**

This is one of the most widely used of those prayers which are meant to be repeated over and over again so that the one praying becomes completely caught up in prayer. Often prayers like this one are intended to be in rhythm with one's breathing.

Lord Jesus Christ,
Son of the living God,
have mercy on me, a sinner.

1164 **THE ROSARY**

The rosary is another prayer which in its repetition draws us into contemplation of the mysteries of our salvation. The rosary begins with the Apostle's Creed (no. 239) and consists of groups of ten Hail Marys, each group preceded by the Lord's Prayer and followed by the Glory to the Father. Each decade has traditionally been given to pondering one aspect of the paschal mystery:

The Joyful Mysteries
    1. The Annunciation (Luke 1:30-33)
    2. The Visitation (Luke 1:50-53)
    3. The Nativity (Luke 2:10-11)
    4. The Presentantion (Luke 2:29-32)
    5. The Finding of Jesus in the Temple (Luke 2:48-52)

The Sorrowful Mysteries
    1. The Agony in the Garden (Matthew 26:38-39)
    2. The Scourging (John 19:1)
    3. The Crowning with Thorns (Mark 15:16-17)
    4. Jesus Carries His Cross (John 19:17)
    5. The Crucifixion (John 19:28-30)

The Glorious Mysteries
    1. The Resurrection (Mark 16:6-8)
    2. The Ascension (Acts 1:10-11)
    3. The Coming of the Holy Spirit (Acts 2:1-4)
    4. The Assumption (Song of Songs 2:3-6)
    5. The Coronation of Mary (Luke 1:51-54)

The prayer which makes up the rosary is the Hail Mary. Its words are drawn from the scriptures and the intercession of the church.

Hail Mary, full of grace,
the Lord is with you!
Blessed are you among women
and blessed is the fruit of your womb, Jesus.
Holy Mary, mother of God,
pray for us sinners,
now and at the hour of our death. Amen.

1165

THE ANGELUS

1166

This is the prayer prayed in early morning, at noon, and at the end of the work day. Through this constant presence in the midst of everyday, the Christian proclaims that all of our time and all of our human space is transformed by the incarnation, the presence of God with us.

The angel spoke God's message to Mary
and she conceived of the Holy Spirit.
Hail Mary...

"I am the lowly servant of the Lord:
let it be done to me according to your word."
Hail Mary...

And the Word became flesh
and lived among us.
Hail Mary...

Pray for us, holy Mother of God,
that we may become worthy of the promises of Christ.

Lord,
fill our hearts with your grace:
once, through the message of an angel
you revealed to us the incarnation of your Son:
now, through his suffering and death
lead us to the glory of his resurrection.

DIVINE PRAISES

1167

These prayers may be used together, or each short line can be repeated over and over (as with the Jesus Prayer).

Blessed be God.
Blessed be his holy name.
Blessed be Jesus Christ, true God and true man.
Blessed be the name of Jesus.
Blessed be his most sacred heart.
Blessed be his most precious blood.
Blessed be Jesus in the most holy sacrament of the altar.
Blessed be the Holy Spirit, the Paraclete.
Blessed be the great mother of God, Mary most holy.
Blessed be her holy and immaculate conception.
Blessed be her glorious assumption.

Blessed be the name of Mary, virgin and mother.
Blessed be Joseph, her most chaste spouse.
Blessed be God in his angels and in his saints.

EVENING PRAYERS

1168 **PRAISE OF GOD FOR CHRIST, OUR LIGHT**
The prayer as day ends has often begun with a verse or hymn in praise of God who has given us in Christ our true light. The ancient hymn Phos Hilaron, *"O Radiant Light," is a beautiful expression of this (nos. 12 and 679). This praise is also contained in the simple invocation:*

Jesus Christ is the light of the world,
a light no darkness can overpower.

1169 **EVENING PSALMS**
Psalm 141 prays:

Let my prayer arise before you like incense,
the raising of my hands like an evening oblation.

This is the primary psalm of evening prayer (no. 74) as it prays for God's protection. Other appropriate psalms of the evening are Psalm 23 (no. 32), Psalm 121 (no. 66) and Psalm 123 (no. 68).

1170 **EVENING HYMNS**
Evening hymns will be found at nos. 676 through 681.

1171 **INTERCESSIONS**
At baptism the Christian receives the responsibility to intercede at all times, to be the voice of all creation and of all people before God. Each day we bring the needs and sufferings of our world. Such prayers are often made in the evening: our work is finished and we place all the world in God's care. The following prayers show how broad is the church's intercession. They may serve as an example for an individual's prayer.

For peace from on high and for our salvation, let us pray to the Lord. Lord, hear our prayer.

For the welfare of all churches and for the unity of the human family, let us pray...

For (name), our pope, (name), our bishop, and (name), our pastor, and for all ministers of the gospel, let us pray...

For nations and governments and for all who serve them, let us pray...

For this city and for every city and community and for all who live in them, let us pray...

For the good earth which God has given us and for the wisdom and will to conserve it, let us pray...

For the safety of travelers, the recovery of the sick, the care of the destitute and the release of prisoners, let us pray...

For an angel of peace to guide and protect us, let us pray...

For a peaceful evening and a night free from sin, let us pray...

THE MAGNIFICAT 1172

The Song of Mary from Luke 1:46-55 has long been a part of evening prayer of Christians. It is strong in its praise and in its vision of justice brought by God. It is found at nos. 87 and 88, with metrical versions at nos. 15 and 534.

NIGHT PRAYERS

CONFESSION 1173

Before sleep, the Christian recalls with sorrow the failures of the day and gives thanks to God for the love which surrounds us. Another prayer, The Act of Contrition, is found at no. 1194.

I confess to almighty God,
and to you, my brothers and sisters,
that I have sinned through my own fault
in my thoughts and in my words,
in what I have done,
and in what I have failed to do;
and I ask blessed Mary, ever virgin,
all the angels and saints,
and you, my brothers and sisters,
to pray for me to the Lord our God.

SHORT PRAYERS 1174

May the almighty Lord give us a restful night
and a peaceful death.

Keep us, Lord, as the apple of your eye
and shelter us in the shadow of you wing.

Protect us, Lord, as we stay awake;
watch over us as we sleep,
that awake, we may keep watch with Christ,
and asleep, rest in his peace.

Into your hands, Lord, I commend my spirit.
O Lord our God, make us lie down in peace
and raise us up to life.

Visit this house,
we beg you, Lord,
and banish from it
the deadly power of the evil one.
May your holy angels dwell here
to keep us in peace,
and may your blessing be always upon us.

Hear us, Lord,
and send your angel from heaven
to visit and protect,
to comfort and defend
all who live in this house.

1175 **NIGHT PSALMS**
The traditional psalms of night are Psalm 4 (no. 25), Psalm 91 (no. 49) and Psalm 134 (no. 72).

1176 **NIGHT HYMNS**
Night hymns are found at nos. 20 and 676 through 681.

1177 **CANTICLE OF SIMEON**
The words spoken by Simeon in the Temple (Luke 2:29-32) are often used as a night prayer for the church. It is found at nos. 22 and 90, with metrical versions at nos. 676 and 691.

1178 **ANTHEMS OF MARY**
The last prayer of night is addressed to our mother. The Salve Regina *(no. 703) is used throughtout the year; during Eastertime it is replaced by the* Regina Caeli *(no. 443). Another appropriate prayer is the* Memorare.

Remember, most loving virgin Mary,
never was it heard
that anyone who turned to you for help
was left unaided.
Inspired by this confidence,
though burdened by my sins,
I run to your protection
for you are my mother.
Mother of the Word of God,
do not despise my words of pleading
but be merciful and hear my prayer.

MEAL PRAYERS
At table we learn to give God thanks and praise for all the fruit of the earth and work of human hands.

1179 **BEFORE MEALS**
Bless us, O Lord, and these thy gifts
which we are about to receive
from thy bounty;
through Christ our Lord. Amen.

Or:

The eyes of all hope in you, Lord,
and you give them food in due season.
You open your hand,
and every creature is filled with your blessing.

Or:

Blessed are you, Lord our God, ruler of the universe,
for you bring forth bread from the earth.

AFTER MEALS

We give you thanks
for all your gifts,
almighty God,
living and reigning
now and for ever.

Or:

Blessed be the Lord
of whose bounty we have received
and by whose goodness we live.

SUNDAY PRAYERS

Sunday is called by Christians "The Lord's Day." On this day Christians assemble, listen to the scriptures, gather at the holy table and share in communion. Sunday is the highest day in our calendar. It is appropriate to prepare for the eucharistic assembly by reading and reflecting on the Sunday's scriptures. Week by week these scriptures are read at the liturgy as a foundation for all our worship and all our lives. In the eucharistic prayer and the holy communion, we "proclaim the death of the Lord until he comes" (1 Corinthians 11:26). Thus each Sunday we gather as the church "to praise and thank God, to remember and make present God's great deeds, to offer common prayer, to realize and celebrate the kingdom of peace and justice" (United States Bishops' Committee on the Liturgy, Environment and Art in Catholic Worship*). Some traditional prayers of preparation for Mass and thanksgiving after Mass are found below. Among the hymns which are especially appropriate for Sunday are nos. 661 through 663. The eucharistic hymns of Thomas Aquinas are fitting prayers both before and after communion: nos. 489, 758, 759 and 813. Among the psalms which have been used as communion prayers are Psalm 23 (no. 32), Psalm 34 (no. 36) and Psalm 147 (no. 78).*

HOW HOLY THIS FEAST

How holy this feast
in which Christ is our food:
his passion is recalled,
grace fills our hearts,
and we receive a pledge of the glory to come.

You gave them bread from heaven to be their food.
And this bread contained all goodness.

Lord Jesus Christ,
you gave us the eucharist
as the memorial of your suffering and death.
May our worship of this sacrament of your body and blood
help us to experience the salvation you won for us
and the peace of the kingdom
where you live with the Father and the Holy Spirit,
one God, for ever and ever. Amen.

1183 **ANIMA CHRISTI**

Soul of Christ, sanctify me.
Body of Christ, heal me.
Blood of Christ, drench me.
Water from the side of Christ, wash me.
Passion of Christ, strengthen me.
Good Jesus, hear me.
In your wounds shelter me.
From turning away keep me.
From the evil one protect me.
At the hour of my death call me.
Into your presence lead me,
to praise you with all your saints
for ever and ever. Amen.

1184 **PRAYER TO THE VIRGIN MARY**

Mary, holy virgin mother,
I have received your Son, Jesus Christ.
With love you became his mother,
gave birth to him, nursed him,
and helped him grow to manhood.
With love I return him to you,
to hold once more,
to love with all your heart,
and to offer him to the Holy Trinity
as our supreme act of worship
for your honor and for the good
of all your children.
Mother, ask God to forgive my sins
and to help me serve him more faithfully.
Keep me true to Christ until death,
and let me come to praise him with you
for ever and ever. Amen.

1185 **PRAYER FOR FRIDAYS**

In their 1983 letter, The Challenge of Peace, *the bishops of the United States called on Catholics to join them in fasting, prayer and charity on Fridays: "As a tangible sign of our need and desire to do penance we, for the cause of peace, commit ourselves to fast and abstinence on each Friday of the year... Every Friday should be a day significantly devoted to prayer, penance, and almsgiving for peace."*

All praise be yours, God our Creator,
as we wait in joyful hope
for the flowering of justice and the fullness of peace.
All praise for this day, this Friday.
By our weekly fasting and prayer
cast out the spirit of war, of fear and mistrust,
and make us grow hungry for human kindness,
thirsty for solidarity

with all the people of your dear earth.
May all our prayer, our fasting and our deeds
be done in the name of Jesus. Amen.

TIMES OF NEED

There are many scriptures, hymns and psalms in this book which give voice to our prayers for our own needs, for the needs of others and of the world. A familiarity with the psalms especially will lead the Christian to many prayers in troubled times.

IN TIMES OF SICKNESS 1186

All-powerful and ever-living God,
the lasting health of all who believe in you,
hear us as we ask your loving help for the sick;
restore their health,
that they may again offer joyful thanks in your Church.

Or:

God of love,
ever caring,
ever strong,
stand by us in our time of need.
Watch over your child who is sick,
Look after him/her in every danger,
and grant him/her your healing and peace.

IN TIME OF SUFFERING 1187

Lord Jesus Christ, by your patience in suffering you hallowed earthly pain
and gave us the example of obedience to your Father's will:
Be near me in my time of weakness and pain;
sustain me by your grace, that my strength and courage may not fail;
heal me, if it be your will;
and help me always to believe that what happens to me here
is of little account if you hold me in eternal life,
my Lord and my God.

WHEN DEATH IS NEAR 1188

Go forth, Christian soul, from this world
in the name of God the almighty Father, who created you,
in the name of Jesus Christ, Son of the living God, who suffered for you,
in the name of the Holy Spirit, who has poured out upon you,
go forth, faithful Christian.
May you live in peace this day,
may your home be with God in Zion,
with Mary, the virgin mother of God,
with Joseph, and all the angels and saints.

Or:

Saints of God, come to his/her aid!
Come to meet him/her, angels of the Lord!

1189 WHEN SOMEONE HAS DIED

Eternal rest grant to him/her/them, O Lord,
and let perpetual light shine upon him/her/them.

Or:

Loving and merciful God,
we entrust our brother/sister to your mercy.
You loved him/her greatly in this life:
now that he/she is freed from all its cares,
give him/her happiness and peace for ever.
The old order has passed away;
welcome him/her now into paradise
where there will be no more sorrow,
no more weeping or pain,
but only peace and joy
with Jesus, your Son,
and the Holy Spirit
for ever and ever. Amen.

Or:

1190 God of all consolation,
in your unending love and mercy for us
you turn the darkness of death
into the dawn of new life.
Show compassion to your people in their sorrow.
Be our refuge and our strength
to lift us from the darkness of this grief
to the peace and light of your presence.
Your Son, our Lord Jesus Christ,
by dying for us, conquered death
and by rising again, restored life.
May we then go forward eagerly to meet him,
and after our life on earth
be reunited with our brothers and sisters
where every tear will be wiped away.
We ask this through Christ our Lord. Amen.

1191 PSALMS IN TIME OF NEED

Among the psalms which are prayed in times of sickness and sorrow are the following: Psalm 6 (no. 26), Psalm 25 (no. 33), Psalm 42 (no. 37), Psalm 63 (no. 42) and Psalm 103 (no. 55).

1192 PRAYER TO MARY

We turn to you for protection,
holy Mother of God.
Listen to our prayers
and help us in our needs.
Save us from every danger,
glorious and blessed Virgin.

PRAYER FOR PEACE 1193

Lord, make me an instrument of your peace:
  where there is hatred, let me sow love;
  where there is injury, pardon;
  where there is doubt, faith;
  where there is despair, hope;
  where there is darkness, light;
  where there is sadness, joy.
O divine Master, grant that I may not so much seek
  to be consoled as to console,
  to be understood as to understand,
  to be loved as to love.
For it is in giving that we receive,
  it is in pardoning that we are pardoned,
  it is in dying that we are born to eternal life.

PENANCE AND RECONCILIATION 1194

The rite of reconciliation for several penitents is at no. 125. When a person alone comes to celebrate the sacrament with a priest, the priest greets the penitent. Then the penitent makes the sign of the cross and the priest invites the penitent to have trust in God. A reading from scripture follows. After this, the penitent may say a prayer of confession (for example, "I confess to almighty God" no. 1173). The penitent then makes a confession of sin and receives counsel from the priest. The penitent may then recite one of the following prayers or use some other way to express sorrow.

My God,
I am sorry for my sins with all my heart.
In choosing to do wrong
and failing to do good,
I have sinned against you
whom I should love above all things.
I firmly intend, with your help,
to do penance,
to sin no more,
and to avoid whatever leads me to sin.

Or:

Our Savior Jesus Christ
suffered and died for us.
In his name, my God, have mercy.

Or:

Lord Jesus, Son of God,
have mercy on me, a sinner.

The priest then extends hands over the penitent's head and speaks the absolution. The priest may then say: "Give thanks to the Lord, for he is good" and the penitent responds: "His mercy endures for ever." Then the priest dismisses the penitent in peace.

1195 VARIOUS PRAYERS OF PENANCE AND RECONCILIATION

Lord,
turn to us in mercy,
and forgive all our sins
that we may serve you in true freedom.

1196 Father of mercies
and God of consolation,
you do not wish the sinner to die
but to be converted and live.
Come to the aid of your people,
that they may turn from their sins
and live for you alone.
May we be attentive to your word,
confess our sins, receive your forgiveness,
and be always grateful for your loving kindness.
Help us to live the truth in love
and grow into the fullness of Christ, your Son,
who lives and reigns for ever and ever. Amen.

1197 Father, all-powerful and ever-living God,
we do well always and everywhere to give you thanks.
When you punish us, you show your justice;
when you pardon us, you show your kindness;
yet always your mercy enfolds us.
When you chastise us, you do not wish to condemn us;
when you spare us, you give us time to amend for ours sins
through Christ our Lord. Amen.

1198 God and Father of us all,
you have forgiven our sins
and sent us your peace.
Help us to forgive each other
and to work together to establish peace in the world.

1199 PSALMS OF PENANCE AND RECONCILIATION
Among the psalms which speak of sin, of sorrow and of forgiveness are the following: Psalm 51 (no. 41), Psalm 90 (no. 48), Psalm 123 (no. 68), Psalm 130 (no. 71) and Psalm 139 (no. 73).

VARIOUS PRAYERS

1200 COME, HOLY SPIRIT
Come, Holy Spirit, fill the hearts of your faithful,
and kindle in them the fire of your love.
Send forth your Spirit and they shall be created,
and you will renew the face of the earth.

Lord, by the light of the Holy Spirit
you have taught the hearts of your faithful.
In the same Spirit
help us to relish what is right
and always rejoice in your consolation.

LITANY OF THE HOLY NAME

Lord, have mercy	Lord, have mercy
Christ, have mercy	Christ, have mercy
Lord, have mercy	Lord, have mercy
God our Father in heaven	have mercy on us
God the Son, Redeemer of the world	have mercy on us
God the Holy Spirit	have mercy on us
Holy Trinity, one God	have mercy on us
Jesus, Son of the living God	have mercy on us
Jesus, splendor of the Father	have mercy on us
Jesus, brightness of the everlasting light	have mercy on us
Jesus, king of glory	have mercy on us
Jesus, dawn of justice	have mercy on us
Jesus, Son of the Virgin Mary	have mercy on us
Jesus, worthy of our love	have mercy on us
Jesus, mighty God	have mercy on us
Jesus, father of the world to come	have mercy on us
Jesus, prince of peace	have mercy on us
Jesus, all-powerful	have mercy on us
Jesus, pattern of patience	have mercy on us
Jesus, model of obedience	have mercy on us
Jesus, gentle and humble of heart	have mercy on us
Jesus, lover of chastity	have mercy on us
Jesus, lover of us all	have mercy on us
Jesus, God of peace	have mercy on us
Jesus, author of life	have mercy on us
Jesus, model of goodness	have mercy on us
Jesus, seeker of souls	have mercy on us
Jesus, our God	have mercy on us
Jesus, our refuge	have mercy on us
Jesus, father of the poor	have mercy on us
Jesus, treasure of the faithful	have mercy on us
Jesus, Good Shepherd	have mercy on us
Jesus, the true light	have mercy on us
Jesus, eternal wisdom	have mercy on us
Jesus, infinite goodness	have mercy on us
Jesus, our way and our life	have mercy on us
Jesus, joy of angels	have mercy on us
Jesus, king of patriarchs	have mercy on us
Jesus, teacher of apostles	have mercy on us
Jesus, master of evangelists	have mercy on us
Jesus, courage of martyrs	have mercy on us
Jesus, light of confessors	have mercy on us
Jesus, purity of virgins	have mercy on us
Jesus, crown of saints	have mercy on us
Lord, be merciful	Jesus, save your people
From all evil	Jesus, save your people
From every sin	Jesus, save your people

From the snares of the devil	Jesus, save your people
From your anger	Jesus, save your people
From the spirit of infidelity	Jesus, save your people
From everlasting death	Jesus, save your people
From the neglect of your Holy Spirit	Jesus, save your people
By the mystery of your incarnation	Jesus, save your people
By your birth	Jesus, save your people
By your childhood	Jesus, save your people
By your hidden life	Jesus, save your people
By your public ministry	Jesus, save your people
By your agony and crucifixion	Jesus, save your people
By your abandonment	Jesus, save your people
By your grief and sorrow	Jesus, save your people
By your death and burial	Jesus, save your people
By your rising to new life	Jesus, save your people
By your return to the Father	Jesus, save your people
By your gift of the holy eucharist	Jesus, save your people
By your joy and glory	Jesus, save your people

1202 LITANY OF LORETTO

Lord, have mercy	Lord, have mercy
Christ, have mercy	Christ, have mercy
Lord, have mercy	Lord, have mercy
God our Father in heaven	have mercy on us
God the Son, Redeemer of the world	have mercy on us
God the Holy Spirit	have mercy on us
Holy Trinity, one God	have mercy on us
Holy Mary	pray for us
Holy Mother of God	pray for us
Most honored of virgins	pray for us
Mother of Christ	pray for us
Mother of the Church	pray for us
Mother of divine grace	pray for us
Mother most pure	pray for us
Mother of chaste love	pray for us
Mother and virgin	pray for us
Sinless Mother	pray for us
Dearest of Mothers	pray for us
Model of motherhood	pray for us
Mother of good counsel	pray for us
Mother of our Creator	pray for us
Mother of our Savior	pray for us
Virgin most wise	pray for us
Virgin rightly praised	pray for us
Virgin rightly renowned	pray for us
Virgin most powerful	pray for us
Virgin gentle in mercy	pray for us
Faithful Virgin	pray for us

Mirror of justice	pray for us
Throne of wisdom	pray for us
Cause of our joy	pray for us
Shrine of the Spirit	pray for us
Glory of Israel	pray for us
Vessel of selfless devotion	pray for us
Mystical Rose	pray for us
Tower of David	pray for us
Tower of ivory	pray for us
House of gold	pray for us
Ark of the covenant	pray for us
Gate of heaven	pray for us
Morning star	pray for us
Health of the sick	pray for us
Refuge of sinners	pray for us
Comfort of the troubled	pray for us
Help of Christians	pray for us
Queen of angels	pray for us
Queen of patriarchs and prophets	pray for us
Queen of apostles and martyrs	pray for us
Queen of confessors and virgins	pray for us
Queen of all saints	pray for us
Queen conceived without sin	pray for us
Queen assumed into heaven	pray for us
Queen of the rosary	pray for us
Queen of peace	pray for us

1203   Acknowledgements

The publisher gratefully acknowledges the following holders of copyright whose permission has been granted for the inclusion of material in this book. Every effort has been made to determine the owner- ship of all tunes, texts and harmonizations used in this edition and to make proper arrangements for their use. The publisher regrets any error or oversight which may have occurred and will readily make proper acknowledgement in future editions if such omission is made known. Acknowledgements are stated in accordance with the requirements of the individual copyright holder.

PSALM TONES

The Gelineau Psalm Tones are © 1963, The Grail, England, GIA Publications, Inc., agent. The own- ership of the remaining psalm tones is as follows (each tone is only listed the first time it appears): Laurence Bevenot, nos. 28, 34, 43, 60 and 66, ©, Ampleforth Abbey Trustees. The Chrysogonus Waddell, OCSO, tone, no. 29, © Gethsemani Abbey. The tones from *Lutheran Worship,* nos. 26 and 87, © 1982, Concordia Publishing House. The tones by A. Gregory Murray, OSB, nos. 25, 35, 797 and 881, © L.J. Carey and Co. Ltd. (Ascherberg, Hopwood & Crew, Ltd.). The tones by Robert Kreutz, no. 76, and Douglas Mews, no. 37, © International Committee on English in the Liturgy, Inc. The tone at no. 24, © 1979, Robert Knox Kennedy. The tone at no. 40, © 1973, David Hurd. All remaining psalm tones are the copyright of GIA Publications, Inc.

SERVICE MUSIC AND HYMNS

Other than the psalm tones, all music found from nos. 1 to 354, and nos. 765 to 1151, is copyright by GIA Publications, Inc., with the exception of those items specified below.

2   Text: © 1969, James Quinn, SJ. By permission of Geoffrey Chapman, a division of Cassell Ltd. Music: © 1980, GIA Publications, Inc.

6   Text: © 1969, James Quinn, SJ. By permission of Geoffrey Chapman, a division of Cassell Ltd. Harm: © Oxford University Press

12   Text: © William G. Storey

92   Music: © 1979, ICEL

112   Music: © 1977, ICEL

176   © 1970, 1977, ICEL

177   Text: © 1985, ICEL

276   Music from *1972 Communion Service* © 1972, Oxford University Press

284   Music: © 1980, ICEL

287   © 1984, Les Presses de Taizé, GIA Publications, Inc., agent.

288   Music: © 1971, Manna Music. Arr.: © 1971,1975, Celebration, P.O. Box 309, Aliquippa, PA 15001 All rights reserved.

292   Music: © 1980, David M. Young

294   Music: © 1980, ICEL

295   © 1980, Les Presses de Taizé, GIA Publications, Inc., agent.

297   © 1984, Les Presses de Taizé, GIA Publications, Inc., agent.

298   © 1979, Les Presses de Taizé, GIA Publications, Inc., agent.

299   © 1977, GIA Publications, Inc.

305   © Studio SM, Paris

309   Adaptation: © 1980, Church Pension Fund. Harm: © 1986, GIA Publications, Inc.

323   Music from *1972 Communion Service* © 1972, Oxford University Press

327   Music: © Huguenin Schola Cantorum

329   © 1980, Les Presses de Taizé, GIA Publications, Inc., agent.

336   © 1984, Les Presses de Taizé, GIA Publications, Inc., agent.

337   © 1980, Les Presses de Taizé, GIA Publications, Inc., agent.

355   Text: © 1982, Hope Publishing Co., Carol Stream, IL 60188

357   Harm: © 1975, GIA Publications, Inc.

358   Text: © 1970, Mayhew McCrimmon Ltd.

359   Text: © David Higham Assoc. Ltd.

360   © 1983, GIA Publications, Inc.

361   © 1980 ICEL.

362   Text: © 1982, Hope Publishing Co., Carol Stream, IL 60188. Music: From *Enlarged Songs of Praise* © Oxford University Press

364   Harm: © National Christian Education Council

365   Text: From *English Praise* © 1975, Oxford University Press. Music: © J. Curwen and Sons

367   Harm: © 1958, Basilian Fathers, assigned to Ralph Jusko Publications, Inc.

368   Text: © 1985, The Church Pension Fund. Harm: © 1986, GIA Publications, Inc.

369   © 1984, Les Presses de Taizé, GIA Publications, Inc., agent.

371   Text: © 1982, Hope Publishing Co., Carol Stream, IL 60188

378   Harm: © Oxford University Press

380   Text: © Fredrick Harris Music Co. Ltd., Oakville, Ontario, Canada. Setting: © 1978, *Lutheran Book of Worship.* Used by permission of Augsburg Publishing House.

381   Text: © Oxford University Press. Harm: © A. R. Mowbray and Co. Ltd., Oxford, England

384   Text: © 1964; Harm: © 1986, GIA Publications, Inc.

385   Text: ''A Christmas Hymn'' from *Advice to A Prophet and Other Poems* © 1961, Richard Wilbur. Reprinted by permission of Harcourt Brace Jovanovich, Inc. Music: © 1984, GIA Publications, Inc.

387   Descant with accompaniment: From *Carols for Choirs,* © 1961, Oxford University Press

388   Translation © 1978, *Lutheran Book of Worship*

389   Text: © 1978, *Lutheran Book of Worship.* Used by permission of Augsburg Publishing House.

390   Text: © 1978, *Lutheran Book of Worship.* Used by permission of Augsburg Publishing House.

392   Descant with accompaniment: From *Carols for Choirs,* © 1961, Oxford University Press

393   Harm: © Rosalind Rusbridge, 44 Archfield Rd., Bristol, BS6 6BQ, England

394   Text: © 1927. Renewed 1955 by Eleanor Farjeon. Reprinted by permission of Harold Ober Assoc. Inc. Music: © The Estate of Leo Sowerby

Acknowledgements/*continued*

395 Text: © 1969, James Quinn, SJ. Printed by permission of Geoffrey Chapman a division of Cassell Ltd.

396 Harm: From the *English Hymnal* © Oxford University Press

397 Text: By permission of Mrs. John W. Work III. Harm: © 1971, Walton Music Corp.

398 Harm: © 1985, GIA Publications, Inc.

401 © 1979, Les Presses de Taizé, GIA Publications, Inc., agent.

402 Harm: © 1957, Novello and Co. Ltd.

404 Harm: © 1986, GIA Publications, Inc.

408 Harm: © Oxford University Press

412 Text: © 1984, Hope Publishing Co., Carol Stream, IL 60188

414 Text: © 1980, International Committee on English in the Liturgy, Inc. All rights reserved. Harm: © 1975, GIA Publications, Inc.

415 Harm: © 1986, GIA Publications, Inc.

416 Psalm Text: © 1963, The Grail. Harm: © 1986, GIA Publications, Inc.

418 © 1985, Oxford University Press, Inc.

420 Text: © Peter J. Scagnelli

421 Text: © 1971, Faber Music Ltd., London. Reprinted from *New Catholic Hymnal* by permission of the publishers. Harm: © 1986, GIA Publications, Inc.

422 Text: From *English Hymnal*, © Oxford University Press

423 © 1981, Les Presses de Taizé, GIA Publications, Inc., agent.

424 Text: © Peter J. Scagnelli. Harm: © 1975, GIA Publications, Inc.

425 © 1980, Les Presses de Taizé, GIA Publications, Inc., agent.

426 Text: © Author. Harm: © 1971, Faber Music Lit., London. Reprinted from *New Catholic Hymnal* by permission of the publishers.

427 Harm: © 1975, GIA Publications, Inc.

429 © 1979, Les Presses de Taizé, GIA Publications, Inc., agent.

430 © 1979, Les Presses de Taizé, GIA Publications, Inc., agent.

431 Text and tune: © 1969, and arr: © 1982, Hope Publishing Co., Carol Stream, IL 60188

432 © Gethsemani Abbey

435 Rhythmic reconstruction: © 1983, Schola Antiqua, Inc. Harm: © 1986, GIA Publications, Inc.

436 Harm: From *The Hymnal, 1940* © 1940, 1943, 1961, Church Pension Fund

437 Harm: © 1986, GIA Publications, Inc.

438 Text: © W. Russell Bowie

439 Music: © John Ireland Trust, 35 St. Mary's Mansions, London W2 1SQ, England

440 © 1984, Les Presses de Taizé, GIA Publications, Inc., agent.

441 Text and Tune: © 1973, The Word of God Music, P.O. Box 8617, Ann Arbor, MI 48107. All rights reserved. Harm. and Desc: © 1979, Celebration, P.O. Box 309, Aliquippa, PA 15001 All rights reserved.

443 Harm: © 1986, GIA Publications, Inc.

444 Text: © Oxford University Press. Music: From *English Hymnal* © Oxford University Press

446 © 1983, GIA Publications, Inc.

447 Harm: © 1975, GIA Publications, Inc.

448 Text: © Peter J. Scagnelli. Harm: © 1975, GIA Publications, Inc.

449 Harm: From *Lutheran Worship* © 1969, Concordia Publishing House

452 Harm: © 1980, GIA Publications, Inc.

453 Text: © Oxford University Press. Harm: © 1986, GIA Publications, Inc.

454 © 1979, Les Presses de Taizé, GIA Publications, Inc., agent.

455 Text: © 1978, *Lutheran Book of Worship*. Used by permission of Augsburg Publishing House.

458 Melody: © 1975, Richard Hillert from Setting One of Holy Communion in the *Lutheran Book of Worship* © 1978. Permission to use the melody in additional arrangements must be obtained from the copyright holder.

465 © 1984, Les Presses de Taizé, GIA Publications, Inc., agent.

466 Text: © 1975, Hope Publishing Co., Carol Stream, IL 60188

469 Harm: From the *English Hymnal* © Oxford University Press

470 Text: © 1978, Jeffery W. Rowthorn. Music: © 1942. Renewal 1970, Hope Publishing Co., Carol Stream, IL 60188

472 Music: From the *English Hymnal* © Oxford University Press

473 © 1979, Les Presses de Taizé, GIA Publications, Inc., agent.

474 Text: © Oxford University Press

475 Text: © 1971, John Webster Grant. Harm: © 1975, GIA Publications, Inc.

477 Text: From *English Praise* © 1975, Oxford University Press. Music: © 1983, GIA Publications, Inc.

478 © 1969, Hope Publishing Co., Carol Stream, IL 60188.

479 Harm: © 1975, GIA Publications, Inc.

480 Music: © 1986, GIA Publications, Inc. Text: © 1968, Hope Publishing Co., Carol Stream, IL 60188

481 Text: © 1984, Hope Publishing Co., Carol Stream, IL 60188. Music: © 1974, 1986, Harold Flammer, Inc., Delaware Water Gap, PA 18327, International copyright secured. All rights reserved. Used with permission.

482 Harm: © 1986, GIA Publications, Inc.

483 Text: *A Monastic Breviary* © Order of the Holy Cross, West Park, New York. Music: © 1983, Hank Beebe. All rights reserved.

484 Text: © 1959, 1965, 1966, 1977, Order of St. Benedict, Inc. Published by Liturgical Press, Collegeville, MN 56321. Harm: © 1958, Basilian Fathers, assigned to Ralph Jusko Publications, Inc.

488 Text: © 1955, GIA Publications, Inc.

489 Trans: © 1971, Faber Music Ltd., London. Reprinted from *New Catholic Hymnal* by permission of the publishers. Harm. © 1986, GIA Publications, Inc.

490 Harm: From the *English Hymnal* © Oxford University Press

495 Harm: © 1975, GIA Publications, Inc.

497 Text: © 1941, Irene C. Mueller. Harm: © 1986, GIA Publications, Inc.

499 Music: From *Enlarged Songs of Praise* © Oxford University Press

500 Text: From *Enlarged Songs of Praise* © Oxford University Press

501 Text: © 1966,1984, Willard F. Jabusch. Harm: © 1986, GIA Publications, Inc.

503 Text: © 1971, Walton Music Corp. Harm: © 1986, GIA Publications, Inc.

504 Text: © 1982, Hope Publishing Co., Carol Stream, IL 60188

506 Text: © 1981, Hope Publishing Co., Carol Stream, IL 60188. Music: © 1986, GIA Publications, Inc.

507 Music: From *Enlarged Songs of Praise* © Oxford University Press

508 Harm: From *English Praise* © 1975, Oxford University Press

509 Text: © 1982, Hope Publishing Co., Carol Stream, IL 60188. Music: From *Revised Church Hymnary 1927*, © Oxford University Press

510 © 1970,1975, Celebration, P.O. Box 309, Aliquippa, PA 15001 All rights reserved.

511 Text: © 1969, Concordia Publishing House

513 Text: © 1969, James Quinn, SJ. Printed by permission of Geoffrey Chapman, a division of Cassell Ltd.

514 Text: © 1954, Renewal 1982, and music: Music: © 1966, Hope Publishing Co., Carol Stream, IL 60188

515 Text: © 1970, Mayhew McCrimmon Ltd. Music: © 1979, Carl Schalk

516 Text: © 1953. Renewal 1981, Hymn Society of America, Texas Christian University, Fort Worth, TX 76129

517 © 1968, Augsburg Publishing House. Used by permission.

518 Text: © 1982, Hope Publishing Co., Carol Stream, IL 60188. Music: © 1971, Walton Music Corp.

519 © 1980, Les Presses de Taizé, GIA Publications, Inc., agent.

520 Text: © J. Curwen and Sons. Harm: From the *English Hymnal* © Oxford University Press

522 Text: © 1975 and Music © 1973, Hope Publishing Co., Carol Stream, IL 60188.

525 Text: Courtesy of Charles Scribner's Sons

526 Text: © 1972, GIA Publications, Inc.

Acknowledgements/*continued*

527 Trans: © 1978, Church Pension Fund
529 Music: © 1973, Hope Publishing Co., Carol Stream, IL 60188.
531 © 1979, Hope Publishing Co., Carol Stream, IL 60188
532 Music: © Oxford University Press
533 Text: © 1974, and harm: © 1977, Hope Publishing Co., Carol Stream, IL 60188
534 Text: © 1962, Hope Publishing Co., Carol Stream, IL 60188. Music: © Oxford University Press
535 Text: © 1982, Hope Publishing Co., Carol Stream, IL 60188
536 Music: © 1975, The Church Pension Fund
538 Text: © Canon John E. Bowers. Music From *English Hymnal* © Oxford University Press
540 Text: © Hope Publishing Co., Carol Stream, IL 60188. Harm: © 1978, GIA Publications, Inc.
541 Text: © 1982, Hope Publishing Co., Carol Stream, IL 60188
542 Text: © 1980, Hope Publishing Co., Carol Stream, IL 60188. Music: © 1980, GIA Publications, Inc.
543 Text: © 1969, Hope Publishing Co., Carol Stream, IL 60188
544 Text: © 1970, Mayhew McCrimmon Ltd. Tune: © Composer
545 © 1973, Hope Publishing Co., Carol Stream, IL 60188.
547 Descant: © 1953, Novello and Co. Ltd.
548 © 1979, Les Presses de Taizé, GIA Publications, Inc., agent.
549 Text: © 1972, Hope Publishing Co., Carol Stream, IL 60188
550 © 1973, Hope Publishing Co., Carol Stream, IL 60188.
552 Music: 1974, 1986 Harold Flammer, Inc., Delaware Water Gap, PA 18327. International copyright secured. All rights reserved. Used with permission.
553 © 1979, Les Presses de Taizé, GIA Publications, Inc., agent.
554 Text: © 1972, GIA Publications, Inc.
555 © 1979, Les Presses de Taizé, GIA Publications, Inc., agent.
556 Text: © Hope Publishing Co., Carol Stream, IL 60188. Music: © J. Curwen and Sons.
557 Music: From *Revised Church Hymnary 1927*, © Oxford University Press
558 Text: © 1940, The Church Pension Fund
559 Text: © 1939, E.C. Schirmer Music Co. Harm: Executors of G.H. Knight
561 © 1982, Les Presses de Taizé, GIA Publications, Inc., agent.
562 Text: © 1970, Hope Publishing Co., Carol Stream, IL 60188. Music: © Francis Jackson
563 Text: © 1979, Hope Publishing Co., Carol Stream, IL 60188
564 Text: © 1982, Hope Publishing Co., Carol Stream, IL 60188. Music: © 1986, GIA Publications, Inc.
565 Text: © 1954. Renewal 1982, Hymn Society of America, Texas Christian University, Fort Worth, TX 76129
566 Text: © 1979, Stainer and Bell, Ltd. Used by permission of Galaxy Music Corp., New York, NY, sole US agent. Music: © 1986, GIA Publications, Inc.
567 Music: © 1986, Praise Publications
568 Text: From *Enlarged Songs of Praise* © Oxford University Press. Harm: © 1985, Hope Publishing Co., Carol Stream, IL 60188
569 Music: © 1911, Stainer and Bell, Ltd. Used by permission of Galaxy Music Corp., New York, NY, sole US agent.
570 Text: © 1941, The Church Pension Fund
572 Harm: © 1986, GIA Publications, Inc.
573 Text: © 1984, Hope Publishing Co., Carol Stream, IL 60188
574 © 1985, Oxford University Press, Inc.
575 Text: © 1982, Hope Publishing Co., Carol Stream, IL 60188
576 Text: © 1982, Hope Publishing Co., Carol Stream, IL 60188
577 Text: © 1974, Hope Publishing Co., Carol Stream, IL 60188 Music: © SEFIM, Secretariat des Editeurs, 13 Avenue Savornin, 94240, L'hay-les-roses, France
578 Text: © 1970, Mayhew McCrimmon Ltd., 10-12 High Street, Great Wakering, Essex, England. All rights reserved. Music: © 1986, GIA Publications, Inc.

580 © 1972, Maranatha! Music
581 Text: © 1984, Hope Publishing Co., Carol Stream, IL 60188
582 Text: © 1971, Faber Music Ltd., London. Reprinted from *New Catholic Hymnal* by permission of the publishers. Music: © Mrs. Alfred M. Smith
583 Harm: © Hope Publishing Co., Carol Stream, IL 60188.
584 Text: © 1982, Carl P. Daw, Jr. Tune: © Skinner Chavez-Melo. Used by permission.
585 Harm: © 1975, GIA Publications, Inc.
586 Text: By permission of Augsburg Publishing House
587 Text: © J.W. Shore. Tune: © Composer
589 Text: © 1985, and music: © 1969, Hope Publishing Co., Carol Stream, IL 60188
590 Text: © 1969, James Quinn, SJ. By permission of Geoffrey Chapman, a division of Cassell Ltd. Harm: © Estate of T.H. Weaving
591 Music: Reprinted from "Six Wesley Songs for the Young" ©, 1971 Josef Weinberger Ltd.
592 Text: © 1968, Hope Publishing Co., Carol Stream, IL 60188. Music: © J. Curwen and Sons
593 Music: © 1969, Faith and Life Press
594 Text: © in this version, 1982 Hope Publishing Co., Carol Stream, IL 60188.
596 Music: © 1977, GIA Publications, Inc.
597 © 1983, Thomas H. Troeger and Carol Doran
598 Trans: © 1975, 1986, GIA Publications, Inc. Harm: © 1986, GIA Publications, Inc.
599 Text: © 1970, Mayhew McCrimmon Ltd. Music: © 1986, GIA Publications, Inc.
600 Harm: From *Cantate Domino* © 1980, Oxford University Press
602 Text and music: © 1969, Concordia Publishing House
603 Texts from *Revised Standard Version* © Division of Christian Education of the National Council of the Churches of Christ in the USA. Music: © 1974, Novello and Co. Ltd.
604 © 1979, Les Presses de Taizé, GIA Publications, Inc., agent.
606 Harm: © 1975, GIA Publications, Inc.
607 Harm: From the *English Hymnal* © Oxford University Press
608 Harm: © 1986, GIA Publications, Inc.
609 Harm: © A. Gregory Murray, Downside Abbey, Stratton on the Fosse, Bath BA3 4RH
612 Tune: © The Jesuit Fathers, London. Reprinted by permission of Peter Janson-Smith, Ltd., London. Harm: © 1934, Oxford University Press
613 Harm: © 1986, GIA Publications, Inc.
614 Text: © 1974, Hope Publishing Co., Carol Stream, IL 60188. Harm: © 1986, GIA Publications, Inc.
615 Text: © Mrs. M. Rees
616 Text: © 1982, Hope Publishing Co., Carol Stream, IL 60188
618 Text: © Christian Conference of Asia
619 © 1972, GIA Publications, Inc.
620 Harm: © 1985, GIA Publications, Inc.
621 Text: © 1969, Galliard Ltd. Used by permission of Galaxy Music Corp., New York, NY, sole US agent. Music: © 1969, Hope Publishing Co., Carol Stream, IL 60188
622 Text: © 1982, Hope Publishing Co., Carol Stream, IL 60188. Music: Reprinted from "Six Wesley Songs for the Young" © 1971, Josef Weinberger Ltd.
623 Text: © 1975, and music: © 1980, Hope Publishing Co., Carol Stream, IL 60188
624 Text: © Oxford University Press. Music: © 1969, Hope Publishing Co., Carol Stream, IL 60188
625 Text: © 1968, Hope Publishing Co., Carol Stream, IL 60188. Harm: © Executors of the late Dr. Basil Harwood
626 Text: © 1971, Hope Publishing Co., Carol Stream, IL 60188. Music: © 1971, Faber Music Limited. Reprinted from the *New Catholic Hymnal* by permission of the publisher and copyright owner.
627 Text: © 1969, James Quinn, SJ. By permission of Geoffrey Chapman, a division of Cassell Ltd.
628 Text: © 1955, 1964, Abingdon Press
629 Text: © 1980, Hope Publishing Co., Carol Stream, IL 60188
630 Text: © Oxford University Press
631 Text: © 1961, Hymn Society of America, Texas Christian University, Fort Worth, TX 76129

Acknowledgements/*continued*

632 Text: From *Songs of Praise* © Oxford University Press. Harm: © 1975, GIA Publications, Inc.

633 Text: © 1986, and music: © 1970, GIA Publications, Inc.

635 Text and tune: © 1972, Chantry Music Press, Inc. Harm: © 1975, GIA Publications, Inc.

636 Text and Harm: © 1963, Galliard Ltd. Used by permission of Galaxy Music Corp., New York, NY, sole US agent.

637 Text: © 1982, Hope Publishing Co., Carol Stream, IL 60188. Tune: © 1986, GIA Publications, Inc.

638 Text: © Oxford University Press. Music: From the *Clarendon Hymnbook* © Oxford University Press

639 Text: © 1983, Hope Publishing Co., Carol Stream, IL 60188. Tune: © 1986, GIA Publications, Inc.

640 Text: "Baptism By Fire" from *Incendiary Fellowship* © 1967, David Elton Trueblood. Reprinted by permission of Harper & Row, Publishers, Inc. Harm: © 1975, Broadman Press. All rights reserved. International Copyright Secured. Used by Permission.

641 © 1927, Edward B. Marks. By permission of Hal Leonard Corporation, Milwaukee, WI 53213

642 Text: © Lee M. Baldwin

643 Text: © 1968, Hope Publishing Co., Carol Stream, IL 60188

644 © 1963, Galliard Ltd. Used by permission of Galaxy Music Corp., New York, NY, sole US agent.

645 Text: From *Enlarged Songs of Praise* © Oxford University Press. Harm: © 1975, GIA Publications, Inc.

646 Text: © 1954. Renewal 1982, Hymn Society of America, Texas Christian University, Fort Worth, TX 76129. Music: From the *Revised Church Hymnary* © 1927, Oxford University Press

647 Text: © 1968, Hope Publishing Co., Carol Stream, IL 60188. Music: © 1971, Faber Music Ltd., London. Reprinted from *New Catholic Hymnal* by permission of the publishers.

648 Text: © 1967, Hope Publishing Co., Carol Stream, IL 60188. Setting: © 1969, *Contemporary Worship I: Hymns*. Used by permission of Augsburg Publishing House.

649 Text: © 1968, Hope Publishing Co., Carol Stream, IL 60188. Tune: © 1975, GIA Publications, Inc.

650 Text: © 1958, Hymn Society of America, Texas Christian University, Fort Worth, TX 76129. Music: © 1975, GIA Publications, Inc.

651 Text: © George Utech. Music: © 1986, GIA Publications, Inc.

653 Text: © American Peace Society. Reprinted with permission of the Helen Dwight Reid Educational Foundation, 400 Albemarle St., NW, Washington, DC 20016. Tune: © 1985, GIA Publications, Inc.

654 Text: © 1982, Carl P. Daw, Jr. Tune: © 1916. 1944, Roberton Publications. Reproduced by permission of the publisher: Theodore Presser Co., sole representative. Harm: © 1986, GIA Publications, Inc.

655 Text: © Stewart Cross. Tune: © 1942, The Church Pension Fund

656 Text: © 1975, Hope Publishing Co., Carol Stream, IL 60188. Harm: From the *English Hymnal* © Oxford University Press

657 © 1984, Les Presses de Taizé, GIA Publications, Inc., agent.

658 © 1968, Hope Publishing Co., Carol Stream, IL 60188

659 Text: © American Tract Society, Garland, Texas

660 Text: © 1969, James Quinn, SJ. By permission of Geoffrey Chapman, a division of Cassell Ltd.

661 Text: © 1983 and Music © 1982, Hope Publishing Co., Carol Stream, IL 60188

663 Text: © 1968, Hope Publishing Co., Carol Stream, IL 60188. Music: From the *Clarendon Hymnbook* © Oxford University Press

664 © 1973, Hope Publishing Co., Carol Stream, IL 60188

665 © 1982, GIA Publications, Inc.

666 Harm: © 1969, Concordia Publishing House

667 Text: © 1979, and music: © 1942. Renewal 1970, Hope Publishing Co., Carol Stream, IL 60188

668 © 1969, Hope Publishing Co., Carol Stream, IL 60188

670 Music: © 1973, Concordia Publishing House

671 Music: © 1983, GIA Publications, Inc.

672 © 1975, Celebration, P.O. Box 309, Aliquippa, PA 15001 All rights reserved.

673 Text: © 1969, James Quinn, SJ. By permission of Geoffrey Chapman, a division of Cassell Ltd. Harm: © A. Gregory Murray, Downside Abbey, Stratton on the Fosse, Bath BA3 4RH

674 Text: From "The Children's Bells", pub. Oxford University Press © David Higham Assoc. Ltd.

676 © 1980, Les Presses de Taizé, GIA Publications, Inc., agent.

677 Text: © 1969, James Quinn, SJ. By permission of Geoffrey Chapman, a division of Cassel Ltd.

680 Text: © Benedictine Nuns, St. Mary's Abbey, West Malling

681 Text: © Anne LeCroy. Music: © 1985, GIA Publications, Inc.

682 Text: © Oxford University Press. Harm: © A. Gregory Murray, Downside Abbey, Stratton on the Fosse, Bath BA3 4RH

683 Text: © John Arlott. Harm: © National Christian Education Council

684 Text: © 1973, Hope Publishing Co., Carol Stream, IL 60188. Music: © 1986, GIA Publications, Inc.

685 Text: © Harper and Row. Harm: © 1940, The Church Pension Fund

687 Harm: © 1986, GIA Publications, Inc.

688 Music: © 1986, GIA Publications, Inc.

689 Harm: © 1986, GIA Publications, Inc.

690 Harm: © 1975, GIA Publications, Inc.

691 Text: © 1969, James Quinn, SJ. By permission of Geoffrey Chapman, a division of Cassell Ltd. Harm: © 1975, GIA Publications, Inc.

692 Music: © 1986, GIA Publications, Inc.

693 © 1972, Canadian Catholic Conference, Ottawa, Canada. Reproduced with permission.

694 Text: © 1979, Hymn Society of America, Texas Christian University, Fort Worth, TX 76129. Harm: © 1975, GIA Publications, Inc.

695 © 1961, H. Freeman and Co., London WC2H 0LD

697 Text: © 1980, Hope Publishing Co., Carol Stream, IL 60188. Music: © Boekencentrum, Gravenhage, Netherlands

699 Text: © Anne LeCroy. Music: © Boekencentrum, Gravenhage, Netherlands

700 Text: © Esme. D. E. Bird

701 Text: © 1977, and music: © 1985, Hope Publishing Co., Carol Stream, IL 60188

702 Harm: © Willis Music Company

703 Trans: © 1954 and harm: © 1986, GIA Publications, Inc.

704 © 1978, Hope Publishing Co., Carol Stream, IL 60188

705 Music: From the *English Hymnal* © Oxford University Press

706 Text: © 1985, The Church Pension Fund

707 Text and Harm: From the *English Hymnal* © Oxford University Press.

708 Text: © 1971, Faber Music Ltd., London. Reprinted from *New Catholic Hymnal* by permission of the publishers.

709 Text: © 1967, Gooi en Sticht bv. Hilversum, The Netherlands. International copyright secured. Revised translation © 1984, TEAM Publications

710 Stanzas 1-3: © Board of Publication, Lutheran Church in America. Stanza 4: © 1958, *Service Book and Hymnal*. Used by permission of Augsburg Publishing House. Harm: © 1983, Hope Publishing Co., Carol Stream, IL 60188

711 © 1971, Faber Music Ltd., London. Reprinted from *New Catholic Hymnal* by permission of the publishers.

713 Harm: © 1986, GIA Publications, Inc.

714 Text: From *English Praise* © 1975, Oxford University Press

715 The text "Let us with joy our voices raise", has been reprinted with permission of the copyright owner, F.E.L Publications, Ltd., 2545 Chandler Ave., Suite 5, Las Vegas, NV 89120, Phone: (702)736-9420. Further reproduction (even words only or one time usage) is not permitted without F.E.L.'s written permission.

717 Text: © Peter J. Scagnelli. Harm: © 1969, Condordia Publishing House

719 Harm: © 1975, GIA Publications, Inc.

720 Text: © 1982, Hope Publishing Co., Carol Stream, IL 60188. Harm: © A. Gregory Murray, Downside Abbey, Stratton on the Fosse, Bath BA3 4RH

721 Text: © John B. Geyer

722 Text: © 1978, Thomas E. Herbranson, from *Lutheran Book of Worship*. Music: © 1964, Abingdon Press

723 Text: © 1971, Faber Music Ltd., London. Reprinted from *New Catholic Hymnal* by permission of the publishers.

724 © 1969, Hope Publishing Co., Carol Stream, IL 60188

Acknowledgements/*continued*

725 Harm: © A. Gregory Murray, Downside Abbey, Stratton on the Fosse, Bath BA3 4RH
726 Text: © 1971, Hope Publishing Co., Carol Stream, IL 60188. Harm: © 1938, J. Fisher and Bro.
727 Harm: © 1983, GIA Publications, Inc.
728 Harm: © 1986, GIA Publications, Inc.
730 Harm: © 1986, GIA Publications, Inc.
731 Text: From *Enlarged Songs of Praise* © Oxford University Press. Tune: © 1957, H.W. Gray Co., Inc., a division of Belwin-Mills Publishing Corporation. Copyright renewed. Used with permission. All rights reserved. Harm: © Christian Board of Education, Christian Church (Disciples of Christ)
734 © 1984, Les Presses de Taizé, GIA Publications, Inc., agent.
735 Harm: © 1986, GIA Publications, Inc.
736 © 1977, Archdiocese of Philadelphia
738 © 1970, GIA Publications, Inc.
739 Text: © 1968, Hope Publishing Co., Carol Stream, IL 60188
742 Text: © 1971, GIA Publications, Inc. Harm: © National Christian Education Council
745 Text and Harm: © 1983, Hope Publishing Co., Carol Stream, IL 60188
746 Text: © 1980, ICEL
747 Text: © 1969, Hope Publishing Co., Carol Stream, IL 60188
748 Text: © Board of Publication, Lutheran Church in America. Setting: © 1978, *Lutheran Book of Worship.* Used by permission of Augsburg Publishing House.
749 Text: © 1982, Hope Publishing Co., Carol Stream, IL 60188. Music: © 1971, Faber Music Limited. Reprinted from the *New Catholic Hymnal* by permission of the publisher and copyright owner.
750 Text: © 1986, GIA Publications, Inc.
751 © 1984, Oxford University Press, Inc.
752 Text: © 1965, GIA Publications, Inc. Harm: © 1986, GIA Publications, Inc.
754 Text: © Oxford University Press. Harm: Executors of G.H. Knight
755 Text: © 1980, International Committee on English in the Liturgy, Inc.
756 Harm: © 1979, Church of the Redeemer Episcopal, Houston, TX
758 Trans: © 1969, James Quinn, SJ. By permission of Geoffrey Chapman, a division of Cassell Ltd.
759 Harm: © 1986, GIA Publications, Inc.
760 Text: © J. Curwen and Sons
805 Rhythmic Reconstruction: © 1984, Schola Antiqua Inc. Harm: © 1985, GIA Publications, Inc.
813 Text: © 1969, James Quinn, SJ. By permission of Geoffrey Chapman, a division of Cassell Ltd.
830 Music: © 1977, International Committee on English in the Liturgy, Inc.
837 Trans: © 1983, Peter J. Scagnelli
857 Trans: © 1986, Peter J. Scagnelli; Acc: © Boekencentrum, Gravenhage, Netherlands

PRAYERS

1158, 1174 (Protect us, Lord) from *Liturgy of the Hours* © 1970, International Committee on English in the Liturgy, Inc. All rights reserved.
1166, 1173, 1174 (Visit this house, and Hear us, Lord), 1178, 1180, 1182, 1183, 1184, 1192, 1200-1202 from *A Book of Prayers*, © 1982, International Committee on English in the Liturgy, Inc. All rights reserved.
1185 © Archdiocese of Chicago
1186, 1188-1190, from *Pastoral Care of the Sick* © 1982, International Committee on English in the Liturgy, Inc. All rights reserved.
1187 From *The Book of Common Prayer*, 1979
1194-1198 From *Rite of Penance* © 1974, International Committee on English in the Liturgy, Inc. All rights reserved.

Scripture Passages Related to Hymns 1204

GENESIS

1:	God, Who Stretched the Spangled Heavens 648
	Many and Great, O God, Are Your Works 503
	Over the Chaos of the Empty Waters 483
	Praise the Spirit in Creation 477
	Thy Strong Word Didst Cleave the Darkness 511
	This Is the Day When Light Was First Created 663
1:1-5	God, Whose Almighty Word 486
1:2-3	On This Day, the First of Days 662
1:3	God, Omnipotent, Eternal 563
	Let There Be Light 653
1:3-5	Morning Has Broken 674
	This Is the Day When Light Was First Created 663
1:12	I Sing the Mighty Power of God 502
1:26-27	On This Day, the First of Days 662
1:31	All Things Bright and Beautiful 505
2:2-3	On This Day, the First of Days 662
8:22	Now Join We to Praise the Creator 647
12:1	The God of Abraham Praise 537
14:18	The God of Abraham Praise 537
22:1-18	God Spoke to Our Father Abraham 578
22:16-17	The God of Abraham Praise 537

EXODUS

3:6	The God of Abraham Praise 537
3:14	The God of Abraham Praise 537
14:29	Come, Ye Faithful, Raise the Strain 456
15:	At the Lamb's High Feast We Sing 459, 460
	Come, Ye Faithful, Raise the Strain 456
	When Israel Was in Egypt's Land 508
	Who Can Measure Heaven and Earth 509
15:2	The God of Abraham Praise 537
16 & 17	Shepherd of Souls 728
19.4	The God of Abraham Praise 537
19:20	The Glory of These Forty Days 422
20:	O Come, O Come, Emmanuel 357
33:14	The God of Abraham Praise 537
33:18-23	Holy, Holy, Holy! Lord God Almighty 485

NUMBERS

24:17	What Star Is This 407

DEUTERONOMY

6:2-6	God Be in My Head 567
8:3	Shepherd of Souls 728
30:19-20	Come, Let Us Love the Unborn Generations 639
32:3	Sing Praise to God Who Reigns Above 528

JOSHUA

3:14-17	Let Saints on Earth in Concert Sing 741

I SAMUEL

15:29	All Hail the Power of Jesus' Name 494, 495

I KINGS

8:30,36,39	Only Begotten, Word of God Eternal 666
19:	He Comes to Us as One Unknown 573

II KINGS

2:11	The Glory of These Forty Days 422

Scripture Passages Related to Hymns/*continued*

Scripture Passages Related to Hymns/*continued*

	To Jesus Christ, Our Sovereign King 497
72:5-17	Crown Him with Many Crowns 496
	From All That Dwell below the Skies 521
72:12-13	The Church of Christ in Every Age 626
78:25	Alleluia! Sing to Jesus 737
90:1-5	O God, Our Help in Ages Past 579
95:	Rejoice, the Lord Is King 493
95:1-2,6-7,8-9	O for a Heart to Praise My God 591
96:	Let All on Earth Their Voices Raise 716
	Sing a New Song to the Lord 550
	The King Shall Come When Morning Dawns 373
	The Royal Banners Forward Go 435
98:	Earth and All Stars 517
	New Songs of Celebration 533
	Sing to the Lord a Joyful Song 532
	Sing a New Song to the Lord 550
98:	The King Shall Come When Morning Dawns 373
98:49	Joy to the World 399
100:	All People That On Earth Do Dwell 669, 670
	Come, Rejoice before Your Maker 664
	Christians, Lift Up Your Hearts 538
	Jubilate Deo 555
	Let All the World in Every Corner Sing 536
	Praise to the Lord, the Almighty 547
102:1-7	Great God of Mercy 746
	O Christ, the Healer 747
103:	Praise, My Soul, the King of Heaven 530
	Praise to the Lord, the Almighty 547
104:	All Things Bright and Beautiful 505
	Fire of God, Titanic Spirit 478
	God Sends Us His Spirit 724
	Joyful, Joyful, We Adore You 525
	O That I Had a Thousand Voices 546
	Over the Chaos of the Empty Waters 483
	Praise and Thanksgiving 682
	The Works of the Lord Are Created in Wisdom 504
105:	All Creatures of Our God and King 520
	For the Beauty of the Earth 557
	Thanks Be to God 526
105:40-41	Shepherd of Souls 728
106:4	Love Divine, All Loves Excelling 588
109:	The Works of the Lord Are Created in Wisdom 504
113:1-2	From All That Dwell below the Skies 521
113:1-6	The Day You Gave Us, Lord, Is Ended 678
116:13	By Gracious Powers 577
117:	From All That Dwell below the Skies 521
	Laudate Dominum 519
	Sing Praise to the Lord 539
118:	Christus Resurrexit 465
118:14	Christians, Lift Up Your Hearts 538
118:24	Christ Is Made the Sure Foundation 617
	This Is the Day When Light Was First Created 663
118:25-27	All Glory, Laud, and Honor 428, 805
118:26	Benedictus Qui Venit 429
118:19-20	Only Begotten, Word of God Eternal 666
127:	O Father, All Creating 744
137:	Alleluia, Song of Gladness 413
	By the Babylonian Rivers 426
	Confitemini Domino 561
142:5	Amazing Grace 583
145:	Let All Things Now Living 559

Scripture Passages Related to Hymns/*continued*

Scripture Passages Related to Hymns/*continued*

40:28	Sing to the Lord a Joyful Song 532
40:10	How Firm a Foundation 585
42:1-4	The Church of Christ in Every Age 626
42:1-9	The Voice of God Goes Out through All the World 358
43:1-2	How Firm a Foundation 585
49:	In Christ There Is No East or West 659
49:14-15	Christian, Do You Hear the Lord 594
51:1-3	The Voice of God Goes Out through All the World 358
52:7	Come, O Long Expected Jesus 364
55:1-2	Come and Let Us Drink of That New River 723
55:6	We Walk by Faith 572
55:10-11	Word of God, Come Down on Earth 513
61:1-2	Come, O Long Expected Jesus 364
	The Voice of God Goes Out through All the World 358
61:3	The God of Abraham Praise 537
62:3	All Hail the Power of Jesus' Name 494, 495
63:3	Mine Eyes Have Seen the Glory 686
66:1	Mine Eyes Have Seen the Glory 686

JEREMIAH
8:22	There Is a Balm in Gilead 608
23:5-6	The God of Abraham Praise 537
24:23	The God of Abraham Praise 537
31:33	O for a Heart to Praise My God 591
51:8	Sing Praise to God Who Reigns Above 528

LAMENTATIONS
1:12	All You Who Pass This Way 440
2:21	By Gracious Powers 577
3:19	All Hail the Power of Jesus' Name 494, 495

BARUCH
4-5	City of God, Jerusalem 362

EZECHIEL
21:14-15	Mine Eyes Have Seen the Glory 686
36:26	O for a Heart to Praise My God 591
48:35	All Who Love and Serve Your City 621

DANIEL
6-7	The Glory of These Forty Days 422
7:9	Immortal, Invisible, God Only Wise 512
7:9,22	Come, Now Almighty King 487
	The God of Abraham Praise 537

HOSEA
6:3	Mine Eyes Have Seen the Glory 686

JOEL
2:12-18	Again We Keep This Solemn Fast 420
2:17	Parce Domine 416
3:1-5	God Sends Us His Spirit 724
	Praise the Spirit in Creation 477

AMOS
6:1-7	O Christ, the Healer 747

MICAH
5:2	O Little Town of Bethlehem 386
6:6-8	What Does the Lord Require 624
	When Jesus Came Preaching the Kingdom of God 614

Scripture Passages Related to Hymns/*continued*

Scripture Passages Related to Hymns/*continued*

Scripture Passages Related to Hymns/*continued*

Scripture Passages Related to Hymns/*continued*

13:5-13	Go Make of All Disciples 628
13:24	Hills of the North, Rejoice 365
	The King Shall Come When Morning Dawns 373
14:22-25	Hail Our Savior's Glorious Body/Pange Lingua 813
14:26	When in Our Music God Is Glorified 549
15:17-18	O Sacred Head Surrounded 434
16:15-20	Go Make of All Disciples 628

LUKE

1:26-31	Hail Our Savior's Glorious Body/Pange Lingua 813
1:26-37	Ave Maria 713
1:26-38	Immaculate Mary 708
	Sing We of the Blessed Mother 714
1:26-45	Savior of the Nations, Come 372
1:28	Mary, How Lovely the Light of Your Glory 711
1:40-42	Hail, Queen of Heaven/Salve Regina 703
1:46	Magnificat 553
1:46-55	My Soul Gives Glory to the Lord 15
	Tell Out, My Soul, the Greatness of the Lord 534
1:68-79	Blessed Be the God of Israel 6
1:78-79	O Come, Divine Messiah 367
	O Come, O Come, Emmanuel 357
2:1-10	The First Nowell 408
2:1-18	From Heaven Above 388
2:1-20	A Child Is Born in Bethlehem 384
2:6-7	Savior of the Nations, Come 372
2:6-14	Silent Night, Holy Night 379
2:6-18	Angels, from the Realms of Glory 377
	God Rest You Merry, Gentlemen 383
	Go Tell It on the Mountain 397
	Infant Holy, Infant Lowly 393
	What Child Is This 411
2:7	A Child Is Born in Bethlehem 384
	A Stable Lamp Is Lighted 385
	Away in a Manger 378
	Christ Was Born on Christmas Day 396
	Good Christian Friends, Rejoice 391
	Lo, How a Rose E'er Blooming 374
	Now Every Child That Dwells on Earth 394
	Once in Royal David's City 402
	Sing of Mary, Pure and Lowly 404
	Unto Us a Boy Is Born 381
2:7-18	Angel Voices Richly Blending 395
	'Twas in the Moon of Wintertime 380
2:8-14	See amid the Winter's Snow 375
	While Shepherds Watched 382
2:10-11	God Rest You Merry, Gentlemen 383
	Good Christian Friends, Rejoice 391
	Go Tell It on the Mountain 397
	It Came upon the Midnight Clear 400
	O Come, All Ye Faithful/Adeste Fideles 392
2:10-11,14	From Heaven Above 388
2:10-14	Immaculate Mary 708
2:13-14	All Glory Be to God on High 527
2:13-15	O Come, All Ye Faithful/Adeste Fideles 392
2:13-18	Angels We Have Heard on High 376
2:14	From Heaven Above 388
	Gloria, Gloria 401
	Glory Be to God in Heaven 518
	Glory to God in the Highest 542
2:15	O Come, All Ye Faithful/Adeste Fideles 392

Scripture Passages Related to Hymns/*continued*

Scripture Passages Related to Hymns/*continued*

Scripture Passages Related to Hymns/*continued*

Scripture Passages Related to Hymns/*continued*

Scripture Passages Related to Hymns/*continued*

Scripture Passages Related to Hymns/*continued*

Scripture Passages Related to Hymns/*continued*

Scripture Passages Related to Hymns/*continued*

Scripture Passages Related to Hymns/*continued*

Hymns for the Church Year   1205

The following hymns are suggested for the Sundays of the three-year lectionary cycle. Those with an asterisk (*) are directly related to the scriptures of the day, while the others are suggested because of their relationship to the predominant focus of the day's readings.

ADVENT I
A - Wake, O Wake, and Sleep No Longer   371
B - Wake, O Wake, and Sleep No Longer   371
C - Now the Day of the Lord Is at Hand*   687

ADVENT II
A - On Jordan's Bank*   356
    Lo, How a Rose E'er Blooming*   374
B - Comfort, Comfort, O My People*   370
    Take Comfort, God's People*   361
    On Jordan's Bank*   356
C - City of God, Jerusalem*   362
    On Jordan's Bank*   356

ADVENT III
A - When the King Shall Come Again*   355
B - On Jordan's Bank*   356
    The Voice of God Goes Out through All the
        World*   358
C - On Jordan's Bank*   356

ADVENT IV
A - O Come, O Come, Emmanuel*   357
    Lift Up Your Heads, O Mighty Gates*   363
B - The Angel Gabriel from Heaven Came*   695
C - Savior of the Nations, Come   372

CHRISTMAS
see nos. 374-401

HOLY FAMILY
Once in Royal David's City   402

MARY MOTHER OF GOD
see nos. 403-405

EPIPHANY
see nos. 406-411

BAPTISM OF THE LORD
When John Baptized by Jordan's River   412

LENT I
A - Forty Days and Forty Nights*   419
B - Lord, Who throughout These Forty Days*   417
C - Forty Days and Forty Nights*   419

LENT II
A - 'Tis Good, Lord, to Be Here*   700
B - God Spoke to Our Father Abraham*   578
    'Tis Good, Lord, to Be Here*   700
C - 'Tis Good, Lord, to Be Here*   700

LENT III
A - I Heard the Voice of Jesus Say*   607
B - Christ Is Made the Sure Foundation   617
    The Stars Declare His Glory   506

C - The God of Abraham Praise   537

LENT IV
A - He Healed the Darkness of My Mind*   749
B - A Spendthrift Lover Is the Lord*   597
    By the Babylonian Rivers*   426
C - Our Father, We Have Wandered*   755

LENT V
A - I Am the Bread of Life*   738
B - Before the Fruit Is Ripened by the Sun*   418
    Lift High the Cross*   704
    O God beyond All Praising   541
C - Forgive Our Sins*   754

PASSION SUNDAY
see nos. 428-430

HOLY THURSDAY
see nos. 431-432

GOOD FRIDAY
see nos. 433-440

EASTER VIGIL
see nos. 441-467

EASTER
see nos. 441-467

EASTER II
A - O Sons and Daughters*   447
    We Walk by Faith*   572
B - O Sons and Daughters*   447
    We Walk by Faith*   572
C - O Sons and Daughters*   447
    We Walk by Faith*   572

EASTER III
A - Daylight Fades*   448
B - Daylight Fades   448
C - Christian, Do You Hear the Lord*   594

EASTER IV
A - Jesus, Shepherd of Our Souls*   649
B - A Single Unmatched Stone*   574
    Jesus, Shepherd of Our Souls   649
C - A Multitude Comes from the East and the
        West   688
    Jesus, Shepherd of Our Souls   649

EASTER V
A - Come, My Way, My Truth, My Life*   569
    I Know That My Redeemer Lives*   445
B - This Is My Will   590
C - Lord of All Nations, Grant Me Grace*   602
    Love Is His Word*   599

Hymns for the Church Year/*continued*

Hymns for the Church Year/*continued*

EIGHTEENTH SUNDAY
A - You Satisfy the Hungry Heart   736
B - Shepherd of Souls*   728
C - O the Beautiful Treasures   689

NINETEENTH SUNDAY
A - How Firm a Foundation*   585
    I Sought the Lord*   593
B - I Am the Bread of Life*   738
C - This World, My God, Is Held within Your
    Hand*   582
    What Does the Lord Require   624

TWENTIETH SUNDAY
A - O God, Empower Us   642
B - I Am the Bread of Life*   738
C - God, Whose Purpose Is to Kindle*   640

TWENTY-FIRST SUNDAY
A - Christ's Church Shall Glory in His Power   616
B - I Am the Bread of Life*   738
    The Church of Christ in Every Age   626
    The Kingdom of God   615
C - A Multitude Comes from the East and the
    West*   688

TWENTY-SECOND SUNDAY
A - Take Up Your Cross*   634
B - O for a Heart to Praise My God   591
C - Gather Us In   665

TWENTY-THIRD SUNDAY
A - Draw Us in the Spirit's Tether*   731
B - O Son of God, in Galilee*   748
C - Take Up Your Cross*   634

TWENTY-FOURTH SUNDAY
A - Forgive Our Sins*   754
B - Take Up Your Cross*   634
C - Our Father, We Have Wandered*   755

TWENTY-FIFTH SUNDAY
A - There's a Wideness in God's Mercy   595, 596
B - The Church of Christ in Every Age   626
C - God, Whose Giving Knows No Ending   631

TWENTY-SIXTH SUNDAY
A - At the Name of Jesus*   499
    Our Father, We Have Wandered   755
B - How Good the Name of Jesus Sounds   610
C - God, Whose Purpose Is to Kindle   640

TWENTY-SEVENTH SUNDAY
A - A Single Unmatched Stone*   574
    Christ Is Made the Sure Foundation   617
B - A Spendthrift Lover Is the Lord   597
    Our Father, by Whose Name   570
C - The Church of Christ in Every Age   626

TWENTY-EIGHTH SUNDAY
A - City of God, Jerusalem*   362

Gather Us In*   665
B - Weary of All Trumpeting   635
C - Surely It Is God Who Saves Me   584

TWENTY-NINTH SUNDAY
A - Reap Me the Earth   544
B - The Church of Christ in Every Age   626
C - God Is My Great Desire   581

THIRTIETH SUNDAY
A - Lord of All Nations, Grant Me Grace*   602
B - Your Hands, O Lord, in Days of Old   750
C - What Does the Lord Require   624

THIRTY-FIRST SUNDAY
A - What Does the Lord Require   624
B - God Be in My Head   567
C - I Heard the Voice of Jesus Say   607

THIRTY-SECOND SUNDAY
A - Wake, O Wake, and Sleep No Longer*   371
    Who Can Measure Heaven and Earth   509
B - Where Temple Offerings Are Made*   622
C - God Is My Great Desire   581
    The God of Abraham Praise   537

THIRTY-THIRD SUNDAY
A - God, Whose Giving Knows No Ending*   631
    O the Beautiful Treasures   689
B - Now the Day of the Lord Is at Hand   687
C - Now the Day of the Lord Is at Hand   687

CHRIST THE KING
see nos. 492-501

1206   Liturgical Index

Liturgical Index/*continued*

Liturgical Index/*continued*

Liturgical Index/*continued*

Liturgical Index/*continued*

Liturgical Index/*continued*

RITES OF THE CHURCH

BAPTISM OF CHILDREN

CHRISTIAN INITIATION OF ADULTS

Liturgical Index/*continued*

Liturgical Index/*continued*

MARRIAGE

PASTORAL CARE OF THE SICK

Liturgical Index/*continued*

Topical Index   1207

Topical Index/*continued*

Topical Index/*continued*

Topical Index/*continued*

Topical Index/*continued*

Topical Index/*continued*

Topical Index/*continued*

Topical Index/*continued*

Topical Index/*continued*

Topical Index/*continued*

Topical Index/*continued*

Topical Index/*continued*

Topical Index/*continued*

Topical Index/*continued*

Topical Index/*continued*

Topical Index/*continued*

Topical Index/*continued*

1208   Hymns Which May Be Sung in Canon

To be sung unaccompanied, at the distance of one measure, and usually at the interval of one octave.

Index of Composers, Authors and Sources   1209

Index of Composers, Authors and Sources/*continued*

Index of Composers, Authors and Sources/*continued*

Index of Composers, Authors and Sources/*continued*

Index of Composers, Authors and Sources/*continued*

Index of Composers, Authors and Sources/*continued*

Metrical Index of Tunes 1210

Metrical Index of Tunes/*continued*

Metrical Index of Tunes/*continued*

Metrical Index of Tunes/*continued*

Index of Tunes   1211

Index of Tunes/*continued*

Index of Tunes/*continued*

1212   Psalm Refrains Set to Music

Psalm Refrains Set to Music/*continued*

Psalm Refrains Set to Music/*continued*

Psalm Refrains Set to Music/*continued*

1213 Index of First Lines and Common Titles

Indented listings represent alternate titles by which some hymns are commonly known.

Index of First Lines and Common Titles/*continued*

Index of First Lines and Common Titles/*continued*

Index of First Lines and Common Titles/*continued*

Index of First Lines and Common Titles/*continued*